C000243695

Newnes Mechanical Engineer's Pocket Book

Newnes

Mechanical Engineer's Pocket Book

Roger Timings and Tony May

Newnes
An imprint of Butterworth-Heinemann Ltd
Linacre House, Jordan Hill, Oxford OX2 8DP

A member of the Reed Elsevier plc group

OXFORD LONDON BOSTON
MUNICH NEW DELHI SINGAPORE SYDNEY
TOKYO TORONTO WELLINGTON

First published 1990
Reprinted 1992, 1993, 1995 (twice)

British Library Cataloguing in Publication Data
Timings, Roger
Newnes mechanical engineer's pocket book
1. Mechanical engineering
I. Title II. May, Tony
621

ISBN 0 7506 0919 2

Printed and bound in Great Britain by Clays Ltd, St Ives plc

Contents

Preface

This pocket book has been prepared as an aid to mechanical engineers engaged in design and manufacture, together with others who require a quick, day-to-day reference for useful workshop information. For easy reference this book is divided into five main parts, namely:

1 Engineering Mathematics and Science
2 Engineering Design Data
3 Engineering Materials
4 Computer Aided Engineering
5 Cutting Tools

In turn, these five main sections have been subdivided into main topic areas. For example: part 2, Engineering Design Data, has been subdivided into the following topic areas:

2.1 Screwed fastenings
2.2 Riveted joints;
2.3 Self-secured joints;
2.4 Miscellaneous fasteners
2.5 Power transmission: gears
2.6 Power transmission: belt drives
2.7 Power transmission: shafts

Within these subsections, the material has been assembled in a logical sequence for easy reference and a comprehensive list of contents has been provided which leads the reader directly to the item required.

This pocket book is not a textbook but is a compilation of useful data. The authors are indebted to the British Standards Institution and to all the industrial and commercial companies in the UK and abroad who have cooperated in providing up-to-date data in so many technical areas. Unfortunately, limitation of space has allowed only abstracts to be included from the wealth of material provided. Therefore, the reader is strongly recommended to consult the complete standard, industrial manual or catalogue after an initial perusal of the tables of data found in this book. To this end, an appendix is provided listing the names and addresses of libraries, institutions and companies where the complete standards, manuals and catalogues may be consulted or purchased. Many industrial manuals and catalogues are available free of charge to bona fide users.

The section on computer aided engineering is only a very brief introduction to a very complex and broadly-based area of engineering. It is intended to follow up this section with a series of pocket books specializing in such topic areas as computer numerical control, computer aided design, industrial robotics and programmable logic controllers.

Finally it is intended, within the restraints of commercial viability, to produce new and updated editions of this book from time to time. Therefore, the authors would appreciate (via the publishers) suggestions from the users of this book for additions or deletions to be taken into account when producing new editions.

Roger Timings
Tony May

Acknowledgements

We would like to thank all the companies who have kindly given permission for their material to be used: Continental Gummi-Werke AG (sections 2.6.4-2.6.14); David Brown Gears Ltd (section 2.5.1); National Broach & Machine Co (sections 2.5.8-2.5.15); Sandvik Coromant UK (sections 5.5.1-5.5.16); Tucker Fasteners (section 2.2.8). We are also grateful to Hodder and Stoughton for allowing us to reproduce material from Higgins, R.A., *Properties of Materials* in sections 3.2.2., 3.2.3., 3.2.5-3.2.7 and 3.2.13 and to Longman for permission to reproduce material from Timings, R. *Materials Technology Level 2* and *Materials Technology Level 3* in sections 3.1.1.-3.1.21.

Extracts from British Standards are reproduced with permission of BSI. Complete copies of the documents can be obtained by post from BSI Sales, Linford Wood Milton Keynes, Bucks MK14 6LE.

Part 1 Engineering Mathematics and Science

1.1 Engineering mathematics

1.1.1 The Greek alphabet

Name	*Symbol* *Capital*	*Lower case*	*Examples of use*
alpha	Α	α	angles, angular acceleration, various coefficients
beta	Β	β	angles, coefficients
gamma	Γ	γ	shear strain, surface tension, kinematic viscosity
delta	Δ	δ	differences, damping coefficient
epsilon	Ε	ε	linear strain
zeta	Ζ	ζ	
eta	Η	η	dynamic viscosity, efficiency
theta	Θ	θ	angles, temperature, volume strain
iota	Ι	ι	
kappa	Κ	κ	compressibility
lambda	Λ	λ	wavelength, thermal conductivity
mu	Μ	μ	Poisson's ratio, coefficient of friction
nu	Ν	ν	dynamic viscosity
xi	Ξ	ξ	
omicron	Ο	o	
pi	Π	π	mathematical constant
rho	Ρ	ρ	density
sigma	Σ	σ	normal stress, standard deviation, sum of
tau	Τ	τ	shear stress
upsilon	Υ	υ	
phi	Φ	ϕ	angles, heat flow rate, potential energy
chi	Χ	χ	
psi	Ψ	ψ	helix angle (gears)
omega	Ω	ω	angular velocity, solid angle (ω) electrical resistance (Ω)

1.1.2 Mathematical symbols

is equal to	$=$	is not equal to	$\neq$
is identically equal to	$\equiv$	is approximately equal to	$\approx$
approaches	$\rightarrow$	is proportional to	$\propto$
is smaller than	$<$	is larger than	$>$
is smaller than or equal to	$\leqslant$	is larger than or equal to	$\geqslant$
magnitude of a	$\lvert a \rvert$	a raised to power n	a^n
square root of a	$\sqrt{a}$	nth root of a	$\sqrt[n]{a}$
mean value of a	$\bar{a}$	factorial a	$a!$
sum	Σ	product	Π
complex operator	i,j	real part of z	Re z
imaginary part of z	Im z	modulus of z	$\lvert z \rvert$
argument of z	arg z	complex conjugate of z	z^*

a multiplied by b	ab, $a.b$, $a \times b$
a divided by b	a/b, $\frac{a}{b}$, ab^{-1}
function of x	$f(x)$
variation of x	δx
finite increment of x	Δx
limit to which $f(x)$ tends as x approaches a	$\lim_{x \to a} f(x)$
differential coefficient of $f(x)$ with respect to x	$\frac{\mathrm{d}f}{\mathrm{d}x}$, $\mathrm{d}f/\mathrm{d}x$, $f'(x)$
indefinite integral of $f(x)$ with respect to x	$\int f(x)\mathrm{d}x$
increase in value of $f(x)$ as x increases from a to b	$[f(x)]_a^b$
definite integral of $f(x)$ from $x=a$ to $x=b$	$\int_a^b f(x)\mathrm{d}x$
logarithm to the base 10 of x	lg x, $\log_{10} x$
logarithm to the base a of x	$\log_a x$
exponential of x	exp x, e^x
natural logarithm	ln x, $\log_e x$
inverse sine of x	arcsin x
inverse cosine of x	arccos x
inverse tangent of x	arctan x

inverse secant of x	arcsec x
inverse cosecant of x	arccosec x
inverse cotangent of x	arccot x
inverse hyperbolic sine of x	arsinh x
inverse hyperbolic cosine of x	arcosh x
inverse hyperbolic tangent of x	artanh x
inverse hyperbolic cosecant of x	arcosech x
inverse hyperbolic secant of x	arsech x
inverse hyperbolic cotangent of x	arcoth x
vector	**A**
magnitude of vector **A**	$\|\mathbf{A}\|, A$
scalar products of vectors **A** and **B**	**A.B**
vector products of vectors **A** and **B**	$\mathbf{A} \times \mathbf{B}$, $\mathbf{A} \wedge \mathbf{B}$

1.1.3 Units: SI

Basic and supplementary units

The International System of Units (SI) is based on nine physical quantities.

Physical quantity	*Unit name*	*Unit symbol*
length	metre	m
mass	kilogram	kg
time	second	s
plane angle	radian	rad
amount of substance	mole	mol
electric current	ampere	A
luminous intensity	candela	cd
solid angle	steradian	sr
thermodynamic temperature	kelvin	K

Derived units

By dimensionally appropriate multiplication and/or division of the units shown on page 5, derived units are obtained. Some of these are given special names.

Physical quantity	*Unit name*	*Unit symbol*	*Derivation*
electric capacitance	farad	F	$(A^2 s^4)/(kg\,m^2)$
electric charge	coulomb	C	A s
electric conductance	siemens	S	$(A^2 s^3)/(kg\,m^2)$
electric potential difference	volt	V	$(kg\,m^2)/(A\,s^3)$
electrical resistance	ohm	Ω	$(kg\,m^2)/(A^2 s^3)$
energy	joule	J	$(kg\,m^2)/s^2$
force	newton	N	$(kg\,m)/s^2$
frequency	hertz	Hz	1/s
illuminance	lux	lx	$(cd\,sr)/m^2$
inductance	henry	H	$(kg\,m^2)/(A^2 s^2)$
luminous flux	lumen	lm	cd sr
magnetic flux	weber	Wb	$(kg\,m^2)/(A\,s^2)$
magnetic flux density	tesla	T	$kg/(A\,s^2)$
power	watt	W	$(kg\,m^2)/s^3$
pressure	pascal	Pa	$kg/(m\,s^2)$

Some other derived units not having special names.

Physical quantity	*Unit*	*Unit symbol*
acceleration	metre per second squared	m/s^2
angular velocity	radian per second	rad/s
area	square metre	m^2
current density	ampere per square metre	A/m^2
density	kilogram per cubic metre	kg/m^3
dynamic viscosity	pascal second	Pa s
electric charge density	coulomb per cubic metre	C/m^3
electric field strength	volt per metre	V/m

energy density	joule per cubic metre	J/m^3
heat capacity	joule per kelvin	J/K
heat flux density	watt per square metre	W/m^2
kinematic viscosity	square metre per second	m^2/s
luminance	candela per square metre	cd/m^2
magnetic field strength	ampere per metre	A/m
moment of force	newton metre	N m
permeability	henry per metre	H/m
permittivity	farad per metre	F/m
specific volume	cubic metre per kilogram	m^3/kg
surface tension	newton per metre	N/m
thermal conductivity	watt per metre kelvin	W/(m K)
velocity	metre per second	m/s
volume	cubic metre	m^3

See also 1.2.1 (page 54).

1.1.4 Units: not SI

Some of the units which are not part of the SI system, but which are recognized for continued use with the SI system, are as shown.

Physical quantity	*Unit name*	*Unit symbol*	*Definition*
angle	degree	°	$(\pi/180)$ rad
angle	minute	′	$(\pi/10\,800)$ rad
angle	second	″	$(\pi/648\,000)$ rad
Celsius temperature	degree Celsius	°C	K − 273.2 (For K see 1.1.3)
dynamic viscosity	poise	P	10^{-1} Pa s
energy	calorie	cal	≈4.18 J
Fahrenheit temperature	degree Fahrenheit	°F	$(\frac{9}{5})$°C + 32
force	kilogram force	kgf	≈9.807 N
kinematic viscosity	stokes	St	10^{-4} m^2/s

continued

Physical quantity	*Unit name*	*Unit symbol*	*Definition*
length	inch	in	2.54×10^{-2} m
length	micron	μm	10^{-6} m
mass	pound	lb	≈0.454 kg
mass	tonne	t	10^3 kg
pressure	atmosphere	atm	101 325 Pa
pressure	bar	bar	10^5 Pa
pressure	millimetre of mercury	mm Hg	≈133.322 Pa
pressure	torr	torr	≈133.322 Pa
thermodynamic temperature	degree Rankine	°R	°F+459.7
time	minute	min	60 s
time	hour	h	3600 s
time	day	d	86 400 s

See also 1.2.1 (page 54).

1.1.5 Notes on writing symbols

(a) Symbols should be in roman type lettering: thus cm, not *cm*.

(b) Symbols should remain unaltered in the plural: thus cm, not cms.

(c) There should be a space between the product of two symbols: thus N m, not Nm.

(d) Index notation may be used: thus m/s may be written as $\mathrm{m\,s^{-1}}$ and W/(m K) as $\mathrm{W\,m^{-1}\,K^{-1}}$.

1.1.6 Decimal multiples of units

For quantities which are much larger or much smaller than the units so far given, decimal multiples of units are used. Internationally agreed multiples are as shown.

For small quantities

Multiple	*Prefix*	*Symbol*
10^{-1}	deci	d
10^{-2}	centi	c
10^{-3}	milli	m
10^{-6}	micro	μ
10^{-9}	nano	n
10^{-12}	pico	p
10^{-15}	femto	f
10^{-18}	atto	a

For large quantities

Multiple	*Prefix*	*Symbol*
10	deca	da
10^2	hecto	h
10^3	kilo	k
10^6	mega	M
10^9	giga	G
10^{12}	tera	T
10^{15}	peta	P
10^{18}	exa	E

Notes

(a) A prefix is used with the gram, not the kilogram: thus Mg, not kkg.

(b) A prefix may be used for one or more of the unit symbols: thus kN m, N mm and kN mm are all acceptable.

(c) Compound prefixes should not be used: thus ns, not mμs.

1.1.7 Conversion factors for units

The conversion factors shown below are accurate to five significant figures where FPS is the foot-pound-second system.

FPS to SI units		SI to FPS units	
Acceleration			
1 ft/s^2	=0.304 80 m/s^2	1 m/s^2	=3.2808 ft/s^2
Angular velocity			
1 rev/min	=0.104 72 rad/s	1 rad/s	=9.5493 rev/min
Area			
1 in^2	=6.4516 cm^2	1 cm^2	=0.155 00 in^2
1 ft^2	=0.092 903 m^2	1 m^2	=10.764 ft^2
1 yd^2	=0.836 13 m^2	1 m^2	=1.1960 yd^2
1 acre	=0.404 69 ha	1 ha	=2.4711 acre
Density			
1 lb/ft^3	=16.018 kg/m^3	1 kg/m^3	=0.062 428 lb/ft^3

continued

FPS to SI units / SI to FPS units

FPS to SI units		SI to FPS units	
Energy			
1 ft pdl	=0.042 140 J	1 J	=23.730 ft pdl
1 ft lbf	=1.355 82 J	1 J	=0.737 56 ft lbf
1 kW h	=3.6000 MJ	1 MJ	=0.277 78 kW h
1 therm	=0.105 51 GJ	1 GJ	=9.4781 therm
Force			
1 pdl	=0.138 26 N	1 N	=7.2330 pdl
1 lbf	=4.4482 N	1 N	=0.224 81 lbf
Length			
1 in	=2.5400 cm	1 cm	=0.393 70 in
1 ft	=0.304 80 m	1 m	=3.2808 ft
1 yd	=0.914 40 m	1 m	=1.0936 yd
1 mi	=1.6093 km	1 km	=0.621 37 mi
Mass			
1 oz	=28.350 g	1 g	=0.035 274 oz
1 lb	=0.453 59 kg	1 kg	=2.2046 lb
1 cwt	=50.802 kg	1 kg	=0.019 684 cwt
1 ton	=1.0161 tonne	1 tonne	=0.984 21 ton
Moment of force			
1 lbf ft	=1.3558 N m	1 N m	=0.737 56 lbf ft
Plane angle			
1°	=0.017 45 rad	1 rad	=57.296°
Power			
1 ft lbf/s	=1.3558 W	1 W	=0.737 56 ft lbf/s
1 hp	=0.745 70 kW	1 kW	=1.3410 hp
Pressure and stress			
1 in Hg	=33.864 mbar	1 mbar	=0.029 53 in Hg
1 lbf/in^2	=6.8948 kPa	1 kPa	=0.145 04 lbf/in^2
1 tonf/in^2	=15.444 N/mm^2	1 N/mm^2	=0.064 749 tonf/in^2
Specific heat capacity			
1 Btu/(lb°F)	=4.1868 kJ/(kg°C)	1 kJ/(kg °C)	=0.238 85 Btu/(lb °F)
Velocity			
1 ft/s	=0.304 80 m/s	1 m/s	=3.2808 ft/s
1 mi/h	=1.6093 km/h	1 km/h	=0.621 37 mi/h
Volume			
1 in^3	=16.387 cm^3	1 cm^3	=0.061 024 in^3
1 ft^3	=0.028 317 m^3	1 m^3	=35.315 ft^3
1 yd^3	=0.764 56 m^3	1 m^3	=1.3080 yd^3
1 pt	=0.568 26 litre	1 litre	=1.7598 pt
1 gal	=4.5461 litre	1 litre	=0.219 97 gal

1.1.8 Conversion table: millimetres to inches

mm	in	mm	in	mm	in
0.01	0.000 394	36	1.417 323	89	3.503 937
0.02	0.000 787	37	1.456 693	90	3.543 307
0.03	0.001 181	38	1.496 063	91	3.582 677
0.04	0.001 575	39	1.535 433	92	3.622 047
0.05	0.001 969	40	1.574 803	93	3.661 417
0.06	0.002 362	41	1.614 173	94	3.700 788
0.07	0.002 756	42	1.653 543	95	3.740 158
0.08	0.003 150	43	1.692 913	96	3.779 528
0.09	0.003 543	44	1.732 283	97	3.818 898
0.10	0.003 937	45	1.771 654	98	3.858 268
0.20	0.007 874	46	1.811 024	99	3.897 638
0.30	0.011 810	47	1.850 394	100	3.937 008
0.40	0.015 748	48	1.889 764	200	7.874 016
0.50	0.019 685	49	1.929 134	300	11.811 02
0.60	0.023 622	50	1.968 504	400	15.748 03
0.70	0.027 559	51	2.007 874	500	19.685 04
0.80	0.031 496	52	2.047 244	600	23.622 05
0.90	0.035 433	53	2.086 614	700	27.559 06
1	0.039 370	54	2.125 984	800	31.496 06
2	0.078 740	55	2.165 354	900	35.433 07
3	0.118 110	56	2.204 725	1000	39.370 08
4	0.157 480	57	2.244 095	1100	43.307 09
5	0.196 850	58	2.283 465	1200	47.244 09
6	0.236 221	59	2.322 835	1300	51.181 10
7	0.275 591	60	2.362 205	1400	55.118 11
8	0.314 961	61	2.401 575	1500	59.055 12
9	0.354 331	62	2.440 945	1600	62.992 13
10	0.393 701	63	2.480 315	1700	66.929 14
11	0.433 071	64	2.519 685	1800	70.866 14
12	0.472 441	65	2.559 055	1900	74.803 15
13	0.511 811	66	2.598 425	2000	78.740 16
14	0.551 181	67	2.637 795	2100	82.677 17
15	0.590 551	68	2.677 166	2200	86.614 17
16	0.629 921	69	2.716 536	2300	90.551 19
17	0.669 291	70	2.755 906	2400	94.488 19

continued

mm	in	mm	in	mm	in
18	0.708 661	71	2.795 276	2500	98.425 2
19	0.748 032	72	2.834 646	2600	102.362 2
20	0.787 402	73	2.874 016	2700	106.299 2
21	0.826 772	74	2.913 386	2800	110.236 2
22	0.866 142	75	2.952 756	2900	114.173 2
23	0.905 512	76	2.992 126	3000	118.110 2
24	0.944 882	77	3.031 496	3100	122.047 2
25	0.984 252	78	3.070 866	3200	125.984 3
26	1.023 622	79	3.110 236	3300	129.921 3
27	1.062 992	80	3.149 606	3400	133.858 3
28	1.102 362	81	3.188 977	3500	137.795 3
29	1.141 732	82	3.228 347	3600	141.732 3
30	1.181 102	83	3.267 717	3700	145.669 3
31	1.220 472	84	3.307 087	3800	149.606 3
32	1.259 843	85	3.346 457	3900	153.543 3
33	1.299 213	86	3.385 827	4000	157.480 3
34	1.338 583	87	3.425 197	4100	161.417 3
35	1.377 953	88	3.464 567	4200	165.354 3

1.1.9 Conversion table: minutes of arc to degrees

min	degree	min	degree	min	degree
0.1	0.001 667	14	0.233 333	38	0.633 333
0.2	0.003 333	15	0.250 000	39	0.650 000
0.25	0.004 167	16	0.266 667	40	0.666 667
0.3	0.005 000	17	0.283 333	41	0.683 333
0.4	0.006 667	18	0.300 000	42	0.700 000
0.5	0.008 333	19	0.316 667	43	0.716 667
0.6	0.010 000	20	0.333 333	44	0.733 333
0.7	0.011 667	21	0.350 000	45	0.750 000
0.75	0.012 500	22	0.366 667	46	0.766 667
0.8	0.013 333	23	0.383 333	47	0.783 333
0.9	0.015 000	24	0.400 000	48	0.800 000

1	0.016 667	25	0.416 667	49	0.816 667
2	0.033 333	26	0.433 333	50	0.833 333
3	0.050 000	27	0.450 000	51	0.850 000
4	0.066 667	28	0.466 667	52	0.866 667
5	0.083 333	29	0.483 333	53	0.883 333
6	0.100 000	30	0.500 000	54	0.900 000
7	0.116 667	31	0.516 667	55	0.916 667
8	0.133 333	32	0.533 333	56	0.933 333
9	0.150 000	33	0.550 000	57	0.950 000
10	0.166 667	34	0.566 667	58	0.966 667
11	0.183 333	35	0.583 333	59	0.983 333
12	0.200 000	36	0.600 000	60	1.000 000
13	0.216 667	37	0.616 667		

1.1.10 Conversion table: fractions to decimals

Fraction	*Decimal*	*Fraction*	*Decimal*	*Fraction*	*Decimal*
1/64	0.015 625	11/32	0.343 750	43/64	0.671 875
1/32	0.031 250	23/64	0.359 375	11/16	0.687 500
3/64	0.046 875	3/8	0.375 000	45/64	0.703 125
1/16	0.062 500	25/64	0.390 625	23/32	0.718 750
5/64	0.078 125	13/32	0.406 250	47/64	0.734 375
3/32	0.093 750	27/64	0.421 875	3/4	0.750 000
7/64	0.109 375	7/16	0.437 500	49/64	0.765 625
1/8	0.125 000	29/64	0.453 125	25/32	0.781 250
9/64	0.140 625	15/32	0.468 750	51/64	0.796 875
5/32	0.156 250	31/64	0.484 375	13/16	0.812 500
11/64	0.171 875	1/2	0.500 000	53/64	0.828 125
3/16	0.187 500	33/64	0.515 625	27/32	0.843 750
13/64	0.203 125	17/32	0.531 250	55/64	0.859 375
7/32	0.218 750	35/64	0.546 875	7/8	0.875 000
15/64	0.234 375	9/16	0.562 500	57/64	0.890 625
1/4	0.250 000	37/64	0.578 125	29/32	0.906 250
17/64	0.265 625	19/32	0.593 750	59/64	0.921 875
9/32	0.281 250	39/64	0.609 375	15/16	0.937 500
19/64	0.296 875	5/8	0.625 000	61/64	0.953 125
5/16	0.312 500	41/64	0.640 625	31/32	0.968 750
21/64	0.328 125	21/32	0.656 250	63/64	0.984 375

1.1.11 Conversion table: temperature, −50° to 210°

In the table below, look up the reading in the °F°C column: read corresponding Celsius temperature in the left hand column and Fahrenheit temperature in the right hand column.

°C	← °F°C →	°F	°C	← °F°C →	°F	°C	← °F°C →	°F
−45.56	−50	−58	−0.56	31	87.8	27.22	81	177.8
−42.78	−45	−49	0	32	89.6	27.78	82	179.6
−40	−40	−40	0.56	33	91.4	28.33	83	181.4
−37.22	−35	−31	1.11	34	93.2	28.89	84	183.2
−34.44	−30	−22	1.67	35	95	29.44	85	185
−31.67	−25	−13	2.22	36	96.8	30	86	186.8
−28.89	−20	−4	2.78	37	98.6	30.56	87	188.6
−26.11	−15	5	3.33	38	100.4	31.11	88	190.4
−23.33	−10	14	3.89	39	102.2	31.67	89	192.2
−22.78	−9	15.8	4.44	40	104	32.22	90	194
−22.22	−8	17.6	5	41	105.8	32.78	91	195.8
−21.67	−7	19.4	5.56	42	107.6	33.33	92	197.6
−21.11	−6	21.2	6.11	43	109.4	33.89	93	199.4
−20.56	−5	23	6.67	44	111.2	34.44	94	201.2
−20	−4	24.8	7.22	45	113	35	95	203
−19.44	−3	26.6	7.78	46	114.8	35.56	96	204.8
−18.89	−2	28.4	8.33	47	116.6	36.11	97	206.6
−18.33	−1	30.2	8.89	48	118.4	36.67	98	208.4
−17.78	0	32	9.44	49	120.2	37.22	99	210.2
−17.22	1	33.8	10	50	122	37.78	100	212
−16.67	2	35.6	10.56	51	123.8	38.33	101	213.8

−16.11	3	37.4	11.11	52	125.6	38.89	102	215.6
−15.56	4	39.2	11.67	53	127.4	39.44	103	217.4
−15	5	41	12.22	54	129.2	40	104	219.2
−14.44	6	42.8	12.78	55	131	40.56	105	221
−13.89	7	44.6	13.33	56	132.8	41.11	106	222.8
−13.33	8	46.4	13.89	57	134.6	41.67	107	224.6
−12.78	9	48.2	14.44	58	136.4	42.22	108	226.4
−12.22	10	50	15	59	138.2	42.78	109	228.2
−11.67	11	51.8	15.56	60	140	43.33	110	230
−11.11	12	53.6	16.11	61	141.8	46.11	115	239
−10.56	13	55.4	16.67	62	143.6	48.89	120	248
−10	14	57.2	17.22	63	145.4	51.67	125	257
−9.44	15	59	17.78	64	147.2	54.44	130	266
−8.89	16	60.8	18.33	65	149	57.22	135	275
−8.33	17	62.6	18.89	66	150.8	60	140	284
−7.78	18	64.4	19.44	67	152.6	62.78	145	293
−7.22	19	66.2	20	68	154.4	65.56	150	302
−6.67	20	68	20.56	69	156.2	68.33	155	311
−6.11	21	69.8	21.11	70	158	71.11	160	320
−5.56	22	71.6	21.67	71	159.8	73.89	165	329
−5	23	73.4	22.22	72	161.6	76.67	170	338
−4.44	24	75.2	22.78	73	163.4	79.44	175	347
−3.89	25	77	23.33	74	165.2	82.22	180	356
−3.33	26	78.8	23.89	75	167	85	185	365
−2.78	27	80.6	24.44	76	168.8	87.78	190	374
−2.22	28	82.4	25	77	170.6	90.56	195	383
−1.67	29	84.2	25.56	78	172.4	93.33	200	392
−1.11	30	86	26.11	79	174.2	96.11	205	401
			26.67	80	176	98.89	210	410

1.1.12 Conversion table: temperature, 215° to 3000°

In the table below, look up the reading in the °F°C column: read corresponding Celsius temperature in the left hand column and Fahrenheit temperature in the right hand column.

°C	°F°C	°F	°C	°F°C	°F	°C	°F°C	°F
101.67	215	419	482.22	900	1652	1026.67	1880	3416
104.44	220	428	493.33	920	1688	1037.78	1900	3452
107.22	225	437	504.44	940	1724	1048.89	1920	3488
110	230	446	515.56	960	1760	1060	1940	3524
112.78	235	455	526.67	980	1796	1071.11	1960	3560
115.56	240	464	537.78	1000	1832	1082.22	1980	3596
118.33	245	473	548.89	1020	1868	1093.33	2000	3632
121.11	250	482	560	1040	1904	1104.44	2020	3668
123.89	255	491	571.11	1060	1940	1115.56	2040	3704
126.67	260	500	582.22	1080	1976	1126.67	2060	3740
129.44	265	509	593.33	1100	2012	1137.78	2080	3776
132.22	270	518	604.44	1120	2048	1148.89	2100	3812
135	275	527	615.56	1140	2084	1160	2120	3848
137.78	280	536	626.67	1160	2120	1171.11	2140	3884
140.56	285	545	637.78	1180	2156	1182.22	2160	3920
143.33	290	554	648.89	1200	2192	1193.33	2180	3956
146.11	295	563	660	1220	2228	1204.44	2200	3992
148.89	300	572	671.11	1240	2264	1215.56	2220	4028
151.67	305	581	682.22	1260	2300	1226.67	2240	4064
154.44	310	590	693.33	1280	2336	1237.78	2260	4100

160	320	608	704.44	1300	2372	1248.89	2280	4136
171.11	340	644	715.56	1320	2408	1260	2300	4172
182.22	360	680	726.67	1340	2444	1271.11	2320	4208
193.33	380	716	737.77	1360	2480	1282.22	2340	4244
204.44	400	752	748.89	1380	2516	1293.33	2360	4280
215.56	420	788	760	1400	2552	1304.44	2380	4316
226.67	440	824	771.11	1420	2588	1315.56	2400	4352
237.78	460	860	782.22	1440	2624	1326.67	2420	4388
248.89	480	896	793.33	1460	2660	1337.78	2440	4424
260	500	932	804.44	1480	2696	1348.89	2460	4460
271.11	520	968	815.56	1500	2732	1360	2480	4496
282.22	540	1004	826.67	1520	2768	1371.11	2500	4532
293.33	560	1040	837.78	1540	2804	1382.22	2520	4568
304.44	580	1076	848.89	1560	2840	1393.33	2540	4604
315.56	600	1112	860	1580	2876	1404.44	2560	4640
326.67	620	1148	871.11	1600	2912	1415.56	2580	4676
337.78	640	1184	882.22	1620	2948	1426.67	2600	4712
348.89	660	1220	893.33	1640	2984	1437.78	2620	4748
360	680	1256	904.44	1660	3020	1448.89	2640	4784
371.11	700	1292	915.56	1680	3056	1460	2660	4820
382.22	720	1328	926.67	1700	3092	1471.11	2680	4856
393.33	740	1364	937.78	1720	3128	1493.33	2720	4928
404.44	760	1400	948.89	1740	3164	1515.56	2760	5000
415.56	780	1436	960	1760	3200	1537.78	2800	5072
426.67	800	1472	971.11	1780	3236	1560	2840	5144
437.78	820	1508	982.22	1800	3272	1582.22	2880	5216
448.89	840	1544	993.33	1820	3308	1604.44	2920	5288
460	860	1580	1004.44	1840	3344	1626.67	2960	5360
471.11	880	1616	1015.56	1860	3380	1648.89	3000	5432

1.1.13 Conversion tables: low pressure

in *water*	in *mercury*	mm *mercury*	lbf/in^2	kPa (kN/m^2)
1	0.0736	1.868	0.0361	0.2491
2	0.1471	3.737	0.0723	0.4982
3	0.2207	5.605	0.1084	0.7473
4	0.2942	7.473	0.1445	0.9964
5	0.3678	9.342	0.1806	1.2454
6	0.4413	11.210	0.2168	1.4945
7	0.5149	13.078	0.2529	1.7436
8	0.5884	14.947	0.2890	1.9927
9	0.6620	16.815	0.3251	2.2418
10	0.7356	18.683	0.3613	2.4909
11	0.8091	20.552	0.3974	2.7400
12	0.8827	22.420	0.4335	2.9891
13	0.9562	24.288	0.4697	3.2382
14	1.0300	26.156	0.5058	3.4872
15	1.1033	28.025	0.5419	3.7363

in *mercury*	mm *mercury*	lbf/in^2	kPa (kN/m^2)
1	25.4	0.491	3.386
2	50.8	0.982	6.773
3	76.2	1.473	10.159
4	101.6	1.965	13.546
5	127.0	2.456	16.932
6	152.4	2.947	20.318
7	177.8	3.438	23.705
8	203.2	3.929	27.091
9	228.6	4.420	30.478
10	254.0	4.912	33.864
11	279.4	5.403	37.250
12	304.8	5.894	40.637
13	330.2	6.385	44.023
14	355.6	6.876	47.409
15	381.0	7.367	50.796

16	406.4	7.858	54.182
17	431.8	8.350	57.569
18	457.2	8.841	60.955
19	482.6	9.332	64.341
20	508.0	9.832	67.728
21	533.4	10.314	71.114
22	558.8	10.805	74.501
23	584.2	11.297	77.887
24	609.6	11.788	81.273
25	635.0	12.279	84.660
26	660.4	12.770	88.046
27	685.8	13.261	91.433
28	711.2	13.752	94.819
29	736.6	14.243	98.205
30	762.0	14.735	101.592

1.1.14 Conversion table: high pressure

lbf/in^2	kPa (kN/m^2)	lbf/in^2	kPa (kN/m^2)	lbf/in^2	kPa (kN/m^2)
1	6.89	51	351.63	150	1 034.21
2	13.79	52	358.53	200	1 378.95
3	20.68	53	365.42	250	1 723.69
4	27.58	54	372.32	300	2 068.43
5	34.47	55	379.21	350	2 413.16
6	41.37	56	386.11	400	2 757.90
7	48.26	57	393.00	450	3 102.64
8	55.16	58	399.90	500	3 447.38
9	62.05	59	406.79	550	3 792.12
10	68.95	60	413.69	600	4 136.85
11	75.84	61	420.58	650	4 481.59
12	82.74	62	427.47	700	4 826.33
13	89.63	63	434.37	750	5 171.07
14	96.53	64	441.26	800	5 515.81
15	103.42	65	448.16	850	5 860.54
16	110.32	66	455.05	900	6 205.28
17	117.21	67	461.95	950	6 550.02
18	124.11	68	468.84	1000	6 894.76
19	131.00	69	475.74	1050	7 239.49

continued

Section 1.1.14 (*continued*)

lbf/in^2	kPa (kN/m^2)	lbf/in^2	kPa (kN/m^2)	lbf/in^2	kPa (kN/m^2)
20	137.90	70	482.63	1100	7 584.23
21	144.79	71	489.53	1150	7 928.97
22	151.68	72	496.42	1200	8 273.71
23	158.58	73	503.32	1250	8 618.45
24	165.47	74	510.21	1300	8 963.18
25	172.37	75	517.11	1350	9 307.92
26	179.26	76	524.00	1400	9 652.66
27	186.16	77	530.90	1450	9 997.40
28	193.05	78	537.79	1500	10 342.14
29	199.95	79	544.69	1550	10 686.87
30	206.84	80	551.58	1600	11 031.61
31	213.74	81	558.48	1650	11 376.35
32	220.63	82	565.37	1700	11 721.09
33	227.53	83	572.26	1750	12 065.82
34	234.42	84	579.16	1800	12 410.56
35	241.32	85	586.05	1850	12 755.30
36	248.21	86	592.95	1900	13 100.04
37	255.11	87	599.84	1950	13 444.78
38	262.00	88	606.74	2000	13 789.51
39	268.90	89	613.63	2050	14 134.25
40	275.79	90	620.53	2100	14 478.99
41	282.69	91	627.42	2150	14 823.73
42	289.58	92	634.32	2200	15 168.47
43	296.47	93	641.21	2300	15 857.94
44	303.37	94	648.11	2400	16 547.42
45	310.26	95	655.00	2500	17 236.89
46	317.16	96	661.90	2600	17 926.37
47	324.05	97	668.79	2700	18 615.84
48	330.95	98	675.69	2800	19 305.32
49	337.84	99	682.58	2900	19 994.79
50	344.74	100	689.48	3000	20 684.27

Bar

For pressure in bar, 1 bar = 100 kPa, e.g. 3000 lbf/in^2 = 206.84 bar

1.1.15 Conversion table: stress, $tonf/in^2$ to N/mm^2 (MN/m^2)

$tonf/in^2$	N/mm^2 (MN/m^2)	$tonf/in^2$	N/mm^2 (MN/m^2)	$tonf/in^2$	N/mm^2 (MN/m^2)	$tonf/in^2$	N/mm^2 (MN/m^2)
1	15.44	23	355.22	45	694.99	67	1034.77
2	30.89	24	370.66	46	710.44	68	1050.21
3	46.33	25	386.11	47	725.88	69	1065.66
4	61.78	26	401.55	48	741.33	70	1081.10
5	77.22	27	417.00	49	756.77	71	1096.55
6	92.67	28	432.44	50	772.22	72	1111.99
7	108.11	29	447.88	51	787.66	73	1127.43
8	123.55	30	463.33	52	803.10	74	1142.88
9	139.00	31	478.77	53	818.55	75	1158.32
10	154.44	32	494.22	54	833.99	76	1173.77
11	169.89	33	509.66	55	849.44	78	1204.66
12	185.33	34	525.11	56	864.88	80	1235.54
13	200.78	35	540.55	57	880.33	82	1266.43
14	216.22	36	555.99	58	895.77	84	1297.32
15	231.66	37	571.44	59	911.21	86	1328.21
16	247.11	38	586.88	60	926.66	88	1359.10
17	262.55	39	602.33	61	942.10	90	1389.99
18	278.00	40	617.77	62	957.55	92	1420.88
19	293.44	41	633.22	63	972.99	94	1451.76
20	308.89	42	648.66	64	988.44	96	1482.65
21	324.33	43	664.10	65	1003.88	98	1513.54
22	339.77	44	679.55	66	1019.32	100	1544.43

1.1.16 Conversion table: stress, kgf/mm^2 to N/mm^2 (MN/m^2)

kgf/mm^2	N/mm^2 (MN/m^2)	kgf/mm^2	N/mm^2 (MN/m^2)	kgf/mm^2	N/mm^2 (MN/m^2)	kgf/mm^2	N/mm^2 (MN/m^2)
1	9.81	23	225.55	45	441.30	67	657.05
2	19.61	24	235.36	46	451.11	68	666.85
3	29.42	25	245.17	47	460.91	69	676.66
4	39.23	26	254.97	48	470.72	70	686.47
5	49.03	27	264.78	49	480.53	71	696.27
6	58.84	28	274.59	50	490.33	72	706.08
7	68.65	29	284.39	51	500.14	73	715.89
8	78.45	30	294.20	52	509.95	74	725.69
9	88.26	31	304.01	53	519.75	75	735.50
10	98.07	32	313.81	54	529.56	76	745.31
11	107.87	33	323.62	55	539.37	78	764.92
12	117.68	34	333.43	56	549.17	80	784.53
13	127.49	35	343.23	57	558.98	82	804.15
14	137.29	36	353.04	58	568.79	84	823.76
15	147.10	37	362.85	59	578.59	86	843.37
16	156.91	38	372.65	60	588.40	88	862.99
17	166.71	39	382.46	61	598.21	90	882.60
18	176.52	40	392.27	62	608.01	92	902.21
19	186.33	41	402.07	63	617.82	94	921.83
20	196.13	42	411.88	64	627.63	96	941.44
21	205.94	43	421.69	65	637.43	98	961.05
22	215.75	44	431.49	66	647.24	100	980.67

1.1.17 Conversion table: degrees to radians

degree	rad	degree	rad	degree	rad	degree	rad	degree	rad
1	0.0175	19	0.3316	37	0.6458	55	0.9599	73	1.2741
2	0.0349	20	0.3491	38	0.6632	56	0.9774	74	1.2915
3	0.0524	21	0.3665	39	0.6807	57	0.9948	75	1.3090
4	0.0698	22	0.3840	40	0.6981	58	1.0123	76	1.3265
5	0.0873	23	0.4014	41	0.7156	59	1.0297	77	1.3439
6	0.1047	24	0.4189	42	0.7330	60	1.0472	78	1.3614
7	0.1222	25	0.4363	43	0.7505	61	1.0647	79	1.3788
8	0.1396	26	0.4538	44	0.7679	62	1.0821	80	1.3963
9	0.1571	27	0.4712	45	0.7854	63	1.0996	81	1.4137
10	0.1745	28	0.4887	46	0.8029	64	1.1170	82	1.4312
11	0.1920	29	0.5061	47	0.8203	65	1.1345	83	1.4486
12	0.2094	30	0.5236	48	0.8378	66	1.1519	84	1.4661
13	0.2269	31	0.5411	49	0.8552	67	1.1694	85	1.4835
14	0.2443	32	0.5585	50	0.8727	68	1.1868	86	1.5010
15	0.2618	33	0.5760	51	0.8901	69	1.2043	87	1.5184
16	0.2793	34	0.5934	52	0.9076	70	1.2217	88	1.5359
17	0.2967	35	0.6109	53	0.9250	71	1.2392	89	1.5533
18	0.3142	36	0.6283	54	0.9425	72	1.2566	90	1.5708

1.1.18 Preferred numbers

When one is buying, say, an electric lamp for use in the home, the normal range of lamps available is 15 W, 25 W, 40 W, 60 W, 100 W and so on. These watt values approximately follow a geometric progression, roughly giving a uniform percentage change in light emission between consecutive sizes. In general, the relationship between the sizes of a commodity is not random but based on a system of *preferred numbers.*

Preferred numbers are based on *R numbers* devised by Colonel Charles Renard. The principal series used are R5, R10, R20, R40 and R80 and subsets of these series. The values within a series are approximate geometric progressions based on common ratios of $\sqrt[5]{10}$, $\sqrt[10]{10}$, $\sqrt[20]{10}$, $\sqrt[40]{10}$ and $\sqrt[80]{10}$, representing changes between various sizes within a series of 58% for the R5 series, 26% for the R10, 12% for the R20, 6% for the R40 and 3% for the R80 series.

Further details on the values and use of preferred numbers may be found in BS 2045 : 1965. The rounded values for the R5 series are given as 1.00, 1.60, 2.50, 4.00, 6.30 and 10.00; these values indicate that the electric lamp sizes given above are based on the R5 series. Many of the standards in use are based on series of preferred numbers and these include such standards as sheet and wire gauges, nut and bolt sizes, standard currents (amperes) and rotating speeds of machine tool spindles.

1.1.19 Use of a calculator

In addition to normal arithmetic functions, 'scientific' type calculators have trigonometric, logarithmic and exponential function keys and complex calculations can be performed without the use of pencil and paper. Ways of using a calculator to solve various types of problems are shown below.

Symbols used

Symbol	Meaning	Symbol	Meaning
△ a	input data, i.e. input the value of a	○	perform operation shown in the circle
[M]	store in the memory	[M+]	add to the data in the memory
[MR]	recall contents of the memory to the display	[D]	the value displayed

Problems

$I = PlAN$ △P ○× △l ○× △A ○× △N ○= answer □D

$E = \dfrac{Wl}{Ax}$ △A ○× △x ○= □M △W ○× △l ○= ○÷ □MR ○= answer □D

$v = \sqrt{(2gh)}$ △2 ○× △g ○× △h ○= ○√ answer □D

$v = \sqrt{(u^2 + 2as)}$ △u ○sq □M △2 ○× △a ○× △s ○= ○+ □MR ○= ○√ answer □D

$l = \dfrac{\pi h}{4a^2}(D^2 - d^2)$ △D ○sq □M △d ○sq □M+ □MR ○× △π ○× △h ○= ○÷ △4 ○÷ △a ○÷ △a ○= answer □D

$A = \sqrt{[s(s-a)\,(s-b)\,(s-c)]}$ △s ○− △a ○= □M △s ○− △b ○= ○× □MR ○= □M △s ○− △c ○= ○× □MR ○= □M
△s ○× □MR ○= ○√ answer □D

$a = \dfrac{b \sin A}{\sin B}$ △B ○sin □M △A ○sin ○× △b ○= ○÷ □MR ○= answer □D

$a = \sqrt{(b^2 + c^2 - 2bc \cos A)}$ △b ○sq □M △c ○sq □M+ △A ○cos ○× △2 ○× △b ○× △c ○± □M+ □MR ○√ answer □D

$A = \arctan(\theta + \varphi)$ △θ ○+ △φ ○= ○inv ○tan answer □D

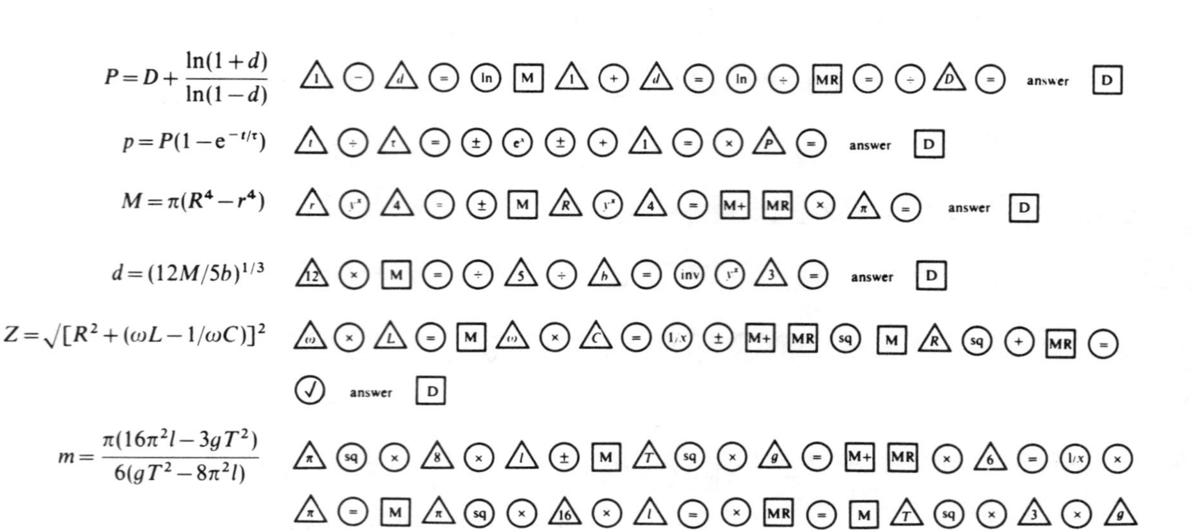

$P = D + \frac{\ln(1+d)}{\ln(1-d)}$
answer
$p = P(1 - e^{-t/\tau})$
answer
$M = \pi(R^4 - r^4)$
answer
$d = (12M/5b)^{1/3}$
answer
$Z = \sqrt{[R^2 + (\omega L - 1/\omega C)]^2}$
answer
$m = \frac{\pi(16\pi^2 l - 3gT^2)}{6(gT^2 - 8\pi^2 l)}$
answer

1.1.20 Mensuration

Planes

Square

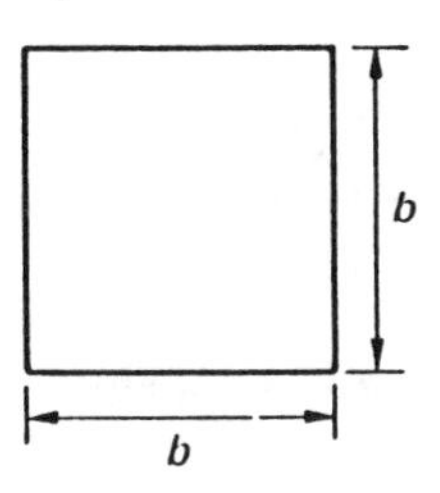

area $= b^2$
length of diagonal $= \surd(2) \times b$

Rectangle

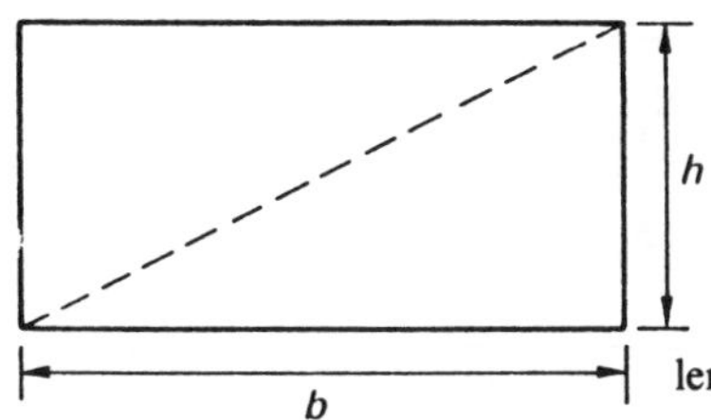

area $= b \times h$
length of diagonal $= \surd(b^2 + h^2)$

Parallelogram

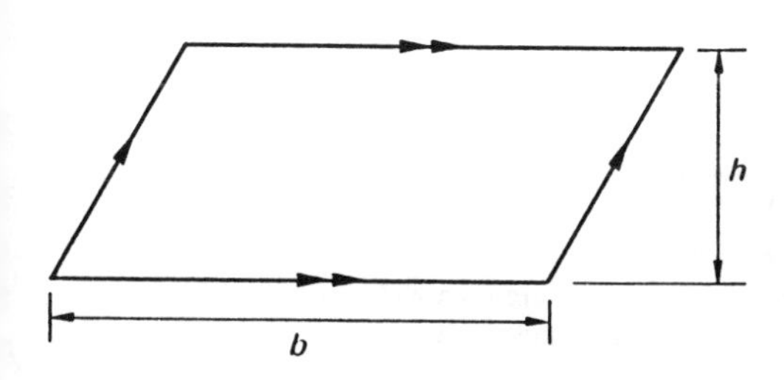

area $= b \times h$

Trapezium

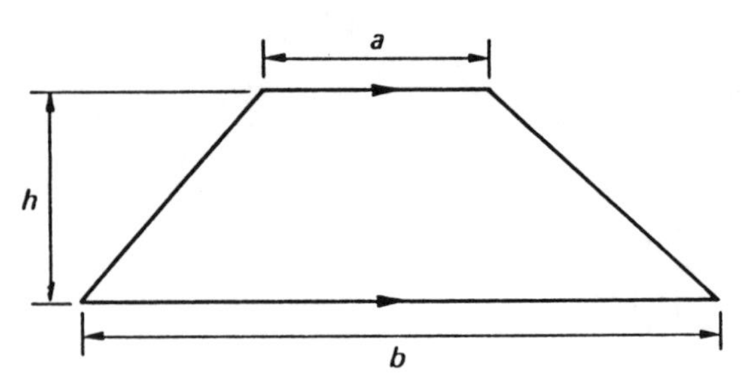

area $= \frac{1}{2} \times (a+b) \times h$

Triangle

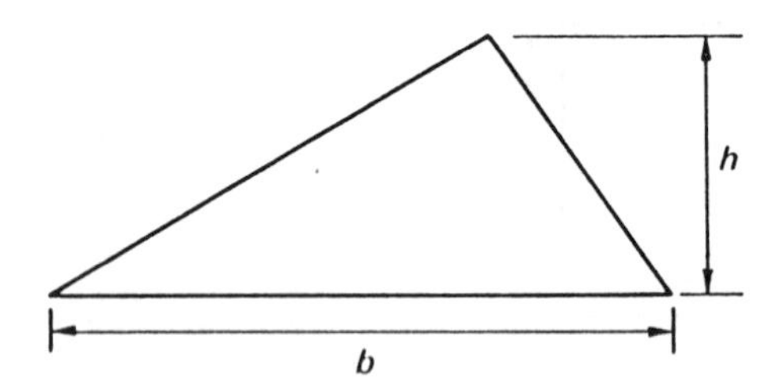

area $= \frac{1}{2} \times b \times h$

Circle

area $= \pi \times r^2$
perimeter $= 2 \times \pi \times r$

Sector of circle

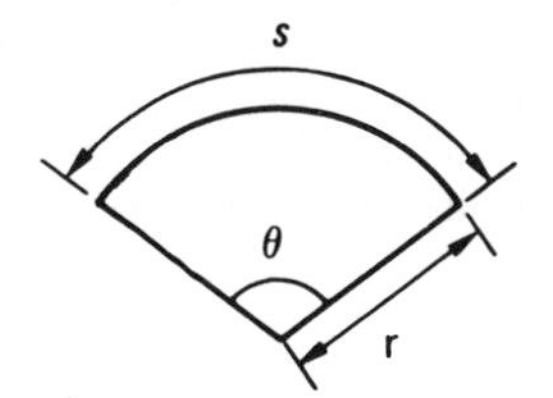

$$\text{area} = \tfrac{1}{2} \times r^2 \times \theta$$
arc length $s = r \times \theta$
(θ is in radians)

Ellipse

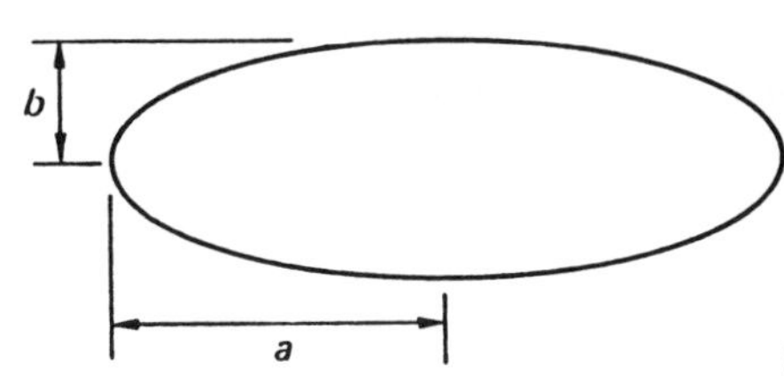

$$\text{area} = \pi \times a \times b$$
$$\text{perimeter} = \pi \times (a + b)$$

Irregular plane

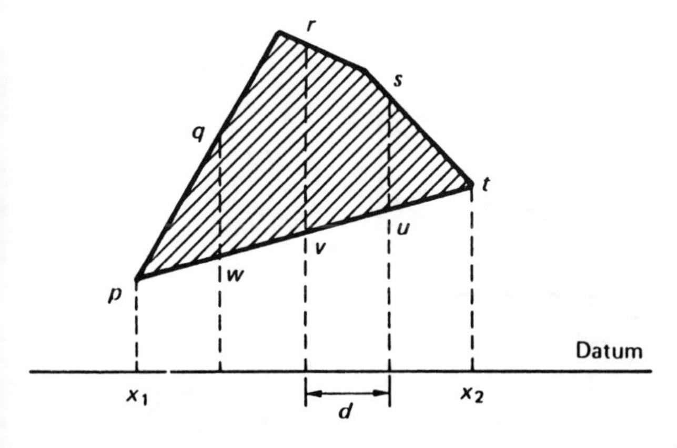

Several methods are used to find the shaded area, such as the mid-ordinate rule, the trapezoidal rule and Simpson's rule. As an example of these, Simpson's rule is as shown. Divide x_1x_2 into an even number of equal parts of width d. Let p, q, r, . . . be the lengths of vertical lines measured from some datum, and let A be the approximate area of the irregular plane, shown shaded. Then

$$A=\frac{d}{3}\,[(p+t)+4\,(q+s)+2r]-\frac{d}{3}\,[(p+t)+4(u+w)+2v]$$

In general, the statement of Simpson's rule is

approximate area $=(d/3)\times[$(first + last) + 4 × (sum of evens) + 2 × (sum of odds)$]$

where first, last, evens, odds refer to ordinate lengths and d is the width of the equal parts of the datum line.

Solids

Rectangular prism

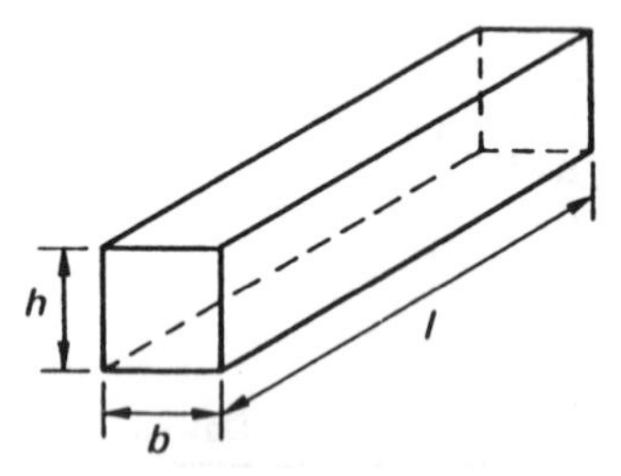

volume $=bhl$

total surface area $=2\,(bh+hl+lb)$

Cylinder

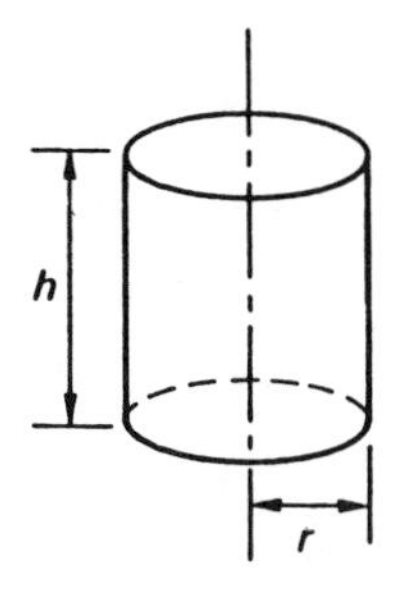

volume $=\pi r^2 h$
total surface area $=2\pi r(r+h)$

Cone

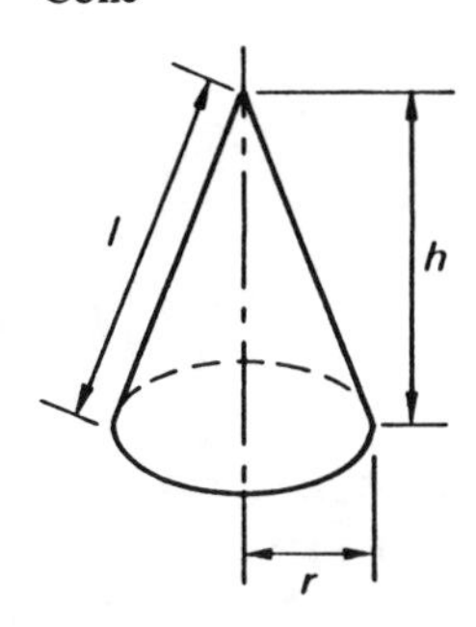

volume $=(1/3)\ \pi r^2 h$
total surface area $=\pi r(l+r)$

Frustrum of cone

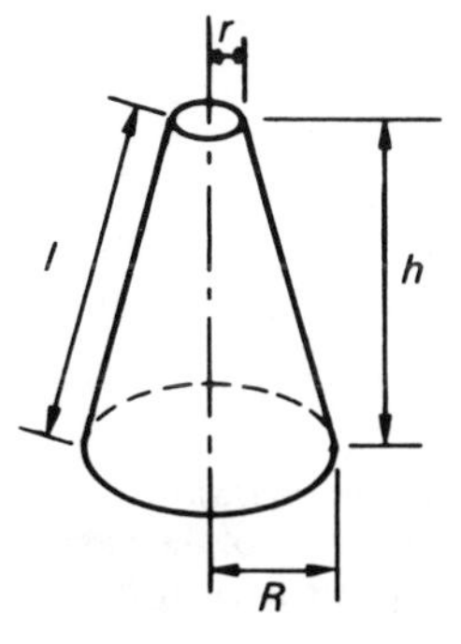

volume $=(1/3)\pi h(R^2+Rr+r^2)$
total surface area $=\pi l(R+r)+\pi(R^2+r^2)$

Sphere

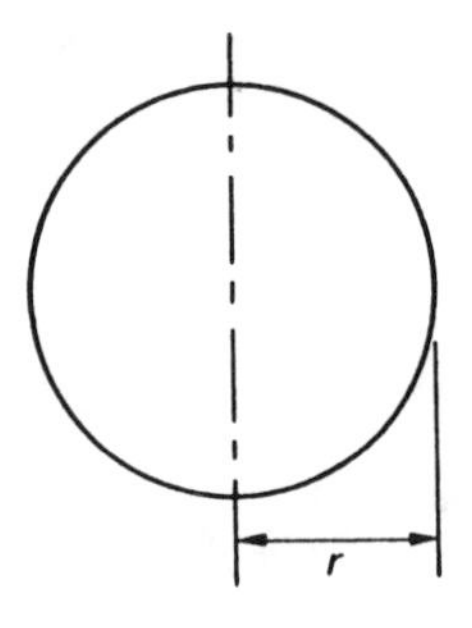

volume $= (4/3)\pi r^3$
total surface area $= 4\pi r^2$

Zone of sphere

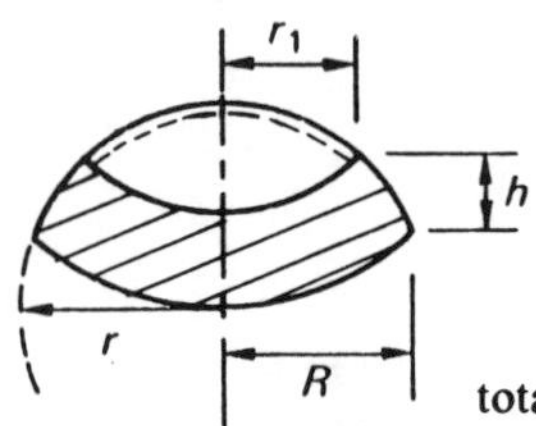

volume $= (\pi h/6)\ (h^2 + 3R^2 + 3r_1{}^2)$
total surface area $= 2\pi rh + \pi(R^2 + r_1{}^2)$
where r is the radius of the sphere

Pyramid

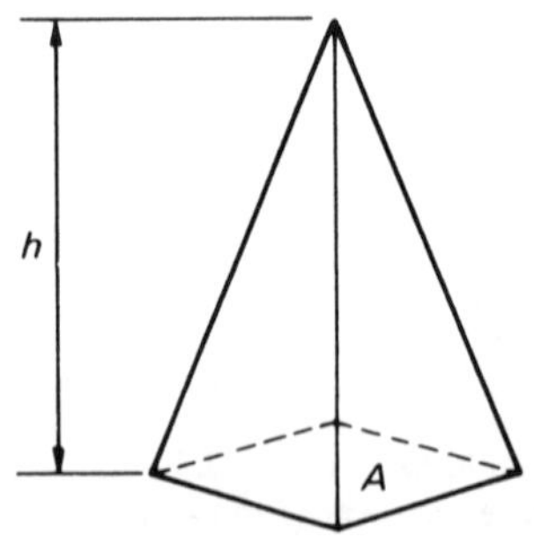

volume $= (1/3)Ah$
where A is the area of the base
and h is the perpendicular height

Regular solids

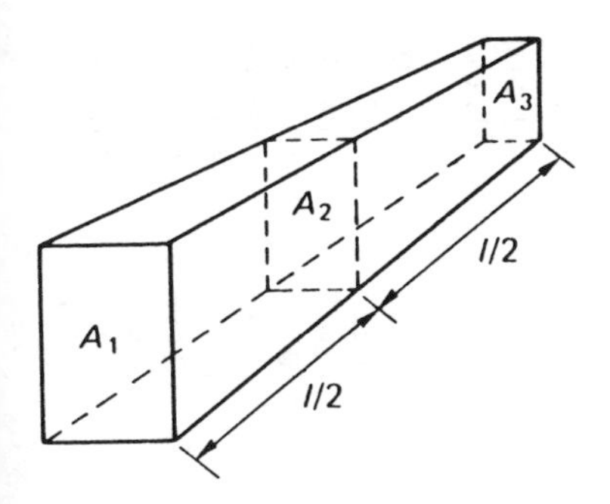

The volume of any regular solid can be found by using the prismoidal rule. Three parallel planes of areas A_1, A_3, A_2, are considered to be at the ends and at the centre of the solid respectively. Then

volume $= (l/6)\ (A_1 + 4A_2 + A_3)$

where l is the length of the solid.

Irregular solids

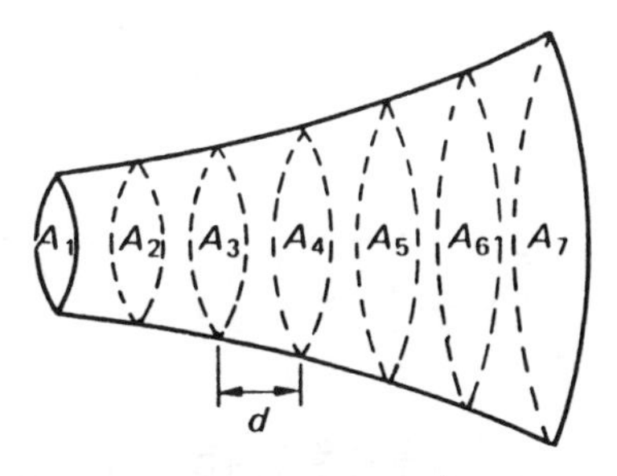

Various methods can be used to determine volumes of irregular solids; one of these is by applying the principles of Simpson's rule (see earlier this section). The solid is considered to be divided into an even number of sections by equally spaced, parallel planes, distance d apart and having areas of A_1, A_2, A_3, ... Assuming, say, seven such planes, then approximate volume $= (d/3)[(A_1 + A_7) + 4(A_2 + A_4 + A_6) + 2(A_3 + A_5)]$

1.1.21 Powers, roots and reciprocals

n	n^2	$\sqrt{n}$	$\sqrt{(10n)}$	n^3	$\sqrt[3]{n}$	$\sqrt[3]{(10n)}$	$\sqrt[3]{(100n)}$	$1/n$
1	1	1.000	3.162	1	1.000	2.154	4.642	1.000 00
2	4	1.414	4.472	8	1.260	2.714	5.848	0.500 00
3	9	1.732	5.477	27	1.442	3.107	6.694	0.333 33
4	16	2.000	6.325	64	1.587	3.420	7.368	0.250 00
5	25	2.236	7.071	125	1.710	3.684	7.937	0.200 00
6	36	2.449	7.746	216	1.817	3.915	8.434	0.166 67
7	49	2.646	8.367	343	1.913	4.121	8.879	0.142 86
8	64	2.828	8.944	512	2.000	4.309	9.283	0.125 00
9	81	3.000	9.487	729	2.080	4.481	9.655	0.111 11
10	100	3.162	10.000	1 000	2.154	4.642	10.000	0.100 00
11	121	3.317	10.488	1 331	2.224	4.791	10.323	0.090 91
12	144	3.464	10.954	1 738	2.289	4.932	10.627	0.083 33
13	169	3.606	11.402	2 197	2.351	5.066	10.914	0.076 92
14	196	3.742	11.832	2 744	2.410	5.192	11.187	0.071 43
15	225	3.873	12.247	3 375	2.466	5.313	11.447	0.066 67
16	256	4.000	12.649	4 096	2.520	5.429	11.696	0.062 50
17	289	4.123	13.038	4 913	2.571	5.540	11.935	0.058 82
18	324	4.243	13.416	5 832	2.621	5.646	12.164	0.055 56
19	361	4.359	13.784	6 859	2.668	5.749	12.386	0.052 63

20	400	4.472	14.142	8000	2.714	5.848	12.599	0.050 00
21	441	4.583	14.491	9261	2.759	5.944	12.806	0.047 62
22	484	4.690	14.832	10 648	2.802	6.037	13.006	0.045 45
23	529	4.796	15.166	12 167	2.844	6.127	13.200	0.043 48
24	576	4.899	15.492	13 824	2.884	6.214	13.389	0.041 67
25	625	5.000	15.811	15 625	2.924	6.300	13.572	0.040 00
26	676	5.099	16.125	17 576	2.962	6.383	13.751	0.038 46
27	729	5.196	16.432	19 683	3.000	6.463	13.925	0.037 04
28	784	5.292	16.733	21 952	3.037	6.542	14.095	0.035 71
29	841	5.385	17.029	24 389	3.072	6.619	14 260	0.034 48
30	900	5.477	17.321	27 000	3.107	6.694	14.422	0.033 33
31	961	5.568	17.607	29 791	3.141	6.768	14.581	0.032 26
32	1024	5.657	17.889	32 768	3.175	6.840	14.736	0.031 25
33	1089	5.745	18.166	35 937	3.208	6.910	14.888	0.030 30
34	1156	5.831	18.439	39 304	3.240	6.980	15.037	0.029 41
35	1225	5.916	18.708	42 875	3.271	7.047	15.183	0.028 57
36	1296	6.000	18.974	46 656	3.302	7.114	15.326	0.027 78
37	1369	6.083	19.235	50 653	3.332	7.179	15.467	0.027 03
38	1444	6.164	19.494	54 872	3.362	7.243	15.605	0.026 32
39	1521	6.245	19.748	59 319	3.391	7.306	15.741	0.025 64
40	1600	6.325	20.000	64 000	3.420	7.368	15.874	0.025 00
41	1681	6.430	20.248	68 921	3.448	7.429	16.005	0.024 39
42	1764	6.481	20.494	74 088	3.476	7.489	16.134	0.023 81
43	1849	6.557	20.736	79 507	3.503	7.548	16.261	0.023 26

continued

n	n^2	$\sqrt{n}$	$\sqrt{(10n)}$	n^3	$\sqrt[3]{n}$	$\sqrt[3]{(10n)}$	$\sqrt[3]{(100n)}$	$1/n$
44	1936	6.633	20.976	85 184	3.530	7.606	16.386	0.022 73
45	2025	6.708	21.213	91 125	3.557	7.663	16.510	0.022 22
46	2116	6.782	21.448	97 336	3.583	7.719	16.631	0.021 74
47	2209	6.856	21.679	103 823	3.609	7.775	16.751	0.021 28
48	2304	6.928	21.909	110 592	3.634	7.830	16.869	0.020 83
49	2401	7.000	22.136	117 649	3.659	7.884	16.985	0.020 41
50	2500	7.071	22.361	125 000	3.684	7.937	17.100	0.020 00
51	2601	7.141	22.583	132 651	3.708	7.990	17.213	0.019 61
52	2704	7.211	22.804	140 608	3.733	8.041	17.325	0.019 23
53	2809	7.280	23.022	148 877	3.756	8.093	17.435	0.018 87
54	2916	7.348	23.238	157 464	3.780	8.143	17.544	0.018 52
55	3025	7.416	23.452	166 375	3.803	8.193	17.652	0.018 18
56	3136	7.483	23.664	175 616	3.826	8.243	17.758	0.017 86
57	3249	7.550	23.875	185 193	3.849	8.291	17.863	0.017 54
58	3364	7.616	24.083	195 112	3.871	8.340	17.967	0.017 24
59	3481	7.681	24.290	205 379	3.893	8.387	18.070	0.016 95
60	3600	7.746	24.495	216 000	3.915	8.434	18.171	0.016 67
61	3721	7.810	24.698	226 981	3.936	8.481	18.272	0.016 39
62	3844	7.874	24.900	238 328	3.958	8.527	18.371	0.016 13
63	3969	7.937	25.100	250 047	3.979	8.573	18.469	0.015 87
64	4096	8.000	25.298	262 144	4.000	8.618	18.566	0.015 62

65	4225	8.062	25.495	274 625	4.021	8.662	18.663	0.015 38
66	4356	8.124	25.690	287 496	4.041	8.707	18.758	0.015 15
67	4489	8.185	25.884	300 763	4.062	8.750	18.852	0.014 93
68	4624	8.246	26.077	314 432	4.082	8.794	18.945	0.014 71
69	4761	8.307	26.268	328 509	4.102	8.837	19.038	0.014 49
70	4900	8.367	26.458	343 000	4.121	8.879	19.129	0.014 29
71	5041	8.426	26.646	357 911	4.141	8.921	19.220	0.014 08
72	5184	8.485	26.833	373 248	4.160	8.963	19.310	0.013 89
73	5329	8.544	27.019	389 017	4.179	9.004	19.399	0.013 70
74	5476	8.602	27.203	405 224	4.198	9.045	19.487	0.013 51
75	5625	8.660	27.386	421 875	4.217	9.086	19.574	0.013 33
76	5776	8.718	27.568	438 976	4.236	9.126	19.661	0.013 16
77	5929	8.775	27.749	456 533	4.254	9.166	19.747	0.012 99
78	6084	8.832	27.928	474 552	4.273	9.205	19.832	0.012 82
79	6241	8.888	28.107	493 039	4.291	9.244	19.916	0.012 66
80	6400	8.944	28.284	512 000	4.309	9.283	20.000	0.012 50
81	6561	9.000	28.460	531 441	4.327	9.322	20.083	0.012 35
82	6724	9.055	28.636	551 368	4.344	9.360	20.165	0.012 20
83	6889	9.110	28.810	571 787	4.362	9.398	20.247	0.012 05
84	7056	9.165	28.983	592 704	4.380	9.435	20.328	0.011 90
85	7225	9.220	29.155	614 125	4.397	9.473	20.408	0.011 76
86	7396	9.274	29.326	636 056	4.414	9.510	20.488	0.011 63
87	7569	9.327	29.496	658 503	4.431	9.546	20.567	0.011 49
88	7744	9.381	29.665	681 472	4.448	9.583	20.646	0.011 36
89	7921	9.434	29.833	704 969	4.465	9.619	20.724	0.011 24

continued

Section 1.1.21 (*continued*)

n	n^2	$\sqrt{n}$	$\sqrt{(10n)}$	n^3	$\sqrt[3]{n}$	$\sqrt[3]{(10n)}$	$\sqrt[3]{(100n)}$	$1/n$
90	8100	9.487	30.000	729 000	4.481	9.655	20.801	0.011 11
91	8281	9.539	30.166	753 571	4.498	9.691	20.878	0.010 99
92	8464	9.592	30.332	778 688	4.514	9.726	20.954	0.010 87
93	8649	9.644	30.496	804 357	4.531	9.761	21.029	0.010 75
94	8836	9.695	30.659	830 584	4.547	9.796	21.105	0.010 64
95	9025	9.747	30.822	857 375	4.563	9.830	21.179	0.010 53
96	9216	9.798	30.984	884 736	4.579	9.865	21.253	0.010 42
97	9409	9.849	31.145	912 673	4.595	9.899	21.327	0.010 31
98	9604	9.899	31.305	941 192	4.610	9.933	21.400	0.010 20
99	9801	9.950	31.464	970 299	4.626	9.967	21.472	0.010 10

1.1.22 Progressions

A set of numbers in which one number is connected to the next number by some law is called a *series* or a *progression.*

Arithmetic progressions

The relationship between consecutive numbers in an arithmetic progression is that they are connected by a *common difference.* For the set of numbers 3, 6, 9, 12, 15, . . ., the series is obtained by adding 3 to the preceding number; that is, the common difference is 3. In general, when a is the first term and d is the common difference, the arithmetic progression is of the form

Term	1st	2nd	3rd	4th	last
Value	a,	$a+d$,	$a+2d$,	$a+3d, \ldots,$	$a+(n-1)d$

where n is the number of terms in the progression

The sum S_n of all the terms is given by the average value of the terms times the number of terms; that is,

$$S_n = [(\text{first}+\text{last})/2] \times (\text{number of terms})$$
$$= [(a+a+(n-1)d)/2] \times n$$
$$= (n/2)\,[2a+(n-1)d]$$

Geometric progressions

The relationship between consecutive numbers in a geometric progression is that they are connected by a *common ratio.* For the set of numbers 3, 6, 12, 24, 48, . . ., the series is obtained by multiplying the preceding number by 2. In general, when a is the first term and r is the common ratio, the geometric progression is of the form

Term	1st	2nd	3rd	4th	last
Value	a,	ar,	ar^2,	$ar^3, \ldots,$	ar^{n-1}

where n is the number of terms in the progression.

The sum S_n of all the terms may be found as follows:

$$S_n = a + ar + ar^2 + ar^3 + \ldots + ar^{n-1} \qquad (1)$$

Multiplying each term of (1) by r gives

$$rS_n = \quad ar + ar^2 + ar^3 + \ldots + ar^{n-1} + ar^n \qquad (2)$$

Subtracting (2) from (1) gives

$$S_n(1-r)=a-ar^n \tag{3}$$
$$S_n=[a(1-r^n)]/(1-r)$$

Alternatively, multiplying both numerator and denominator by -1 gives

$$S_n=[a(r^n-1)]/(r-1) \tag{4}$$

It is usual to use equation (3) when $r < 1$ and (4) when $r > 1$.

When $-1>r>1$, each term of a geometric progression is smaller than the preceding term and the terms are said to *converge*. It is possible to find the sum of all the terms of a converging series. In this case, such a sum is called the sum to infinity. The term $[a(1-r^n)]/(1-r)$ can be rewritten as $[a/(1-r)]-[ar^n/(1-r)]$. Since r is less than 1, r^n becomes smaller and smaller as n grows larger and larger. When n is very large, r^n effectively becomes zero, and thus $[ar^n/(1-r)]$ becomes zero. It follows that the *sum to infinity of a geometric progression* is $a/(1-r)$, which is valid when $-1>r>1$.

Harmonic progressions

The relationship between numbers in a harmonic progression is that the *reciprocals* of consecutive terms form an arithmetic progression. Thus for the arithmetic progression 1, 2, 3, 4, 5, . . ., the corresponding harmonic progression is 1, 1/2, 1/3, 1/4, 1/5, ...

1.1.23 Trigonometric formulae

Basic definitions

In the right-angled triangle shown, a is the side *opposite* to angle A, b is the *hypotenuse* of the triangle and c is the side *adjacent* to angle A. By definition:

$$\sin A=\text{opp/hyp}=a/b$$
$$\cos A=\text{adj/hyp}=c/b$$
$$\tan A=\text{opp/adj}=a/c$$
$$\text{cosec } A=\text{hyp/opp}=b/a=1/\sin A$$
$$\sec A=\text{hyp/adj}=b/c=1/\cos A$$
$$\cot A=\text{adj/opp}=c/a=1/\tan A$$

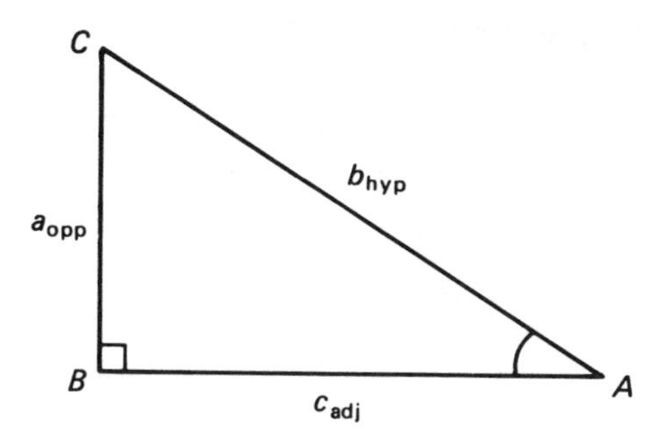

Identities

$$\sin^2 A + \cos^2 A = 1$$
$$1 + \tan^2 A = \sec^2 A$$
$$1 + \cot^2 A = \mathrm{cosec}^2 A$$
$$\sin(-A) = -\sin A$$
$$\cos(-A) = \cos A$$
$$\tan(-A) = -\tan A$$

Compound and double angle formulae

$$\sin(A+B) = \sin A \cos B + \cos A \sin B$$
$$\sin(A-B) = \sin A \cos B - \cos A \sin B$$
$$\cos(A+B) = \cos A \cos B - \sin A \sin B$$
$$\cos(A-B) = \cos A \cos B + \sin A \sin B$$
$$\tan(A+B) = (\tan A + \tan B)/(1 - \tan A \tan B)$$
$$\tan(A-B) = (\tan A - \tan B)/(1 + \tan A \tan B)$$
$$\sin 2A = 2 \sin A \cos A$$
$$\cos 2A = \cos^2 A - \sin^2 A = 2\cos^2 A - 1 = 1 - 2\sin^2 A$$
$$\tan 2A = (2 \tan A)/(1 - \tan^2 A)$$

'Product to sum' formulae

$$\sin A \cos B = \tfrac{1}{2}[\sin(A+B) + \sin(A-B)]$$
$$\cos A \sin B = \tfrac{1}{2}[\sin(A+B) - \sin(A-B)]$$
$$\cos A \cos B = \tfrac{1}{2}[\cos(A+B) + \cos(A-B)]$$
$$\sin A \sin B = -\tfrac{1}{2}[\cos(A+B) - \cos(A-B)]$$

Triangle formulae

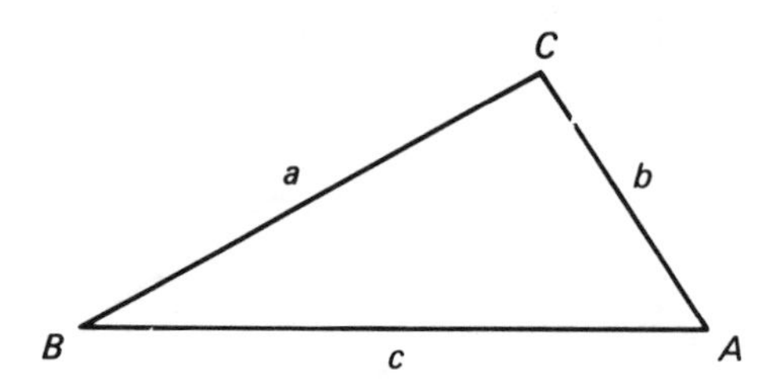

With reference to the figure:

Sine rule: $a/\sin A = b/\sin B = c/\sin C$

Cosine rule: $a^2 = b^2 + c^2 - 2bc \cos A$
$b^2 = c^2 + a^2 - 2ca \cos B$
$c^2 = a^2 + b^2 - 2ab \cos C$

Area: $\text{area} = \frac{1}{2}ab \sin C = \frac{1}{2}bc \sin A = \frac{1}{2}ca \sin B$

Also:

$$\text{area} = \sqrt{[s(s-a)(s-b)(s-c)]}$$

where s is the semi-perimeter, that is $(a+b+c)/2$.

1.1.24 Circles: some definitions and properties

For a circle of diameter d and radius r:

The *circumference* is πd or $2\pi r$
The area is $\pi d^2/4$ or πr^2.

An *arc* of a circle is part of the circumference.

A *tangent* to a circle is a straight line which meets the circle at one point only. A radius drawn from the point where a tangent meets a circle is at right angles to the tangent.

A *sector* of a circle is the area between an arc of the circle and two radii. The area of a sector is $\frac{1}{2}r^2\theta$, where θ is the angle in radians between the radii.

A *chord* is a straight line joining two points on the circumference of a circle. When two chords intersect, the product of the parts of one chord is equal to the products of the parts of the other chord. In the figure, $AE \times BE = CE \times ED$.

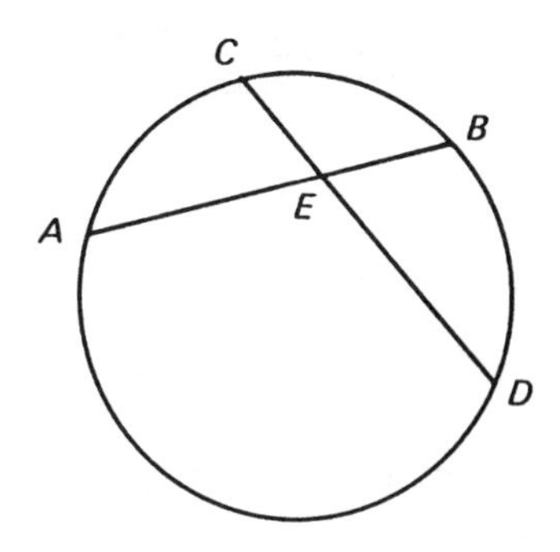

A *segment* of a circle is the area bounded by a chord and an arc. Angles in the same segment of a circle are equal: in the figure, angle A = angle B.

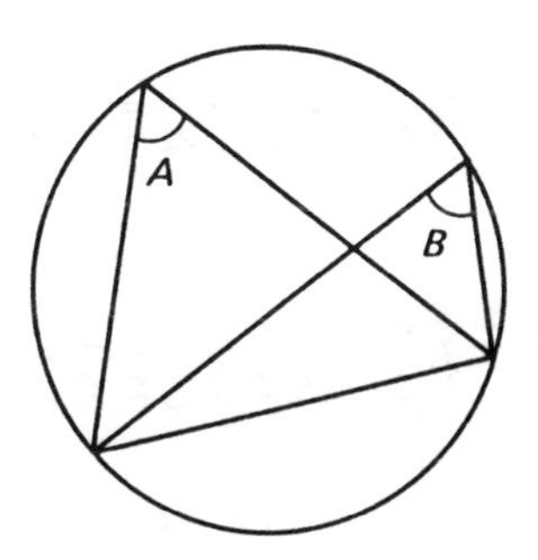

1.1.25 Circles: areas and circumferences

Dia.	*Area*	*Cir*	*Dia.*	*Area*	*Cir.*	*Dia.*	*Area*	*Cir.*
1	0.7854	3.142	34	907.92	106.8	67	3525.7	210.5
2	3.1416	6.283	35	962.11	110.0	68	3631.7	213.6
3	7.0686	9.425	36	1017.9	113.1	69	3739.3	216.8
4	12.566	12.57	37	1075.2	116.2	70	3848.5	219.9
5	19.635	15.71	38	1134.1	119.4	71	3959.2	223.1
6	28.274	18.85	39	1194.6	122.5	72	4071.5	226.2
7	38.485	21.99	40	1256.6	125.7	73	4185.4	229.3
8	50.265	25.13	41	1320.3	128.8	74	4300.8	232.5
9	63.617	28.27	42	1385.4	131.9	75	4417.9	235.6
10	78.540	31.42	43	1452.2	135.1	76	4536.5	238.8
11	95.033	34.56	44	1520.5	138.2	77	4656.6	241.9
12	113.10	37.70	45	1590.4	141.4	78	4778.4	245.0
13	132.73	40.84	46	1661.9	144.5	79	4901.7	248.2
14	153.94	43.98	47	1734.9	147.7	80	5026.5	251.3
15	176.71	47.12	48	1809.6	150.8	81	5153.0	254.5
16	201.06	50.27	49	1885.7	153.9	82	5381.0	257.6
17	226.98	53.41	50	1963.5	157.1	83	5410.6	260.8
18	254.47	56.55	51	2042.8	160.2	84	5541.8	263.9
19	283.53	59.69	52	2123.7	163.4	85	5674.5	267.0

20	314.16	62.83	53	2206.2	166.5	86	5808.8	270.2
21	346.36	65.97	54	2290.2	169.6	87	5944.7	273.3
22	380.13	69.11	55	2375.8	172.8	88	6082.1	276.5
23	415.48	72.26	56	2463.0	175.9	89	6221.1	279.6
24	452.39	75.40	57	2551.8	179.1	90	6361.7	282.7
25	490.87	78.54	58	2642.1	182.2	91	6503.9	285.9
26	530.93	81.68	59	2734.0	185.4	92	6647.6	289.0
27	572.56	84.82	60	2827.4	188.4	93	6792.9	292.2
28	616.75	87.96	61	2922.5	191.6	94	6939.8	295.3
29	660.52	91.11	62	3019.1	194.8	95	7088.2	298.5
30	706.86	94.25	63	3117.2	197.9	96	7238.2	301.6
31	754.77	97.39	64	3217.0	201.1	97	7389.8	304.7
32	804.25	100.5	65	3318.3	204.2	98	7543.0	307.9
33	855.30	103.7	66	3421.2	207.3	99	7697.7	311.0

1.1.26 Coordinate systems

The position of geometrical features on a workpiece are usually related to three mutually perpendicular axes. In addition, on numerically controlled machines and machine tools such as jig boring machines, it is necessary to define the position and movement of the workpiece relative to the cutting tool. Again it is usual to use a system of three mutually perpendicular axes.

The axes used in both these cases are given designations such as P, Q and R or X, Y and Z. The X axis is often selected to be on a horizontal plane, parallel to the work holding surface, and is considered to have positive values in the direction of cutting. The Y axis, in this system, is also on a horizontal plane and is at right angles to the X axis. The Z axis is taken to be normal (at right angles) to the work holding surface.

To determine the positive directions of the Y and Z axes, a 'right hand rule' can be used. The thumb, first and second fingers of the right hand are extended so that they are mutually at right angles and positioned so that the thumb and first finger are in a horizontal plane. The positive directions of the axes are then taken to be the directions in which the fingers are pointing, as shown in the figure.

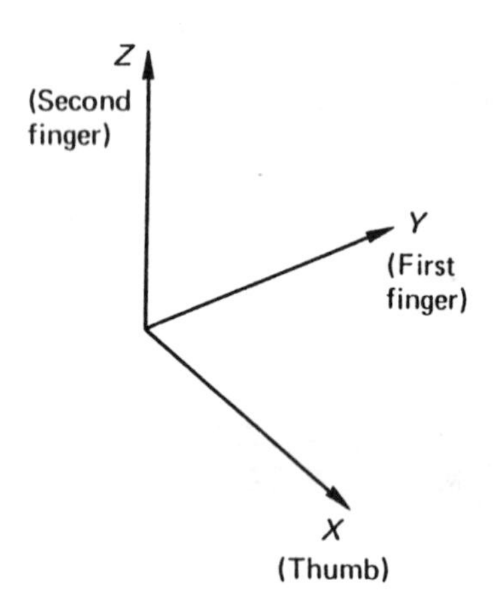

Rotation about the X, Y and Z axes is normally referred to as A, B and C respectively. The direction which will advance a right handed screw is taken as positive rotation, as shown in the figure.

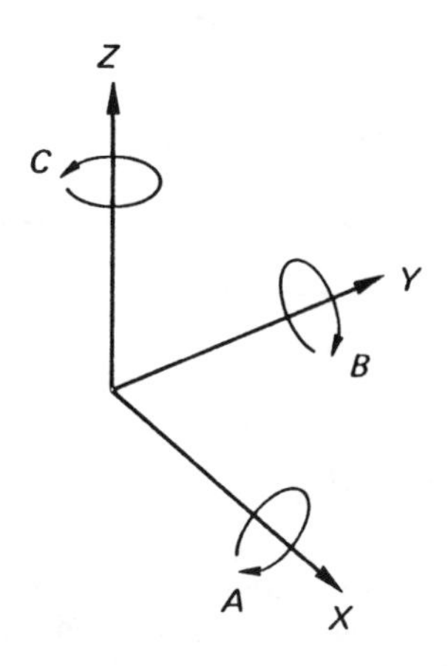

The system outlined above is used where power is transmitted to the tool to make it change its position. When the system is such that power is used to move the work holding surface relative to the tool, then designations such as X', Y' and Z' are used, since a negative movement of the work holding surface relative to a stationary tool has the same effect as a positive movement of the tool. (See also section 4.1.4.)

Rectangular (cartesian) coordinates

Here, features on a drawing or solid component are positioned by dimensioning from two mutually perpendicular datum surfaces, as shown in the figure.

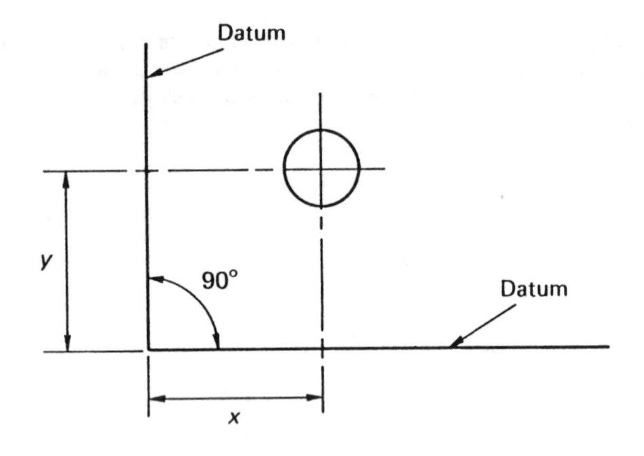

Polar coordinates

Here, features on a drawing or solid component are dimensioned by a radial distance from a datum point and an angular displacement from a datum line or datum edge (surface), as shown in the figure.

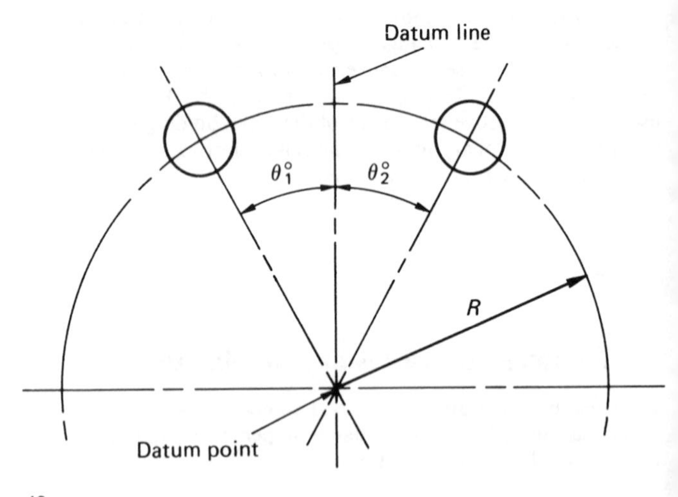

1.1.27 Statistics: an introduction

Basic concepts

To understand the fairly advanced statistics underlying quality control, a certain basic level of statistics is assumed by most texts dealing with this subject. The brief introduction given below should help to lead readers into the various texts dealing with quality control.

The *arithmetic mean*, or *mean*, is the average value of a set of data. Its value can be found by adding together the values of the members of the set and then dividing by the number of members in the set. Mathematically:

$$X=(X_1+X_2+\ldots+X_N)/N$$

Thus the mean of the set of numbers 4, 6, 9, 3 and 8 is $(4+6+9+3+8)/5=6$.

The *median* is either the middle value or the mean of the two middle values of a set of numbers arranged in order of magnitude. Thus the numbers 3, 4, 5, 6, 8, 9, 13 and 15 have a median value of $(6+8)/2=7$, and the numbers 4, 5, 7, 9, 10, 11, 15, 17 and 19 have a median value of 10.

The *mode* is the value in a set of numbers which occurs most frequently. Thus the set 2, 3, 3, 4, 5, 6, 6, 6, 7, 8, 9, and 9 has a modal value of 6.

The *range* of a set of numbers is the difference between the largest value and the smallest value. Thus the range of the set of numbers 3, 2, 9, 7, 4, 1, 12, 3, 17 and 4 is $17-1=16$.

The *standard deviation*, sometimes called the *root mean square deviation*, is defined by

$$s=\sqrt{\{[X_1-X)^2+(X_2-X)^2+\ldots+(X_N-X)^2]/N\}}$$

Thus for the numbers 2, 5 and 11, the mean is $(2+5+11)/3$, that is 6. The standard deviation is

$$s=\sqrt{\{[(2-6)^2+(5-6)^2+(11-6)^2]/3\}}$$
$$=\sqrt{[(16+1+25)/3]}=\sqrt{14}\approx 3.74$$

Usually s is used to denote the standard deviation of a population (the whole set of values) and σ is used to denote the standard deviation of a sample.

Probability

When an event can happen x ways out of a total of n possible and equally likely ways, the *probability* of the occurrence of the event is given by $p = x/n$. The probability of an event occurring is therefore a number between 0 and 1. If q is the probability of an event not occurring it also follows that $p + q = 1$. Thus when a fair six-sided dice is thrown, the probability of getting a particular number, say a three, is 1/6, since there are six sides and the number three only appears on one of the six sides.

Binomial distribution

The *binomial distribution* as applied to quality control may be stated as follows:

The probability of having 0, 1, 2, 3, . . ., n defective items in a sample of n items drawn at random from a large population, whose probability of a defective item is p and of a non-defective item is q, is given by the successive terms of the expansion of $(q+p)^n$, taking terms in succession from the right.

Thus if a sample of, say, 4 items is drawn at random from a machine producing an average of 5% defective items, the probability of having 0, 1, 2, 3 or 4 defective items in the sample can be determined as follows. By repeated multiplication,

$$(q+p)^4 = q^4 + 4q^3p + 6q^2p^2 + 4qp^3 + p^4$$

The values of q and p are $q = 0.95$ and $p = 0.05$. Thus

$$\begin{aligned}(0.95+0.05)^4 &= 0.95^4 + (4 \times 0.95^3 \times 0.05) + (6 \times 0.95^2 \times 0.05^2) \\ &\quad + (4 \times 0.95 \times 0.05^3) + 0.05^4 \\ &= 0.8145 + 0.1715 + 0.011\,354 + \ldots\end{aligned}$$

This indicates that

(a) 81% of the samples taken are likely to have no defective items in them.
(b) 17% of the samples taken are likely to have one defective item.
(c) 1% of the samples taken are likely to have two defective items.
(d) There will hardly ever be three or four defective items in a sample.

As far as quality control is concerned, if by repeated sampling these percentages are roughly maintained, the inspector is satisfied that the machine is continuing to produce about 5% defective items. However, if the percentages alter then it is likely that the defect rate has also altered. Similarly, a customer receiving a large batch of items can, by random sampling, find the number of defective items in the samples and by using the binomial distribution can predict the probable number of defective items in the whole batch.

Poisson distribution

The calculations involved in a binomial distribution can be very long when the sample number n is larger than about six or seven, and an approximation to them can be obtained by using a *Poisson distribution.* A statement for this is:

When the chance of an event occurring at any instant is constant and the expectation np of the event occurring is λ, then the probabilities of the event occurring 0, 1, 2, 3, 4, . . . times are given by

$$e^{-\lambda}, \lambda e^{-\lambda}, \lambda^2 e^{-\lambda}/2!, \lambda^3 e^{-\lambda}/3!, \lambda^4 e^{-\lambda}/4!, \ldots$$

where e is the constant 2.718 28 . . . and $2! = 2 \times 1$, $3! = 3 \times 2 \times 1$, $4! = 4 \times 3 \times 2 \times 1$, and so on (where 4! is read 'four factorial').

Applying the Poisson distribution statement to the machine producing 5% defective items, used above to illustrate a use of the binomial distribution, gives

expectation $np = 4 \times 0.05 = 0.2$
probability of no defective items is $e^{-\lambda} = e^{-0.2} = 0.8187$
probability of 1 defective item is $\lambda e^{-\lambda} = 0.2e^{-0.2} = 0.1637$
probability of 2 defective items is $\lambda^2 e^{-\lambda}/2! = 0.2^2 e^{-0.2}/2 = 0.0164$

It can be seen that these probabilities of approximately 82%, 16% and 2% compare quite well with the results obtained previously.

Normal distribution

Data associated with measured quantities such as mass, length, time and temperature is called *continuous*, that is, the data can

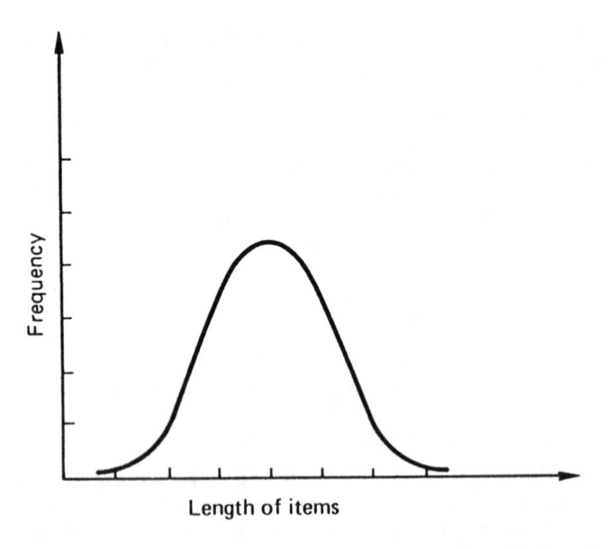

have any values between certain limits. Suppose that the lengths of items produced by a certain machine tool were plotted as a graph, as shown in the figure; then it is likely that the resulting shape would be mathematically definable. The shape is given by $y=(1/\sigma)e^z$, where $z=-x^2/2\sigma^2$, σ is the standard deviation of the data, and x is the frequency with which the data occurs. Such a curve is called a *normal probability* or a *normal distribution curve.* Important properties of this curve to quality control are:

(a) The area enclosed by the curve and vertical lines at ± 1 standard deviation from the mean value is approximately 67% of the total area.
(b) The area enclosed by the curve and vertical lines at ± 2 standard deviation from the mean value is approximately 95% of the total area.
(c) The area enclosed by the curve and vertical lines at ± 3 standard deviations from the mean value is approximately 99.75% of the total area.
(d) The area enclosed by the curve is proportional to the frequency of the population.

To illustrate a use of these properties, consider a sample of 30 round items drawn at random from a batch of 1000 items produced by a machine. By measurement it is established that the mean diameter of the samples is 0.503 cm and that the standard deviation of the samples is 0.0005 cm. The normal distribution curve theory may be used to predict the reject rate if, say, only items having a diameter of 0.502 to 0.504 cm are acceptable. The range of items accepted is $0.504 - 0.502 = 0.002$ cm. Since the standard deviation is 0.0005 cm, this range corresponds to ± 2 standard deviations. From (b) above, it follows that 95% of the items are acceptable, that is, that the sample is likely to have 28 to 29 acceptable items and the batch is likely to have 95% of 1000, that is, 950 acceptable items.

This example was selected to give exactly ± 2 standard deviations. However, sets of tables are available of *partial areas under the standard normal curve*, which enable any standard deviation to be related to the area under the curve.

1.2 Engineering science

1.2.1 Weight and mass

The SI system of units does not define weight. The relationship between force and mass is that a force of 1 newton imparts an acceleration of 1 metre per second squared to a mass of 1 kilogram. For a mass of 1 kg on a horizontal, frictionless plane, a force of 1 N is needed to impart an acceleration of 1 m/s^2. To lift the same mass vertically at the same acceleration, the force needed is about 9.81 N. It is this vertical force which just overcomes the gravitational force which is called the weight.

Since weight is frequently used when buying goods, a metric technical system of units (MKSA), based on a gravitational system, is widely used in Europe. Both the SI and MKSA systems use the kilogram as the unit of mass, but the MKSA system recognizes weight (representing a force) as 'kilogram force', signified by kgf. Unit kilogram force is defined as the force which imparts unit gravitational acceleration to unit mass.

For the principal systems of units, weight may be defined as

1 lbf per 1 lb in the FPS system
1 kgf per 1 kg in the MKSA system
9.806 65 N per 1 kg in the SI system

1.2.2 Heat

Temperature

The basic unit of thermodynamic temperature, the kelvin, is usually used in heat calculations which are equated to absolute zero temperature (0 K). The degree Celsius is the customary unit, where °C = K − 273.15, and for this scale the ice point of water is 0 °C and the boiling point of water at 1 standard atmosphere is 100 °C. The degree Fahrenheit is based on an ice point of water of 32 °F and a boiling point at 1 standard atmosphere of 212 °F, where °F = 32 + 1.8 × °C.

Specific heat capacity

This is the quantity of heat energy needed to raise the temperature of 1 kg of a substance by 1 °C, the unit being J/(kg °C) or J/(kg K). The specific heat capacity of water is normally taken as 4190 J/(kg °C). The quantity of heat energy Q needed to raise m kg of a substance having a specific heat capacity of c J/(kg °C) from t_1 °C to t_2 °C is given by

$$Q = m \times c \times (t_2 - t_1) \quad \text{joule}$$

Change of state

The specific latent heat of fusion is the heat required to convert 1 kg of the solid at its melting point into a liquid at the same temperature. For ice it is about 335 kJ/kg at 0 °C.

The specific heat of vaporization is the heat required to convert 1 kg of a liquid at its melting point to a gaseous state at the same temperature. For water it is about 2257 kJ/kg at 100 °C.

Conduction

The rate of heat flow ($\mathrm{d}Q/\mathrm{d}t$) through a surface, measured at right angles to the surface, is given by the product thermal conductivity (λ) × area (A) × temperature gradient ($\mathrm{d}T/\mathrm{d}x$), i.e.

$$\frac{\mathrm{d}Q}{\mathrm{d}t} = -\lambda \times A \times \frac{\mathrm{d}T}{\mathrm{d}x}$$

Typical values of thermal conductivity in W/(m °C) are glass 0.8, brick 0.6 and glass wool 0.04.

1.2.3 Sound

Velocity

The approximate velocity of sound in metres per second for some substances is as follows:

air 330	lead 1200
water 1500	brass 3500
oak 3850	iron 5000
glass 5000	aluminium 5100

Intensity

The loudness of sounds is measured in decibels (dB), and

$$\text{sound intensity} = 20 \times \log_{10}\left(\frac{P}{P_0}\right)$$

where P is the measured sound intensity and $P_0 = 2 \times 10^{-5}$ Pa. Some typical values are: 10 dB virtual silence; 40 dB a quiet street; 70 dB loud conversation; 120 dB near an aeroplane engine.

1.2.4 Electrical formulae

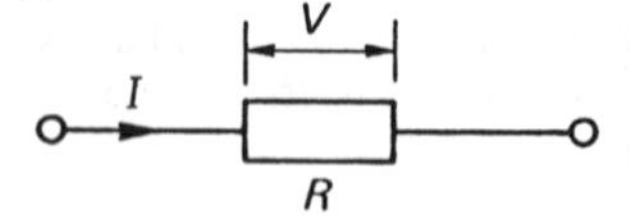

Resistors

$R = V/I$ where R = resistance (ohm, Ω)
$V = IR$ $\quad I$ = current (ampere, A)
$I = V/R$ $\quad V$ = potential difference or pd (volt, V)

Power

$P = IV$
$P = I^2R$
$P = V^2/R$ where P = power (watt, W)

Resistors in series

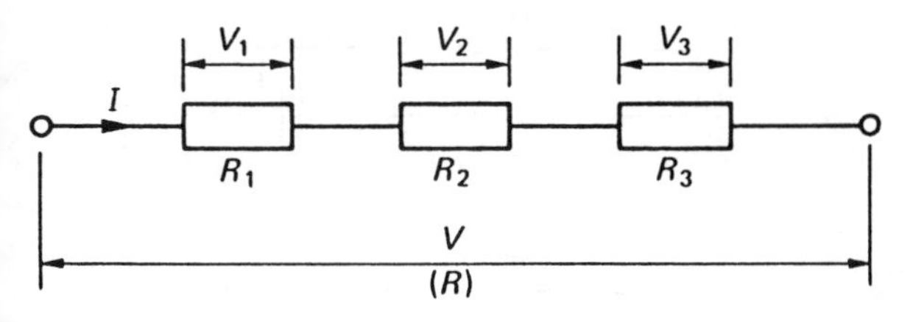

$R = R_1 + R_2 + R_3 + \ldots$
$V = V_1 + V_2 + V_3 + \ldots$
I is constant throughout the circuit.

Resistors in parallel

$1/R = 1/R_1 + 1/R_2 + 1/R_3 + \ldots$
$I = I_1 + I_2 + I_3 + \ldots$
V is constant across each limb of the circuit.

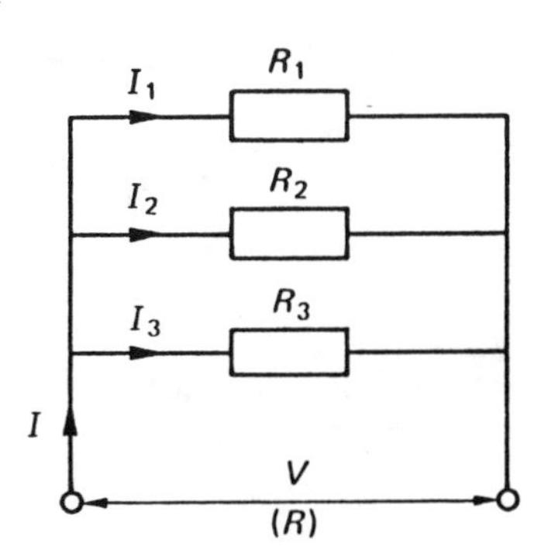

Capacitors

$Q = VC$ where Q = charge (coulomb, C)
V = potential difference (volt, V)
C = capacitance (farad, F)

$X_c = 1/2\pi fC$ where X_c = capacitive reactance (ohm, Ω)
$I = V/X_C$ f = frequency (hertz, Hz)
C = capacitance (farad, F)

Capacitors in series

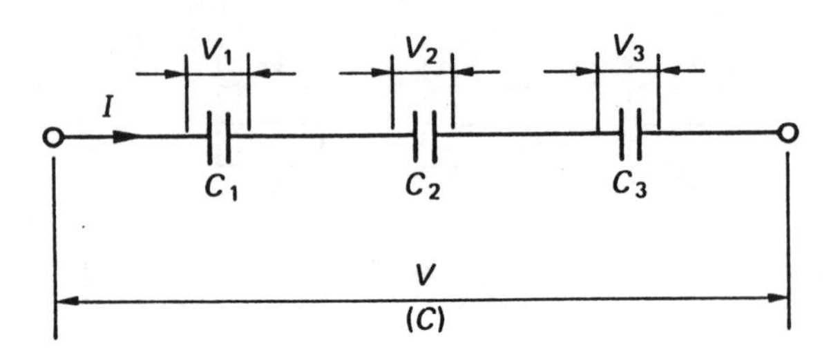

$1/C = 1/C_1 + 1/C_2 + 1/C_3$
$V = V_1 + V_2 + V_3$
$= Q/C_1 + Q/C_2 + Q/C_3$
I is constant throughout the circuit.

Capacitors in parallel

$C = C_1 + C_2 + C_3$
$I = I_1 + I_2 + I_3$
V is constant across each limb of the circuit.

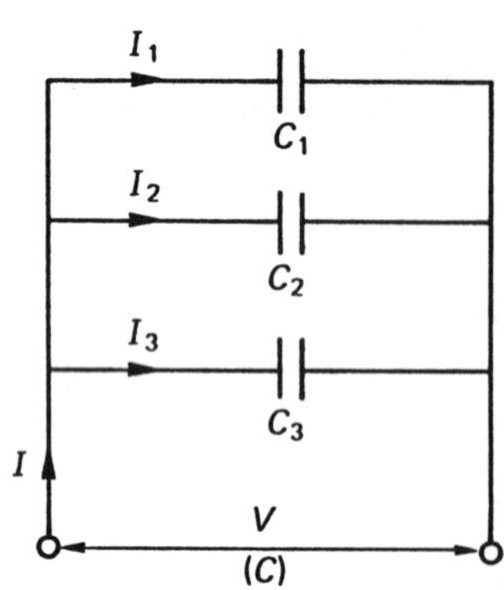

Time constant: resistance and capacitance

$\tau = RC$
where τ = time constant (s)
R = resistance (Ω)
C = capacitance (F)

The time constant (Greek letter tau, τ) for a resistance-capacitance series circuit is defined as the time taken for the pd across the capacitor to reach 63% of its final steady state value. For all practical purposes the steady state value is assumed to be reached in 5τ seconds.

Inductive reactance

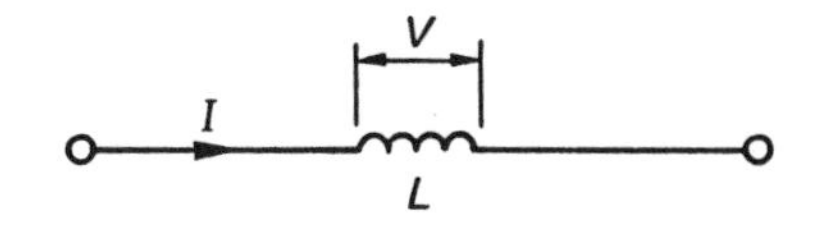

$X_L = 2\pi fL$ where X_L = inductive reactance (Ω)
f = frequency (Hz)
$I = V/X_L$ L = inductance (henrys, H)

Impedance: resistance and capacitance

$Z = \sqrt{(R^2 + X_C^2)}$

$R = V_R/I$

$X_C = V_C/I$

$Z = V/I$

$\tan\phi = \frac{X_c}{R}$

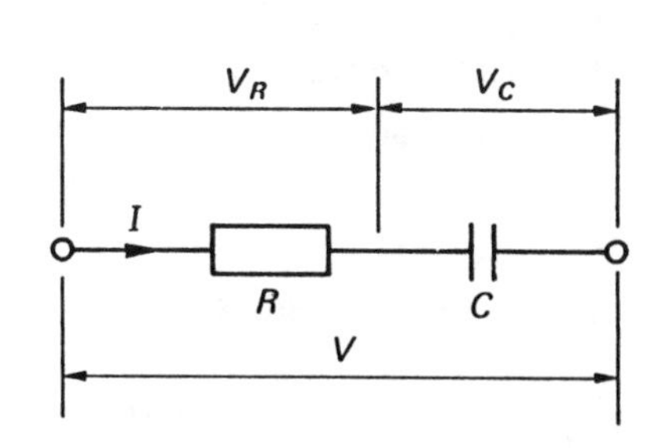

where:
Z = impedance (Ω)
R = resistance (Ω)
X_C = capacitive reactance (Ω)
I = current (A)
V_R = pd across resistor (V)
V_C = pd across capacitor (V)
V = pd across circuit (V)
ϕ = phase angle

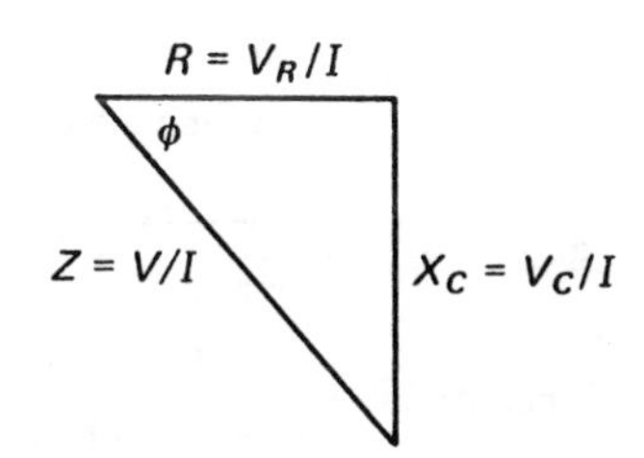

Impedance: resistance and inductance

$Z=\sqrt{(R^2+X_L^2)}$

$R=V_R/I$

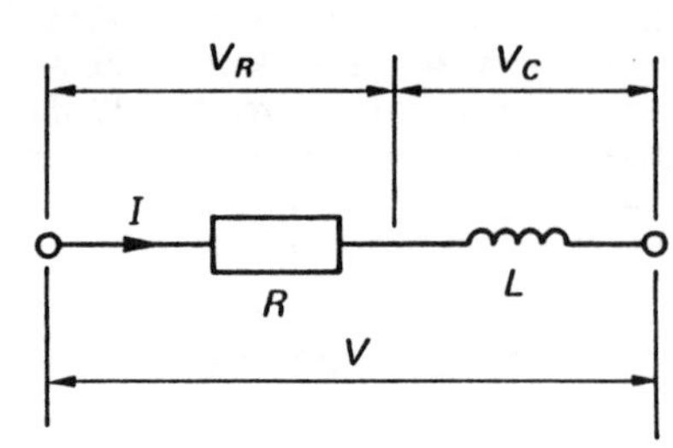

$X_L=V_L/I$

$Z=V/I$

$\tan\phi=\dfrac{X_L}{R}$

where:
Z = impedance (Ω)
R = resistance (Ω)
X_L = inductive reactance (Ω)

I = current (A)
V_R = pd across resistor (V)
V_L = pd across inductor (V)
V = pd across circuit (V)

ϕ = phase angle

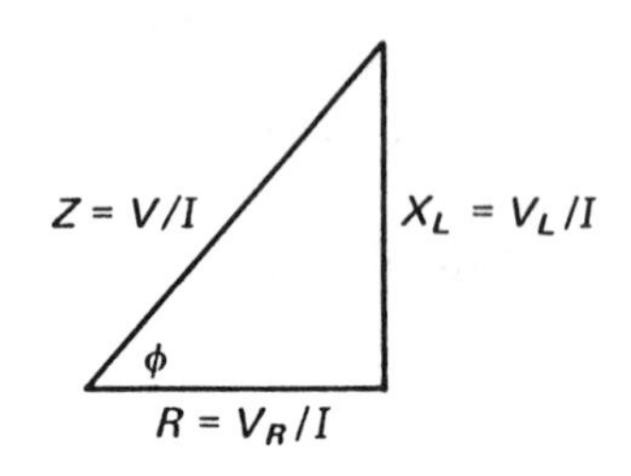

1.2.5 Stress and strain

$$\text{Direct stress } \sigma=\frac{\text{applied force } F}{\text{cross-sectional area } A}$$

$$\text{Direct strain } \varepsilon=\frac{\text{change in length } \delta l}{\text{original length } l}$$

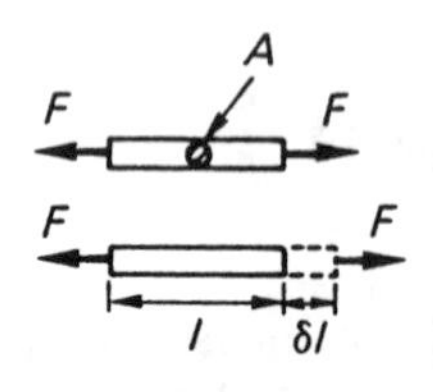

$$\text{Shear stress } \tau=\frac{\text{shear force } Q}{\text{area in shear } A}$$

$$\text{Shear strain } \gamma=\frac{\text{deformation } x}{\text{original dimension } l}$$

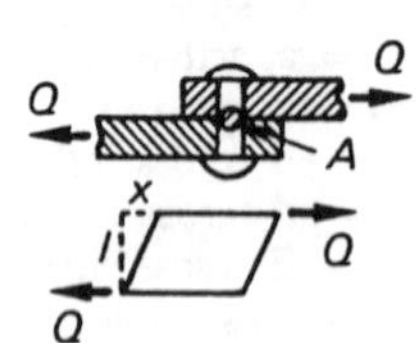

Modulus of elasticity $E = \dfrac{\text{direct stress } \sigma}{\text{direct strain } \varepsilon}$

Modulus of rigidity $G = \dfrac{\text{shear stress } \tau}{\text{shear strain } \gamma}$

For metallic materials:
Stress is usually of sufficient magnitude to be measured in MN/m^2 (meganewtons per square metre).
The modulus of elasticity or rigidity is measured in GN/m^2 (giganewtons per square metre).

Torsional stress

When a shaft of circular cross-section is acted upon by a torque T:

(a) All sections of the shaft remain circular and of unchanged diameter
(b) Plane cross-sections remain plane (circular only) providing the angle of twist is small.

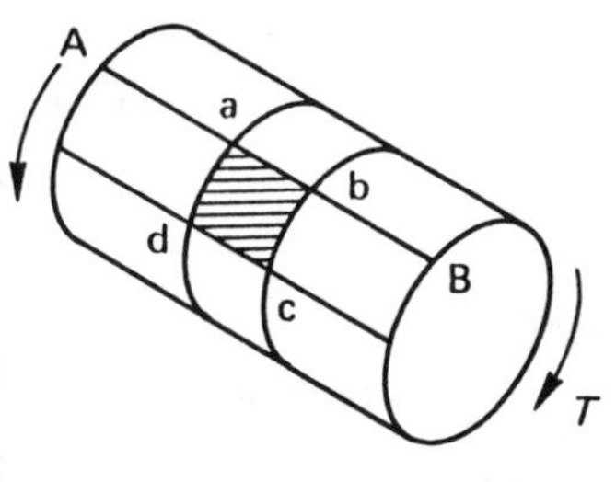

AB is parallel to the axis when *no* torque is applied.

For the isolated cylindrical element from the shaft, the end faces remain plane and any rectangular surface element abcd will be in a state of pure shear. Shear stresses along ad and bc will induce complementary shear stress along ab and cd.

Longitudinal twisting of the shaft occurs so that the lengths ab and cd are sheared through angle ϕ. The original line AB will have twisted through angle ϕ to AB_1.

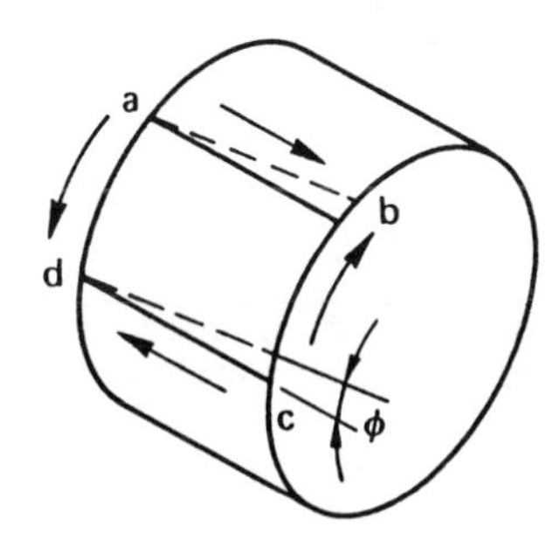

For pure shear and small angles of twist, angle ϕ represents shear strain and τ is the shear stress at the surface of the shaft. Thus

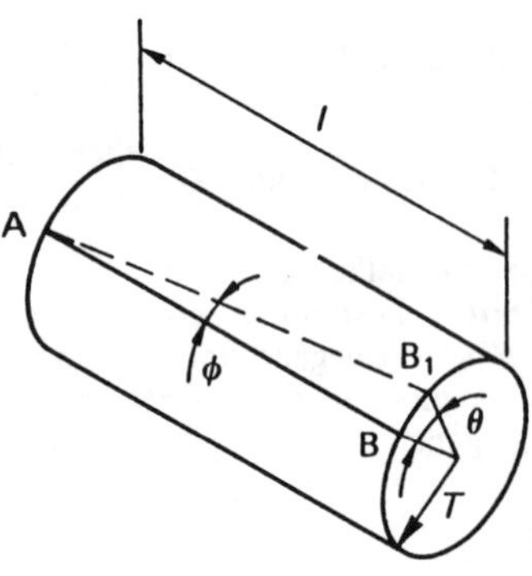

$$\frac{\text{shear stress } \tau}{\text{shear strain } \phi} = \text{modulus of rigidity } G \tag{1}$$

Also

arc $BB_1 = l\phi$ providing ϕ is small

and

arc $BB_1 = r^{\theta}$

where

r = radius of shaft and θ = angle of twist over full length l of shaft.

Therefore

$$l\phi = \text{arc } BB_1 = r\theta$$
$$\phi = r\theta/l$$

Substituting for ϕ in (1):

$$G = \frac{\tau}{r\theta/l} \text{ or } \frac{\tau}{r} = \frac{G\theta}{l}$$

Note

Since G and l are constant for any given shaft and θ is constant for all radii at any particular cross-section, then

$$\frac{\tau}{r} = \text{constant}$$

Thus the shear stress at any point within a given cross-section is proportional to the radius, and the stress increases uniformly from zero at the centre of the shaft to a maximum at the outside radius. For this reason it is apparent that a hollow shaft can transmit a greater torque than a solid shaft of the same cross-sectional area.

1.2.6 Stress in thin cylindrical shells

Hoop stress

P = pressure acting radially on thin shell

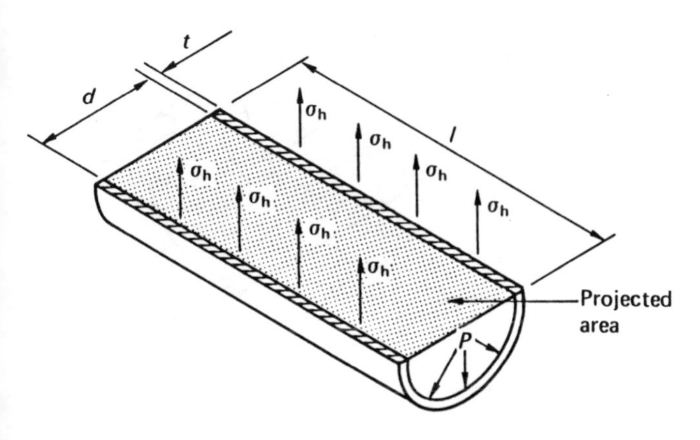

Internal pressure P tends to increase the diameter of the cylinder. This stretches the cylinder walls circumferentially and sets up a tensile stress known as the hoop stress σ_h.

The force due to the internal pressure P is balanced by the hoop stress σ_h. Hence:

hoop stress × area = pressure × projected area

$$\sigma_h \times 2lt = P \times dl$$

$$\sigma_h = Pd/2t$$

Longitudinal stress

The internal pressure P also induces a tensile stress in the longitudinal direction known as the longitudinal stress σ_l.

Hence the pressure P acting over the area $\pi d^2/4$ is balanced by the longitudinal stress σ_l acting over the area πdt. (Strictly the mean diameter should be used, but as the wall thickness t is small compared with the diameter, the approximation is adequate.) Thus

$$P \times \frac{\pi d^2}{4} = \sigma_l \times \pi dt$$

$$\sigma_l = \frac{\pi P d^2}{4\pi dt}$$

$$\sigma_l = \frac{Pd}{4t}$$

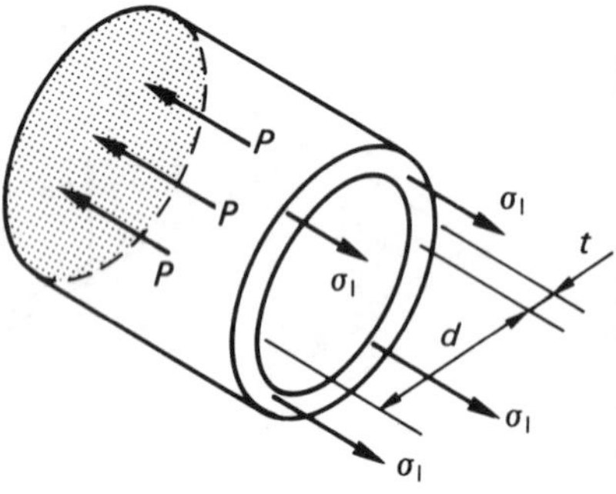

Note

The equations for σ_h and σ_l assume stresses are, for all practical purposes, constant over the wall thickness. This is only valid if the ratio of thickness to internal diameter is less than 1:20.

1.2.7 Beams: shearing force and bending moment diagrams

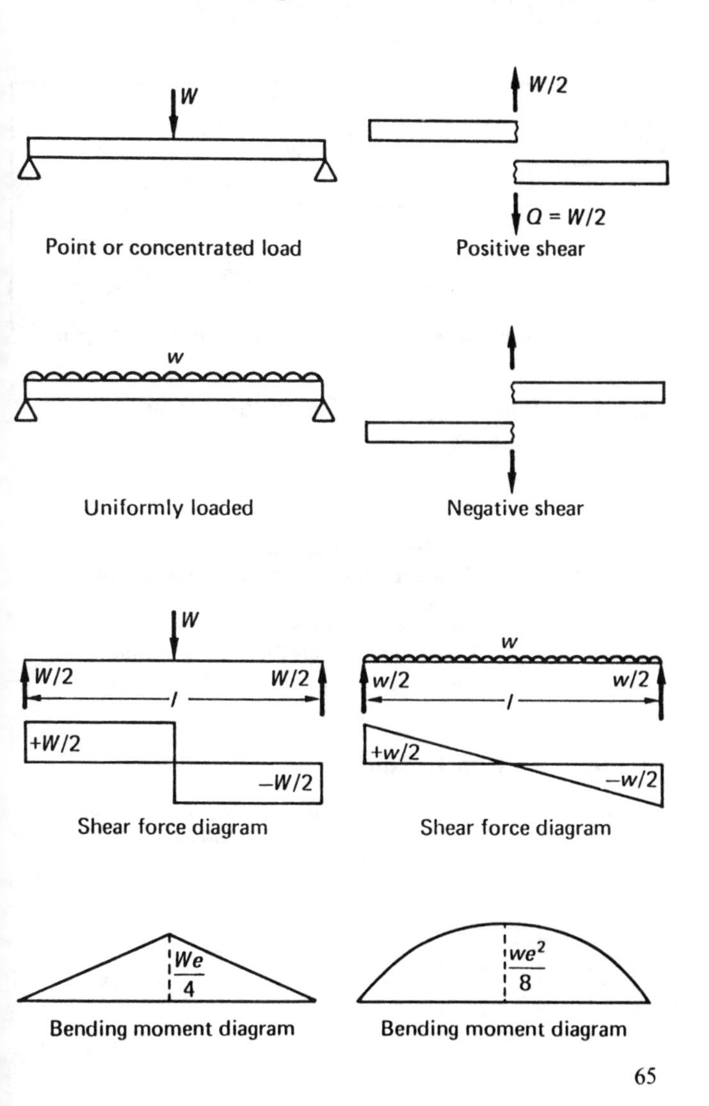

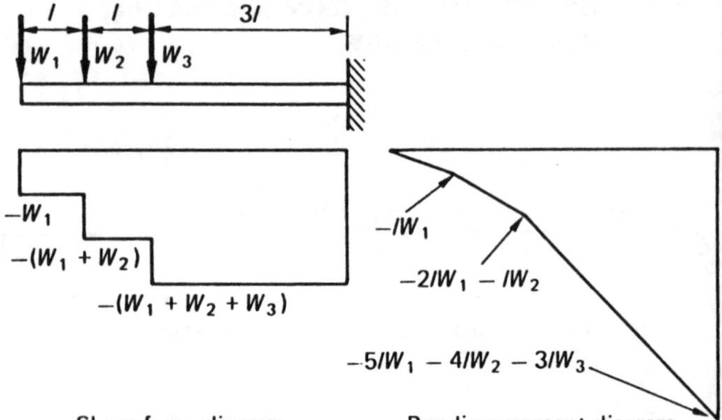

Shear force diagram

Bending moment diagram

1.2.8 Beams: general formulae for simple bending

$$\frac{M}{I}=\frac{\sigma}{y}=\frac{E}{R}$$ where

M = bending moment
I = second moment of area (moment of inertia)
σ = stress
y = distance from neutral axis
E = elastic modulus for beam material
R = radius of curvature of beam

1.2.9 Section formulae

Section	*Second moment of area* I_{XX}	*Section modulus* $z = I/y$	*Radius of gyration* $k=\sqrt{(I/A)}$
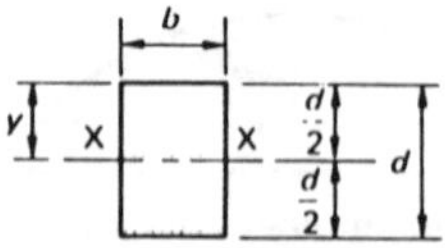	$\frac{bd^3}{12}$	$\frac{bd^2}{6}$	$\frac{d}{\sqrt{12}}$

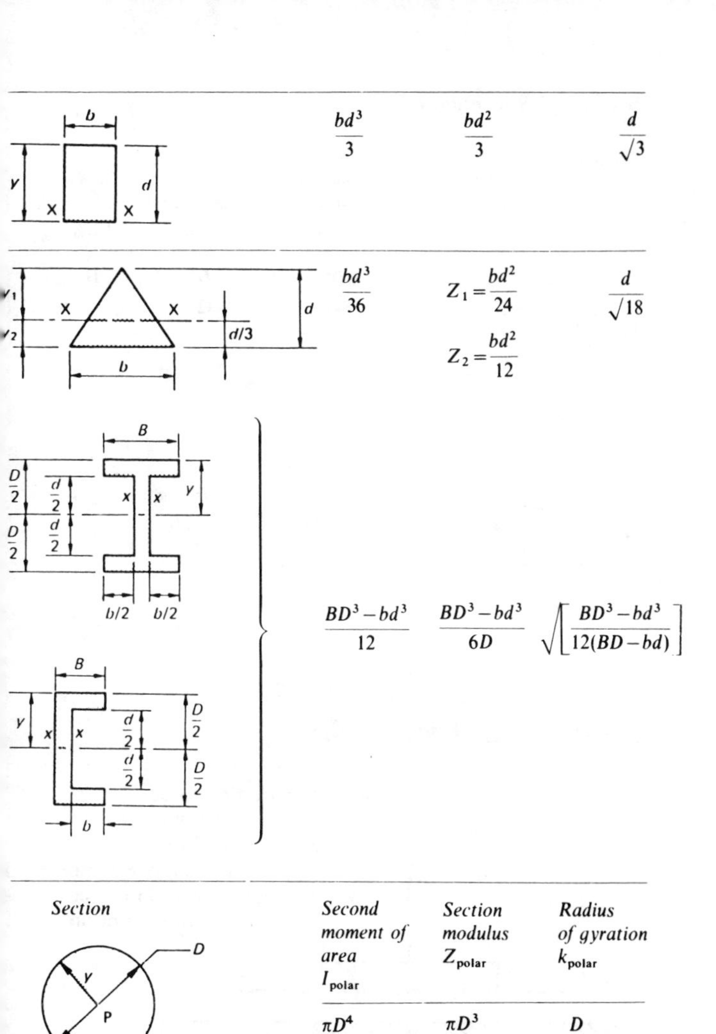

Rectangle (about base)	$\frac{bd^3}{3}$	$\frac{bd^2}{3}$	$\frac{d}{\sqrt{3}}$
Triangle	$\frac{bd^3}{36}$	$Z_1 = \frac{bd^2}{24}$ $Z_2 = \frac{bd^2}{12}$	$\frac{d}{\sqrt{18}}$
I-section and channel section	$\frac{BD^3 - bd^3}{12}$	$\frac{BD^3 - bd^3}{6D}$	$\sqrt{\left[\frac{BD^3 - bd^3}{12(BD - bd)}\right]}$

Section	*Second moment of area* I_{polar}	*Section modulus* Z_{polar}	*Radius of gyration* k_{polar}
Circle	$\frac{\pi D^4}{32}$	$\frac{\pi D^3}{16}$	$\frac{D}{\sqrt{8}}$

continued

Section	*Second moment of area* I_{polar}	*Section modulus* Z_{polar}	*Radius of gyration* k_{polar}
D, Y, X, X	$\dfrac{\pi D^4}{64}$	$\dfrac{\pi D^3}{32}$	$\dfrac{D}{4}$
D, d, Y, X, X	$\dfrac{\pi(D^4 - d^4)}{64}$	$\dfrac{\pi(D^4 - d^4)}{32D}$	$\dfrac{\sqrt{(D^2 - d^2)}}{4}$

1.2.10 Static friction: dry

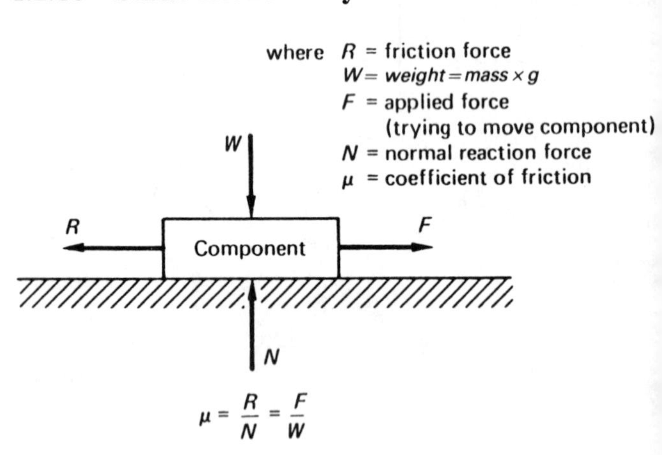

$$\mu = \frac{R}{N} = \frac{F}{W}$$

Values of μ for various combinations of materials

Steel on steel	0.8
Steel on copper-lead alloy	0.22
Steel on phosphor-bronze	0.35
Steel or brass	0.35
Steel on cast iron	0.4
Steel on Teflon	0.04
Cast iron on cast iron	1.0
Cast iron on Ferodo brake lining: dry	0.4
wet	0.2

1.2.11 Levers

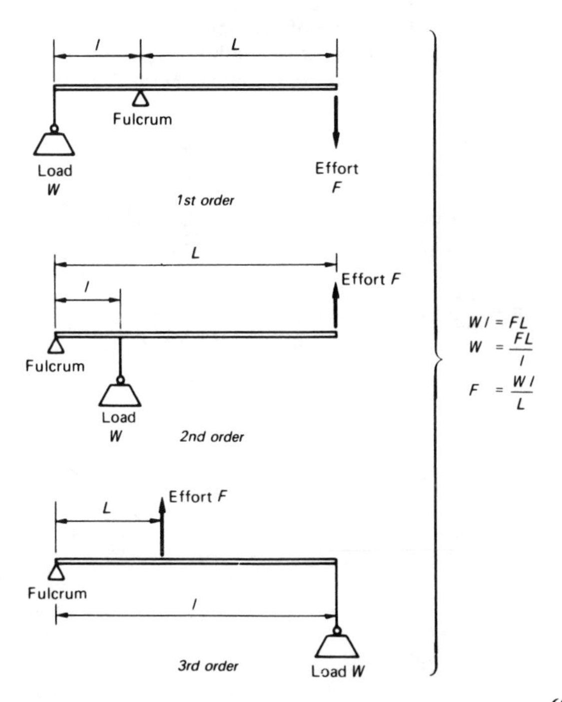

1.2.12 Formulae relating to rotary motion

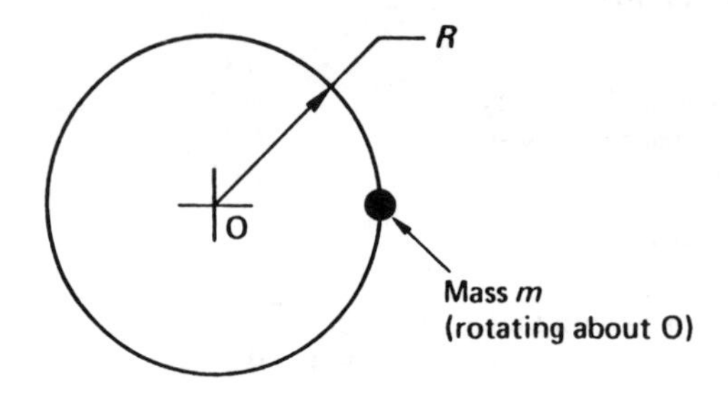

where F = centrifugal force (N)
m = mass of revolving body (kg)
v = rotational velocity (m/s)
R = radius of rotation (m)
n = number of revolutions per minute
g = gravitational acceleration (9.81 m/s^2)

$$F = \frac{mv^2}{R} \qquad R = \frac{mv^2}{F}$$

$$F = \frac{4mR\pi^2n^2}{60^2} \qquad n = \sqrt{\left(\frac{900F}{\pi^2mR}\right)}$$

$$m = \frac{FR}{v^2} \qquad v = \sqrt{\left(\frac{FR}{m}\right)}$$

Part 2 Engineering Design Data

2.1 Screwed fastenings

2.1.1 Drawing proportions

Bolts and screws

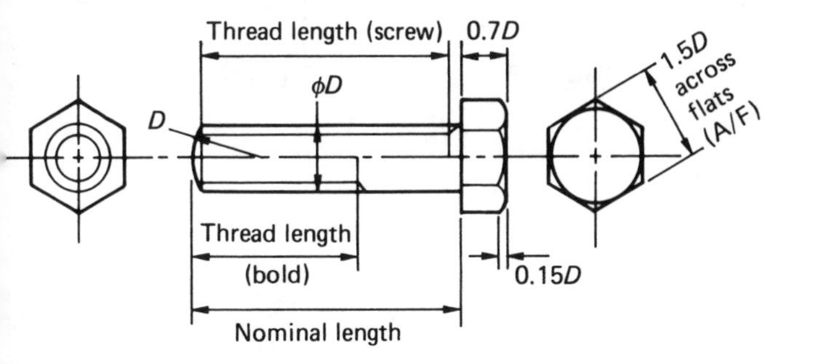

Studs

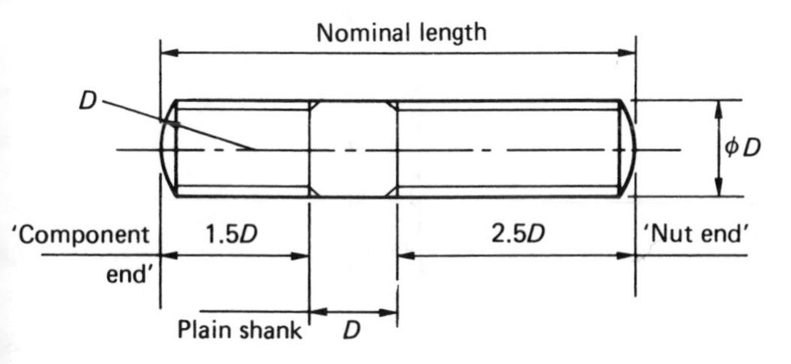

Standard nut

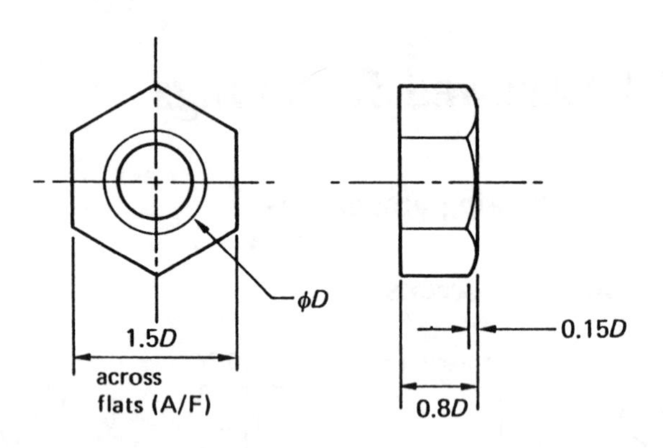

Thin (lock) nut

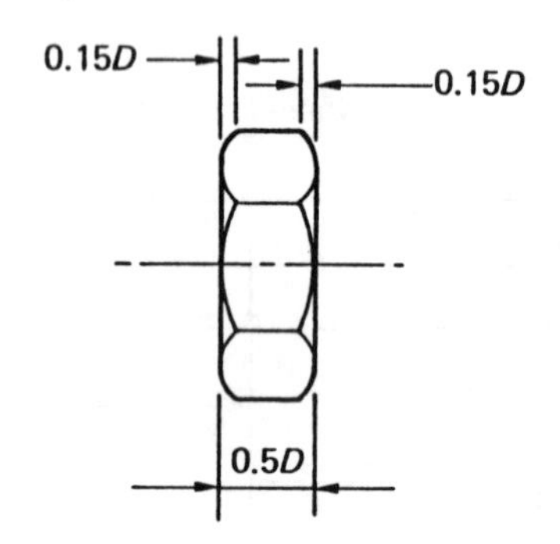

Plain washer

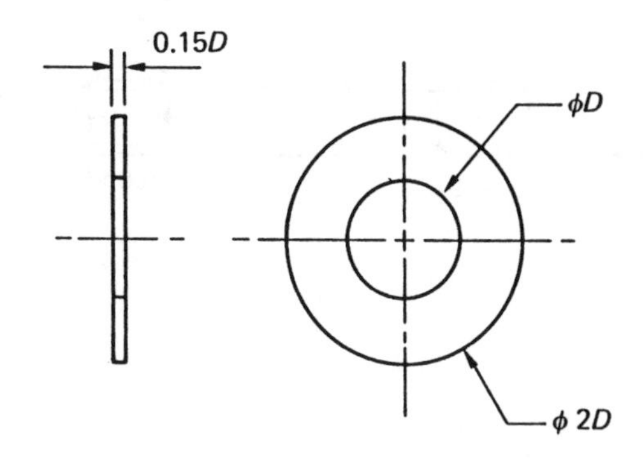

2.1.2 Alternative screw heads

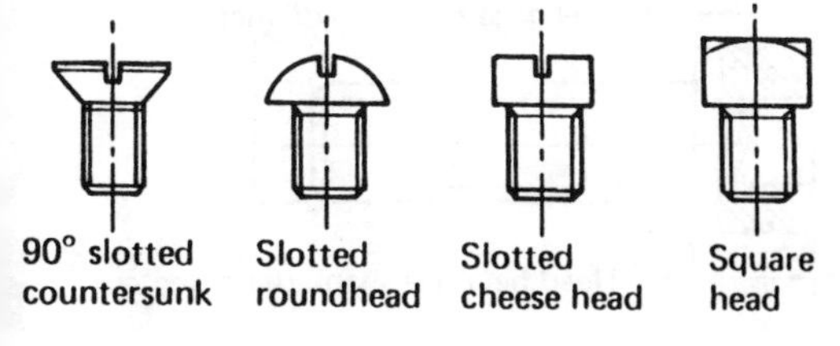

2.1.3 Alternative screw points

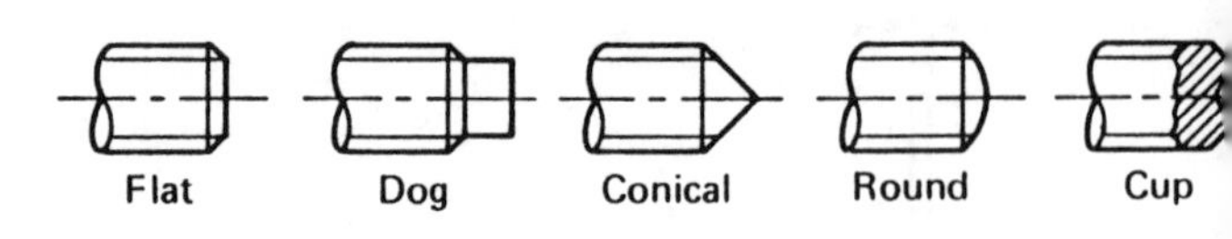

2.1.4 Hexagon socket cap head screw

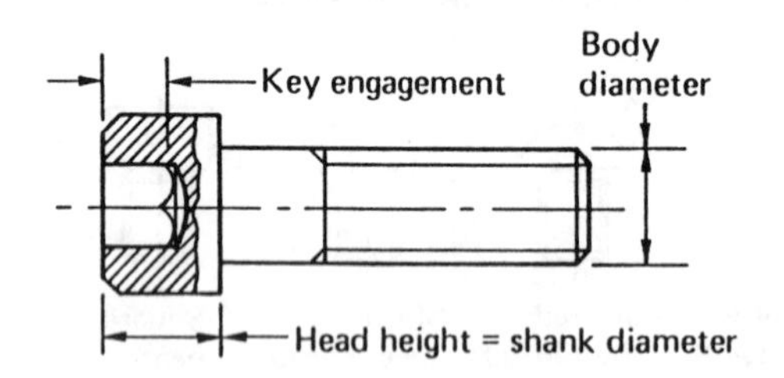

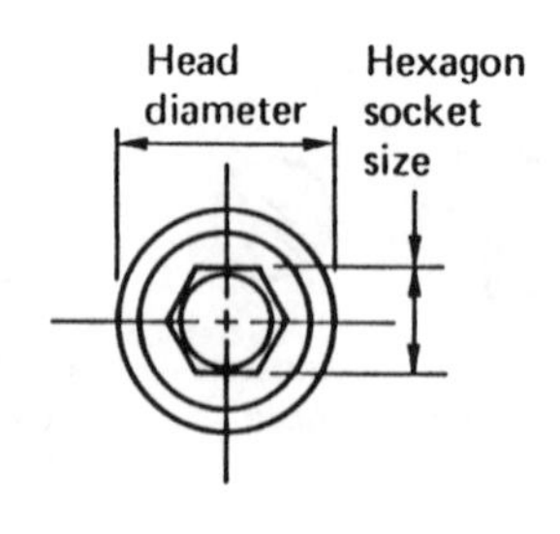

2.1.5 Applications of screwed fasteners

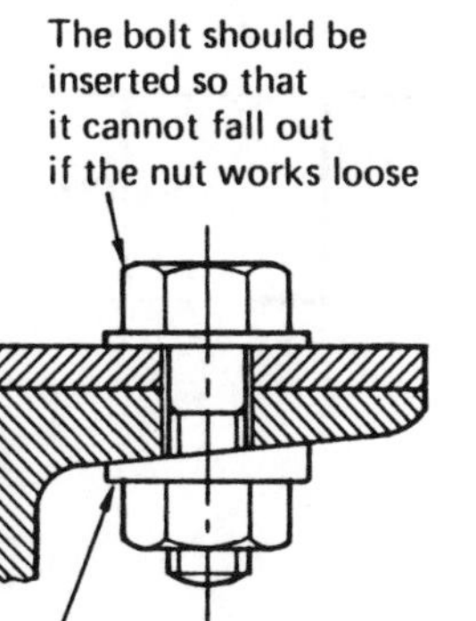

Tapered washers should be used in structural steelwork to ensure a flat seating

The joint face should lie across the plain shank of the bolt, *never* across the threads

The bolt should pass through a hole of the correct clearance

At least two threads should show beyond the nut when tightened to ensure full engagement

2.1.6 Acme thread form

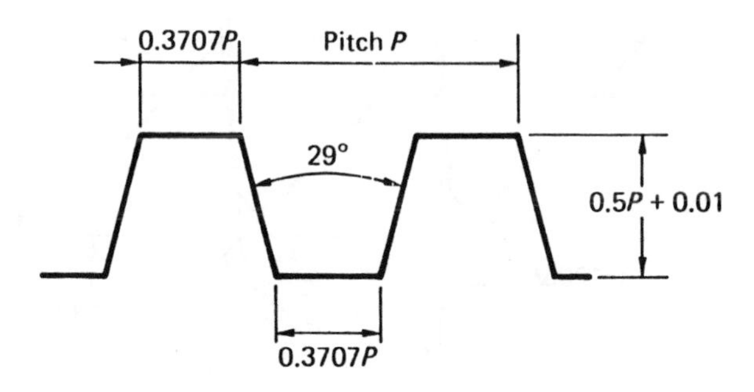

2.1.7 Square thread form

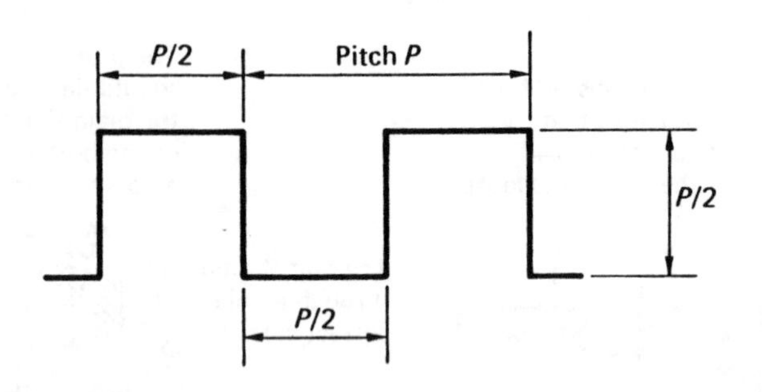

2.1.8 Buttress thread form

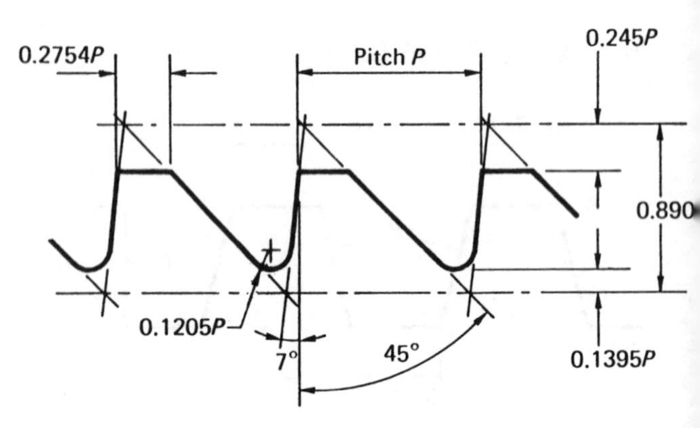

2.1.9 V-thread form

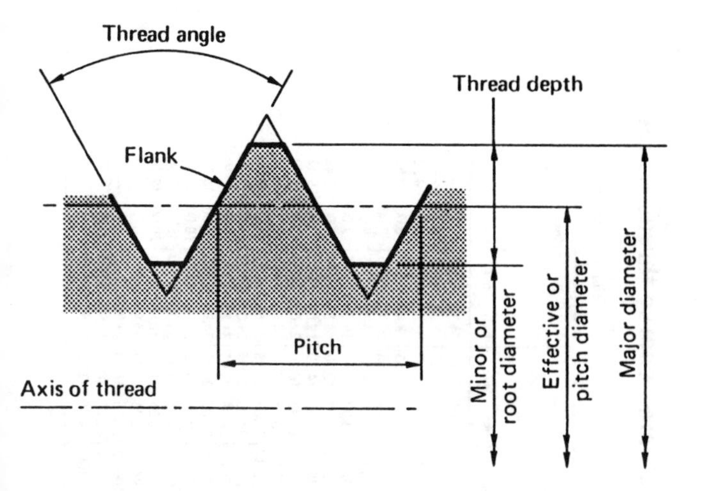

2.1.10 ISO metric and ISO unified thread forms

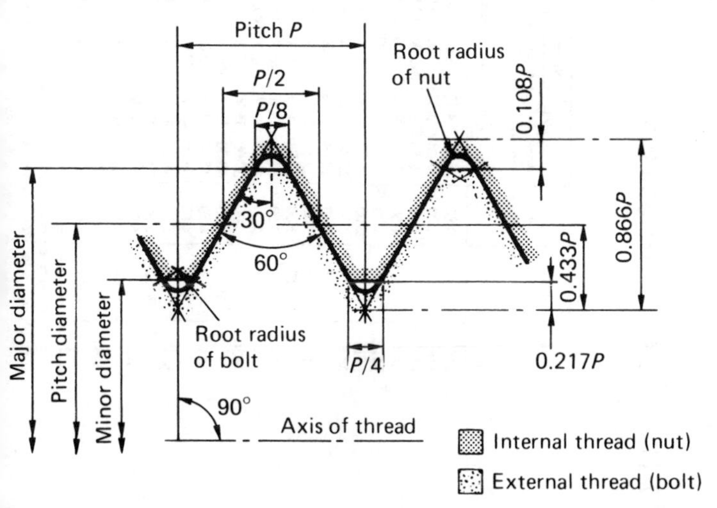

2.1.11 ISO metric black hexagon bolts and nuts, coarse thread series

Dimensions in millimetres

Nominal size and thread diameter		Pitch of thread	Unthreaded shank diameter		Hexagon bolts and nuts				Height of bolt head		Nut thickness			
					Across flats (A/F)		Across corners				Normal		Thin	
1st	2nd choice		max.	min.	max.	min.	max.	min.	max.	min.	max.	min.	max.	min.
M5		0.80	5.48	4.52	8.00	7.64	9.20	8.63	3.88	3.13	4.38	3.63	—	—
M6		1.00	6.48	5.52	10.00	9.64	11.50	10.89	4.38	3.63	5.38	4.63	—	—
M8		1.25	8.58	7.42	13.00	12.57	15.00	14.20	5.88	5.13	6.88	6.13	5.00	4.52
M10		1.50	10.58	9.42	17.00	16.57	19.60	18.72	7.45	6.55	8.45	7.55	6.00	5.52
M12		1.75	12.70	11.30	19.00	18.48	21.90	20.88	8.45	7.55	10.45	9.55	7.00	6.42
M16		2.00	16.70	15.30	24.00	23.16	27.70	26.17	10.45	9.55	13.55	12.45	9.00	8.42
M20		2.50	20.84	19.16	30.00	29.16	34.60	32.95	13.90	12.10	16.55	15.45	9.00	8.42
	M22	2.50	22.84	21.16	32.00	31.61	36.90	35.03	14.90	13.10	18.55	17.45	10.00	9.42
M24		3.00	24.84	23.16	36.00	35.00	41.60	39.55	15.90	14.10	19.65	18.35	10.00	9.42
	M27	3.00	27.84	26.16	41.00	40.38	47.30	45.20	17.90	16.10	22.65	21.35	12.00	11.30
M30		3.50	30.84	29.16	46.00	45.00	53.10	50.85	20.05	17.95	24.65	23.35	12.00	11.30
	M33	3.50	34.00	32.00	50.00	49.00	57.70	55.37	22.05	19.95	26.65	25.35	14.00	13.30
M36		4.00	37.00	35.00	55.00	53.80	63.50	60.79	24.05	21.95	29.65	28.35	14.00	13.30
	M39	4.00	40.00	38.00	60.00	58.80	69.30	66.44	26.05	23.95	31.80	30.20	16.00	15.30
M42		4.50	43.00	41.00	65.00	63.80	75.10	72.09	27.05	24.95	34.80	33.20	16.00	15.30
	M45	4.50	46.00	44.00	70.00	68.80	80.80	77.74	29.05	26.95	36.80	35.20	18.00	17.30
M48		5.00	49.00	47.00	75.00	73.80	86.60	83.39	31.05	28.95	38.80	37.20	18.00	17.30
	M52	5.00	53.20	50.80	80.00	78.80	92.40	89.04	34.25	31.75	42.80	41.20	20.00	19.16
M56		5.50	57.20	54.80	85.00	83.60	98.10	94.47	36.25	33.75	45.80	44.20	—	—
	M60	5.50	61.20	58.80	90.00	86.60	103.90	100.12	39.25	36.75	48.80	47.20	—	—
M64		6.00	65.20	62.80	95.00	93.60	109.70	105.77	41.25	38.75	51.95	50.05	—	—
	M68	6.00	69.20	66.80	100.00	98.60	115.50	111.42	44.25	41.75	54.95	53.05	—	—

Bolts: tolerance class 8g. Nuts: tolerance class 7H.
For full range of sizes and further information see BS 4190.

2.1.12 ISO metric precision hexagon bolts and nuts, coarse thread series

Dimensions in millimetres

Nominal size		Pitch of thread	Major diameter (bolt)		Pitch diameter (bolt)		Minor diameter (bolt)		Major diameter (nut)	Minor diameter (nut)		Head height (bolt)	Thickness (nut)	Hexagon (bolt and nut)		
														Across flats (A/F)		Across corners (A/C)
1st choice	2nd choice		max.	min.	max.	min.	max.	min.		max.	min.	max.	max.	max.	min.	max.
M.16		0.35	1.581	1.496	1.354	1.291	1.151	1.063	1.600	1.321	1.221	1.225	1.30	3.20	3.08	3.70
M2		0.40	1.981	1.886	1.721	1.654	1.490	1.394	2.000	1.679	1.567	1.525	1.60	4.00	3.88	4.60
M2.5		0.45	2.480	2.380	2.188	2.117	1.928	1.825	2.500	2.138	2.013	1.825	2.00	5.00	4.88	5.80
M3		0.50	2.980	2.874	2.655	2.580	2.367	2.256	3.000	2.599	2.459	2.125	2.40	5.50	5.38	6.40
M4		0.70	3.978	3.838	3.523	3.433	3.119	2.979	4.000	3.422	3.242	2.925	3.20	7.00	6.85	8.10
M5		0.80	4.976	4.826	4.456	4.361	3.995	3.842	5.000	4.334	4.134	3.650	4.00	8.00	7.85	9.20
M6		1.00	5.974	5.794	5.324	5.212	4.747	4.536	6.000	5.153	4.917	4.150	5.00	10.00	9.78	11.50
M8		1.25	7.972	7.760	7.160	7.042	6.438	6.230	8.000	6.912	6.647	5.650	6.50	13.00	12.73	15.00
M10		1.50	9.968	9.732	8.994	8.862	8.128	7.888	10.000	8.676	8.376	7.180	8.00	17.00	16.73	19.60
M12		1.75	11.966	11.701	10.829	10.679	9.819	9.543	12.000	10.441	10.106	8.180	10.00	19.00	18.67	22.10
	M14	2.00	13.962	13.682	12.663	12.503	11.508	11.204	14.000	12.210	11.835	9.180	11.00	22.00	21.67	25.40
M16		2.00	15.922	15.662	14.663	14.503	13.508	13.204	16.000	14.210	13.835	10.180	13.00	24.00	23.67	27.70
	M18	2.50	17.958	17.623	16.334	16.164	14.891	14.541	18.000	15.744	15.294	12.215	15.00	27.00	26.67	31.20
M20		2.50	19.958	19.623	18.334	18.164	16.891	16.541	20.000	17.744	17.294	13.215	16.00	30.00	29.67	34.60
	M22	2.50	21.958	21.623	20.334	20.164	18.891	18.541	22.000	19.744	19.294	14.215	18.00	32.00	31.61	36.90
M24		3.00	23.952	23.577	22.003	21.803	20.271	19.855	24.000	21.252	20.752	15.215	19.00	36.00	35.58	41.60
	M27	3.00	26.952	26.577	25.003	24.803	23.271	22.855	27.000	24.252	23.752	17.215	22.00	41.00	40.38	47.30
M30		3.50	29.947	29.522	27.674	27.462	25.653	25.189	30.000	26.771	26.211	19.260	24.00	46.00	45.38	53.10
	M33	3.50	32.947	32.522	30.674	30.462	28.653	28.189	33.000	29.771	29.211	21.260	26.00	50.00	49.38	57.70
M36		4.00	35.940	35.465	33.342	33.118	31.033	30.521	36.000	32.270	31.670	23.260	29.00	55.00	54.26	63.50
	M39	4.00	38.940	38.465	36.342	36.118	34.033	33.521	39.000	35.270	34.670	25.260	31.00	60.00	59.26	69.30
M42		4.50	41.937	41.437	39.014	38.778	36.416	35.855	42.000	37.799	37.129	26.260	34.00	65.00	64.26	75.10
	M45	4.50	44.937	44.437	42.014	41.778	39.416	38.855	45.000	40.799	40.129	28.260	36.00	70.00	69.26	80.80
M48		5.00	47.929	47.399	44.681	44.431	41.795	41.184	48.000	43.297	42.587	30.260	38.00	75.00	74.26	86.60
	M52	5.00	51.929	51.399	48.681	48.431	45.795	45.184	52.000	47.297	46.587	33.310	42.00	80.00	79.26	92.40

Bolts: tolerance class 6g. Nuts: tolerance class 6H.
For full range and further information see BS 3692.

2.1.13 ISO metric precision hexagon bolts and nuts, fine thread series

Dimensions in millimetres

Nominal size		Pitch of thread	Major diameter (bolt)		Pitch diameter (bolt)		Minor diameter (bolt)		Major diameter (nut)	Minor diameter (nut)		Head height (bolt)	Thickness (nut)	Hexagon (bolt and nut) Across flats (A/F)		Hexagon (bolt and nut) Across corners (A/C)
1st choice	2nd choice		max.	min.	max.	min.	max.	min.		max.	min.	max.	max.	max.	min.	max.
M6		0.75	5.978	5.838	5.491	5.391	5.058	4.909	6.000	5.378	5.188	4.150	5.00	10.00	9.78	11.50
M8		1.00	7.974	7.794	7.324	7.212	6.747	6.563	8.000	7.153	6.917	5.650	6.50	13.00	12.73	15.00
M10		1.25	9.972	9.760	9.160	9.042	8.439	8.231	10.000	8.912	8.647	7.180	8.00	17.00	16.73	19.60
M12		1.25	11.972	11.760	11.160	11.028	10.439	10.217	12.000	10.912	10.647	8.180	10.00	19.00	18.67	22.10
	M14	1.50	13.968	13.732	12.994	12.854	12.127	11.879	14.000	12.676	12.376	9.180	11.00	22.00	21.67	25.40
M16		1.50	15.968	15.732	14.994	14.854	14.127	13.879	16.000	14.676	14.376	10.180	13.00	24.00	23.67	27.70
	M18	1.50	17.968	17.732	16.994	16.854	16.127	15.879	18.000	16.676	16.376	12.215	15.00	27.00	26.67	31.20
M20		1.50	19.968	19.732	18.994	18.854	18.127	17.879	20.000	18.676	18.376	13.215	16.00	30.00	29.67	34.60
	M22	1.50	21.968	21.732	20.994	20.854	20.127	19.879	22.000	20.676	20.376	14.215	18.00	32.00	31.61	36.90
M24		2.00	23.962	23.682	22.663	22.493	21.508	21.194	24.000	22.210	21.835	15.215	19.00	36.00	35.38	41.60
	M27	2.00	26.962	26.682	25.663	25.493	24.508	24.194	27.000	25.210	24.835	17.215	22.00	41.00	40.38	47.30
M30		2.00	29.962	29.682	28.663	28.493	27.508	27.194	30.000	28.210	27.835	19.260	24.00	46.00	45.38	53.10
	M33	2.00	32.962	32.682	31.663	31.493	30.508	30.194	33.000	31.210	31.835	21.260	26.00	50.00	49.38	57.70
M36		3.00	35.952	35.577	34.003	33.803	32.271	31.855	36.000	33.252	32.752	23.260	29.00	55.00	54.26	63.50
	M39	3.00	38.952	38.577	37.003	36.803	35.271	34.855	39.000	36.252	35.752	25.260	31.00	60.00	59.26	69.30
M42		3.00	41.952	41.577	40.003	39.803	38.271	37.855	42.000	39.252	38.752	26.260	34.00	65.00	64.26	75.10

Bolts: Tolerance class 6g. Nuts: tolerance class 6H.
For full range of sizes and further information see BS 3692.

2.1.14 ISO metric hexagon socket head screws

Cap head screws

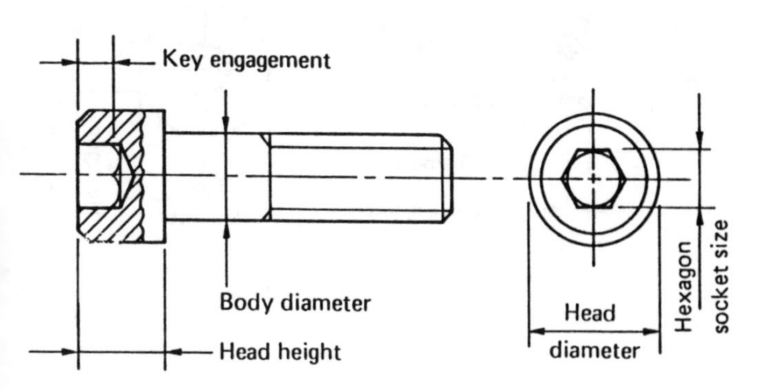

Dimensions in millimetres

Nominal size 1st choice	*Body diameter and head height*		*Head diameter*		*Hexagon socket size*	*Key engage-ment*
	max.	*min.*	*max.*	*min.*		*min.*
M3	3.00	2.86	5.50	5.20	2.50	1.30
M4	4.00	3.82	7.00	6.64	3.00	2.00
M5	5.00	4.82	8.50	8.14	4.00	2.70
M6	6.00	5.82	10.00	9.64	5.00	3.30
M8	8.00	7.78	13.00	12.57	6.00	4.30
M10	10.00	9.78	16.00	15.57	8.00	5.50
M12	12.00	11.73	18.00	17.57	10.00	6.60
M16	16.00	15.73	24.00	23.48	14.00	8.80
M20	20.00	19.67	30.00	29.48	17.00	10.70
M24	24.00	23.67	36.00	35.38	19.00	12.90

90° countersunk head screws

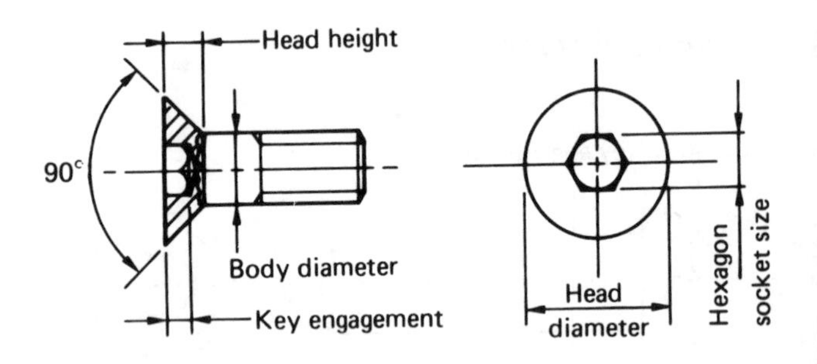

Dimensions in millimetres

Nominal size 1st *choice*	*Body diameter* max.	*Body diameter* min.	*Head diameter* max.	*Head diameter* min.	*Head height*	*Hexagon socket size*	*Key engagement min.*
M3	3.00	2.86	6.00	5.82	1.86	2.00	1.05
M4	4.00	3.82	8.00	7.78	2.48	2.50	1.49
M5	5.00	4.82	10.00	9.78	3.10	3.00	1.86
M6	6.00	5.82	12.00	11.73	3.72	4.00	2.16
M8	8.00	7.78	16.00	15.73	4.96	5.00	2.85
M10	10.00	9.78	20.00	19.67	6.20	6.00	3.60
M12	12.00	11.73	24.00	23.67	7.44	8.00	4.35
M16	16.00	15.73	32.00	29.67	8.80	10.00	4.89
M20	20.00	19.67	40.00	35.61	10.16	12.00	5.45

For full range and further information see BS 4168 (metric) and BS 2470 (inch).

2.1.15 ISO unified precision internal screw threads, coarse series

Dimensions in inches

Designation	Major diameter min.	Pitch (effective) diameter		Minor diameter		Hexagon (nut)				
						Max. width across flats (A/F)	Max. width across corners (A/C)	Nut thickness		
		max.	min.	max.	min.			Thick	Normal	Thin
$\frac{1}{4}$-20 UNC-2B	0.2500	0.2223	0.2175	0.2074	0.1959	0.4375	0.505	0.286	0.224	0.161
$\frac{5}{16}$-18 UNC-2B	0.3125	0.2817	0.2764	0.2651	0.2524	0.5000	0.577	0.333	0.271	0.192
$\frac{3}{8}$-16 UNC-2B	0.3750	0.3401	0.3344	0.3214	0.3073	0.5625	0.650	0.411	0.333	0.224
$\frac{7}{16}$-14 UNC-2B	0.4375	0.3972	0.3911	0.3760	0.3602	0.6875	0.794	0.458	0.380	0.255
$\frac{1}{2}$-13 UNC-2B	0.5000	0.4565	0.4500	0.4336	0.4167	0.7500	0.866	0.567	0.442	0.317
$\frac{9}{16}$-12 UNC-2B*	0.5625	0.5152	0.5084	0.4904	0.4723	0.8750	1.010	0.614	0.489	0.349
$\frac{5}{8}$-11 UNC-2B	0.6250	0.5732	0.5660	0.5460	0.5266	0.9375	1.083	0.724	0.552	0.380
$\frac{3}{4}$-10 UNC-2B	0.7500	0.6927	0.6850	0.6627	0.6417	1.1250	1.300	0.822	0.651	0.432
$\frac{7}{8}$-9 UNC-2B	0.8750	0.8110	0.8028	0.7775	0.7547	1.3125	1.515	0.916	0.760	0.494
1-8 UNC-2B	1.0000	0.9276	0.9188	0.8897	0.8647	1.5000	1.732	1.015	0.874	0.562
$1\frac{1}{8}$-7 UNC-2B	1.1250	1.0416	1.0322	0.9980	0.9704	1.6875	1.948	1.176	0.989	0.629

continued

Dimensions in inches

Designation	Major diameter	Pitch (effective) diameter		Minor diameter		Hexagon (nut)				
						Max. width across flats (A/F)	Max. width across corners (A/C)	Nut thickness		
	min.	max.	min.	max.	min.			Thick	Normal	Thin
$1\frac{1}{4}$-7 UNC-2B	1.2500	1.1668	1.1572	1.1230	1.0954	1.8750	2.165	1.275	1.087	0.744
$1\frac{3}{8}$-6 UNC-2B*	1.3750	1.2771	1.2667	1.2252	1.1946	2.0625	2.382	1.400	1.197	0.806
$1\frac{1}{2}$-6 UNC-2B	1.5000	1.4022	1.3917	1.3502	1.3196	2.2500	2.598	1.530	1.311	0.874
$1\frac{3}{4}$-5 UNC-2B	1.7500	1.6317	1.6201	1.5675	1.5335	2.6250	3.031	—	1.530	0.999
2-$4\frac{1}{2}$ UNC-2B	2.0000	1.8681	1.8557	1.7952	1.7594	3.0000	3.464	—	1.754	1.129
$2\frac{1}{4}$-$4\frac{1}{2}$ UNC-2B	2.2500	2.1183	2.1057	2.0452	2.0094					
$2\frac{1}{2}$-4 UNC-2B	2.5000	2.3511	2.3376	2.2669	2.2294					
$2\frac{3}{4}$-4 UNC-2B	2.7500	2.6013	2.5876	2.5169	2.4794					
3-4 UNC-2B	3.0000	2.8515	2.8376	2.7669	2.7294					
$3\frac{1}{4}$-4 UNC-2B	3.2500	3.1017	3.0876	3.0169	2.9794					
$3\frac{1}{2}$-4 UNC-2B	3.5000	3.3519	3.3376	3.2669	3.2294					
$3\frac{3}{4}$-4 UNC-2B	3.7500	3.6021	3.5876	3.5169	3.4794					
4-4 UNC-2B	4.0000	3.8523	3.8376	3.7669	3.7294					

* To be dispensed with wherever possible.
For full range and further information see BS 1768.

Example

The interpretation of designation $\frac{1}{2}$-13 UNC-2B is as follows: nominal diameter $\frac{1}{2}$ inch; threads per inch 13; ISO unified thread, coarse series; thread tolerance classification 2B.

2.1.16 ISO unified precision external screw threads, coarse series

Dimensions in inches

Designation	Major diameter		Pitch (effective) diameter		Minor diameter		Shank diameter		Hexagon head (bolt)		
	max.	min.	max.	min.	max.	min.	max.	min.	Max. width across flats (A/F)	Max. width across corners (A/C)	Max. height
$\frac{1}{4}$-20 UNC-2A	0.2489	0.2408	0.2164	0.2127	0.1876	0.1803	0.2500	0.2465	0.4375	0.505	0.163
$\frac{5}{16}$-18 UNC-2A	0.3113	0.3026	0.2752	0.2712	0.2431	0.2351	0.3125	0.3090	0.5000	0.577	0.211
$\frac{3}{8}$-16 UNC-2A	0.3737	0.3643	0.3331	0.3287	0.2970	0.2881	0.3750	0.3715	0.5625	0.650	0.243
$\frac{7}{16}$-14 UNC-2A	0.4361	0.4258	0.3897	0.3850	0.3485	0.3387	0.4375	0.4335	0.6250	0.722	0.291
$\frac{1}{2}$-13 UNC-2A	0.4985	0.4876	0.4485	0.4435	0.4041	0.3936	0.5000	0.4960	0.7500	0.866	0.323
$\frac{9}{16}$-12 UNC-2A*	0.5609	0.5495	0.5068	0.5016	0.4587	0.4475	0.5625	0.5585	0.8125	0.938	0.371
$\frac{5}{8}$-11 UNC-2A	0.6234	0.6113	0.5644	0.5589	0.5119	0.4999	0.6250	0.6190	0.9375	1.083	0.403
$\frac{3}{4}$-10 UNC-2A	0.7482	0.7353	0.6832	0.6773	0.6255	0.6124	0.7500	0.7440	1.1250	1.300	0.483
$\frac{7}{8}$-9 UNC-2A	0.8731	0.8592	0.8009	0.7946	0.7368	0.7225	0.8750	0.8670	1.3125	1.515	0.563
1-8 UNC-2A	0.9980	0.9830	0.9168	0.9100	0.8446	0.8288	1.0000	0.9920	1.5000	1.732	0.627
$1\frac{1}{8}$-7 UNC-2A	1.1228	1.1064	1.0300	1.0228	0.9475	0.9300	1.1250	1.1170	1.6875	1.948	0.718
$1\frac{1}{4}$-7 UNC-2A	1.2478	1.2314	1.1550	1.1476	1.0725	1.0548	1.2500	1.2420	1.8750	2.165	0.813
$1\frac{3}{8}$-6 UNC-2A*	1.3726	1.3544	1.2643	1.2563	1.1681	1.1481	1.3750	1.3650	2.0625	2.382	0.878

continued

Designation	Major diameter		Pitch (effective) diameter		Minor diameter		Shank diameter		Hexagon head (bolt)		
	max.	min.	max.	min.	max.	min.	max.	min.	Max. width across flats (A/F)	Max. width across corners (A/C)	Max. height
$1\frac{1}{2}$-6 UNC-2A	1.4976	1.4794	1.3893	1.3812	1.2931	1.2730	1.5000	1.4900	2.2500	2.598	0.974
$1\frac{3}{4}$-5 UNC-2A	1.7473	1.7268	1.6174	1.6085	1.5019	1.4786	1.7500	1.7400	2.6250	3.031	1.134
2-$4\frac{1}{2}$ UNC-2A	1.9971	1.9751	1.8528	1.8433	1.7245	1.6990	2.000	1.9900	3.000	3.464	1.263
$2\frac{1}{4}$-$4\frac{1}{2}$ UNC-2A	2.2471	2.2251	2.1028	2.0931	1.9745	1.9488					
$2\frac{1}{2}$-4 UNC-2A	2.4969	2.4731	2.3345	2.3241	2.1902	2.1618					
$2\frac{3}{4}$-4 UNC-2A	2.7468	2.7230	2.5844	2.5739	2.4401	2.4116					
3-4 UNC-2A	2.9968	2.9730	2.8344	2.8237	2.6901	2.6614					
$3\frac{1}{4}$-4 UNC-2A	3.2467	3.2229	3.0843	3.0734	2.9400	2.9111					
$3\frac{1}{2}$-4 UNC-2A	3.4967	3.4729	3.3343	3.3233	3.1900	3.1610					
$3\frac{3}{4}$-4 UNC-2A	3.7466	3.7228	3.5842	3.5730	3.4399	3.4107					
4-4 UNC-2A	3.9966	3.9728	3.8342	3.8229	3.6899	3.6606					

*To be dispensed with wherever possible
For full range and further information see BS 1768.

Example

The interpretation of designation $\frac{1}{4}$-13 UNC-2A is as follows: nominal diameter $\frac{1}{4}$ inch; threads per inch 13; ISO

2.1.17 ISO unified precision internal screw threads, fine series

Dimensions in inches

Designation	Major diameter min.	Pitch (effective) diameter max.	Pitch (effective) diameter min.	Minor diameter max.	Minor diameter min.	Hexagon (nut) Max. width across flats (A/F)	Hexagon (nut) Max. width across corners (A/C)	Nut thickness Thick	Nut thickness Normal	Nut thickness Thin
1/4-28 UNF-2B	0.2500	0.2311	0.2268	0.2197	0.2113	0.4375	0.505	0.286	0.224	0.161
5/16-24 UNF-2B	0.3125	0.2902	0.2854	0.2771	0.2674	0.5000	0.577	0.333	0.271	0.192
3/8-24 UNF-2B	0.3750	0.3528	0.3479	0.3396	0.3299	0.5625	0.650	0.411	0.333	0.224
7/16-20 UNF-2B	0.4375	0.4104	0.4050	0.3949	0.3834	0.6875	0.794	0.458	0.380	0.255
1/2-20 UNF-2B	0.5000	0.4731	0.4675	0.4574	0.4459	0.7500	0.866	0.567	0.442	0.317
9/16-18 UNF-2B*	0.5625	0.5323	0.5264	0.5151	0.5024	0.8750	1.010	0.614	0.489	0.349
5/8-18 UNF-2B	0.6250	0.5949	0.5889	0.5776	0.5649	0.9375	1.083	0.724	0.552	0,380
3/4-16 UNF-2B	0.7500	0.7159	0.7094	0.6964	0.6823	1.1250	1.300	0.822	0.651	0.432
7/8-14 UNF-2B	0.8750	0.8356	0.8286	0.8135	0.7977	1.3125	1.515	0.916	0.760	0.494
1-12 UNF-2B	1.000	0.9535	0.9459	0.9279	0.9098	1.5000	1.732	1.015	0.874	0.562
1 1/8-12 UNF-2B	1.1250	1.0787	1.0709	1.0529	1.0348	1.6875	1.948	1.176	0.984	0.629
1 1/4-12 UNF-2B	1.2500	1.2039	1.1959	1.1779	1.1598	1.8750	2.165	1.275	1.087	0.744
1 3/8-12 UNF-2B*	1.3750	1.3291	1.3209	1.3029	1.2848	2.0625	2.382	1.400	1.197	0.806
1 1/2-12 UNF-2B	1.500	1.4542	1.4459	1.4279	1.4098	2.2500	2.598	1.530	1.311	0.874

*To be dispensed with wherever possible
For full range and further information see BS 1768.

Example

The interpretation of designation 1/2-20 UNF-2B is as follows: nominal diameter 1/2 inch; threads per inch 20; ISO unified thread, fine series; thread tolerance classification 2B.

2.1.18 **ISO unified precision external screw threads, fine series**

Dimensions in inches

Designation	Major diameter		Pitch (effective) diameter		Minor diameter		Shank diameter		Hexagon head (bolt)		
	max.	min.	max.	min.	max.	min.	max.	min.	Max. width across flats (A/F)	Max. width across corners (A/C)	Max. height
$\frac{1}{4}$-28 UNF-2A	0.2490	0.2425	0.2258	0.2225	0.2052	0.1993	0.2500	0.2465	0.4375	0.505	0.163
$\frac{5}{16}$-24 UNF-2A	0.3114	0.3042	0.2843	0.2806	0.2603	0.2536	0.3125	0.3090	0.5000	0.577	0.211
$\frac{3}{8}$-24 UNF-2A	0.3739	0.3667	0.3468	0.3430	0.3228	0.3160	0.3750	0.3715	0.5625	0.650	0.243
$\frac{7}{16}$-20 UNF-2A	0.4362	0.4281	0.4037	0.3995	0.3749	0.3671	0.4375	0.4335	0.6250	0.722	0.291
$\frac{1}{2}$-20 UNF-2A	0.4987	0.4906	0.4662	0.4615	0.4374	0.4295	0.5000	0.4960	0.7500	0.866	0.323
$\frac{9}{16}$-18 UNF-2A*	0.5611	0.5524	0.5250	0.5205	0.4929	0.4844	0.5625	0.5585	0.8125	0.938	0.371
$\frac{5}{8}$-18 UNF-2A	0.6236	0.6149	0.5875	0.5828	0.5554	0.5467	0.6250	0.6190	0.9375	1.083	0.403
$\frac{3}{4}$-16 UNF-2A	0.7485	0.7391	0.7079	0.7029	0.6718	0.6623	0.7500	0.7440	1.1250	1.300	0.483
$\frac{7}{8}$-14 UNF-2A	0.8734	0.8631	0.8270	0.8216	0.7858	0.7753	0.8750	0.8670	1.3125	1.515	0.563
1-12 UNF-2A	0.9982	0.9868	0.9441	0.9382	0.8960	0.8841	1.0000	0.9920	1.5000	1.732	0.627
$1\frac{1}{8}$-12 UNF-2A	1.1232	1.1118	1.0691	1.0631	0.0210	1.0090	1.1250	1.1170	1.6875	1.948	0.718
$1\frac{1}{4}$-12 UNF-2A	1.2482	1.2368	1.1941	1.1879	1.1460	1.1338	1.2500	1.2420	1.8750	2.165	0.813
$1\frac{3}{8}$-12 UNF-2A*	1.3731	1.3617	1.3190	1.3127	1.2709	1.2586	1.3750	1.3650	2.0625	2.382	0.878
$1\frac{1}{2}$-12 UNF-2A	1.4981	1.4867	1.4440	1.4376	1.3959	1.3835	1.500	1.4900	2.2500	2.598	0.974

*To be dispensed with wherever possible
For full range and further information see BS 1768.

Example

The interpretation of designation $\frac{1}{4}$-20 UNF-2A is as follows: nominal diameter $\frac{1}{4}$ inch; threads per inch 20; ISO

2.1.19 ISO metric screw threads, miniature series

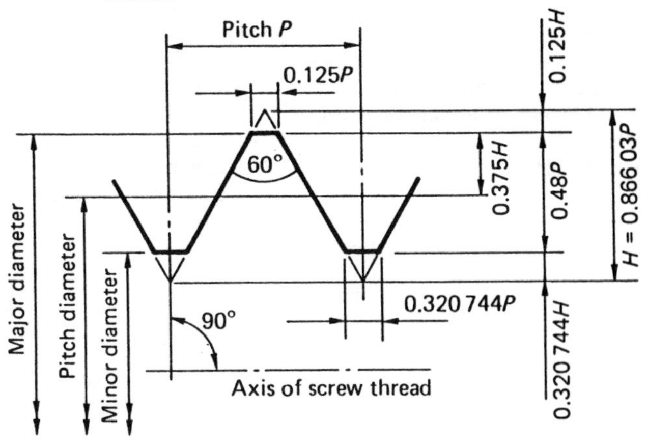

Dimensions in millimetres

Nominal size		*Pitch of thread*			
1st choice	*2nd choice*	*P*	*Major diameter*	*Pitch (effective) diameter*	*Minor diameter*
S-0.3		0.080	0.300 000	0.248 038	0.223 200
	S-0.35	0.090	0.350 000	0.291 543	0.263 600
S-0.4		0.100	0.400 000	0.335 048	0.304 000
	S-0.45	0.100	0.450 000	0.385 048	0.354 000
S-0.5		0.125	0.500 000	0.418 810	0.380 000
	S-0.55	0.125	0.550 000	0.468 810	0.430 000
S-0.6		0.150	0.600 000	0.502 572	0.456 000
	S-0.7	0.175	0.700 000	0.586 334	0.532 000
S-0.8		0.200	0.800 000	0.670 096	0.608 000
	S-0.9	0.225	0.900 000	0.753 858	0.684 000
	S-1	0.250	1.000 000	0.837 620	0.760 000
	S-1.1	0.250	1.100 000	0.937 620	0.860 000
	S-1.2	0.250	1.200 000	1.037 620	0.960 000
	S-1.4	0.300	1.400 000	1.205 144	1.112 000

For full range and further information see BS 4827.

2.1.20 Basis for standard metric thread lengths

Nominal length of bolt l	*Length of thread b*
Up to and including 125 mm	$2d+6$ mm
Over 125 mm up to and including 200 mm	$2d+12$ mm
over 200 mm	$2d+25$ mm
	where d = nominal diameter

2.1.21 Strength grade designation of metric steel bolts and screws

Strength grade designation (*BS* 3692)	4.6	4.8	5.6	5.8	6.6	6.8	8.8	10.9	12.9	14.9
Tensile strength										
R_m (min.) kgf/mm^2	40	40	50	50	60	60	80	100	120	140
N/mm^2	392.4	392.4	490.5	490.5	588.6	588.6	784.8	981.0	1177.2	1373.4
Yield stress										
R_e (min.) kgf/mm^2	24	32	30	40	36	48	—	—	—	—
N/mm^2	235.4	314.0	294.3	392.4	353.2	470.9	—	—	—	—
Stress at permanent set limit										
$R_{0.2}$ kgf/mm^2	—	—	—	—	—	—	64	90	108	126
N/mm^2							627.8	882.9	1059.5	1236.0

Being in accordance with ISO/DR 911, the strength grade designation system for steel bolts and screws consists of two figures: the first is one-tenth of the minimum tensile strength in kgf/mm^2 and the second is one-tenth of the ratio between the minimum yield stress (or stress at permanent set limit $R_{0.2}$) and the minimum tensile strength, expressed as a percentage as illustrated below. For strength grade 8.8 in accordance with the above table:

(a) 1/10 minimum tensile strength of 80 kgf/mm^2 gives symbol 8.

(b) 1/10 ratio $\frac{\text{stress at permanent set limit } R_{0.2}}{\text{minimum tensile strength}}\% = \frac{1}{10} \times \frac{64}{80} \times 100 = \text{symbol } 8.$

(c) Therefore strength grade designation is 8.8 in accordance with the above table.

(d) Multiplication of these two grade code figures will give the stress at permanent set limit $R_{0.2}$ (or yield stress), e.g. $8 \times 8 = 64\ kgf/mm^2$.

2.1.22 Strength grade designation of metric steel nuts

Strength grade designation (*BS* 3692)	4	5	6	8	12	14
Proof load stress kg/mm^2	40	50	60	80	120	140
N/mm^2	392.4	490.5	588.6	784.8	1177.2	1373.4

2.1.23 Recommended metric bolt and nut combinations

Grade of bolt	4.6	4.8	5.6	5.8	6.6	6.8	8.8	10.9	12.9	14.9
Grade of nut	4	4	5	5	6	6	8	12	12	14

For further details see BS 3692.

2.1.24 Mechanical properties of metric steel bolts and nuts

Mechanical properties of steel bolts and screws

Mechanical property			Strength grade designation									
			4.6	4.8	5.6	5.8	6.6	6.8	8.8	10.9	12.9	14.9
Tensile strength*	min.	kgf/mm²		40		50		60	80	100	120	140
		N/mm²		392		490		588	785	981	1177	1373
	max.	kgf/mm²		55		70		80	100	120	140	160
		N/mm²		539		686		785	981	1177	1373	1569
Brinell hardness*	min.	H_B		110		140		170	225	280	330	390
	max.	H_B		170		215		245	300	365	425	—
Rockwell hardness*	min.	HRB		62		77		88	—	—	—	—
		HRC		—		—		—	18	27	34	40
	max.	HRB		88		97		102	—	—	—	—
		HRC		—		—		—	31	38	44	49

continued

Mechanical property		*Strength grade designation*									
		4.6	4.8	5.6	5.8	6.6	6.8	8.8	10.9	12.9	14.9
Vickers hardness HV 30*	min. max.		110 170		140 215		170 245	225 300	250 370	330 440	400 510
Yield stress (R_e) min.	kgf/mm² N/mm²	24 235	32 314	30 294	40 392	36 353	48 471	— —	— —	— —	— —
Stress at permanent set limit $R_{0.2}$ min.	kgf/mm² N/mm²	— —	— —	— —	— —	— —	— —	64 628	90 883	108 1059	126 1236
Stress under proof load† S_p	S_p/R_e kgf/mm² N/mm²	0.94 22.6 222	0.91 29.1 286	0.94 28.2 276	0.91 36.4 357	0.94 33.9 333	0.91 43.7 429	0.91 58.2 571	0.88 79.2 777	0.88 95.0 932	0.88 111 1089
Elongation (A) after fracture	min. %	25	14	20	10	16	8	12	9	8	7
Charpy impact strength min.	kgf/cm² ft lbf/in²	— —	— —	— —	— —	— —	— —	6 22	4 14	3 11	3 11

Strength under wedge loading	The value for full size bolts equals the minimum values for tensile strengths shown above.‡
Head soundness	No fracture.§
Decarburization at root of thread	Depth not more than 1/10 of H_1 (see diagram page 98)
Non-decarburized zone	Depth not less than 2/3 of H_1 (see diagram page 98)

* Only for full size bolts.
† The allowed permanent extension is 12.5 micrometres.
‡ The fracture should not take place immediately under the head of the bolt.
§ Where screws are threaded up to the head, this property will be regarded as established even if a crack should appear in the first thread, provided the head does not snap off.

Depth of decarburization in steel bolts and nuts

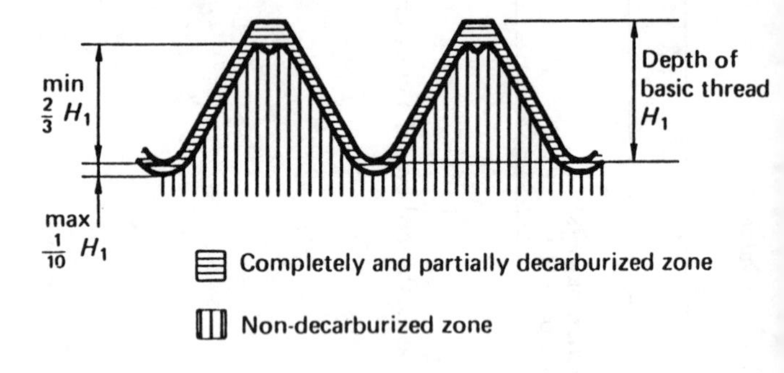

Mechanical properties of steel nuts

Strength grade designation	4	5	6	8	12	14	*Requirement*
Proof load stress* kgf/mm^2	40	50	60	80	120	140	All nuts †
N/mm^2	392	490	588	785	1177	1373	
Brinell hardness H_B (max.)	302	302	302	302	353	375	All nuts
Rockwell hardness‡ HRC (max.)	30	30	30	30	36	39	All nuts
Vickers hardness HV (max.)	310	310	310	310	370	395	All nuts

* Proof load is calculated by multiplying the proof load stress by the tensile stress area of the bolt.

† Nuts with a specified proof load in excess of 35 metric tonnes may be exempt from proof load testing. Such nuts shall meet the minimum hardness as agreed between purchaser and manufacturer.

‡ The conversion from Brinell hardness into Rockwell hardness has been calculated according to EURONORM 8-55.

For further information see BS 3692.

2.1.25 ISO pipe thread forms

Basic Whitworth thread form: parallel threads

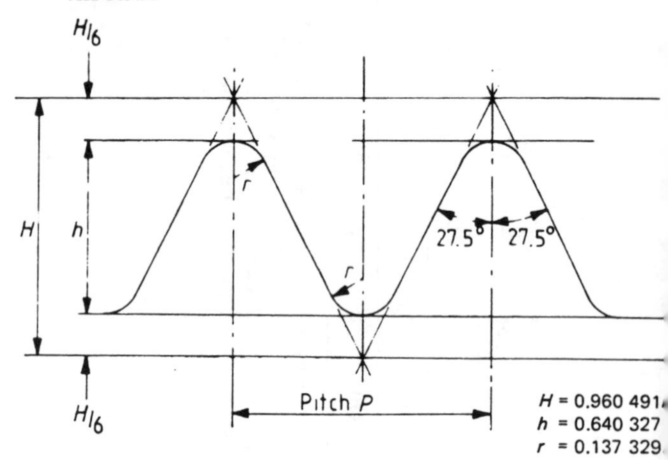

Basic Whitworth thread form: taper threads

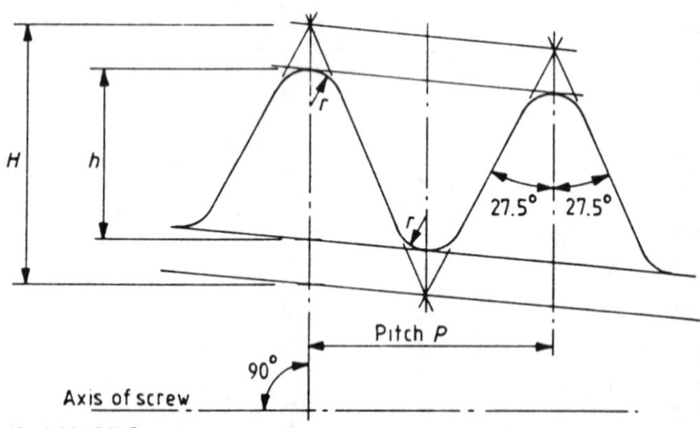

$H = 0.960\ 237P$
$h = 0.640\ 327P$
$r = 0.137\ 278P$

NOTE. The taper is 1 in 16 measured on the diameter (shown exaggerated in the diagram).

Terms relating to taper pipe threads

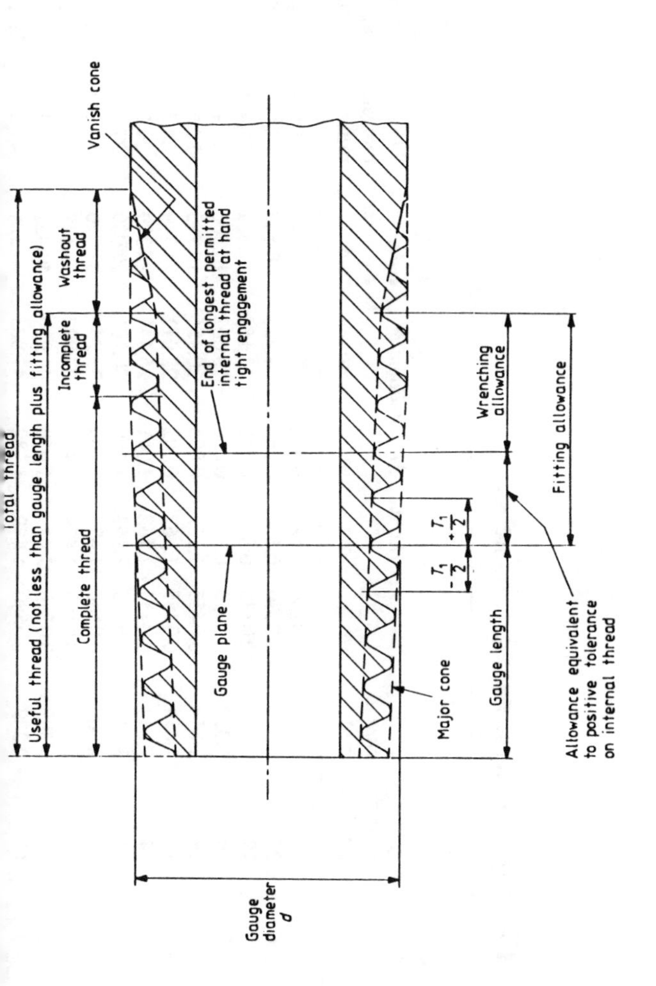

2.1.26 ISO pipe threads, parallel: basic sizes

*Nominal (bore) size of pipe**		*Number of threads*	*Pitch of thread*	*Depth of thread*		*Major diameter*		*Pitch (effective) diameter*	*Minor diameter*	*Minimum length of thread on pipe end*
in	mm	*per inch*	mm	in	mm	in	mm	mm	mm	mm
1/16†	3	28	0.907	0.0230	0.581	0.304	7.723	7.142	6.561	4.9
1/8†	6	28	0.907	0.0230	0.581	0.383	9.728	9.147	8.566	6.5
1/4	8	19	1.337	0.0335	0.856	0.518	13.157	12.301	11.445	9.7
3/8	10	19	1.337	0.0335	0.856	0.656	16.662	15.806	14.950	10.1
1/2	15	14	1.814	0.0455	1.162	0.805	20.455	19.793	18.631	13.2
5/8	—	14	1.814	0.0455	1.162	0.902	22.911	21.749	20.587	13.9
3/4	20	14	1.814	0.0455	1.162	1.041	26.441	25.279	24.117	14.5
7/8	—	14	1.814	0.0455	1.162	1.189	30.201	29.039	27.877	15.7
1	25	11	2.309	0.0580	1.479	1.309	33.249	31.770	30.291	16.8
1 1/8	—	11	2.309	0.0580	1.479	1.492	37.897	36.418	34.939	18.0
1 1/4	32	11	2.309	0.0580	1.479	1.650	41.910	40.431	38.952	19.1
1 1/2	40	11	2.309	0.0580	1.479	1.882	47.803	46.324	44.845	19.1

1¾	—	11	2.309	0.0580	1.479	2.116	53.746	52.267	50.788	21.3
2	50	11	2.309	0.0580	1.479	2.347	59.614	58.135	56.656	23.4
2¼	—	11	2.309	0.0580	1.479	2.587	65.710	64.231	62.752	25.0
2½	65	11	2.309	0.0580	1.479	2.960	75.184	73.705	72.226	26.7
2¾	—	11	2.309	0.0580	1.479	3.210	81.534	80.055	78.576	28.3
3	80	11	2.309	0.0580	1.479	3.460	87.884	84.405	84.926	29.8
3½	90	11	2.309	0.0580	1.479	3.950	100.330	98.851	97.372	31.4
4	100	11	2.309	0.0580	1.479	4.450	113.030	141.551	110.072	35.8
4½	—	11	2.309	0.0580	1.479	4.950	125.730	124.251	122.772	35.8
5	125	11	2.309	0.0580	1.479	5.450	138.430	136.951	135.472	40.1
5½	—	11	2.309	0.0580	1.479	5.950	151.130	149.651	148.172	40.1
6	150	11	2.309	0.0580	1.479	6.450	163.830	162.351	160.872	40.1

* These are nominal pipe size equivalents and are *not* inch/metric conversions. For example, for all practical purposes a pipe of 8 mm nominal bore is the same size as ¼ in nominal bore. The actual bore will lie between these nominal sizes and the O/D of this nominal size of pipe will be approximately 14 mm.

† These sizes are no longer recommended.

ISO pipe threads (parallel and tapered) are based upon the previous British Standard pipe (BSP) threads and retain the Whitworth (55°) thread form. For further information see BS 2779.

2.1.27 ISO pipe threads, tapered: basic sizes

*Nominal (bore) Size of pipe**		*Number of threads per inch*	*Pitch of thread* mm	*Depth of thread* mm	*Basic diameters at gauge plane*		
in	mm				*Major (gauge) diameter* mm	*Pitch (effective) diameter* mm	*Minor diameter* mm
$\frac{1}{8}$	6	28	0.907	0.581	9.728	9.147	8.566
$\frac{1}{4}$	8	19	1.337	0.856	13.157	12.301	11.445
$\frac{3}{8}$	10	19	1.337	0.856	16.662	15.806	14.950
$\frac{1}{2}$	15	14	1.814	1.162	20.955	19.793	18.631
$\frac{3}{4}$	20	14	1.814	1.162	26.441	25.279	24.117
1	25	11	2.309	1.479	33.249	31.770	30.291
$1\frac{1}{4}$	32	11	2.309	1.479	41.910	40.431	38.952
$1\frac{1}{2}$	40	11	2.309	1.479	47.803	46.324	44.845
2	50	11	2.309	1.479	59.614	58.135	56.656
$2\frac{1}{2}$	65	11	2.309	1.479	75.184	73.705	72.226
3	80	11	2.309	1.479	87.884	86.405	84.926
4	100	11	2.309	1.479	113.030	111.551	110.072
5	125	11	2.309	1.479	138.430	136.951	135.472
6	150	11	2.309	1.479	163.830	162.351	160.872

Nominal (bore) Size of pipe* in	mm	Gauge length† Basic	Tolerance ±	max.	min.	Useful thread (min.) Basic	max.	min.	Fitting allowance	Wrenching allowance	Position of gauge plane tolerance‡ ±	Diametral tolerance§ ±
$\frac{1}{8}$	6	$4\frac{3}{8}$ (4.0)	1 (0.9)	$5\frac{3}{8}$ (4.9)	$3\frac{3}{8}$ (3.1)	$7\frac{1}{8}$ (6.5)	$8\frac{1}{8}$ (7.4)	$6\frac{1}{8}$ (5.6)	$2\frac{1}{4}$ (2.5)	$1\frac{1}{2}$ (1.4)	$1\frac{1}{4}$ (1.1)	0.071
$\frac{1}{4}$	8	$4\frac{1}{2}$ (5.0)	1 (1.3)	$5\frac{1}{2}$ (7.3)	$3\frac{1}{2}$ (4.7)	$7\frac{1}{4}$ (9.7)	$8\frac{1}{4}$ (11.0)	$6\frac{1}{4}$ (8.4)	$2\frac{1}{4}$ (3.7)	$1\frac{1}{2}$ (2.0)	$1\frac{1}{4}$ (1.7)	0.104
$\frac{3}{8}$	10	$4\frac{3}{4}$ (6.4)	1 (1.3)	$5\frac{3}{4}$ (7.7)	$3\frac{3}{4}$ (5.1)	$7\frac{1}{2}$ (10.1)	$8\frac{1}{2}$ (11.4)	$6\frac{1}{2}$ (8.8)	$2\frac{1}{4}$ (3.7)	$1\frac{1}{2}$ (2.0)	$1\frac{1}{4}$ (1.7)	0.104
$\frac{1}{2}$	15	$4\frac{1}{2}$ (8.2)	1 (1.8)	$5\frac{1}{2}$ (10.0)	$3\frac{1}{2}$ (6.4)	$7\frac{1}{4}$ (13.2)	$8\frac{1}{4}$ (15.0)	$6\frac{1}{4}$ (11.4)	$2\frac{1}{4}$ (5.0)	$1\frac{1}{2}$ (2.7)	$1\frac{1}{4}$ (2.3)	0.142
$\frac{3}{4}$	20	$5\frac{1}{4}$ (9.5)	1 (1.8)	$6\frac{1}{4}$ (11.3)	$4\frac{1}{4}$ (7.7)	8 (14.5)	9 (16.3)	7 (12.7)	$2\frac{1}{4}$ (5.0)	$1\frac{1}{2}$ (2.7)	$1\frac{1}{4}$ (2.3)	0.142
1	25	$4\frac{1}{2}$ (10.4)	1 (2.3)	$5\frac{1}{2}$ (12.7)	$3\frac{1}{2}$ (8.1)	$7\frac{1}{4}$ (16.8)	$8\frac{3}{4}$ (19.1)	$6\frac{1}{4}$ (14.5)	$2\frac{1}{4}$ (6.4)	$1\frac{1}{2}$ (3.5)	$1\frac{1}{4}$ (2.9)	0.180
$1\frac{1}{4}$	32	$5\frac{1}{2}$ (12.7)	1 (2.3)	$6\frac{1}{2}$ (15.0)	$4\frac{1}{2}$ (10.4)	$8\frac{1}{4}$ (19.1)	$9\frac{1}{4}$ (21.4)	$7\frac{1}{4}$ (16.8)	$2\frac{1}{4}$ (6.4)	$1\frac{1}{2}$ (3.5)	$1\frac{1}{4}$ (2.9)	0.180
$1\frac{1}{2}$	40	$5\frac{1}{2}$ (12.7)	1 (2.3)	$6\frac{1}{2}$ (15.0)	$4\frac{1}{2}$ (10.4)	$8\frac{1}{4}$ (19.1)	$9\frac{1}{4}$ (21.4)	$7\frac{1}{4}$ (16.8)	$2\frac{1}{4}$ (6.4)	$1\frac{1}{2}$ (3.5)	$1\frac{1}{4}$ (2.9)	0.180
2	50	$6\frac{7}{8}$ (15.9)	1 (2.3)	$7\frac{7}{8}$ (18.2)	$5\frac{7}{8}$ (15.6)	$10\frac{1}{8}$ (23.4)	$11\frac{1}{8}$ (25.7)	$9\frac{1}{8}$ (21.1)	$3\frac{1}{4}$ (7.5)	2 (4.6)	$1\frac{1}{4}$ (2.9)	0.180
$2\frac{1}{2}$	65	$7\frac{9}{16}$ (17.5)	$1\frac{1}{2}$ (3.5)	$9\frac{1}{16}$ (21.0)	$6\frac{1}{16}$ (14.0)	$11\frac{9}{16}$ (26.7)	$13\frac{1}{16}$ (30.2)	$10\frac{1}{16}$ (23.2)	4 (9.2)	$2\frac{1}{2}$ (5.8)	$1\frac{1}{2}$ (3.5)	0.216
3	80	$8\frac{15}{16}$ (20.6)	$1\frac{1}{2}$ (3.5)	$10\frac{7}{16}$ (24.1)	$7\frac{7}{16}$ (17.1)	$12\frac{15}{16}$ (29.8)	$14\frac{7}{16}$ (33.3)	$11\frac{7}{16}$ (26.3)	4 (9.2)	$2\frac{1}{2}$ (5.8)	$1\frac{1}{2}$ (3.5)	0.216
4	100	11 (25.4)	$1\frac{1}{2}$ (3.5)	$12\frac{1}{2}$ (28.9)	$9\frac{1}{2}$ (21.9)	$15\frac{1}{2}$ (35.8)	17 (19.3)	14 (32.3)	$4\frac{1}{2}$ (10.4)	3 (6.9)	$1\frac{1}{2}$ (3.5)	0.216
5	125	$12\frac{3}{8}$ (28.6)	$1\frac{1}{2}$ (3.5)	$13\frac{7}{8}$ (32.1)	$10\frac{7}{8}$ (25.1)	$17\frac{3}{8}$ (40.1)	$18\frac{7}{8}$ (43.6)	$15\frac{7}{8}$ (36.6)	5 (11.5)	$3\frac{1}{2}$ (8.1)	$1\frac{1}{2}$ (3.5)	0.216
6	150	$12\frac{3}{8}$ (28.6)	$1\frac{1}{2}$ (3.5)	$13\frac{7}{8}$ (32.1)	$10\frac{7}{8}$ (25.1)	$17\frac{7}{8}$ (40.1)	$18\frac{7}{8}$ (43.6)	$15\frac{7}{8}$ (36.6)	5 (11.5)	$3\frac{1}{2}$ (8.1)	$1\frac{1}{2}$ (3.5)	0.216

* Nominal pipe size equivalents, *not* conversions.
† Gauge length in number of turns of thread {() = linear equivalent to nearest 0.1 mm}.
‡ Tolerance on position of gauge plane relative to face of internally taper threaded parts.
§ Diametral tolerance on parallel internal threads (millimetres).
For further information see BS 2779.

2.1.28 BA thread form

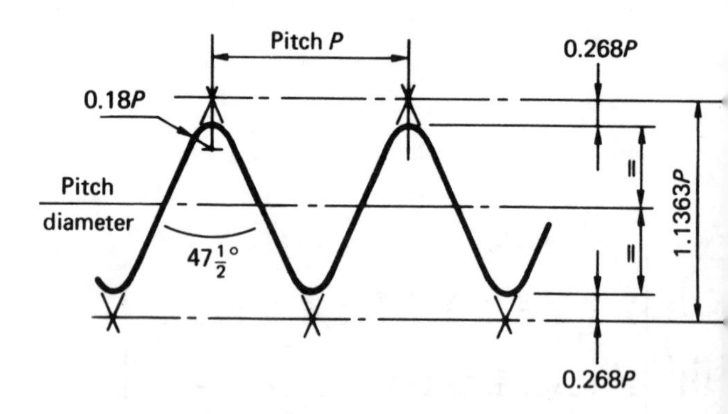

British Association (BA) thread forms are obsolete but are still used in repairs and maintenance.

2.1.29 BA Internal and external screw threads

Dimensions in millimetres

Designation number	*Pitch*	*Depth of thread*	*Major diameter*	*Pitch (effective) diameter*	*Minor diameter*	*Crest radius*	*Root radius*
0	1.0000	0.600	6.00	5.400	4.80	0.1808	0.1808
1	0.9000	0.540	5.30	4.760	4.22	0.1627	0.1627
2	0.8100	0.485	4.70	4.215	3.73	0.1465	0.1465
3	0.7300	0.440	4.10	3.660	3.22	0.1320	0.1320
4	0.6600	0.395	3.60	3.205	2.81	0.1193	0.1193
5	0.5900	0.355	3.20	2.845	2.49	0.1067	0.1067
6	0.5300	0.320	2.80	2.480	2.16	0.0958	0.0958
7	0.4800	0.290	2.50	2.210	1.92	0.0868	0.0868
8	0.4300	0.260	2.20	1.940	1.68	0.0778	0.0778
9	0.3900	0.235	1.90	1.665	1.43	0.0705	0.0705
10	0.3500	0.210	1.70	1.490	1.28	0.0633	0.0633

continued

Section 2.1.29 (*continued*)

Designation number	*Pitch*	*Depth of thread*	*Major diameter*	*Pitch (effective) diameter*	*Minor diameter*	*Crest radius*	*Root radius*
11	0.3100	0.185	1.50	1.315	1.13	0.0561	0.0561
12	0.2800	0.170	1.30	1.130	0.96	0.0506	0.0506
13	0.2500	0.150	1.20	1.050	0.90	0.0452	0.0452
14	0.2300	0.140	1.00	0.860	0.72	0.0416	0.0416
15	0.2100	0.125	0.90	0.775	0.65	0.0380	0.0380
16	0.1900	0.115	0.79	0.675	0.56	0.0344	0.0344
17	0.1700	0.100	0.70	0.600	0.50	0.0307	0.0307
18	0.1500	0.090	0.62	0.530	0.44	0.0271	0.0271
19	0.1400	0.085	0.54	0.455	0.37	0.0253	0.0253
20	0.1200	0.070	0.48	0.410	0.34	0.0217	0.0217
21	0.1100	0.065	0.42	0.355	0.29	0.0199	0.0199
22	0.1000	0.060	0.37	0.310	0.25	0.0181	0.0181
23	0.0900	0.055	0.33	0.275	0.22	0.0163	0.0163
24	0.0800	0.050	0.29	0.240	0.19	0.0145	0.0145
25	0.0700	0.040	0.25	0.210	0.17	0.0127	0.0127

For further information see BS 57 and BS 93.
British Association (BA) thread forms are obsolete but are still used in repairs and maintenance.

Dimensions in millimetres

Pitch of thread	Basic major diameter			Pitch (effective) diameter	Basic minor diameter	
	1st choice	2nd choice	3rd choice		External	Internal
0.25	2.0	—	—	1.84	1.69	1.73
0.25	—	2.2	—	2.04	1.89	1.93
0.35	2.5	—	—	2.27	2.07	2.12
0.35	3.0	—	—	2.77	2.57	2.62
0.35	—	3.5	—	3.27	3.07	3.12
0.50	4.0	—	—	3.68	3.39	3.46
0.50	—	4.5	—	4.18	3.86	3.96
0.50	5.0	—	—	4.68	4.39	4.46
0.50	—	—	5.5	5.18	4.86	4.96
0.75	6.0	—	—	5.51	5.08	5.19
0.75	—	—	7.0	6.51	6.08	6.19
0.75	8.0	—	—	7.51	7.08	7.19
0.75	—	—	9.0	8.51	8.08	8.19
0.75	10.0	—	—	9.51	9.08	9.19
0.75	—	—	11.0	10.51	10.08	10.19

continued

Section 2.1.30 (*continued*)

Pitch of thread	*Basic major diameter*			*Pitch (effective) diameter*	*Basic minor diameter*	
	1st choice	*2nd choice*	*3rd choice*		*External*	*Internal*
1.0	8.0	—	—	7.35	6.77	6.92
1.0	—	—	9.0	8.35	7.77	7.92
1.0	10.0	—	—	9.35	8.77	8.92
1.0	—	—	11.0	10.35	9.77	9.92
1.0	12.0	—	—	11.35	10.77	10.92
1.0	—	14.0	—	13.35	12.77	12.92
1.0	—	—	15.0	14.35	13.77	13.92
1.0	16.0	—	—	15.35	14.77	14.92
1.0	—	—	17.0	16.35	15.77	15.92
1.0	—	18.0	—	17.35	16.77	16.92
1.0	20.0	—	—	19.35	18.77	18.92
1.0	—	22.0	—	21.35	21.77	21.92
1.0	24.0	—	—	23.35	22.77	22.92
1.0	—	—	25.0	24.35	23.77	23.92
1.0	—	27.0	—	26.35	25.77	25.92
1.0	—	—	28.0	27.35	26.77	26.92
1.0	30.0	—	—	29.35	28.77	28.92

1.25	10.0	—	—	9.19	8.47	8.65
1.25	12.0	—	—	11.19	10.47	10.65
1.25*	—	14.0*	—	13.19	12.47	12.65
1.5	12.0	—	—	11.03	10.16	10.38
1.5	—	14.0	—	13.03	12.16	12.38
1.5	—	—	15.0	14.03	13.16	13.38
1.5	16.0	—	—	15.03	14.16	14.38
1.5	—	—	17.0	16.03	15.16	15.38
1.5	—	18.0	—	17.03	16.16	16.38
1.5	20.0	—	—	19.03	18.16	18.38
1.5	—	22.0	—	21.03	20.16	20.38
1.5	24.0	—	—	23.03	22.16	22.38
1.5	—	—	25.0	24.03	23.16	23.38
1.5	—	—	26.0	25.03	24.16	24.38
1.5	—	27.0	—	26.03	25.16	25.38
1.5	—	—	28.0	27.03	26.16	26.38
1.5	30.0	—	—	29.03	28.16	28.38
1.5	—	—	32.0	31.03	30.16	30.38
1.5	—	33.0	—	32.03	31.16	31.38
1.5	—	—	35.0	34.03	33.16	33.38

The 1.5 mm pitch series continues to a maximum diameter of 80 mm.

continued

Pitch of thread	*Basic major diameter*			*Pitch (effective) diameter*	*Basic minor diameter*	
	1st choice	*2nd choice*	*3rd choice*		*External*	*Internal*
2.0	—	18.0	—	16.70	15.55	15.84
2.0	20.0	—	—	18.70	17.55	17.84
2.0	—	22.0	—	20.70	19.55	19.84
2.0	24.0	—	—	22.70	21.55	21.84
2.0	—	—	25.0	23.70	22.55	22.84
2.0	—	—	26.0	24.70	23.55	23.84
2.0	—	27.0	—	25.70	24.55	24.84
2.0	—	—	28.0	26.70	25.55	25.84
2.0	30.0	—	—	28.70	27.55	27.84
2.0	—	—	32.0	30.70	29.55	29.84
2.0	—	33.0	—	31.70	30.55	30.84
2.0	—	—	35.0	33.70	32.55	32.84
The 2.0 mm pitch series continues to a maximum diameter of 150 mm.						
3.0	30.0	—	—	28.05	26.32	26.75
3.0	—	33.0	—	31.05	29.32	29.75
3.0	36.0	—	—	34.05	32.32	32.75
3.0	—	—	38.0	36.05	34.32	34.75
3.0	—	39.0	—	37.05	35.32	35.75
3.0	—	—	40.0	38.05	36.32	36.75

3.0	—	45.0	—	43.05	41.32	41.75
3.0	48.0	—	—	46.05	44.32	44.75
3.0	—	—	50.0	48.05	46.32	46.75
3.0	—	52.0	—	50.05	48.32	48.75
3.0	—	—	55.0	53.05	51.32	51.75
The 3.0 mm pitch series continues to a maximum diameter of 250 mm.						
4.0	42.0	—	—	39.40	37.09	37.67
4.0	—	45.0	—	42.40	40.09	40.67
4.0	48.0	—	—	45.40	43.09	43.67
4.0	—	—	50.0	47.40	45.09	45.67
4.0	—	52.0	—	49.40	47.09	47.67
4.0	—	—	55.0	52.40	50.09	50.67
4.0	56.0	—	—	53.40	51.09	51.67
4.0	—	—	58.0	55.40	53.09	53.67
4.0	—	60.0	—	57.40	55.09	55.67
4.0	—	—	62.0	59.40	57.09	57.67
4.0	64.0	—	—	61.40	59.09	59.67
4.0	—	—	65.0	62.40	60.09	60.67
The 4.0 mm pitch series continues to a maximum diameter of 300 mm.						
6.0	—	—	70.0	66.10	62.64	63.50
6.0	72.0	—	—	68.10	64.64	65.50
6.0	—	76.0	—	72.10	68.64	69.50

continued

Section 2.1.30 (*continued*)

Pitch of thread	*Basic major diameter*			*Pitch (effective) diameter*	*Basic minor diameter*	
	1st choice	*2nd choice*	*3rd choice*		*External*	*Internal*
6.0	80.0	—	—	76.10	72.64	73.50
6.0	—	85.0	—	81.10	77.64	78.50
6.0	90.0	—	—	86.10	82.64	83.50
6.0	—	95.0	—	91.10	87.64	88.50
6.0	100.0	—	—	96.10	92.64	93.50
6.0	—	105.0	—	101.10	97.64	98.50
6.0	110.0	—	—	106.10	102.64	103.50
6.0	—	115.0	—	111.10	107.64	108.50
6.0	—	120.0	—	116.10	112.64	113.50
6.0	125.0	—	—	121.10	117.64	118.50

The 6.0 mm pitch series continues to a maximum diameter of 300 mm.

* This size sparking plugs only.
For further information see BS 3643.

2.1.31 Plain washers, bright: metric series

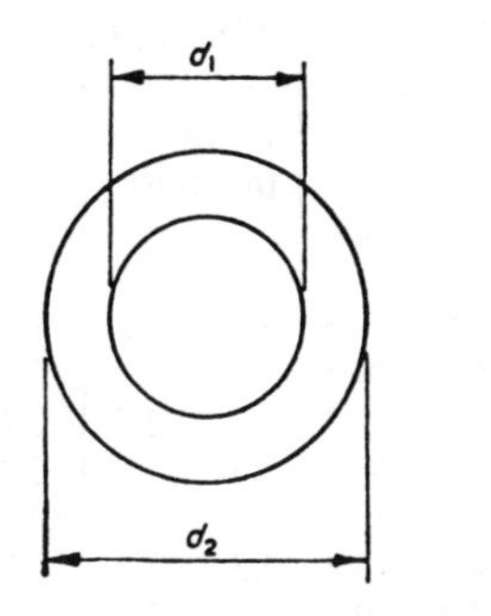

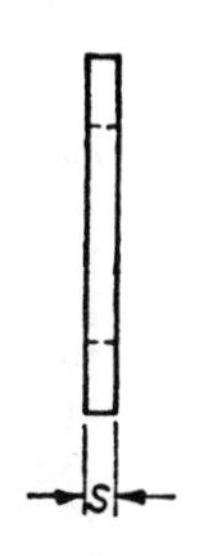

Dimensions in millimetres

Designation (*thread diameter*)*	*Internal diameter* d_1 *max.*	*min.*	*External diameter* d_2 *max.*	*min.*	*Thickness s* *Thick (normal)* *max.*	*min.*	*Thin* *max.*	*min.*
M1.0	1.25	1.1	2.5	2.3	0.4	0.2	—	—
M1.2	1.45	1.3	3.0	2.8	0.4	0.2	—	—
(M1.4)	1.65	1.5	3.0	2.8	0.4	0.2	—	—
M1.6	1.85	1.7	4.0	3.7	0.4	0.2	—	—
M2.0	2.35	2.2	5.0	4.7	0.4	0.2	—	—
(M2.2)	2.55	2.4	5.0	4.7	0.6	0.4	—	—
M2.5	2.85	2.7	6.5	6.2	0.6	0.4	—	—
M3	3.4	3.2	7.0	6.7	0.6	0.4	—	—
(M3.5)	3.9	3.7	7.0	6.7	0.6	0.4	—	—
M4	4.5	4.3	9.0	8.7	0.9	0.7	—	—
(M4.5)	5.0	4.8	9.0	8.7	0.9	0.7	—	—
M5	5.5	5.3	10.0	9.7	1.1	0.9	—	—
M6	6.7	6.4	12.5	12.1	1.8	1.4	0.9	0.7
(M7)	7.7	7.4	14.0	13.6	1.8	1.4	0.9	0.7
M8	8.7	8.4	17.0	16.6	1.8	1.4	1.1	0.9
M10	10.9	10.5	21.0	20.5	2.2	1.8	1.45	1.05
M12	13.4	13.0	24.0	23.5	2.7	2.3	1.8	1.4

continued

Section 2.1.31 (*continued*)

Designation (thread diameter)*	Internal diameter d_1 max.	min.	External diameter d_2 max.	min.	Thickness s: Thick (normal) max.	min.	Thin max.	min.
(M14)	15.4	15.0	28.0	27.5	2.7	2.3	1.8	1.4
M16	17.4	17.0	30.0	29.5	3.3	2.7	2.2	1.8
(M18)	19.5	19.0	34.0	33.2	3.3	2.7	2.2	1.8
M20	21.5	21.0	37.0	36.2	3.3	2.7	2.2	1.8
(M22)	23.5	23.0	39.0	38.2	3.3	2.7	2.2	1.8
M24	25.5	25.0	44.0	43.2	4.3	3.7	2.7	2.3
(M27)	28.5	28.0	50.0	49.2	4.3	3.7	2.7	2.3
M30	31.6	31.0	56.0	55.0	4.3	3.7	2.7	2.3
(M33)	34.6	34.0	60.0	59.0	5.6	4.4	3.3	2.7
M36	37.6	37.0	66.0	65.0	5.6	4.4	3.3	2.7
(M39)	40.6	40.0	72.0	71.0	6.6	5.4	3.3	2.7

* Non-preferred sizes in brackets ().
For full information see BS 4320 : 1968.

2.1.32 **Plain washers, black: metric series**

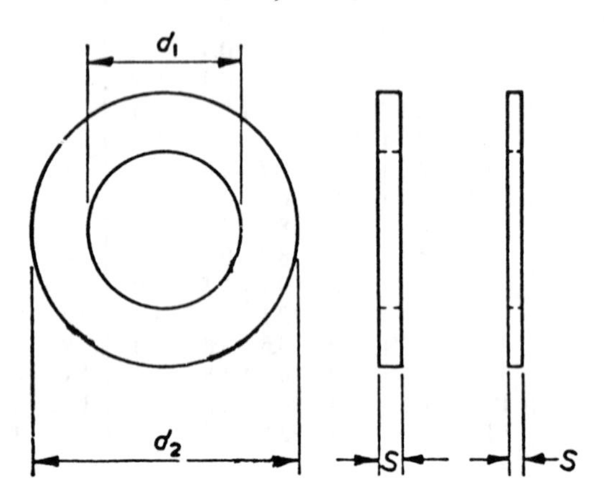

Dimensions in millimetres

Designation (thread diameter)*	Internal diameter d_1 max.	min.	External diameter d_2 max.	min.	Thickness s max.	min.
M5	5.8	5.5	10.0	9.2	1.2	0.8
M6	7.0	6.6	12.5	11.7	1.9	1.3
(M7)	8.0	7.6	14.0	13.2	1.9	1.3
M8	9.4	9.0	17.0	16.2	1.9	1.3
M10	11.5	11.0	21.0	20.2	2.3	1.7
M12	14.5	14.0	24.0	23.2	2.8	2.2
(M14)	16.5	16.0	28.0	27.2	2.8	2.2
M16	18.5	18.0	30.0	29.2	3.6	2.4
(M18)	20.6	20.0	34.0	32.8	3.6	2.4
M20	22.6	22.0	37.0	35.8	3.6	2.4
(M22)	24.6	24.0	39.0	37.8	3.6	2.4
M24	26.6	26.0	44.0	42.8	4.6	3.4
(M27)	30.6	30.0	50.0	48.8	4.6	3.4
M30	33.8	33.0	56.0	54.5	4.6	3.4
(M33)	36.8	36.0	60.0	58.5	6.0	4.0
M36	39.8	39.0	66.0	64.5	6.0	4.0
(M39)	42.8	42.0	72.0	70.5	7.0	5.0
M42	45.8	45.0	78.0	76.5	8.2	5.8
(M45)	48.8	48.0	85.0	83.0	8.2	5.8
M48	53.0	52.0	92.0	90.0	9.2	6.8
(M52)	57.0	56.0	98.0	96.0	9.2	6.8
M56	63.0	62.0	105.0	103.0	10.2	7.8
(M60)	67.0	66.0	110.0	108.0	10.2	7.8
M64	71.0	70.0	115.0	113.0	10.2	7.8
(M68)	75.0	74.0	120.0	118.0	11.2	8.8

* Non-preferred sizes in brackets ().
For full information see BS 4320 : 1968.

2.1.33 Friction locking devices

Lock nut

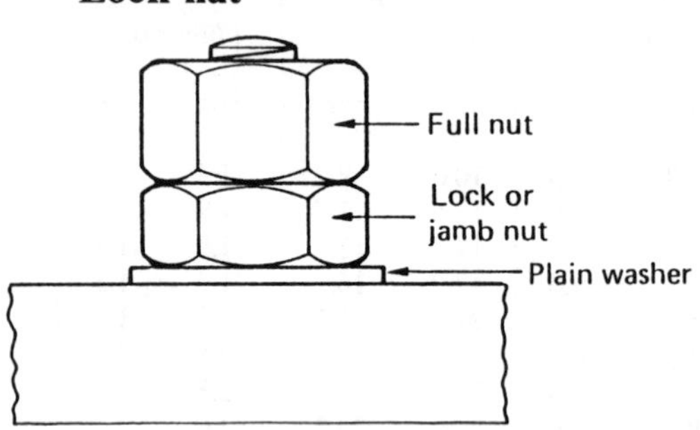

Stiff nut (insert)

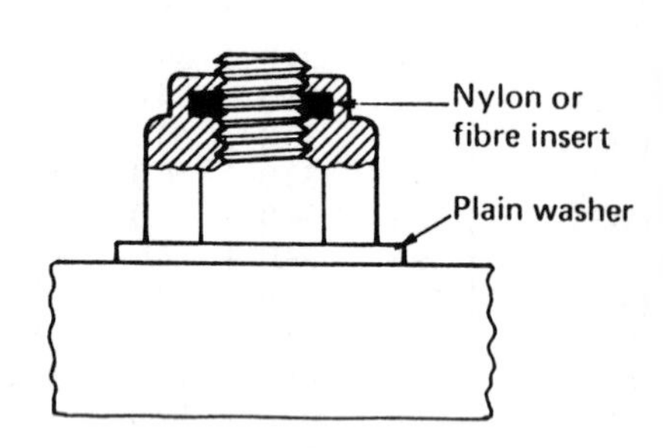

Stiff nut (slit head)

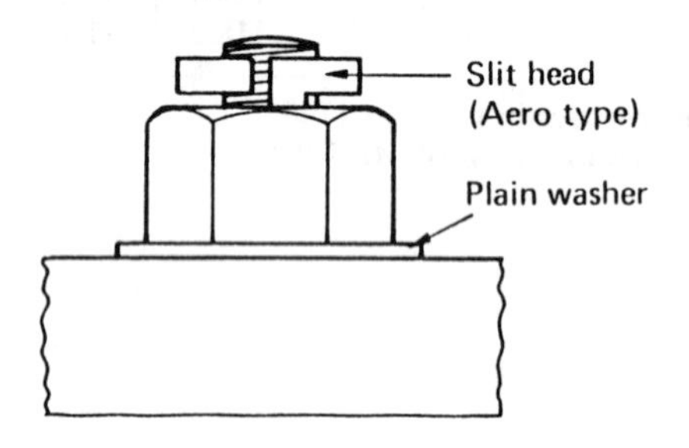

Stiff nut (slit head)

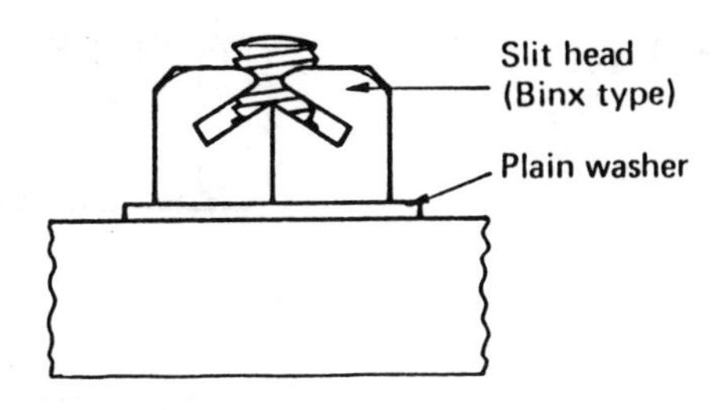

Serrated (toothed) lock washers

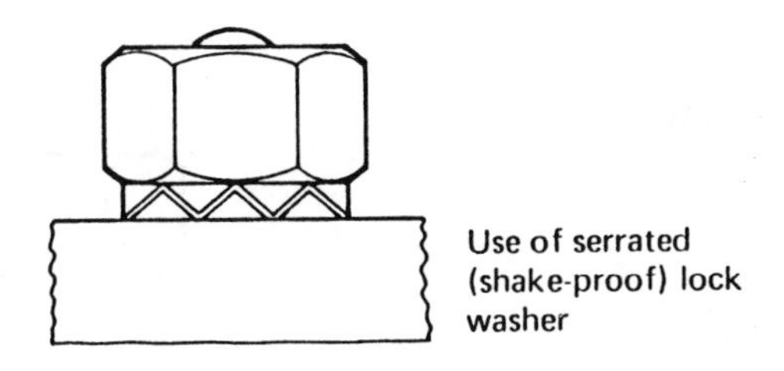

Note:
Serrated lock washers, see 2.1.38, 2.1.39
Spring washers see 2.1.35, 2.1.36, 2.1.37.
Crinkle washers see 2.1.40.

2.1.34 Positive locking devices

Slotted nut

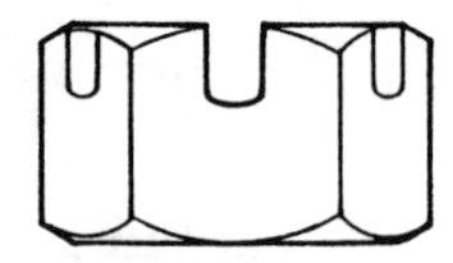

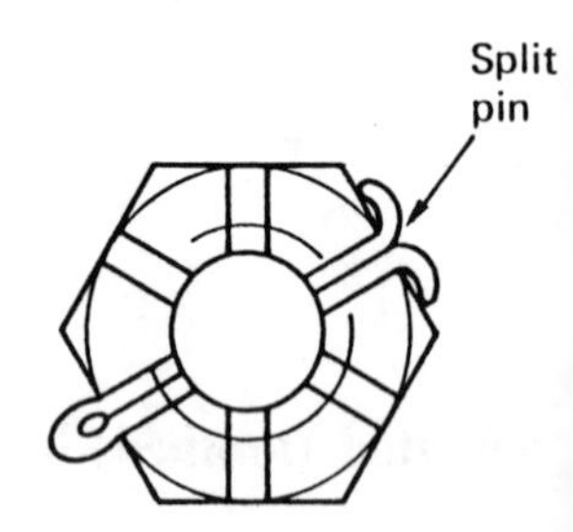

Castle nut

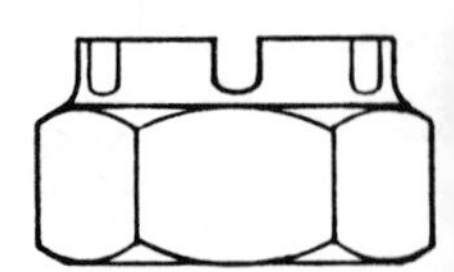

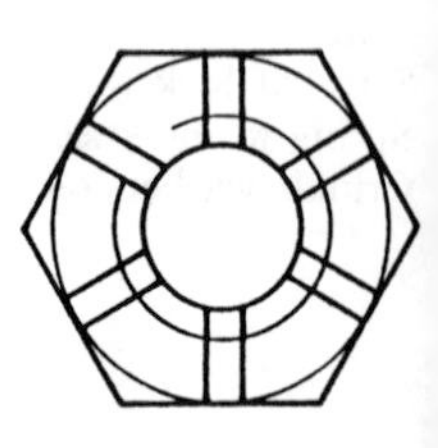

Tab washer

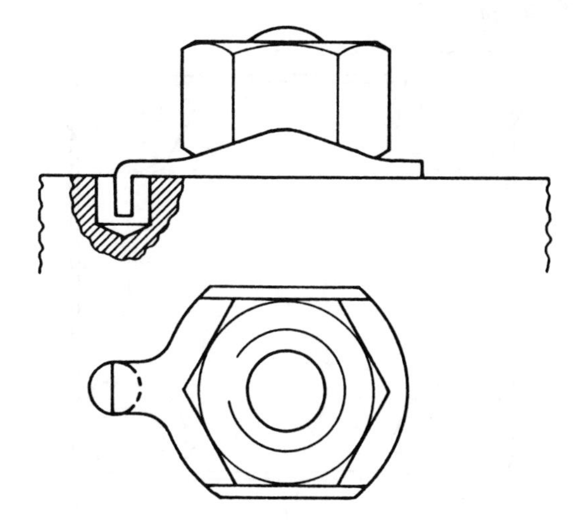

Lock plate

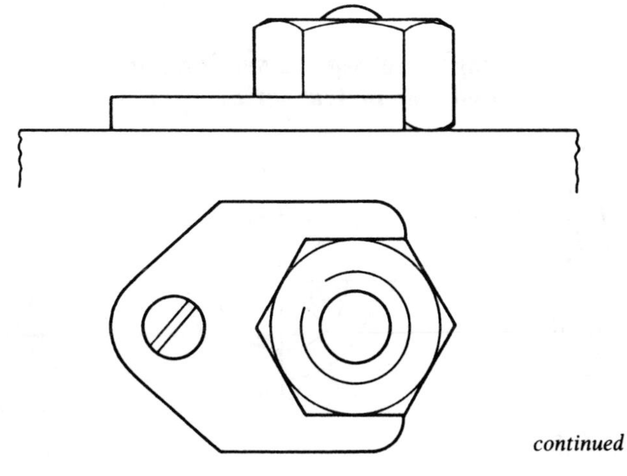

continued

Wiring

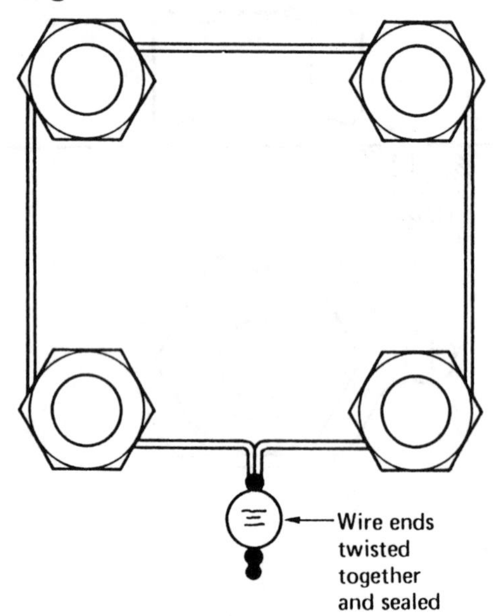

2.1.35 Single coil square section spring washers: metric series, type A

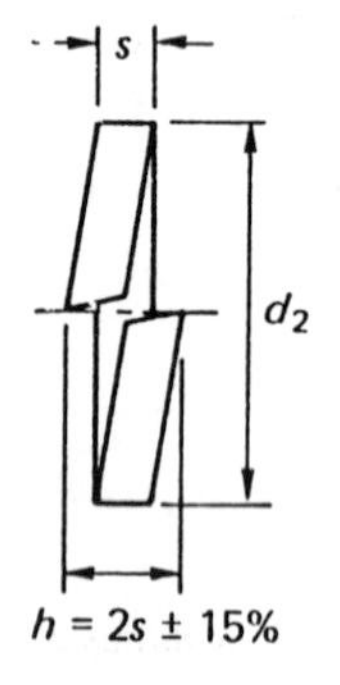

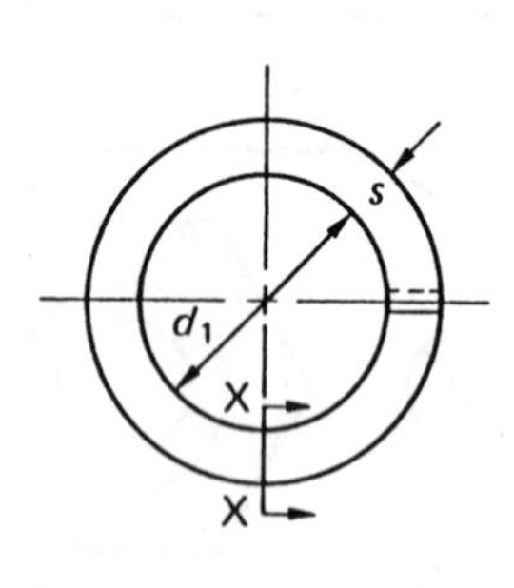

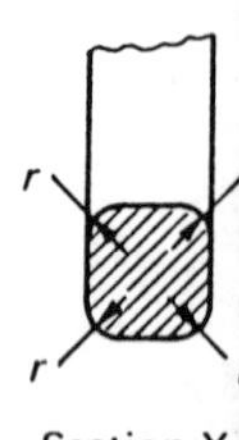

Dimensions in millimetres

*Nominal size and thread diameter** d	*Inside diameter* d_1		*Thickness and width* s	*Outside diameter* d_2	*Radius* r
	max.	*min.*		*max.*	*max.*
M3	3.3	3.1	1 ± 0.1	5.5	0.3
(M3.5)	3.8	3.6	1 ± 0.1	6.0	0.3
M4	4.35	4.1	1.2 ± 0.1	6.95	0.4
M5	5.35	5.1	1.5 ± 0.1	8.55	0.5
M6	6.4	6.1	1.5 ± 0.1	9.6	0.5
M8	8.55	8.2	2 ± 0.1	12.75	0.65
M10	10.6	10.2	2.5 ± 0.15	15.9	0.8
M12	12.6	12.2	2.5 ± 0.15	17.9	0.8
(M14)	14.7	14.2	3 ± 0.2	21.1	1.0
M16	16.9	16.3	3.5 ± 0.2	24.3	1.15
(M18)	19.0	18.3	3.5 ± 0.2	26.4	1.15
M20	21.1	20.3	4.5 ± 0.2	30.5	1.5
(M22)	23.3	22.4	4.5 ± 0.2	32.7	1.5
M24	25.3	24.4	5 ± 0.2	35.7	1.65
(M27)	28.5	27.5	5 ± 0.2	38.9	1.65
M30	31.5	30.5	6 ± 0.2	43.9	2.0
(M33)	34.6	33.5	6 ± 0.2	47.0	2.0
M36	37.6	36.5	7 ± 0.25	52.1	2.3
(M39)	40.8	39.6	7 ± 0.25	55.3	2.3
M42	43.8	42.6	8 ± 0.25	60.3	2.65
(M45)	46.8	45.6	8 ± 0.25	63.3	2.65
M48	50.0	48.8	8 ± 0.25	66.5	2.65

* Sizes shown in brackets are non-preferred and are not usually stock sizes.

For further information see BS 4464.

2.1.36 Single coil rectangular section spring washers: metric series, types B and BP

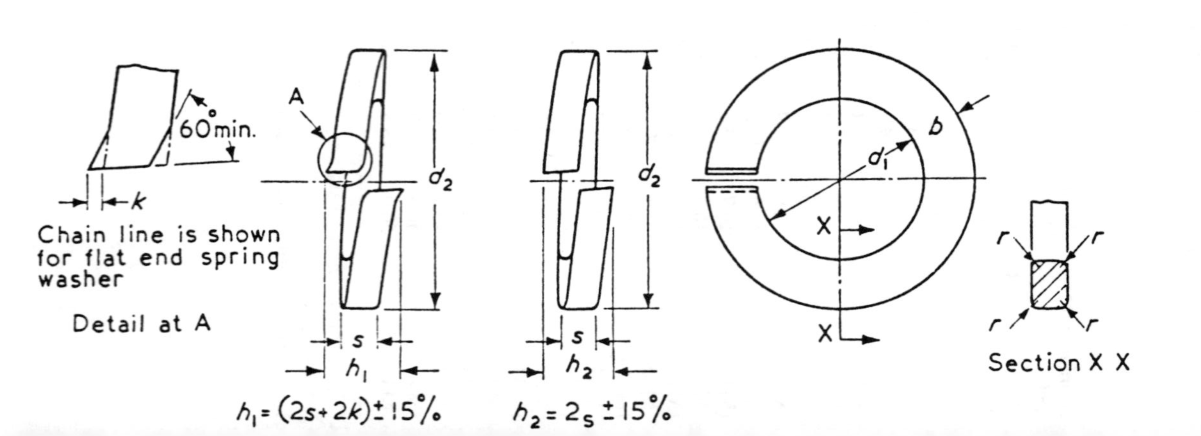

Dimensions in millimetres

Nominal size and thread diameter* d	Inside diameter d_1		Width b	Thickness s	Outside diameter d_2 max.	Radius r max.	k (type BP only)
	max.	min.					
M1.6	1.9	1.7	0.7±0.1	0.4±0.1	3.5	0.15	—
M2	2.3	2.1	0.9±0.1	0.5±0.1	4.3	0.15	—
(M2.2)	2.5	2.3	1.0±0.1	0.6±0.1	4.7	0.2	—
M2.5	2.8	2.6	1.0±0.1	0.6±0.1	5.0	0.2	—
M3	3.3	3.1	1.3±0.1	0.8±0.1	6.1	0.25	—
(M3.5)	3.8	3.6	1.3±0.1	0.8±0.1	6.6	0.25	0.15
M4	4.35	4.1	1.5±0.1	0.9±0.1	7.55	0.3	0.15
M5	5.35	5.1	1.8±0.1	1.2±0.1	9.15	0.4	0.15
M6	6.4	6.1	2.5±0.15	1.6±0.1	11.7	0.5	0.2
M8	8.55	8.2	3±0.15	2±0.1	14.85	0.65	0.3
M10	10.6	10.2	3.5±0.2	2.2±0.15	18.0	0.7	0.3
M12	12.6	12.2	4±0.2	2.5±0.15	21.0	0.8	0.4
(M14)	14.7	14.2	4.5±0.2	3±0.15	24.1	1.0	0.4
M16	16.9	16.3	5±0.2	3.5±0.2	27.3	1.15	0.4
(M18)	19.0	18.3	5±0.2	3.5±0.2	29.4	1.15	0.4
M20	21.1	20.3	6±0.2	4±0.2	33.5	1.3	0.4
(M22)	23.3	22.4	6±0.2	4±0.2	35.7	1.3	0.4

continued

Dimensions in millimetres

Nominal size and thread diameter* d	Inside diameter d_1 max.	Inside diameter d_1 min.	Width b	Thickness s	Outside diameter d_2 max.	Radius r max.	k (type BP only)
M24	25.3	24.4	7±0.25	5±0.2	39.8	1.65	0.5
(M27)	28.5	27.5	7±0.25	5±0.2	43.0	1.65	0.5
M30	31.5	30.5	8±0.25	6±0.25	48.0	2.0	0.8
(M33)	34.6	33.5	10±0.25	6±0.25	55.1	2.0	0.8
M36	37.6	36.5	10±0.25	6±0.25	58.1	2.0	0.8
(M39)	40.8	39.6	10±0.25	6±0.25	61.3	2.0	0.8
M42	43.8	42.6	12±0.25	7±0.25	68.3	2.3	0.8
(M45)	46.8	45.6	12±0.25	7±0.25	71.3	2.3	0.8
M48	50.0	48.8	12±0.25	7±0.25	74.5	2.3	0.8
(M52)	54.1	52.8	14±0.25	8±0.25	82.6	2.65	1.0
M56	58.1	56.8	14±0.25	8±0.25	86.6	2.65	1.0
(M60)	62.3	60.9	14±0.25	8±0.25	90.8	2.65	1.0
M64	66.3	64.9	14±0.25	8±0.25	93.8	2.65	1.0
(M68)	70.5	69.0	14±0.25	8±0.25	99.0	2.65	1.0

* Sizes shown in brackets are non-preferred, and are not usually stock sizes.
For further information see BS 4464.

2.1.37 Double coil rectangular section spring washers: metric series, type D

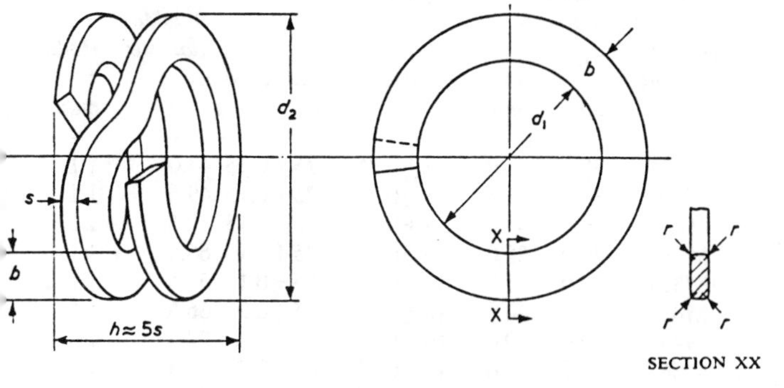

Dimensions in millimetres

*Nominal size and thread diameter** d	*Inside diameter* d_1 *max.*	*Inside diameter* d_1 *min.*	*Width* b	*Thickness* s	*Outside diameter* d_2 *max.*	*Radius* r *max.*
M2	2.4	2.1	0.9 ± 0.1	0.5 ± 0.05	4.4	0.15
(M2.2)	2.6	2.3	1.0 ± 0.1	0.6 ± 0.05	4.8	0.2
M2.5	2.9	2.6	1.2 ± 0.1	0.7 ± 0.1	5.5	0.23
M3.0	3.6	3.3	1.2 ± 0.1	0.8 ± 0.1	6.2	0.25
(M3.5)	4.1	3.8	1.6 ± 0.1	0.8 ± 0.1	7.5	0.25
M4	4.6	4.3	1.6 ± 0.1	0.8 ± 0.1	8.0	0.25
M5	5.6	5.3	2 ± 0.1	0.9 ± 0.1	9.8	0.3
M6	6.6	6.3	3 ± 0.15	1 ± 0.1	12.9	0.33
M8	8.8	8.4	3 ± 0.15	1.2 ± 0.1	15.1	0.4
M10	10.8	10.4	3.5 ± 0.20	1.2 ± 0.1	18.2	0.4
M12	12.8	12.4	3.5 ± 0.2	1.6 ± 0.1	20.2	0.5
(M14)	15.0	14.5	5 ± 0.2	1.6 ± 0.1	25.4	0.5
M16	17.0	16.5	5 ± 0.2	2 ± 0.1	27.4	0.65
(M18)	19.0	18.5	5 ± 0.2	2 ± 0.1	29.4	0.65
M20	21.5	20.8	5 ± 0.2	2 ± 0.1	31.9	0.65
(M22)	23.5	22.8	6 ± 0.2	2.5 ± 0.15	35.9	0.8
M24	26.0	25.0	6.5 ± 0.2	3.25 ± 0.15	39.4	1.1

continued

*Nominal size and thread diameter** *d*	*Inside diameter* d_1 *max.*	*min.*	*Width* *b*	*Thickness* *s*	*Outside diameter* d_2 *max.*	*Radius* *r* *max.*
(M27)	29.5	28.0	7±0.25	3.25±0.15	44.0	1.1
M30	33.0	31.5	8±0.25	3.25±0.15	49.5	1.1
(M33)	36.0	34.5	8±0.25	3.25±0.15	52.5	1.1
M36	40.0	38.0	10±0.25	3.25±0.15	60.5	1.1
(M39)	43.0	41.0	10±0.25	3.25±0.15	63.5	1.1
M42	46.0	44.0	10±0.25	4.5±0.2	66.5	1.5
M48	52.0	50.0	10±0.25	4.5±0.2	72.5	1.5
M56	60.0	58.0	12±0.25	4.5±0.2	84.5	1.5
M64	70.0	67.0	12±0.25	4.5±0.2	94.5	1.5

* Sizes shown in brackets are non-preferred, and are not usually stock sizes.

Note: the free height of double coil washers before compression is normally approximately five times the thickness but, if required, washers with other free heights may be obtained by arrangement between the purchaser and the manufacturer.

For further information see BS 4464.

2.1.38 Toothed lock washers, metric

Type A externally toothed

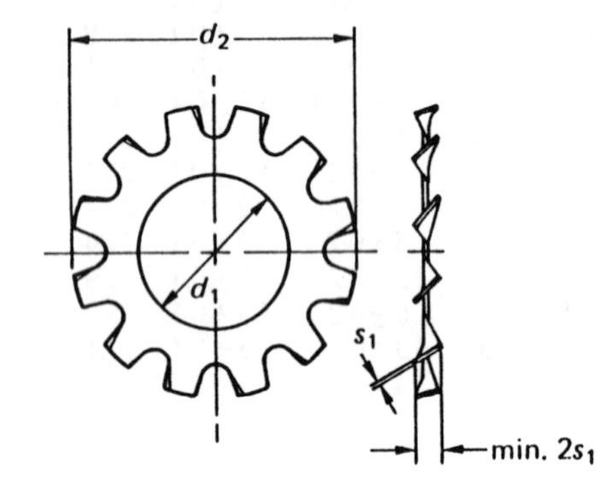

Type J internally toothed

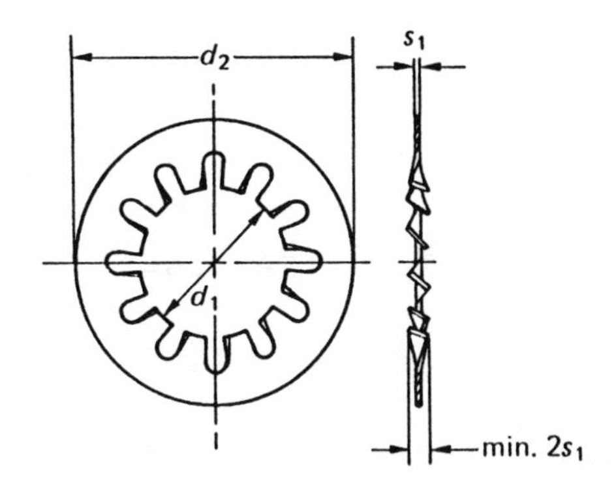

Type V countersunk

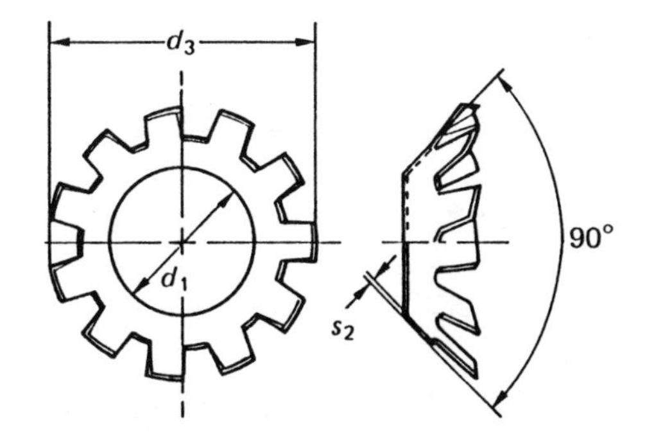

Details left unspecified are to be designed as appropriate.

Designation of a toothed lock washer type J with hole diameter $d_1 = 6.4$ mm of spring steel, surface phosphated for protection against rusting (phr): toothed lock washer J 6.4 DIN 6797 – phr.

If toothed lock washers are required for left hand threaded bolts, the designation reads: toothed lock washer J 6.4 left DIN 6797 – phr.

continued

Section 2.1.38 (*continued*)

Dimensions in millimetres

d_1 (H13)	d_2 (h14)	d_3 ≈	s_1	s_2	Number of teeth min. A and J	V	Weight (7.85 kg/dm³) kg/1000 pieces ≈ A	J	V	For thread diameter
1.7	3.6	—	0.3	—	6	—	0.01	—	—	1.6
1.8	3.8	—	0.3	—	6	—	0.015	—	—	1.7
1.9	4	—	0.3	—	6	—	0.02	0.03	—	1.8
2.2	4.5	4.2	0.3	0.2	6	6	0.025	0.04	0.02	2
2.5	5	—	0.4	0.2	6	6	0.03	0.025	—	2.3
2.7	5.5	5.1	0.4	0.2	6	6	0.04	0.045	0.025	2.5
2.8	5.5	—	0.4	0.2	6	6	0.04	0.045	—	2.6
3.2	6	6	0.4	0.2	6	6	0.045	0.045	0.025	3
3.7	7	7	0.5	0.25	6	6	0.075	0.085	0.04	3.5
4.3	8	8	0.5	0.25	8	8	0.095	0.1	0.05	4
5.1*	9	—	0.5	—	8	—	0.14	0.15	—	5
5.3	10	9.8	0.6	0.3	8	8	0.18	0.2	0.12	5
6.4	11	11.8	0.7	0.4	8	10	0.22	0.25	0.2	6
7.4	12.5	—	0.8	—	8	—	0.3	0.35	—	7
8.2*	14	—	0.8	—	8	—	0.4	0.45	—	8
8.4	15	15.3	0.8	0.4	8	10	0.45	0.55	0.4	8
10.5	18	19	0.9	0.5	9	10	0.8	0.9	0.7	10
12.5	20.5	23	1	0.5	10	10	1.1	1.3	1.2	12
14.5	24	26.2	1	0.6	10	12	1.7	2	1.4	14
16.5	26	30.2	1.2	0.6	12	12	2.1	2.5	1.4	16
19	30	—	1.4	—	12	—	3.5	3.7	—	18
21	33	—	1.4	—	12	—	3.8	4.1	—	20
23	36		1.5	—	14	—	5	6	—	22
25	38	—	1.5	—	14	—	6	6.5	—	24
28	44		1.6	—	14	—	8	8.5	—	27
31	48		1.6	—	14	—	9	9.5	—	30

* Only for hexagon head bolts.
For further details see DIN 6797.

2.1.39 Serrated lock washers, metric

Type A serrated externally

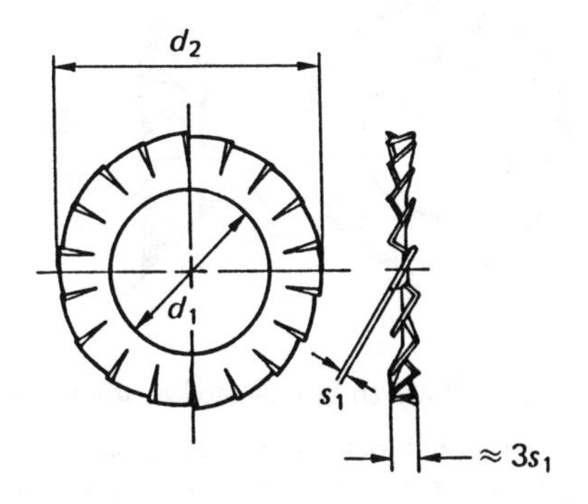

Type J serrated internally

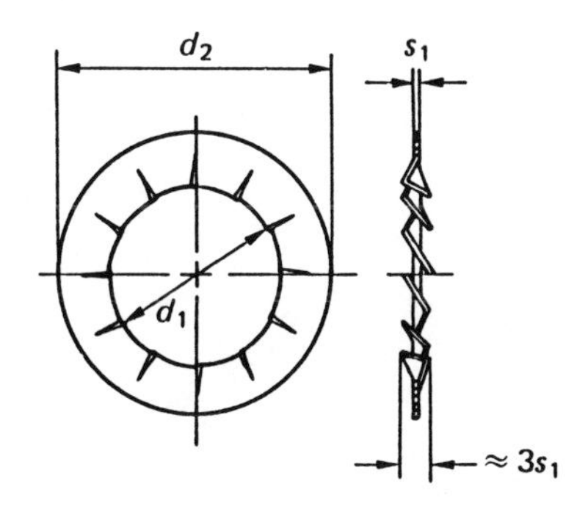

Type V countersunk

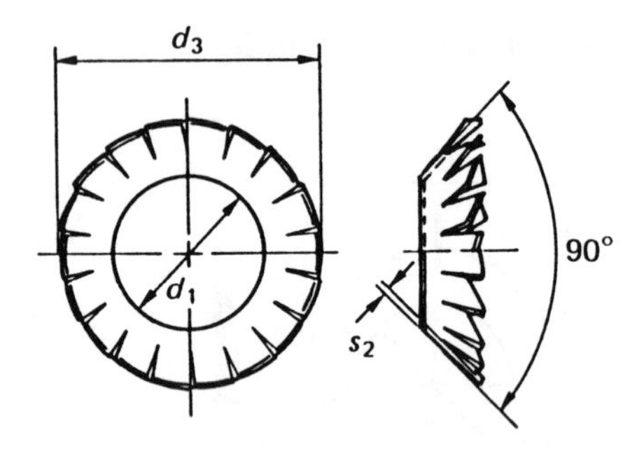

Details left unspecified are to be designed as appropriate.

Designation of a serrated lock washer type J with hole diameter $d_1 = 6.4$ mm in spring steel, surface phosphated for protection against rusting (phr): serrated lock washer J 6.4 DIN 6798 – phr.

If serrated lock washers are required for left hand threaded bolts, the designation reads: serrated lock washer J 6.4 left DIN 6798 – phr.

Dimensions in millimetres

d_1 (H13)	d_2 (h14)	d_3 ≈	s_1	s_2	Number of teeth min. A	J	V	Weight (7.85 kg/dm³) kg/1000 pieces ≈ A and J	V	For thread diameter
1.7	3.6		0.3	—	9	7	—	0.02	—	1.6
1.8	3.8		0.3	—	9	7	—	0.02	—	1.7
1.9	4		0.3	—	9	7	—	0.025	—	—
2.2	4.5	4.2	0.3	0.2	9	7	10	0.03	0.025	2
2.5	5		0.4	0.2	9	7	10	0.04	—	2.3
2.7	5.5	5.1	0.4	0.2	9	7	10	0.045	0.03	2.5
2.8	5.5		0.4	0.2	9	7	10	0.05	—	2.6
3.2	6	6	0.4	0.2	9	7	12	0.06	0.04	3
3.7	7	7	0.5	0.25	10	8	12	0.11	0.075	3.5
4.3	8	8	0.5	0.25	11	8	14	0.14	0.1	4
5.1*	9		0.5	—	11	8	—	0.22	—	5
5.3	10	9.8	0.6	0.3	11	8	14	0.28	0.2	5
6.4	11	11.8	0.7	0.4	12	9	16	0.36	0.3	6
7.4	12.5		0.8	—	14	10	—	0.5	—	7
8.2*	14	—	0.8	—	14	10	—	0.75	—	8
8.4	15	15.3	0.8	0.4	14	10	18	0.8	0.5	8
10.5	18	19	0.9	0.5	16	12	20	1.25	1	10
12.5	20.5	23	1	0.5	16	12	26	1.7	1.5	12
14.5	24	26.2	1	0.6	18	14	28	2.4	2	14
16.5	26	30.2	1.2	0.6	18	14	30	3	2.4	16
19	30	—	1.4	—	18	14	—	5	—	18
21	33	—	1.4	—	20	16	—	6	—	20
23	36	—	1.5	—	20	16	—	7.5	—	22
25	38	—	1.5	—	20	16	—	8	—	24
28	44	—	1.6	—	22	18	—	12	—	27
31	48	—	1.6	—	22	18	—	14	—	30

* Only for hexagon head bolts.
For further details see DIN 6797.

2.1.40 ISO metric crinkle washers: general engineering

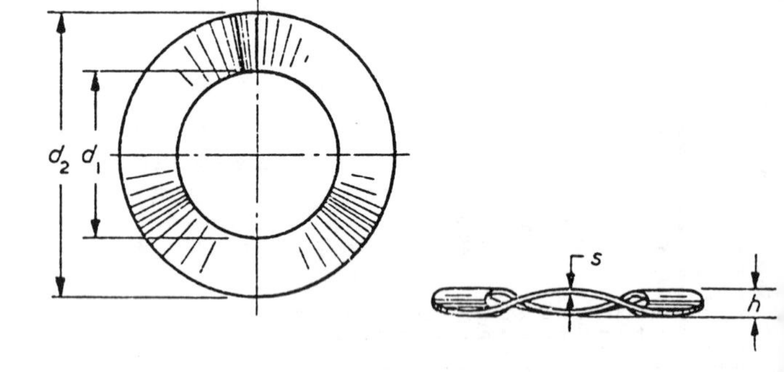

Dimensions in millimetres

Nominal (thread) diameter*	Inside diameter d_1 max.	Inside diameter d_1 min.	Outside diameter d_2 max.	Outside diameter d_2 min.	Height h max.	Height h min.	Thickness s
M1.6	1.8	1.7	3.7	3.52	0.51	0.36	0.16
M2	2.3	2.2	4.6	4.42	0.53	0.38	0.16
M2.5	2.8	2.7	5.8	5.62	0.53	0.38	0.16
M3	3.32	3.2	6.4	6.18	0.61	0.46	0.16
M4	4.42	4.3	8.1	7.88	0.84	0.69	0.28
M5	5.42	5.3	9.2	8.98	0.89	0.74	0.30
M6	6.55	6.4	11.5	11.23	1.14	0.99	0.40
M8	8.55	8.4	15.0	14.73	1.40	1.25	0.40
M10	10.68	10.5	19.6	19.27	1.70	1.55	0.55
M12	13.18	13.0	22.0	21.67	1.90	1.65	0.55
(M14)	15.18	15.0	25.5	25.17	2.06	1.80	0.55
M16	17.18	17.0	27.8	27.47	2.41	2.16	0.70
(M18)	19.21	19.0	31.3	30.91	2.41	2.16	0.70
M20	21.21	21.0	34.7	34.31	2.66	2.16	0.70

* Second choice sizes in brackets ().
For full range and further information see BS 4463.

2.1.41 **Wire thread inserts**

These are used to provide a hard wearing surface which can be renewed for screwed joints which have to be dismantled and reassembled frequently and where the components comprising the assembly are made from relatively soft materials. Wire thread inserts are the subject of BS 4377. The nominal sizes given refer to the male thread which mates with the internal thread of the fitted insert, e.g. an M16 × 2 bolt will screw into a M16 × 2 insert. The tap to produce the internal thread for the insert will, of course, have to be oversize to allow for the thickness of the insert. Such a tap will be marked with the size of the male fastener plus reference to BS 4377. Wire thread inserts are available for preferred sizes of ISO metric coarse series threads. The thread insert is wound from wire of rhombic section in the form of a close coiled helical spring and it is driven into the tapped hole by a special tool which engages a tang on the insert. The tang is removed after insertion.

2.1.42 T-slot profiles

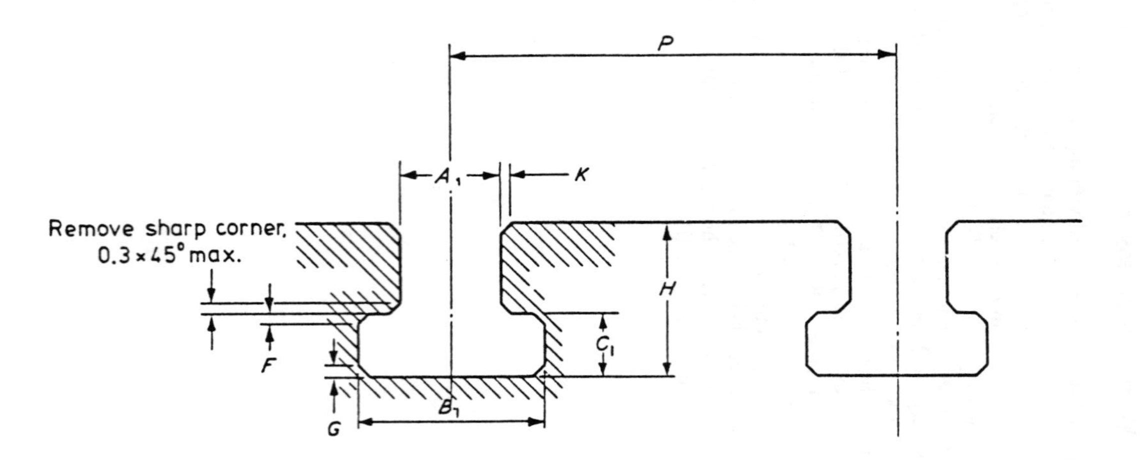

Dimensions in millimetres

Designations of T-slot	Width of throat A_1			Width of recess B_1		Depth of recess c_1		Overall depth of T-slot H		Chamfer × 45° or radius			Pitch P (avoid pitch values in brackets as they lead to weakness)			
	Nominal	Ordinary (H12)	For use as tenon (HB)	min.	max.	min.	max.	min.	max.	K max.	F max.	G max.				
M4	5	+0.12	+0.018	10	11	3.5	4.5	8	10					20	25	32
M5	6	0	0	11	12.5	5	6	11	13					25	32	40
M6	8	+0.15	+0.022	14.5	16	7	8	15	18	1.0		1.0		32	40	50
M8	10	0	0	16	18	7	8	17	21		0.6			40	50	63
M10	12	+0.18	+0.027	19	21	8	9	20	25				(40)	50	63	80
M12	14	0	0	23	25	9	11	23	28				(50)	63	80	100
M16	18			30	32	12	14	30	36	1.6		1.6	(63)	80	100	125
M20	22	+0.21	+0.033	37	40	16	18	38	45				(80)	100	125	160
M24	28	0		46	50	20	22	48	56		1.0	2.5	100	125	160	200
M30	36	+0.25	+0.039	56	60	25	28	61	71				125	160	200	250
M36	42	0	0	68	72	32	35	74	85	2.5	1.6	4.0	160	200	250	320
M42	48			80	85	36	40	84	95		2.0	6.0	200	250	320	400
M48	54	+0.30	+0.046	90	95	40	44	94	106				250	320	400	500
		0	0													

Tolerance on pitches *p* of T-slots

Pitch mm	*Tolerance* mm
20 to 25	±0.2
32 to 100	±0.3
125 to 250	±0.5
320 to 500	±0.8

For further information see BS 2485 : 1987.

2.1.43 Dimensions of T-bolts and T-nuts

T-nut

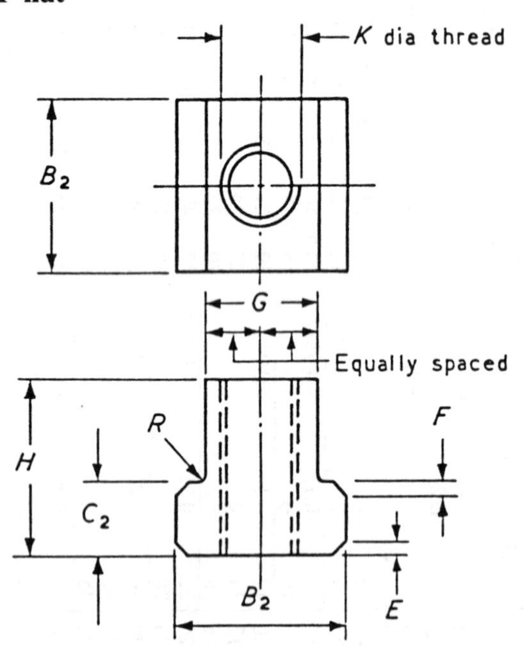

T-bolt

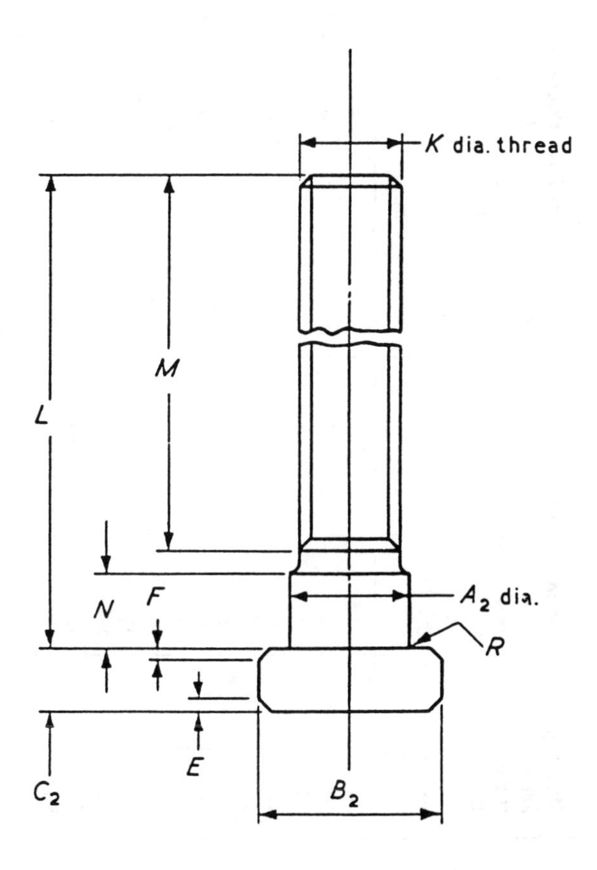

continued

Dimensions of T-bolts and T-nuts

Designation of T-bolt and diameter of thread K	Width of head (square) B_2		Depth of head C_2 tol. ±0.25	Length of shoulder N	Diameter of bolt A_2	Chamfer E	Radius R	Width of T-nut shank G		Height of T-nut H	Chamfer F
	nom.	tol.				max.	max.	nom.	tol.	max.	max.
M4	9		2.5	—	4			5		6	
M5	10		4	—	5			6	−0.3	8	
M6	13		6	—	6	1.0		8	−0.5	10	
M8	15		6	—	8			10		12	
M10	18	0	7	—	10			12		16	
M12	22	−0.5	8	—	12		1.0	14	−0.3	19	0.3
M16	28		10	—	16			18	−0.6	25	×
M20	34		14	—	20			22		30	45°
M24	43		18	20	26	1.5		28		40	
M30	53		23	20	33			36	−0.4	45	
M36	64		28	25	39			42	−0.7	55	
M42	75		32	25	46			48		65	
M48	85		36	30	52	2.5		54	−0.4 −0.8	75	

Dimensions in millimetres

Diameter of thread K	Recommended length of bolt stem L													Length of threaded portion of bolt stem M
M4	30	40	50	60	70	80	100							For $L \leqslant 100$ $M=0.5L$
M5	30	40	50	60	70	80	100							
M6				60	70	80	100							
M8				60	70	80	100							
M10				60	70	80	100	125	160	180				
M12					70	80	100	125	160	180				For $L > 100$ $M=0.3L$
M16					70	80	100	125	160	180	200	250	300	
M20					70	80	100	125	160	180	200	250	300	
M24 M30 M36 M42 M48							100	125	160	180	200	250	300	

For further information see BS 2485 : 1987.

2.1.44 Dimensions of tenons for T-slots

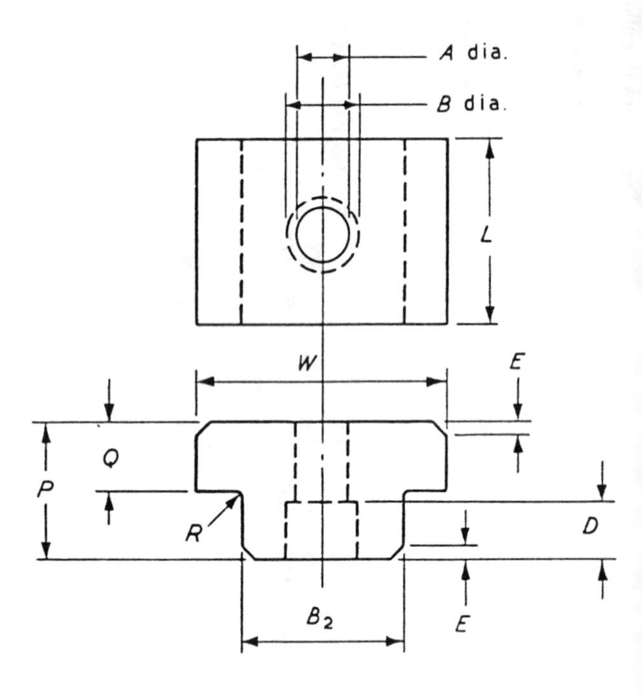

<table>
<tr><th rowspan="3">Designation of T-slot</th><th colspan="2">Width of tenon shank B_2</th><th colspan="2">Overall width of tenon W</th><th rowspan="2">Depth of head of tenon</th><th rowspan="2">Overall height of tenon</th><th rowspan="2">Length of tenon</th><th rowspan="2">Radius R</th><th colspan="4">Fixing hole</th></tr>
<tr><th rowspan="2">nom.</th><th rowspan="2">tol. (h7)</th><th rowspan="2">nom.</th><th rowspan="2">tol. (h7)</th><th rowspan="2">To suit socket head cap screw to BS 4168: Pt 1</th><th rowspan="2">Clearance hole diameter A to BS 4186 medium fit</th><th rowspan="2">Counterbores diameter B tolerance H13</th><th rowspan="2">Counterbore depth D tolerance +0.2</th></tr>
<tr><th>Q</th><th>P</th><th>L</th><th>max.</th></tr>
<tr><td>M4</td><td>5</td><td>0
−0.012</td><td rowspan="3">16</td><td rowspan="3">0
−0.018</td><td rowspan="3">5</td><td rowspan="3">10</td><td rowspan="3">25</td><td rowspan="5">0.6</td><td>M2</td><td>2.4</td><td>4.3</td><td>2.5</td></tr>
<tr><td>M5</td><td>6</td><td rowspan="2">0
−0.015</td><td rowspan="2">M3</td><td rowspan="2">3.4</td><td rowspan="2">6.0</td><td rowspan="2">3.5</td></tr>
<tr><td>M6</td><td>8</td></tr>
<tr><td>M8</td><td>10</td><td rowspan="4">0
−0.018</td><td rowspan="5">30</td><td rowspan="5">0
−0.021</td><td rowspan="5">5.5</td><td rowspan="5">12</td><td rowspan="5">30</td><td rowspan="7">M6</td><td rowspan="7">6.6</td><td rowspan="7">11.0</td><td rowspan="7">6.5</td></tr>
<tr><td>M10</td><td>12</td></tr>
<tr><td>M12</td><td>14</td><td rowspan="5">1.0</td></tr>
<tr><td>M16</td><td>18</td></tr>
<tr><td>M20</td><td>22</td><td rowspan="2">0
−0.021</td></tr>
<tr><td>M24</td><td>28</td><td rowspan="2">50</td><td rowspan="2">0
−0.025</td><td rowspan="2">15</td><td rowspan="2">30</td><td rowspan="2">40</td></tr>
<tr><td>M30</td><td>36</td><td rowspan="3">0
−0.025</td></tr>
<tr><td>M36</td><td>42</td><td rowspan="3">70</td><td rowspan="3">0
−0.030</td><td rowspan="3">25</td><td rowspan="3">40</td><td rowspan="3">60</td><td rowspan="3">1.5</td><td rowspan="3">M8</td><td rowspan="3">9.0</td><td rowspan="3">14.0</td><td rowspan="3">8.5</td></tr>
<tr><td>M42</td><td>48</td></tr>
<tr><td>M48</td><td>54</td><td>0
−0.030</td></tr>
</table>

For further information see BS 2485 : 1987.

2.2 Riveted joints

2.2.1 Typical rivet heads and shanks

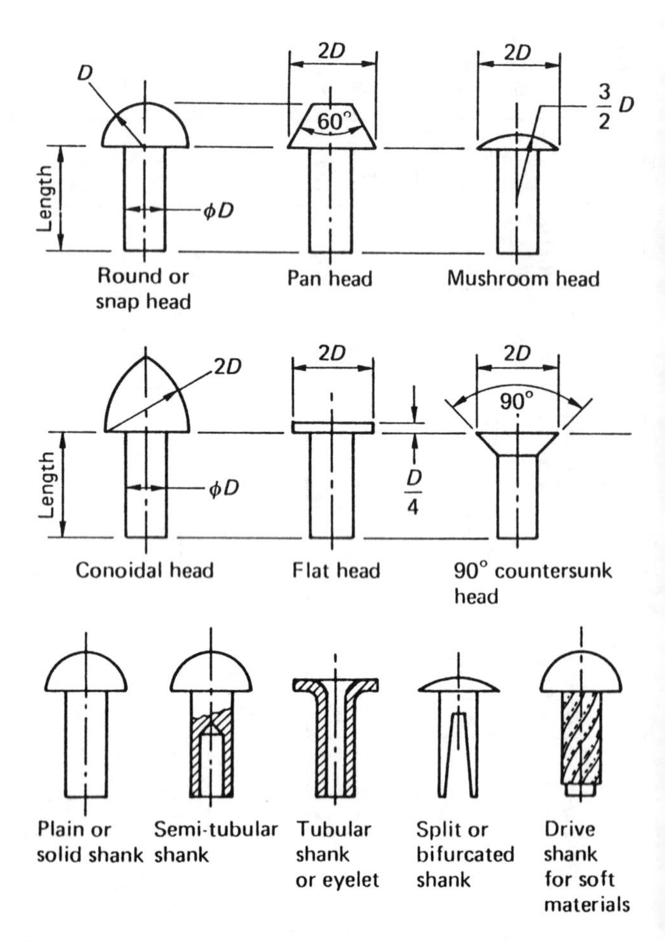

2.2.2 Typical riveted lap joints

Single row lap joint

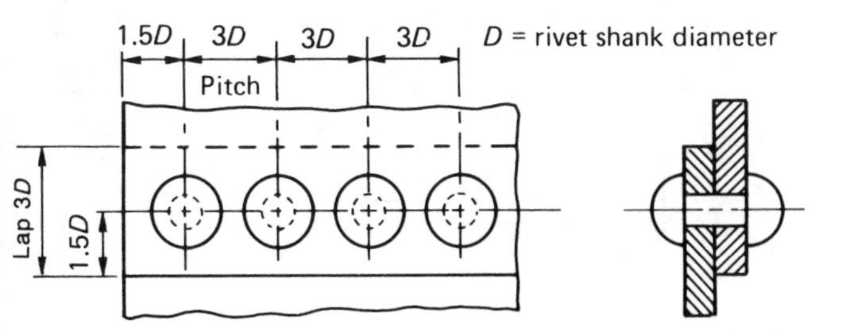

Double Row (chain) lap joint

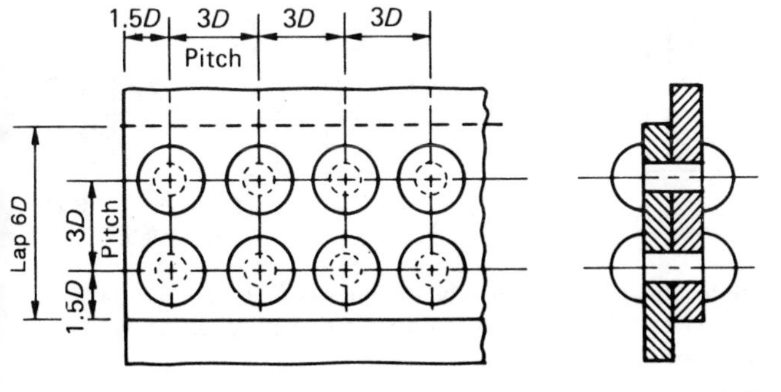

Double row (zigzag) lap joint

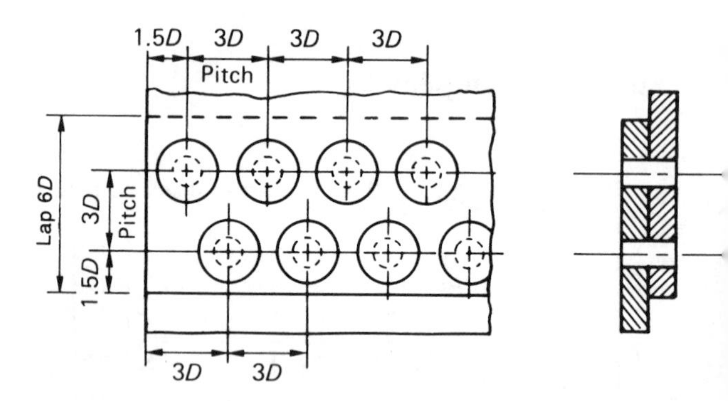

2.2.3 Typical riveted butt joints

Single strap chain riveted butt joint (single row)

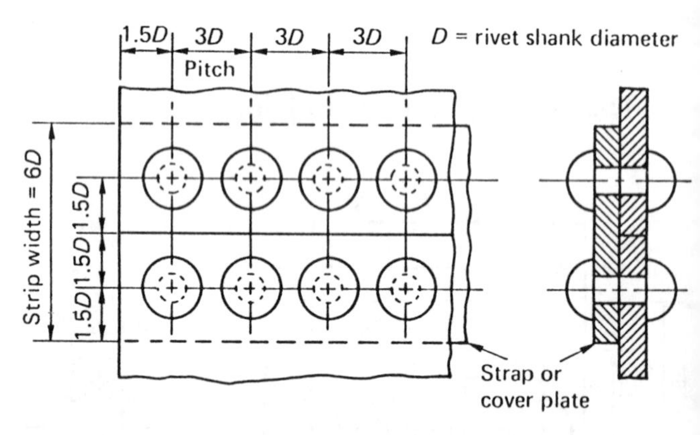

Note: this joint may also be double row riveted, chain or zigzag. The strap width = 12*D* when double riveted (pitch between rows = 3*D*).

Double strap chain riveted butt joint (double row)

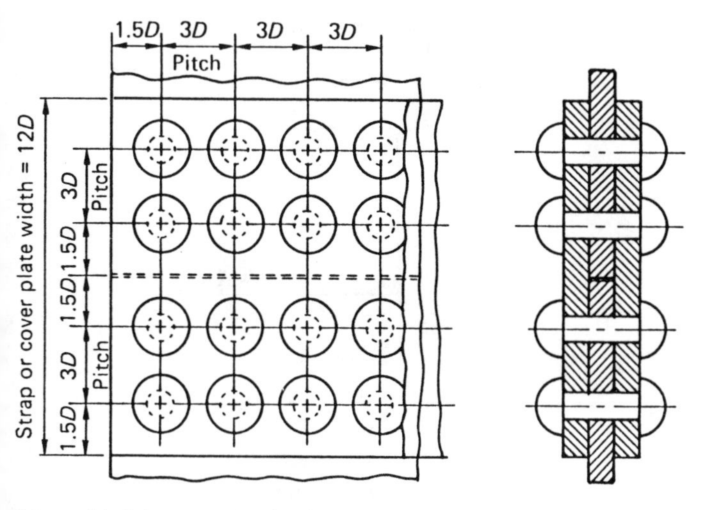

Note: this joint may also be double row zigzag riveted (see 2.2.2) or it may be single riveted as above.

2.2.4 Proportions for hole diameter and rivet length

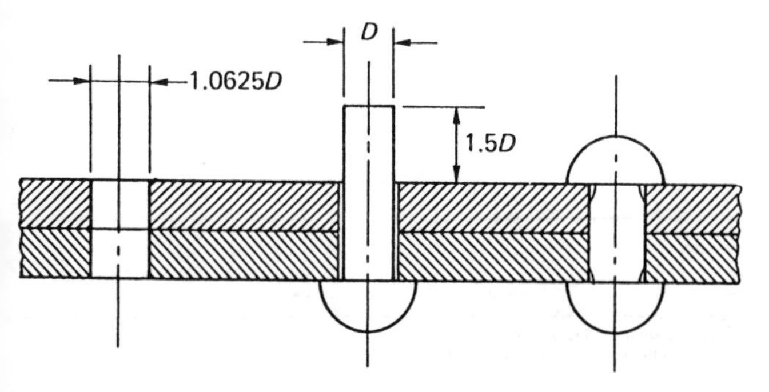

2.2.5 Cold forged snap head rivets

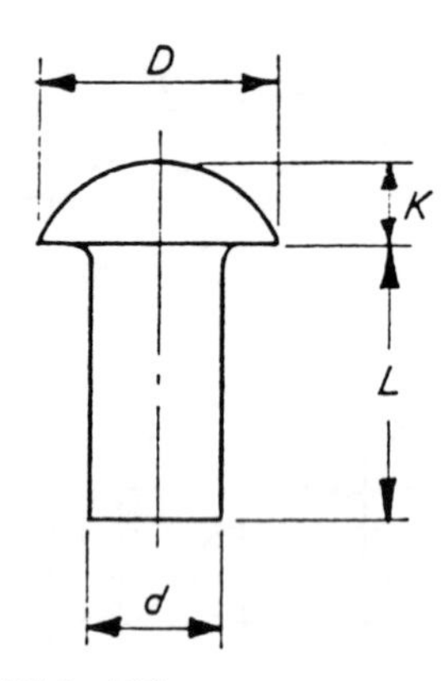

With d 16 mm or smaller

$D = 1{\cdot}75d$

$K = 0{\cdot}6d$

$L =$ Length

Dimensions in millimetres

*Nominal shank diameter** *d*	*Tolerance on diameter* *d*	*Nominal head diameter* *D*	*Tolerance on diameter* *D*	*Nominal head depth* *K*	*Tolerance on head depth* *K*	*Tolerance on length* *L*
1		1.8		0.6	+0.2	
1.2		2.1	±0.2	0.7	−0.0	
1.6	±0.07	2.8		1.0		
2.0		3.5	±0.24	1.2	+0.24	
2.5		4.4		1.5	−0.0	
3.0		5.3		1.8		+0.5
(3.5)		6.1	±0.29	2.1	+0.29	−0.0
4	±0.09	7.0		2.4	−0.0	
5		8.8		3.0		
6		10.5		3.6	+0.35	
			±0.35		−0.0	
(7)		12.3		4.2		+0.8
8	±0.11	14.0		4.8		−0.0
10		18.0		6.0		
12		21.0	±0.42	7.2	+0.42	+1.0
(14)	±0.14	25.0		8.4	−0.0	−0.0
16		28.0		9.6		

* Rivet sizes shown in brackets are non-preferred.
For further information see BS 4620 : 1970.

2.2.6 Hot forged snap head rivets

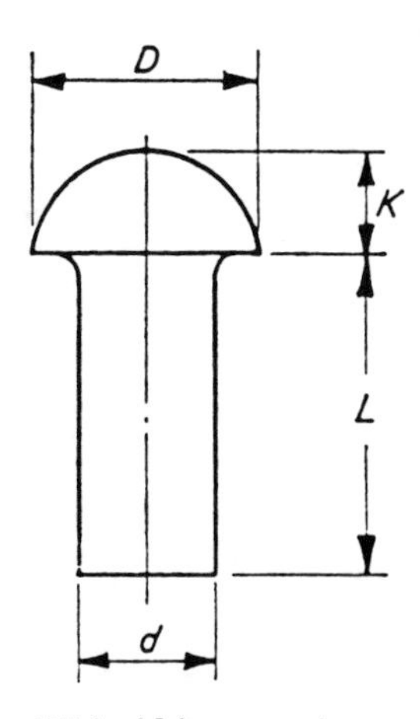

With d 14 mm or larger

$D = 1{\cdot}6d$

$K = 0{\cdot}65d$

L = Length

Dimensions in millimetres

*Nominal shank diameter** *d*	*Tolerance on diameter* *d*	*Nominal head diameter* *D*	*Tolerance on diameter* *D*	*Nominal head depth* *K*	*Tolerance on head depth* *K*	*Tolerance on length* *L*
(14)		22		9		+1.0
16	±0.43	25	±1.25	10.	+1.00	−0.0
18		28		11.5	−0.0	
20		32		13	+1.5	+1.6
(22)	±0.52	36	±1.8	14	−0.0	−0.0
24		40		16		
(27)		43		17	+2.0	
30		48	±2.5	19	−0.0	
(33)	±0.62	53		21		+3.0
						−0.0
36		58	±3.0	23	+2.5	
39		62		25	−0.0	

* Rivet sizes shown in brackets are non-preferred.
For further information see BS 4620 : 1970.

2.2.7 Tentative range of nominal lengths associated with shank diameters

Dimensions in millimetres

Nominal shank diameter* d	Nominal length* L																					
	3	4	5	6	8	10	12	14	16	(18)	20	(22)	25	(28)	30	(32)	35	(38)	40	45	50	55
1.0	×	×	×	×	×	×	×	×	×		×											
1.2	×	×	×	×	×	×	×	×	×		×											
1.6	×	×	×	×	×	×	×	×	×	×		×	×									
2.0	×	×	×	×	×	×	×	×	×		×	×	×									
2.5	×	×	×	×	×	×	×	×	×	×		×	×									
3.0		×	×	×	×	×	×	×	×	×	×	×	×									
(3.5)																						
4.0				×	×	×	×	×	×	×		×	×									
5.0				×	×	×	×	×	×	×	×	×	×	×	×		×	×				
6.0				×	×	×	×	×	×	×	×	×	×	×	×		×	×		×		

* Sizes and lengths shown in brackets are non-preferred and should be avoided if possible. The inclusion of dimensional data is not intended to imply that all the products described are stock production sizes. The purchaser should consult the manufacturer concerning lists of stock production sizes.
For the full range of head types and sizes up to and including 39 mm diameter by 160 mm shank length see BS 4620: 1970.

2.2.8 'Pop'* rivets

'Pop' standard open type rivets
The 'Pop' standard open type rivet is intended for use in all normal blind riveting situations where the materials to be fastened do not present structural problems.

The rivet bodies are available in a range of materials for complete workpiece compatibility. This is a hollow rivet, pre-assembled on to a headed pin or mandrel. The mandrel is designed to fracture at a predetermined point during the setting operation, when the materials to be fastened have been drawn closely together and the joint is tight.

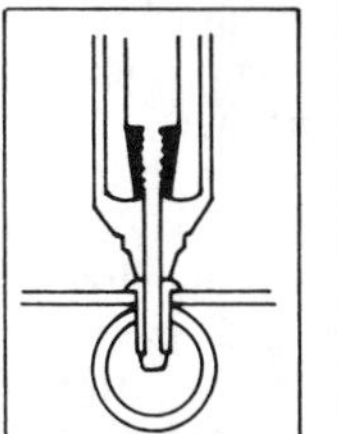

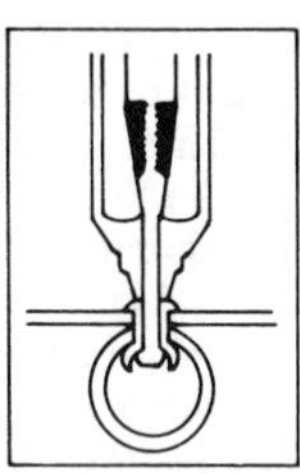

'Pop' sealed type rivets
Designed for use where the fastening to be used has to be pressure or water tight, the 'Pop' sealed blind rivet has a sealed end completely enclosing the mandrel head. The type provides 100% mandrel head retention – an important factor in many applications. This feature, combined with a high rate of radial expansion in setting, ensures that the set rivet will withstand pressures up to 34 bar (500 lbf/in^2) with copper rivets.

The sealed rivet is a fastener of high shear and tensile strength and vibration resistance. Owing to its high rate of expansion in setting, it cannot be recommended for use in very soft or brittle materials.

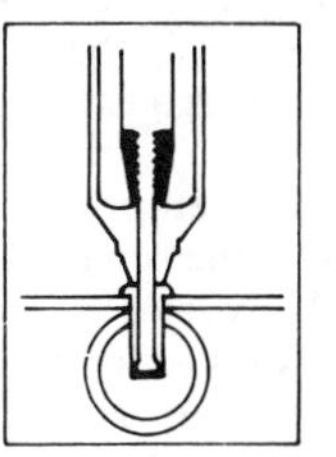

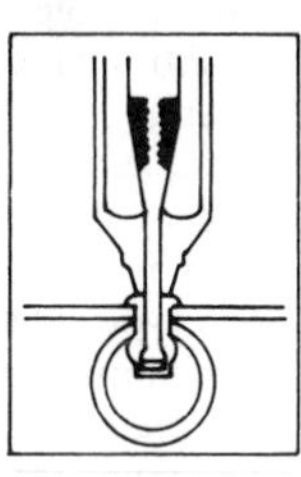

* 'Pop' is a registered trademark of Tucker Fasteners Ltd.

'Pop' peel type rivets
Specifically developed for fastening soft or friable materials, 'Pop' peel type rivets will secure blow moulded or glass reinforced plastic, rubber and plywood, if required to metal panels or sections up to 13.5 mm (0.531 in) thick.

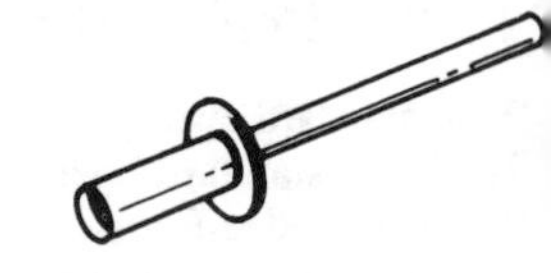

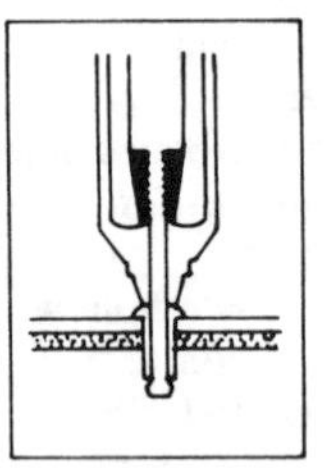

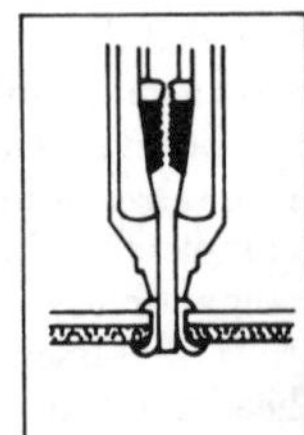

The 'Pop' peel type rivet has an aluminium alloy body and a special carbon steel mandrel. On setting, the rivet body is split into four petals by the action of the mandrel head, producing a large blind-side bearing area capable of withstanding high pull-out loads.

'Pop' grooved type rivets
Developed for use in thick sections of soft or brittle materials such as hardboard, plywood, glassfibre, asbestos board, concrete and brick, the 'Pop' grooved type rivets gain their name from the series of grooves around the shank. These engage into the workpiece on setting, and set inside the material rather than against the rear face.

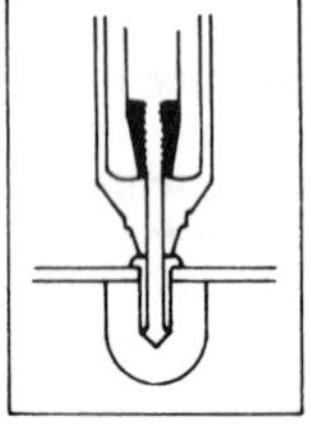

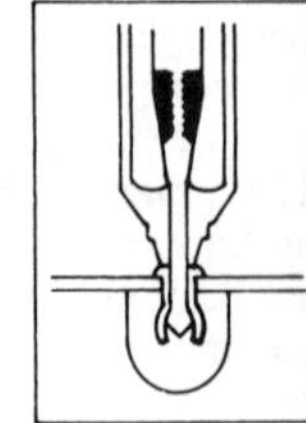

Construction and setting action is similar to the standard open type. The body is of aluminium alloy with a carbon steel mandrel. The grooved type rivet, when set, is capable of withstanding high pull-out loads.

magnesium alloy, BS 1473 Al Mg 3.5)

Nominal rivet diameter	Maximum riveting thickness				Nominal rivet body length		Hole size	Drill size mm
	Domed head		120° csk head					
	mm	in	mm	in	mm	in		
	0.8	0.031	—	—	3.6	0.140	2.46	
2.4 mm	2.4	0.093	3.2	0.126	5.1	0.202	to 2.54 mm	2.45
(0.093 in)	4.8	0.187	5.6	0.220	7.5	0.296	(0.097	
							to 0.100 in)	
	1.6	0.062	2.7	0.105	4.3	0.170		
	3.2	0.125	4.3	0.168	6.1	0.241		
	4.8	0.187	5.8	0.230	7.9	0.310		
	6.4	0.250	7.4	0.293	9.7	0.382	3.28	
3.2 mm	7.9	0.312	9.0	0.355	11.5	0.451	to 3.38 mm	3.30
(0.125 in)	9.5	0.375	10.6	0.418	13.3	0.522	(0.129	
	11.1	0.437	12.2	0.480	15.0	0.592	to 0.133 in)	
	12.7	0.500	13.8	0.543	16.8	0.663		
	14.3	0.562	15.4	0.605	18.6	0.732		
	16.6	0.656	17.7	0.699	20.2	0.795		
	19.8	0.781	20.9	0.824	24.2	0.951		
	3.2	0.125	4.5	0.178	6.8	0.266	For hole size	
4.0 mm	4.8	0.187	6.1	0.240	8.5	0.335	and drill size see	
(0.156 in)	6.4	0.250	7.7	0.303	10.3	0.406	following page	

continued

Section 2.2.8 (*continued*)

Nominal rivet diameter	Maximum riveting thickness: Domed head mm	Domed head in	120° csk head mm	120° csk head in	Nominal rivet body length mm	Nominal rivet body length in	Hole size	Drill size mm
	7.9	0.312	9.3	0.365	12.1	0.476	4.06	
4.0 mm	9.5	0.375	10.9	0.428	13.9	0.547	to 4.16 mm	4.10
(0.156 in)	11.1	0.437	12.4	0.490	15.7	0.617	(0.160	
	12.7	0.500	14.0	0.553	17.4	0.689	to 0.164 in)	
	13.5	0.532	14.8	0.585	18.3	0.722		
	15.9	0.625	17.2	0.678	20.2	0.795		
	17.4	0.687	18.8	0.740	22.3	0.877		
	19.8	0.781	21.2	0.834	24.7	0.971		
	3.2	0.125	4.8	0.188	7.4	0.290		
	4.8	0.187	6.4	0.250	9.2	0.361		
	6.4	0.250	8.0	0.313	10.9	0.431	4.88	
4.8 mm	7.9	0.312	9.5	0.375	12.7	0.501	to 4.98 mm	4.90
(0.187 in)	9.5	0.375	11.1	0.438	14.5	0.572	(0.192	
	11.1	0.437	12.7	0.500	16.3	0.641	to 0.196 in)	
	13.5	0.532	15.1	0.595	19.0	0.748		
	19.8	0.781	21.4	0.844	25.4	1.000		
	26.2	1.031	27.3	1.094	31.8	1.250		
6.4 mm	6.4	0.250	—	—	12.7	0.500	6.53	
(0.250 in)	12.7	0.500	—	—	19.5	0.766	to 6.63 mm	6.50
	19.0	0.750	—	—	26.2	1.032	(0.257	
							to 0.261 in)	

Rivets are also available in: mild steel (see next table); aluminium 5% magnesium alloy; aluminium 2.5% magnesium alloy; copper; nickel copper (BS 3073 NA13) alloy; stainless steel (A2SI 305) alloy.
For full range of standard open types, materials and sizes see Tucker Fastener Ltd data sheet B101-2F

'Pop' blind rivets, standard open type, mild steel

Nominal rivet diameter	Maximum riveting thickness				Nominal rivet body length		Hole size	Drill size
	Domed head		*120 csk head*					
	mm	in	mm	in	mm	in		mm
Low carbon steel, composition BS 1449 CS3								
2.8 mm (0.109 in)	2.3	0.090	—	—	5.3	0.210	2.85 to 2.96 mm (0.113 to 0.117 in)	2.85
6.4 mm (0.253 in)	3.8	0.150	—	—	8.9	0.350	6.53 to 6.63 mm (0.257 to 0.261 in)	6.50
	7.6	0.300	8.4	0.330	12.7	0.500		
	12.7	0.500	13.5	0.530	17.8	0.700		
Low carbon steel, composition SAE 1005								
3.2 mm (0.125 in)	1.6	0.062	2.7	0.105	4.3	0.170	3.28 to 3.38 mm (0.129 to 0.133 in)	3.30
	3.2	0.125	4.3	0.168	6.1	0.241		
	4.8	0.187	5.8	0.230	7.9	0.310		
	6.4	0.250	7.4	0.293	9.7	0.382		
	7.9	0.312	9.0	0.355	11.5	0.451		
	9.5	0.375	10.6	0.418	13.3	0.522		

continued

Nominal rivet diameter	*Maximum riveting thickness*				*Nominal rivet body length*		*Hole size*	*Drill size*
	Domed head		*120° csk head*					
	mm	in	mm	in	mm	in		mm
	3.2	0.125	4.5	0.178	6.8	0.266	4.06	
4.0 mm	4.8	0.187	6.1	0.240	8.5	0.335	to 4.16 mm	
(0.156 in)	6.4	0.250	7.7	0.303	10.3	0.406	(0.160	4.10
	7.9	0.312	9.3	0.365	12.1	0.476	to 0.164 in)	
	9.5	0.375	10.9	0.428	13.9	0.547		
	2.4	0.094	4.0	0.157	6.5	0.255		
	3.2	0.125	4.8	0.188	7.4	0.290		
	4.8	0.187	6.4	0.250	9.2	0.361	4.88	
	6.4	0.250	8.0	0.313	10.9	0.431	to 4.98 mm	
4.8 mm	7.9	0.312	9.5	0.375	12.7	0.501	(0.192	4.90
(0.187 in)	9.5	0.375	11.1	0.438	14.5	0.572	to 0.196 in)	
	11.1	0.437	12.7	0.500	16.3	0.641		
	12.7	0.500	14.3	0.563	18.1	0.712		
	13.5	0.532	15.1	0.595	19.0	0.748		

Rivets are also available in: aluminium–3.5% magnesium alloy (see previous table); aluminium–5% magnesium alloy; aluminium–2.5% magnesium alloy; copper; nickel–copper (BS 3073 NA13) alloy; stainless steel (A1SI 305) alloy.

For full range of standard open types, materials and sizes see Tucker Fasteners Ltd data sheet B101-2E.

'Pop' blind rivets, sealed type

Nominal rivet diameter	Maximum riveting thickness				Nominal rivet body length		Hole size	Drill size
	Domed head		120° csk head					
	mm	in	mm	in	mm	in		mm
Aluminium -5% magnesium alloy (BS 3L58)								
3.2 mm (0.125 in)	1.6	0.062	2.5	0.097	5.9	0.232	3.28 to 3.38 mm (0.129 to 0.133 in)	3.30
	3.2	0.125	4.1	0.160	7.5	0.295		
	4.8	0.187	5.6	0.222	9.1	0.357		
	6.4	0.250	7.2	0.285	10.7	0.420		
	7.9	0.312	8.8	0.347	12.2	0.482		
4.0 mm (0.156 in)	3.2	0.125	4.4	0.175	7.9	0.311	4.06 to 4.16 mm (0.160 to 0.164 in)	4.10
	4.8	0.187	6.0	0.237	9.4	0.372		
	6.4	0.250	7.6	0.300	11.0	0.435		
	7.9	0.312	9.2	0.362	12.6	0.497		
4.8 mm (0.187 in)	3.2	0.125	4.7	0.185	8.3	0.325	4.88 to 4.98 mm (0.192 to 0.196 in)	4.90
	4.8	0.187	6.3	0.247	9.8	0.387		
	6.4	0.250	7.9	0.311	11.4	0.450		
	7.9	0.311	9.4	0.372	13.0	0.512		
	9.5	0.375	11.0	0.435	14.6	0.575		
	12.7	0.500	14.2	0.560	17.8	0.700		
	15.9	0.625	18.4	0.685	21.8	0.860		

continued

Nominal rivet diameter	Maximum riveting thickness				Nominal rivet body length		Hole size	Drill size
	Domed head		120° csk head					
	mm	in	mm	in	mm	in		mm
Copper (BS 2873 C101)								
3.2 mm (0.125 in)	1.6	0.062	2.5	0.097	5.9	0.232	3.28 to 3.38 mm (0.129 to 0.133 in)	3.30
	3.2	0.125	4.1	0.160	7.5	0.296		
	4.8	0.187	5.6	0.222	9.1	0.357		
	7.9	0.312	8.8	0.347	12.2	0.482		
4.0 mm (0.156 in)	4.8	0.187	6.0	0.237	9.4	0.372	4.06 to 4.16 mm (0.160 to 0.164 in)	4.10
	7.9	0.312	9.2	0.362	12.6	0.497		
4.8 mm (0.187 in)	3.2	0.125	4.7	0.185	8.3	0.325	4.88 to 4.98 mm (0.192 to 0.196 in)	4.90
	6.4	0.250	7.9	0.311	11.4	0.450		
	Flat head							
	mm	in						
4.8 mm (0.187 in)	9.5	0.375	—	—	14.6	0.575	4.88 to 4.98 mm (0.192 to 0.196 in)	4.90

Rivets are also available in: 99.5% pure aluminium (BS 1475 A199.5); steel (BS 1449 CS3); stainless steel (A1SI 305); nickel-copper alloy (BS 3073 NA13).

2.3 Self-secured joints

2.3.1 Self-secured joints

Grooved seam

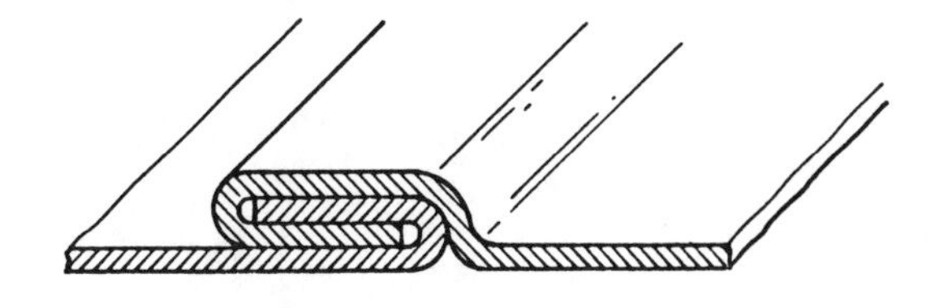

Double grooved seam

Paned down seam

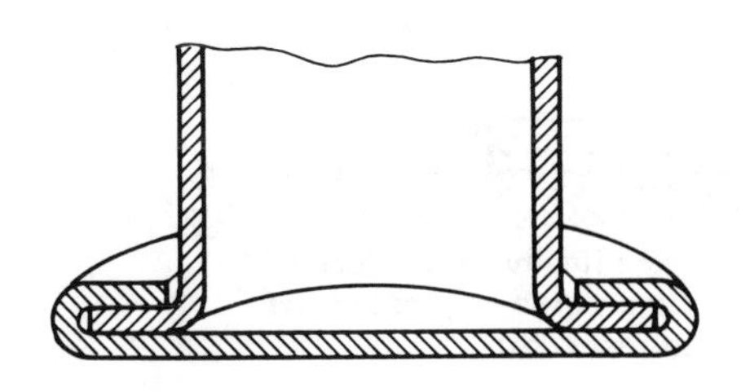

Knocked up seam

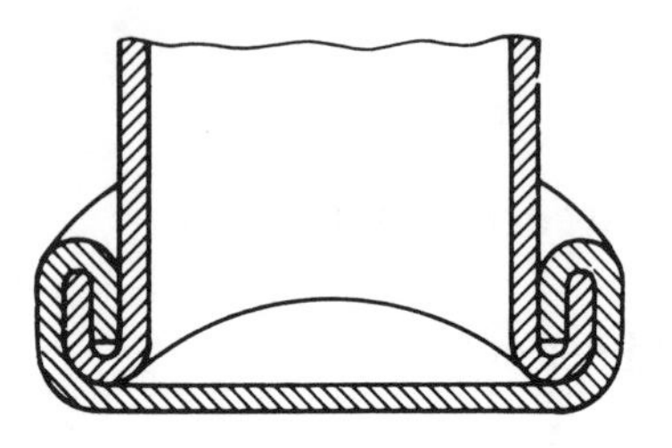

Making a grooved seam

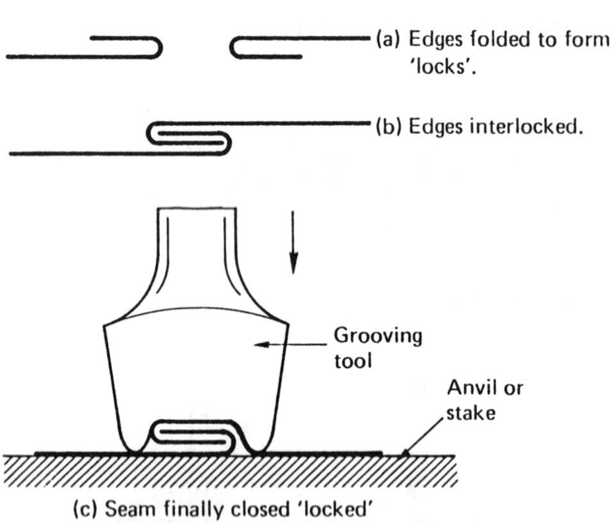

(c) Seam finally closed 'locked' using a grooving tool of the correct width.

2.3.2 Allowances for self-secured joints

Grooved seam

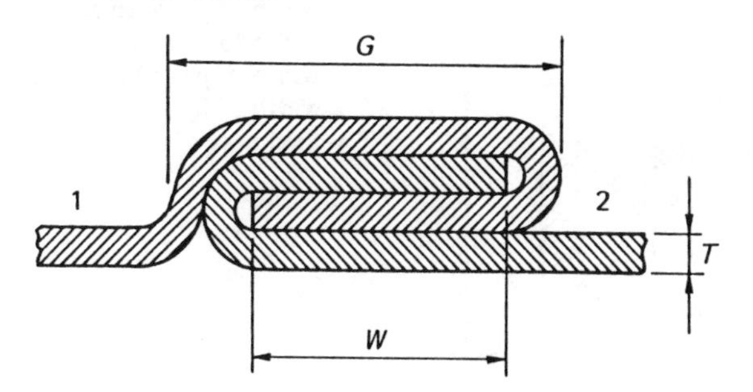

Double grooved seam

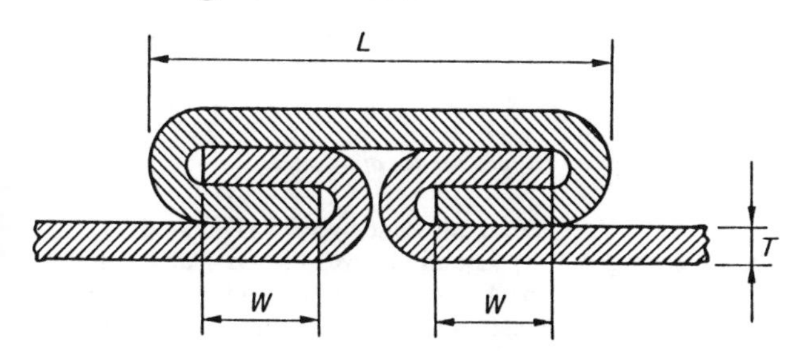

Paned down seam

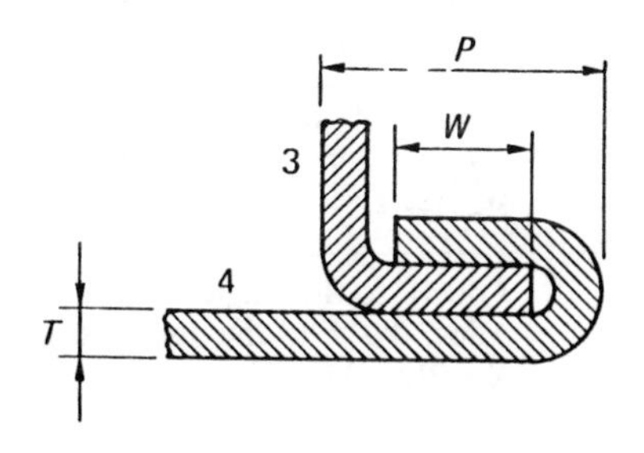

Knocked up seam

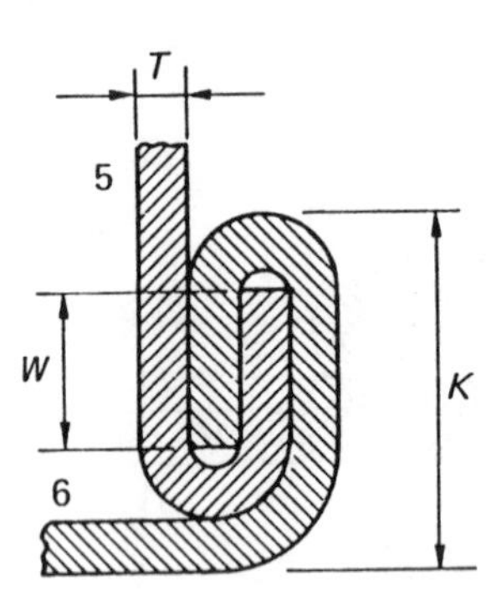

W = width of lock (folded edge)
G = width of grooved seam
L = width locking strip
P = width of paned down seam
K = width of knocked up seam
T = thickness of metal

Type of joint	*Approximate allowance*
Grooved seam	Total allowance $=3G-4T$ shared: (a) Equally between limbs 1 and 2; *or* (b) Two-thirds limb 1 and one-third limb 2 where joint centre position is critical.
Double grooved seam	Add $W-T$ to the edge of each blank to be joined. Allowance for capping strip $=4W+4T$, where $L=2W+4T$.
Paned down seam	Add W to the single edge 3. Add $2W+T$ to the double edge 4. $P=2W+2T$.
Knocked up joint	Add W to the single edge 5. Add $2W+T$ to the double edge 6. $K=2W+3T$.

2.4 Miscellaneous fasteners

2.4.1 Taper pins, unhardened: metric series

Type A: Ground Angle tolerance AT8 Taper 1:50

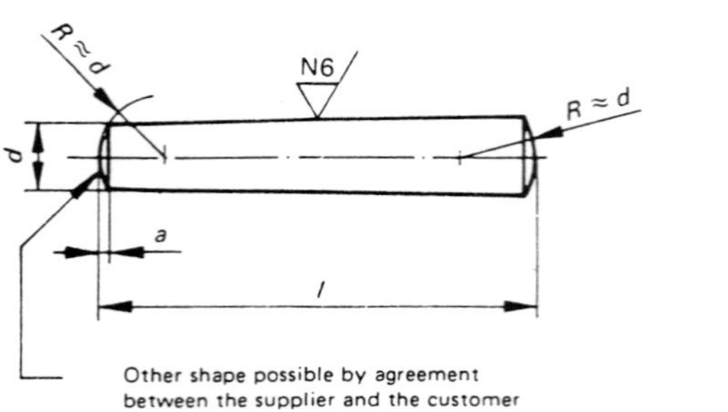

Type B: Turned Angle tolerance AT10 Taper 1:50

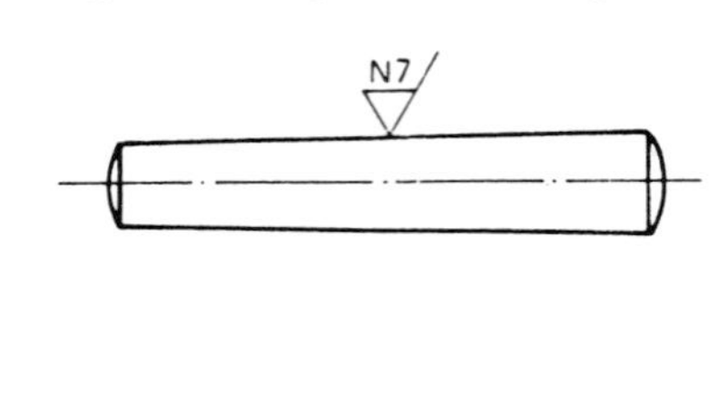

Dimensions in millimetres

Diameter d (h10)	0.6	0.8	1.0	1.2	1.5	2.0	2.5	3.0	4.0	5.0	6.0	8.0	10.0	12.0	16.0	20.0	25.0	30.0	40.0	50.0
$a \approx$	0.08	0.10	0.12	0.16	0.20	0.25	0.30	0.40	0.50	0.63	0.80	1.00	1.20	1.60	2.00	2.50	3.00	4.00	5.00	6.3
Recommend standard length l: sizes inclusive	4 to 8	5 to 12	6 to 16	6 to 20	8 to 25	10 to 35	10 to 35	12 to 45	14 to 55	20 to 60	25 to 90	25 to 130	30 to 160	35 to 180	40 to 200	45 to 200	50 to 200	60 to 200	80 to 200	100 to 200

For further information see BS 5681 : 1979.

2.4.2 Circlips, external: metric series

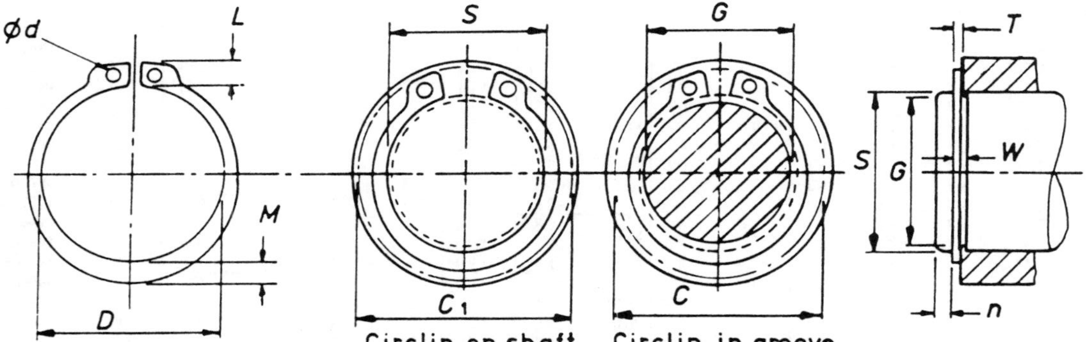

Circlip on shaft

Circlip in groove

continued

Dimensions in millimetres

Reference number of circlip	Shaft diameter S	Groove details					Circlip details							Minimum external clearance	
		Diameter G	Tolerance	Width W	Tolerance	Edge margin (min) n	Diameter D	Tolerance	Thickness T	Tolerance	Beam (approx.) M	Lug depth (max.) L	Lug hole dia- (min.) d	Fitted C	During fitting (C_1)
S003M	3	2.8	0 −0.06	0.5		0.30	2.66		0.4		0.8	1.9	0.8	6.6	7.2
S004M	4	3.8		0.5		0.30	3.64	+0.06	0.4		0.9	2.2	1.0	8.2	8.8
S005M	5	4.8	0	0.7		0.30	4.64	−0.15	0.6	0	1.1	2.5	1.0	9.8	10.6
S006M	6	5.7	−0.075	0.8		0.45	5.54		0.7	−0.04	1.3	2.7	1.15	11.1	12.1
S007M	7	6.7		0.9		0.45	6.45		0.8		1.4	3.1	1.2	12.9	14.0
S008M	8	7.6	0	0.9		0.60	7.35	+0.09	0.8		1.5	3.2	1.2	14.0	15.2
S009M	9	8.6	−0.09	1,1		0.60	8.35	−0.18	1.0		1.7	3.3	1.2	15.2	16.6
S010M	10	9.6		1.1	+0.14	0.60	9.25		1.0		1.8	3.3	1.5	16.2	17.6
S011M	11	10.5		1.1	0	0.75	10.20		1.0		1.8	3.3	1.5	17.1	18.6
S012M	12	11.5		1.1		0.75	11.0		1.0		1.8	3.3	1.7	18.1	19.6
S013M	13	12.4	0	1.1		0.90	11.9		1.0	0	2.0	3.4	1.7	19.2	20.8
S014M	14	13.4	−0.11	1.1		0.90	12.9	+0.18	1.0	−0.06	2.1	3.5	1.7	20.4	22.0
S015M	15	14.3		1.1		1.10	13.8	−0.36	1.0		2.2	3.6	1.7	21.5	23.2
S016M	16	15.2		1.1		1.20	14.7		1.0		2.2	3.7	1.7	22.6	24.4
S017M	17	16.2		1.1		1.20	15.7		1.0		2.3	3.8	1.7	23.8	25.6
S018M	18	17.0		1.3		1.50	16.5		1.2		2.4	3.9	2.0	24.8	26.8
S019M	19	18.0		1.3		1.50	17.5		1.2		2.5	3.9	2.0	25.8	27.8
S020M	20	19.0		1.3		1.50	18.5		1.2		2.6	4.0	2.0	27.0	29.0
S021M	21	20.0		1.3		1.50	19.5		1.2		2.7	4.1	2.0	28.2	30.2
S022M	22	21.0		1.3		1.50	20.5		1.2		2.8	4.2	2.0	29.4	31.4
S023M	23	22.0		1.3		1.50	21.5		1.2		2.9	4.3	2.0	30.6	32.6
S024M	24	22.9	0	1.3		1.70	22.2	+0.21	1.2		3.0	4.4	2.0	31.7	33.8
S025M	25	23.9	−0.21	1.3		1.70	23.2	−0.42	1.2		3.0	4.4	2.0	32.7	34.8

S026M	26	24.9		1.3		1.70	24.2		1.2		3.1	4.5	2.0	33.9	36.0
S027M	27	25.6		1.3		2.10	24.9		1.2		3.1	4.6	2.0	34.8	37.2
S028M	28	26.6		1.6		2.10	25.9		1.5		3.2	4.7	2.0	36.0	38.4
S029M	29	27.6		1.6		2.10	26.9		1.5		3.4	4.8	2.0	37.2	39.6
S030M	30	28.6		1.6	+0.14	2.10	27.9		1.5		3.5	5.0	2.0	38.6	41.0
S031M	31	29.3		1.6	0	2.60	28.6		1.5		3.5	5.1	2.5	39.5	42.2
S032M	32	30.3		1.6		2.60	29.6		1.5		3.6	5.2	2.5	40.7	43.4
S033M	33	31.3		1.6		2.60	30.5		1.5	0	3.7	5.3	2.5	41.9	44.4
S034M	34	32.3		1.6		2.60	31.5		1.5	−0.06	3.8	5.4	2.5	43.1	45.8
S035M	35	33.0		1.6		3.00	32.2		1.5		3.9	5.6	2.5	44.2	47.2
S036M	36	34.0		1.85		3.00	33.2		1.75		4.0	5.6	2.5	45.2	48.2
S037M	37	35.0		1.85		3.00	34.2		1.75		4.1	5.7	2.5	46.4	49.4
S038M	38	36.0		1.85		3.00	35.2		1.75		4.2	5.8	2.5	47.6	50.6
S039M	39	37.0	0	1.85		3.00	36.0	+0.25	1.75		4.3	5.9	2.5	48.8	51.8
S040M	40	37.5	−0.25	1.85		3.80	36.5	−0.50	1.75		4.4	6.0	2.5	49.5	53.0
S041M	41	38.5		1.85		3.80	37.5		1.75		4.5	6.1	2.5	50.7	54.2
S042M	42	39.5		1.85		3.80	38.5		1.75		4.5	6.5	2.5	52.5	56.0
S043M	43	40.5		1.85		3.80	39.5		1.75		4.6	6.6	2.5	53.7	57.2
S044M	44	41.5		1.85		3.80	40.5		1.75		4.6	6.6	2.5	54.7	58.2
S045M	45	42.5		1.85		3.80	41.5		1.75		4.7	6.7	2.5	55.9	59.4
S046M	46	43.5		1.85		3.80	42.5	+0.39	1.75		4.8	6.7	2.5	56.9	60.4
S047M	47	44.5		1.85		3.80	43.5	−0.78	1.75		4.9	6.8	2.5	58.1	61.6
S048M	48	45.5		1.85		3.80	44.5		1.75		5.0	6.9	2.5	59.3	62.8
S049M	49	46.5		1.85		3.80	44.8		1.75		5.0	6.9	2.5	60.3	63.8
S050M	50	47.0		2.15		4.50	45.8		2.00		5.1	6.9	2.5	60.8	64.8
S052M	52	49.0		2.15		4.50	47.8		2.00		5.2	7.0	2.5	63.0	67.0

For full range of sizes and types and for full information see BS 3673 : Pt 4 : 1977.

2.4.3 Circlips, internal: metric series

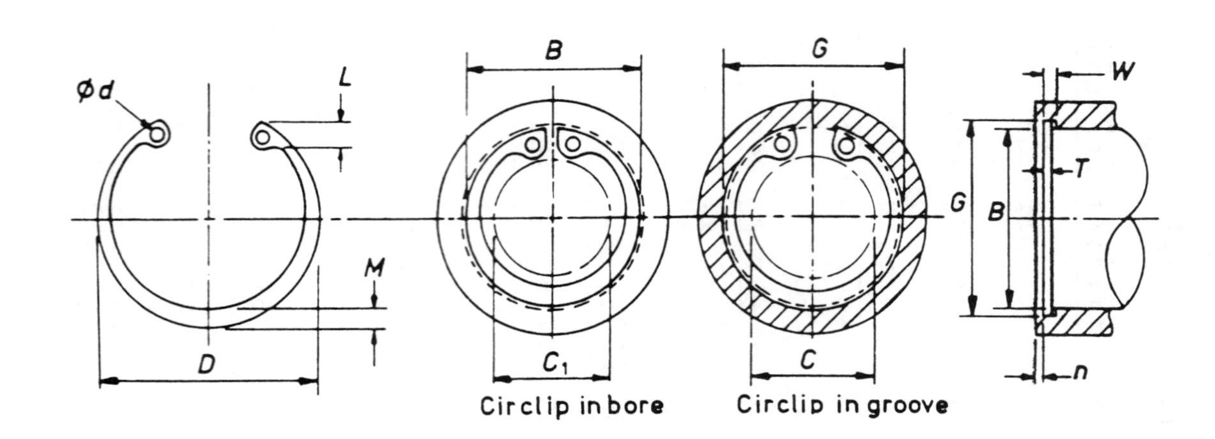

Reference number of circlip	Shaft dia-meter B	Groove details					Circlip details							Minimum internal clearance	
		Dia-meter G	Toler-ance	Width W	Toler-ance	Edge margin (min.) n	Dia-meter D	Toler-ance	Thick-ness T	Toler-ance	Beam (approx.) M	Lug depth (max.) L	Lug hole dia. (min.) d	Fitted C	During fitting C_1
B008M	8	8.4	+0.09	0.9		0.6	8.7		0.8		1.1	2.4	1.0	3.6	2.8
B009M	9	9.4	0	0.9		0.6	9.8		0.8		1.3	2.5	1.0	4.0	3.1
B010M	10	10.4		1.1		0.6	10.8		1.0		1.4	3.2	1.2	4.4	3.6
B011M	11	11.4		1.1		0.6	11.8	+0.36	1.0		1.5	3.3	1.2	4.8	3.9
B012M	12	12.5		1.1		0.75	13.0	−0.18	1.0		1.7	3.4	1.5	5.7	4.7
B013M	13	13.6	+0.11	1.1		0.9	14.1		1.0		1.8	3.6	1.5	6.4	5.3
B014M	14	14.6	0	1.1		0.9	15.1		1.0		1.9	3.7	1.7	7.2	6.1
B015M	15	15.7		1.1	+0.14	1.1	16.2		1.0		2.0	3.7	1.7	8.3	7.1
B016M	16	16.8		1.1	0	1.2	17.3		1.0	0	2.0	3.8	1.7	9.2	7.9
B017M	17	17.8		1.1		1.2	18.3		1.0	−0.06	2.1	3.9	1.7	10.0	8.7
B018M	18	19.0		1.1		1.5	19.5		1.0		2.2	4.1	2.0	10.8	9.3
B019M	19	20.0		1.1		1.5	20.5		1.0		2.2	4.1	2.0	11.8	9.8
B020M	20	21.0		1.1		1.5	21.5	+0.42	1.0		2.3	4.2	2.0	12.6	10.6
B021M	21	22.0		1.1		1.5	22.5	−0.21	1.0		2.4	4.2	2.0	13.6	11.6
B022M	22	23.0	+0.21	1.1		1.5	23.5		1.0		2.5	4.2	2.0	14.6	12.6
B023M	23	24.1	0	1.1		1.5	24.6		1.0		2.5	4.2	2.0	15.7	13.6
B024M	24	25.2		1.1		1.8	25.9		1.0		2.6	4.4	2.0	16.4	14.2
B025M	25	26.2		1.1		1.8	26.9		1.0		2.7	4.5	2.0	17.2	15.0
B026M	26	27.2		1.1		1.8	27.9		1.0		2.8	4.7	2.0	17.8	15.6
B027M	27	28.4		1.1		2.1	29.1		1.0		2.8	4.7	2.0	19.0	16.6
B028M	28	29.4		1.3		2.1	30.1	+0.92	1.2		2.9	4.8	2.0	19.8	17.4
B029M	29	30.4	+0.25	1.3		2.1	31.1	−0.46	1.2		3.0	4.8	2.0	20.8	18.4
B030M	30	31.4	0	1.3		2.1	32.1		1.2		3.0	4.8	2.0	21.8	19.4
B031M	31	32.7		1.3		2.6	33.4		1.2		3.2	5.2	2.5	22.3	19.6

continued

Section 2.4.3 *(continued)*

Dimensions in millimetres

Reference number of circlip	Shaft diameter B	Groove details: Diameter G	Groove details: Tolerance	Groove details: Width W	Groove details: Tolerance	Groove details: Edge margin (min) n	Circlip details: Diameter D	Circlip details: Tolerance	Circlip details: Thickness T	Circlip details: Tolerance	Circlip details: Beam (approx.) M	Circlip details: Lug depth (max.) L	Circlip details: Lug hole diameter (min.) d	Minimum internal clearance: Fitted C	Minimum internal clearance: During fitting C_1
B032M	32	33.7		1.3		2.6	34.4	+0.50	1.2		3.2	5.4	2.5	22.9	20.2
B033M	33	34.7		1.3	+0.14	2.6	35.5	−0.25	1.2		3.3	5.4	2.5	23.9	21.2
B034M	34	35.7		1.6	0	2.6	36.5		1.5		3.3	5.4	2.5	24.9	22.2
B035M	35	37.0		1.6		3.0	37.8		1.5		3.4	5.4	2.5	26.2	23.2
B036M	36	38.0	+0.25	1.6		3.0	38.8		1.5		3.5	5.4	2.5	27.2	24.2
B037M	37	39.0	0	1.6		3.0	39.8		1.5	0	3.6	5.5	2.5	28.0	25.0
B038M	38	40.0		1.6		3.0	40.8		1.5	−0.06	3.7	5.5	2.5	29.0	26.0
B039M	39	41.0		1.6		3.0	42.0		1.5		3.8	5.6	2.5	29.8	26.8
B040M	40	42.5		1.85		3.8	43.5		1.75		3.9	5.8	2.5	30.9	27.4
B041M	41	43.5		1.85		3.8	44.5		1.75		4.0	5.9	2.5	31.7	28.2
B042M	42	44.5		1.85		3.8	45.5	+0.78	1.75		4.1	5.9	2.5	32.7	29.2
B043M	43	45.5		1.85		3.8	46.5	−0.39	1.75		4.2	6.0	2.5	33.5	30.0
B044M	44	46.5		1.85		3.8	47.5		1.75		4.3	6.0	2.5	34.5	31.0
B045M	45	47.5		1.85		3.8	48.5		1.75		4.3	6.2	2.5	35.1	31.6
B046M	46	48.5		1.85		3.8	49.5		1.75		4.4	6.3	2.5	35.9	32.4
B047M	47	49.5		1.85		3.8	50.5		1.75		4.4	6.4	2.5	36.7	33.2
B048M	48	50.5		1.85		3.8	51.5	+0.92	1.75		4.5	6.4	2.5	37.7	34.2
B049M	49	51.5	+0.30	1.85		3.8	52.5	−0.46	1.75		4.5	6.4	2.5	38.7	35.2
B050M	50	53.0	0	2.15		4.5	54.2		2.0		4.6	6.5	2.5	40.0	36.0
B051M	51	54.0		2.15		4.5	55.2		2.0		4.7	6.5	2.5	41.0	37.0
B052M	52	555.0		2.15		4.5	56.2		2.0		4.7	6.7	2.5	41.6	37.6

For full range of sizes and types and for full information see BS 3673: Pt 4: 1977

2.5 Power transmission: gears

2.5.1 Some typical gear drives

Straight tooth spur gears

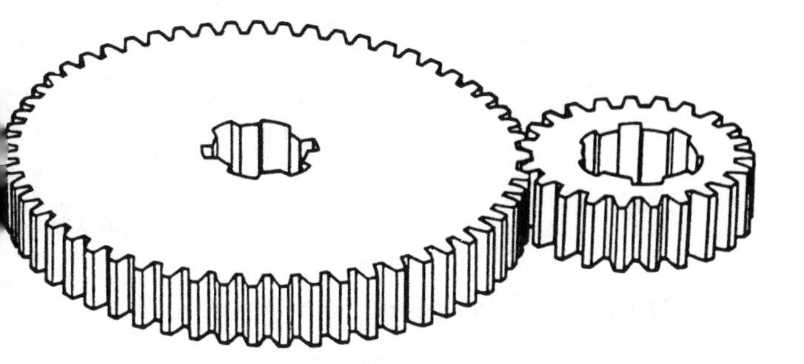

Rack and pinion: converts rotary to linear motion

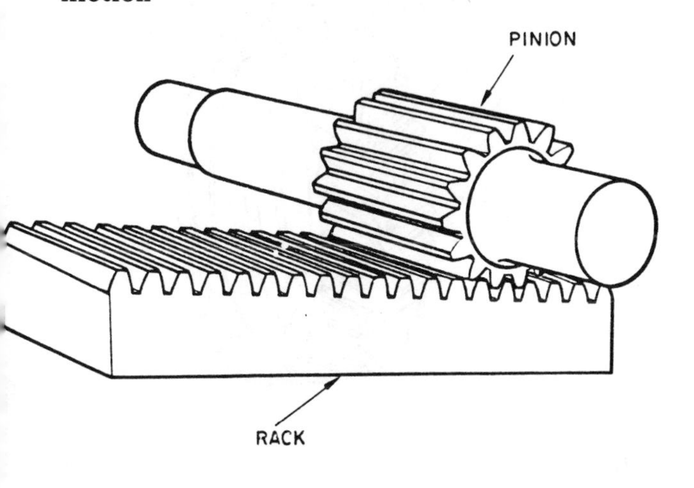

Single helical tooth spur gears

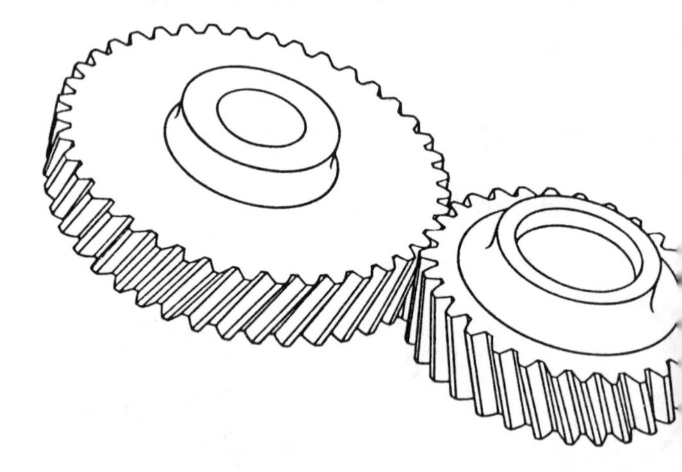

Double helical tooth spur gears

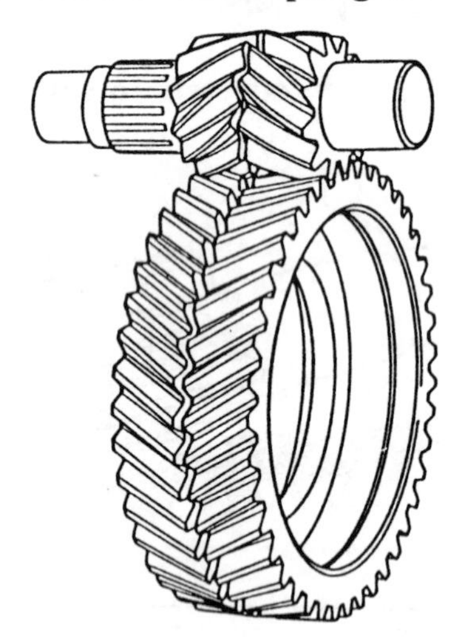

Straight tooth bevel gears

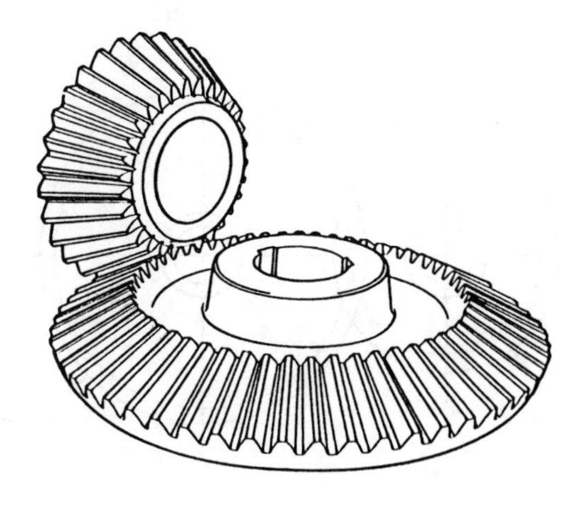

Worm and worm wheel

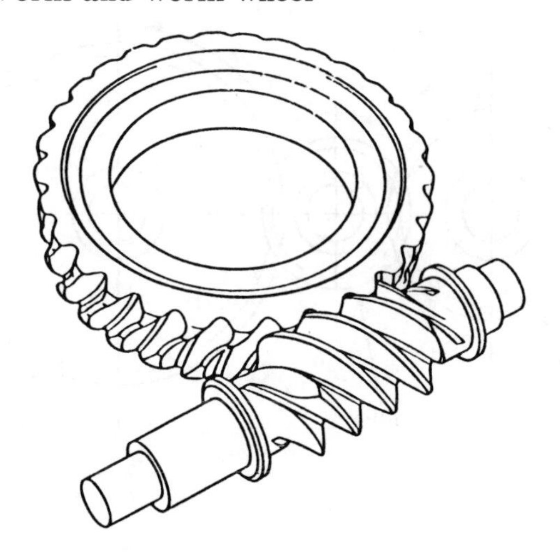

2.5.2 Simple spur gear trains

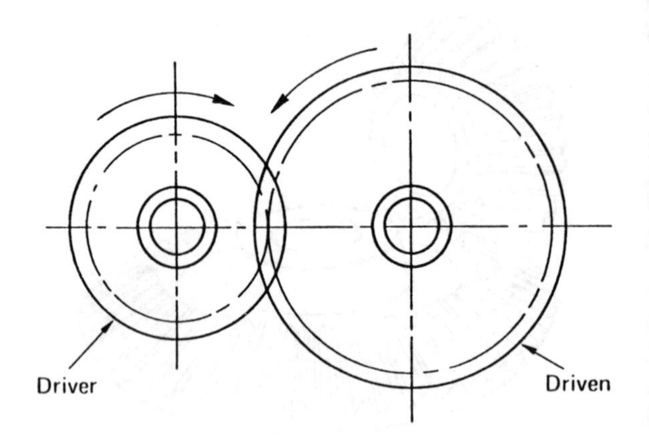

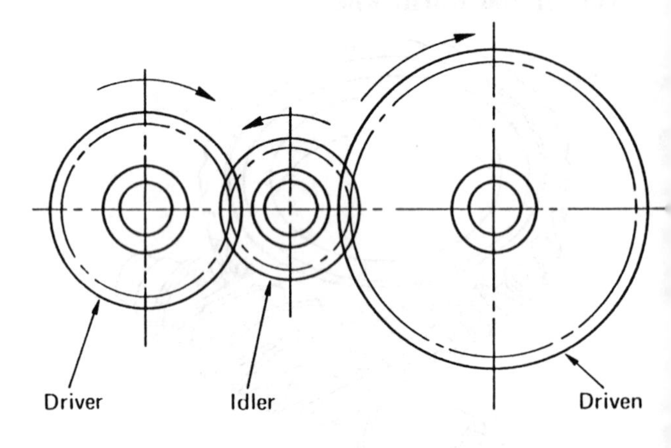

Simple train

(a) Driver and driven gears rotate in opposite directions.
(b) The relative speed of the gears is calculated by the expression

$$\frac{\text{rev/min driver}}{\text{rev/min driven}} = \frac{\text{number of teeth on driven}}{\text{number of teeth on driver}}$$

Example
Calculate the speed of the driven gear if the driving gear is rotating at 120 rev/min. The driven gear has 150 teeth and the driving gear has 50 teeth.

$$\frac{120}{\text{rev/min driven}} = \frac{150}{50}$$

$$\text{rev/min driven} = \frac{120 \times 50}{150} = 40 \text{ rev/min}$$

Simple train with idler gear

(a) Driver and driven gears rotate in the same direction if there is an odd number of idler gears, and in the opposite direction if there is an even number of idler gears.
(b) Idler gears are used to change the direction of rotation and/or to increase the centre distance between the driver and driven gears.
(c) The number of idler gears and the number of teeth on the idler gears do not affect the overall relative speed.
(d) The overall relative speed is again calculated using the expression

$$\frac{\text{rev/min driver}}{\text{rev/min driven}} = \frac{\text{number of teeth on driven}}{\text{number of teeth on driver}}$$

2.5.3 Compound spur gear train

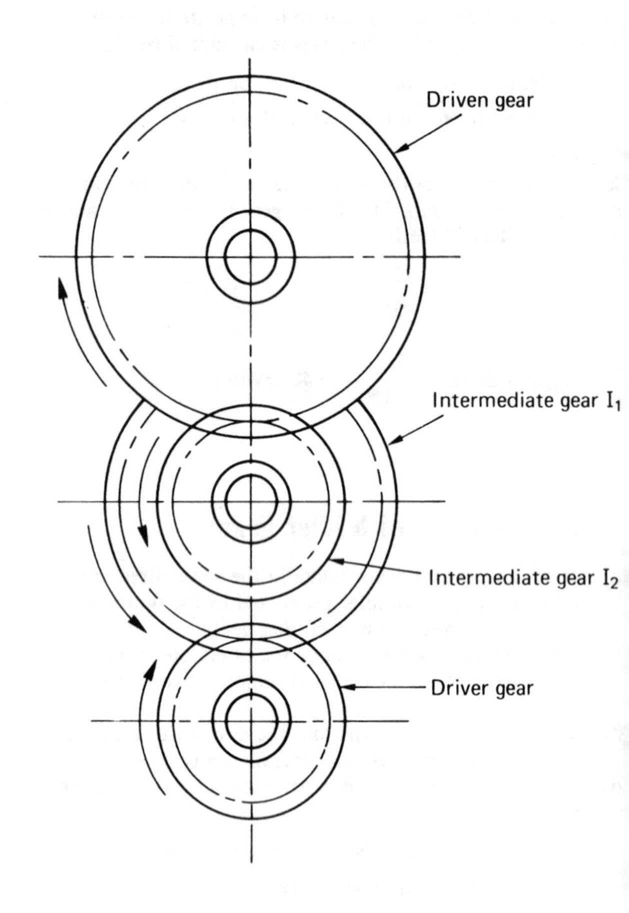

(a) Unlike the idler gear of a simple train, the intermediate gears of a compound train do influence the overall relative speeds of the driver and driven gears.
(b) Both intermediate gears (I_1 and I_2) are keyed to the same shaft and rotate at the same speed.
(c) Driver and driven gears rotate in the same direction. To reverse the direction of rotation an idler gear has to be inserted either between the driver gear and I_1 or between I_2 and the driven gear.
(d) The overall relative speed can be calculated using the expression

$$\frac{\text{rev/min driver}}{\text{rev/min driven}} = \frac{\text{no. of teeth on } I_1}{\text{no. of teeth on driver}} \times \frac{\text{no. of teeth on driven}}{\text{no. of teeth on } I_2}$$

Example
Calculate the speed of the driven gear given that: the driver rotates at 600 rev/min and has 30 teeth; I_1 has 60 teeth; I_2 has 40 teeth; and the driven gear has 80 teeth.

$$\frac{\text{rev/min driver}}{\text{rev/min driven}} = \frac{60 \times 80}{30 \times 40} = \frac{4}{1}$$

$$\text{but speed of driver} = 600 \text{ rev/min}$$

Therefore:

$$\frac{600 \text{ rev/min}}{\text{rev/min driven}} = \frac{4}{1}$$

$$\text{speed driven} = \frac{600 \times 1}{4}$$

$$= \underline{150 \text{ rev/min}}$$

2.5.4 The involute curve

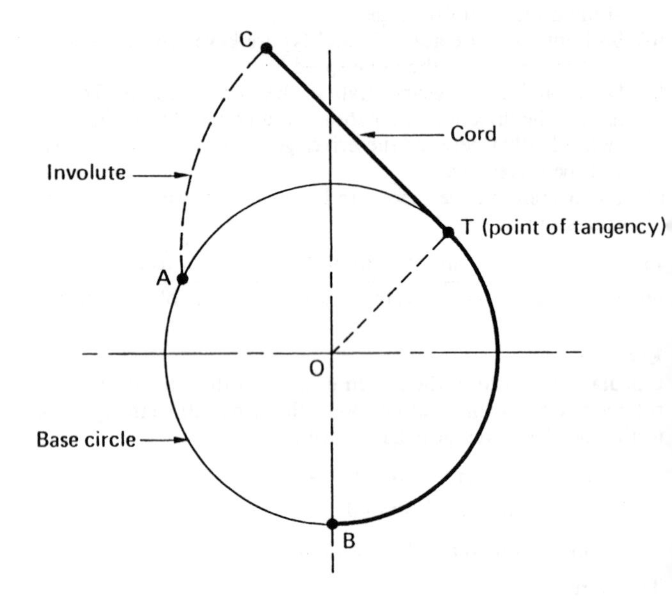

The involute curve is used for the teeth of the majority of industrially produced spur gears. The figure shows that the involute curve can be produced by unwinding an imaginary taut cord BTC from around a base circle, centre O, commencing with the end of the cord at A. The curve AC which is produced this way has an *involute form.*

The curvature of AC depends upon the radius of the base circle. As the radius of the base circle increases, the curvature of the involute decreases. For a base circle of infinite radius, the line AC ceases to be a curve and becomes a straight line. Thus a *rack gear* has teeth with straight sides, since a rack can be considered as part of the circumference of a gear of infinite radius. That is, a rack with straight sided teeth will always mesh satisfactorily with a spur gear of involute form.

The advantages of the involute form for spur gear teeth are as follows:

(a) Involute form teeth produce smooth running gears capable of transmitting heavy loads at a constant velocity.
(b) Mating teeth of involute form make mainly rolling contact between their flanks as they move in and out of mesh. Since sliding contact is minimized, scuffing and wear of the flanks of the teeth is also minimized.
(c) Because of the relationship between the involute form and the straight sided rack form, gear teeth can be rapidly and accurately *generated* using rack type cutters with easily produced straight flank cutting teeth. This has obvious advantages for tooling costs.

2.5.5 Basic gear tooth geometry

In order to develop a practical gear tooth form from the basic involute form considered in 2.5.4, it is necessary to consider two further geometrical relationships:

(a) A tangent to an involute curve, at any point, is always perpendicular to a tangent to the base circle drawn from the same point. Reference to 2.5.4 shows that the line CT is tangential to the base circle and that such a tangent is perpendicular to a tangent drawn to the involute curve at C. It will be shown that the tangent CT is also the line of action of a gear teeth.
(b) The length of the line CT is also equal to the length of the arc AT.

Consider two circles touching at the point P as shown overleaf. The point P is called the *pitch point*, and the circles are called *reference circles*. If the reference circles were friction discs they would drive each other at the required velocity ratio depending upon their relative diameters. However, gears which depended solely upon friction to transmit power would be very limited. In practice they are provided with interlocking teeth to prevent slip. If involute form teeth are used then two additional circles have to be added to the figure as shown. These additional circles are the *base circles* from which the involutes are drawn (2.5.4). Involutes are now drawn from these base circles so that they touch on the *line of action*. This line of action is the common tangent to the base circles and is an extension of the line CT (2.5.4).

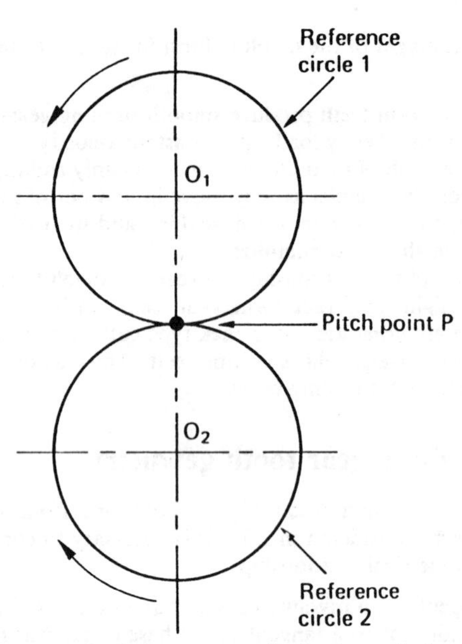

The *pressure angle* ϕ shown opposite is the angle between the line of action and a common tangent to the reference circles drawn through the point P. Experience has shown that a value of $\phi=20^\circ$ gives optimum strength combined with smooth running. This is the value adopted in most modern gears.

To develop a working gear tooth from an abstract involute curve, additional data is required as shown.

Top circle This fixes the height of the tooth and prevents it from interfering with the root of the meshing tooth on the opposite gear.
Root circle This fixes the position of the bottom or root of the tooth and thus fixes the depth to which the tooth form is cut into the gear blank.
Addendum The radial distance between the top circle and the reference circle.
Dedendum The radial distance between the root circle and the reference circle.
Tooth height The radial distance between the top circle and the root circle. That is, tooth height = addendum + dedendum.

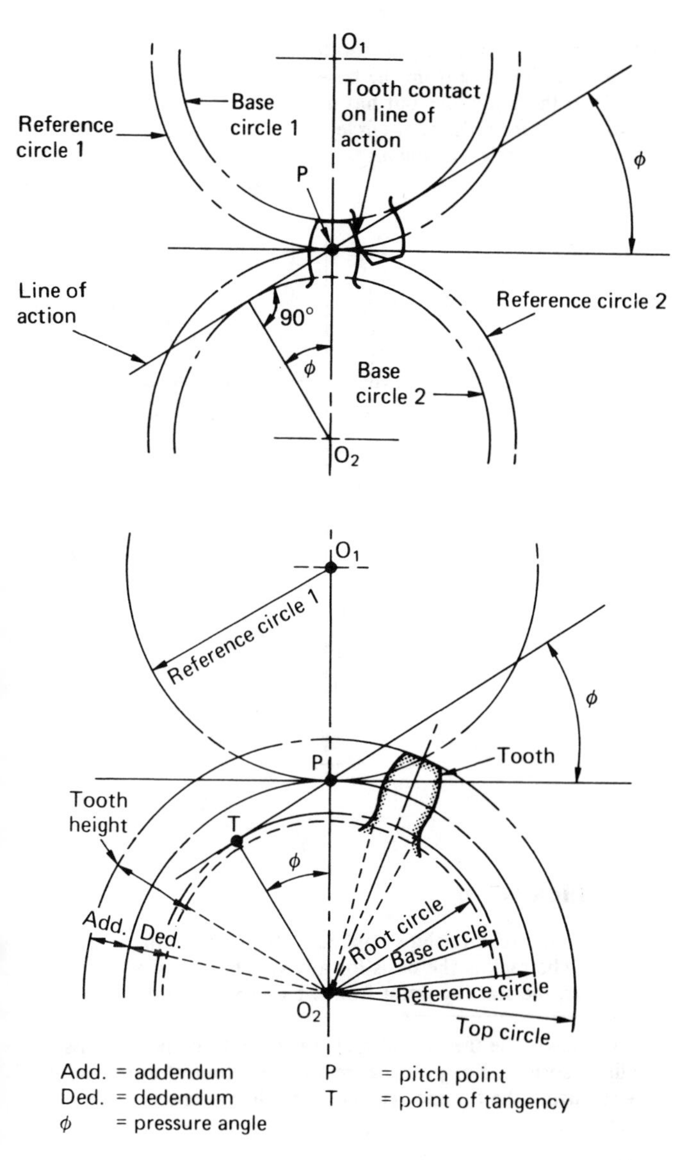
O1
Base circle 1
Tooth contact on line of action
Reference circle 1
P
φ
Line of action
90°
φ
Reference circle 2
Base circle 2
O2
O1
Reference circle 1
φ
Tooth
P
Tooth height
T
φ
Add.
Ded.
Root circle
Base circle
Reference circle
O2
Top circle
Add. = addendum
Ded. = dedendum
φ = pressure angle
P = pitch point
T = point of tangency

Note that the involute gear tooth form is an involute from the base circle to the top circle, but has a radial form from the root circle to the base circle as shown.

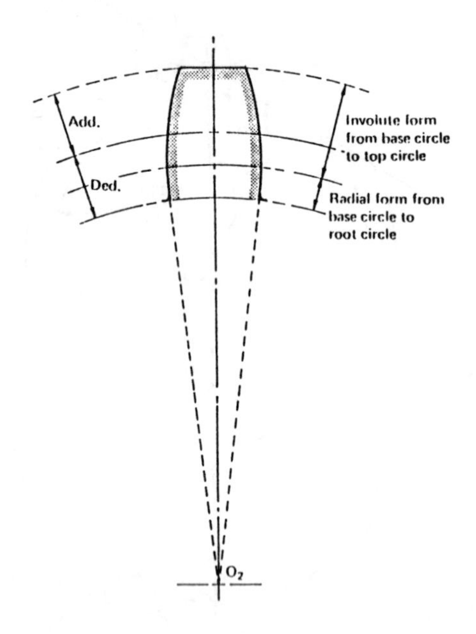

Rack form

The involute relationships applied to the rack tooth are as shown. The rack is the basis for any system of gearing and is, therefore, the starting point from which to build up a series of gears.

As shown, the theoretical rack has straight flanks and sharply defined corners. For practical reasons this tooth form is modified by radiusing the tip and replacing the sharp corners at the root with fillets.

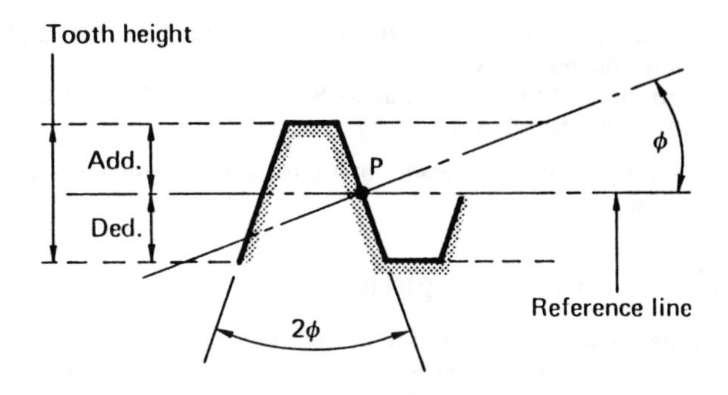

Theoretical rack tooth form

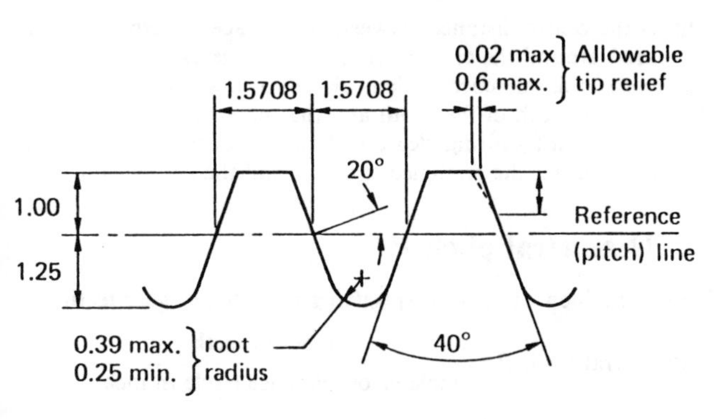

British Standard rack tooth profile
(dimensions for unit modular pitch)

A practical rack tooth form to BS 436 (metric units) is as shown above. This is the British standard basic rack dimensioned for unit modular pitch. For any module other than unity the tooth dimensions are determined by multiplying the figures shown by the module value. For practical reasons this basic rack can be modified further as follows:

(a) Variation of the total depth within the limits of 2.25 to 2.40 times the module value.
(b) Variation of the root radius within the limits of 0.25 to 0.39 times the module value.

Gears are graded in ten grades of accuracy, and these are given in BS 436.

2.5.6 Gear tooth pitch

Spur gear teeth are spaced out around the reference circle at equal intervals (or increments) known as the *pitch*. There are three different systems by which the pitch may be defined.

Circular pitch p

This is the centre distance between two adjacent teeth on a gear measured around the circumference of the reference circle. For this reason the reference circle is also known as the *pitch circle*. As both the width of the tooth and the space between adjacent teeth are equal (ignoring clearance), the thickness of each tooth (as measured on the reference circle) is half the circular pitch.

Diametral pitch P

This is an 'inch' system for specifying the pitch of gear teeth:

$$\text{diametral pitch } P = \frac{\text{number of teeth}}{\text{diameter of reference circle in inches}}$$

Modular pitch m

This is the modern international metric parameter for specifying pitch. It is calculated in a similar manner to diametral pitch:

$$\text{modular pitch } m = \frac{\text{diameter of reference circle in millimetres}}{\text{number of teeth}}$$

2.5.7 Gear tooth height

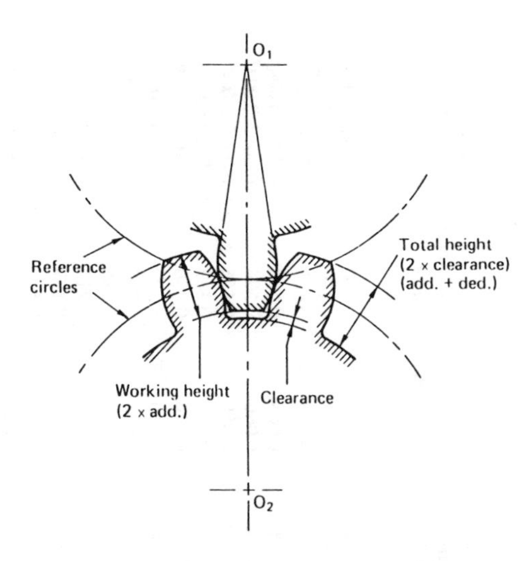

The figure shows that when two gear teeth mesh the reference circles are tangential, and that the addendum of one gear fits into the dedendum space of the mating gear. Since there must be clearance between the top (crest) of one tooth and the roof of the space into which it engages, the dedendum is greater than the addendum by the clearance.

Thus the *working height* of the tooth is twice the addendum, whilst the *total height* is twice the addendum plus the clearance (i.e. the addendum plus the dedendum). Reference to the rack gear (2.5.5) shows that the clearance is equal to the root radius. This is, ideally, 0.25 m to 0.39 m for modular pitch teeth. Hence

addendum = 1.00 m
dedendum = 1.25 m
tooth height (cutting depth) = addendum + dedendum
= 1.00 m + 1.25 m to 1.39 m
= 2.25 m to 2.39 m
working height = addendum + addendum
= 2.00 m
where m = modular pitch.

2.5.8 Standard gear tooth elements, inches

Normal diametral pitch	*Normal circular pitch*	*Standard circular tooth thickness*	*Standard addendum*	*Standard work depth*	**Minimum clearance*	**Minimum whole depth*	*Total shaving stock on tooth thickness*
2.5	1.256637	0.6283	0.4000	0.8000	0.090	0.890	0.0040/0.0050
3	1.047198	0.5236	0.3333	0.6666	0.083	0.750	0.0040/0.0050
3.5	0.897598	0.4488	0.2857	0.5714	0.074	0.645	0.0040/0.0050
4	0.785398	0.3927	0.2500	0.5000	0.068	0.568	0.0035/0.0045
4.5	0.698132	0.3491	0.2222	0.4444	0.060	0.504	0.0035/0.0045
5	0.628319	0.3142	0.2000	0.4000	0.056	0.456	0.0035/0.0045
6	0.523599	0.2618	0.1667	0.3334	0.050	0.383	0.0030/0.0040
7	0.448799	0.2244	0.1429	0.2858	0.044	0.330	0.0030/0.0040
8	0.392699	0.1963	0.1250	0.2500	0.040	0.290	0.0030/0.0040
9	0.349066	0.1745	0.1111	0.2222	0.038	0.260	0.0025/0.0035
10	0.314159	0.1571	0.1000	0.2000	0.035	0.235	0.0025/0.0035
11	0.285599	0.1428	0.0909	0.1818	0.032	0.214	0.0020/0.0030
12	0.261799	0.1309	0.0833	0.1666	0.030	0.197	0.0020/0.0030
14	0.224399	0.1122	0.0714	0.1428	0.026	0.169	0.0020/0.0030
16	0.196350	0.0982	0.0625	0.1250	0.023	0.148	0.0015/0.0025
18	0.174533	0.0873	0.0556	0.1112	0.021	0.132	0.0015/0.0025

* Based on standard tip radius on preshaving hobs and shaper cutters. Increase whole depth by approximately 0.005 in to 0.010 in for crown shaving.

2.5.9 Fine pitch gear tooth elements, inches

Normal diametral pitch	Normal circular pitch	Standard circular tooth thickness	Standard addendum	Standard work depth	*Minimum clearance	*Minimum whole depth	Total shaving stock on tooth thickness
20	0.157080	0.0785	0.0500	0.1000	0.020	0.120	
22	0.142800	0.0714	0.0454	0.0908	0.020	0.111	
24	0.130900	0.0654	0.0417	0.0834	0.020	0.103	
26	0.120830	0.0604	0.0385	0.0770	0.019	0.096	
28	0.112200	0.0561	0.0357	0.0714	0.019	0.090	
30	0.104720	0.0524	0.0333	0.0666	0.018	0.085	0.0005 to 0.0015
32	0.098175	0.0491	0.0312	0.0624	0.018	0.080	
36	0.087266	0.0436	0.0278	0.0556	0.016	0.072	
40	0.078540	0.0393	0.0250	0.0500	0.015	0.065	
44	0.071400	0.0357	0.0227	0.0454	0.014	0.059	
48	0.065450	0.0327	0.0208	0.0416	0.013	0.055	
52	0.060415	0.0302	0.0192	0.0384	0.012	0.050	
56	0.056100	0.0281	0.0178	0.0356	0.011	0.047	
60	0.052360	0.0262	0.0167	0.0334	0.010	0.043	0.0003 to 0.0007
64	0.049087	0.0245	0.0156	0.0312	0.010	0.041	
72	0.043633	0.0218	0.0139	0.0278	0.010	0.038	

* Based on standard tip radius on preshaving hobs and shaper cutter. Increase whole depth by approximately 0.005 in to 0.010 in for crown shaving.

2.5.10 Standard stub gear tooth elements, inches

Normal diametral pitch	*Normal circular pitch*	*Standard circular tooth thickness*	*Standard addendum*	*Standard work depth*	**Minimum clearance*	**Minimum whole depth*	*Total shaving stock on tooth thickness*
3/4	1.047198	0.5236	0.2500	0.5000	0.083	0.583	0.0040/0.0050
4/5	0.785398	0.3927	0.2000	0.4000	0.068	0.468	0.0035/0.0045
5/7	0.628319	0.3142	0.1429	0.2858	0.056	0.342	0.0035/0.0045
6/8	0.523599	0.2618	0.1250	0.2500	0.050	0.300	0.0030/0.0040
7/9	0.448799	0.2244	0.1111	0.2222	0.044	0.266	0.0030/0.0040
8/10	0.392699	0.1963	0.1000	0.2000	0.040	0.240	0.0030/0.0040
9/11	0.349066	0.1745	0.0909	0.1818	0.038	0.220	0.0025/0.0035
10/12	0.314159	0.1571	0.0833	0.1666	0.035	0.202	0.0025/0.0035
12/14	0.261799	0.1309	0.0714	0.1428	0.030	0.173	0.0020/0.0030
14/18	0.224399	0.1122	0.0556	0.1112	0.026	0.137	0.0020/0.0030
16/21	0.196350	0.0982	0.0476	0.0952	0.023	0.118	0.0015/0.0025
18/24	0.174533	0.0873	0.0417	0.0834	0.021	0.104	0.0015/0.0025
20/26	0.157080	0.0785	0.0385	0.0770	0.020	0.097	0.0010/0.0015
22/29	0.142800	0.0714	0.0345	0.0690	0.020	0.089	0.0010/0.0015
24/32	0.130900	0.0654	0.0313	0.0626	0.020	0.083	0.0010/0.0015
26/35	0.120830	0.0604	0.0286	0.0572	0.019	0.076	0.0010/0.0015
28/37	0.112200	0.0561	0.0270	0.0540	0.019	0.073	0.0010/0.0015
30/40	0.104720	0.0524	0.0250	0.0500	0.018	0.068	0.0010/0.0015
32/42	0.098175	0.0491	0.0238	0.0476	0.018	0.066	0.0010/0.0015
34/45	0.092400	0.0462	0.0222	0.0444	0.017	0.061	0.0010/0.0015
36/48	0.087266	0.0436	0.0208	0.0416	0.016	0.058	0.0010/0.0015
38/50	0.082673	0.0413	0.0200	0.0400	0.016	0.056	0.0010/0.0015
40/54	0.078540	0.0393	0.0185	0.0370	0.015	0.052	0.0010/0.0015

2.5.11 Standard gear tooth elements, metric

Normal module	*Normal circular pitch* mm	*Standard circular tooth thickness* mm	**Minimum root clearance* mm	**Minimum whole depth* mm	*Total shaving stock on tooth thickness* mm	*Normal diametral pitch*	*Normal circular pitch* in	*Standard circular tooth thickness* in	*Standard addendum* in	**Minimum root clearance* in	**Minimum whole depth* in
1.0	3.142	1.571	0.390	2.390	0.015/0.040	25.400	0.1237	0.0618	0.0394	0.0154	0.0941
1.25	3.927	1.963	0.480	2.980	0.020/0.045	20.320	0.1546	0.0773	0.0492	0.0189	0.1173
1.50	4.712	2.356	0.560	3.560	0.025/0.050	16.933	0.1855	0.0928	0.0591	0.0220	0.1402
1.75	5.498	2.749	0.640	4.140	0.030/0.055	14.514	0.2164	0.1082	0.0689	0.0252	0.1630
2.0	6.283	3.142	0.720	4.720	0.035/0.060	12.700	0.2474	0.1237	0.0787	0.0283	0.1858
2.25	7.069	3.534	0.790	5.290	0.040/0.065	11.289	0.2783	0.1391	0.0886	0.0311	0.2083
2.50	7.854	3.927	0.860	5.860	0.045/0.070	10.160	0.3092	0.1546	0.0984	0.0339	0.2307
2.75	8.639	4.320	0.920	6.420	0.045/0.070	9.2364	0.3401	0.1701	0.1083	0.0362	0.2528
3.0	9.425	4.712	0.990	6.990	0.050/0.075	8.4667	0.3711	0.1855	0.1181	0.0390	0.2752
3.25	10.210	5.105	1.050	7.550	0.050/0.075	7.8154	0.4020	0.2010	0.1280	0.0413	0.2972
3.50	10.996	5.498	1.110	8.110	0.055/0.080	7.2571	0.4329	0.2165	0.1378	0.0437	0.3193
3.75	11.781	5.890	1.160	8.660	0.055/0.080	6.7733	0.4638	0.2319	0.1476	0.0457	0.3409
4.0	12.566	6.283	1.220	9.220	0.060/0.085	6.3500	0.4947	0.2474	0.1575	0.0480	0.3630
4.25	13.352	6.676	1.270	9.770	0.060/0.085	5.9765	0.5256	0.2628	0.1673	0.0500	0.3846
4.50	14.137	7.069	1.320	10.320	0.060/0.085	5.6444	0.5566	0.2783	0.1772	0.0520	0.4063
4.75	14.923	7.461	1.370	10.870	0.065/0.090	5.3474	0.5875	0.2938	0.1870	0.0539	0.4280
5.0	15.708	7.854	1.420	11.420	0.065/0.090	5.0800	0.6184	0.3092	0.1969	0.0559	0.4496

continued

Section 2.5.11 (*continued*)

Normal module	*Normal circular pitch* mm	*Standard circular tooth thickness* mm	**Minimum root clearance* mm	**Minimum whole depth* mm	*Total shaving stock on tooth thickness* mm	*Normal diametral pitch*	*Normal circular pitch* in	*Standard circular tooth thickness* in	*Standard addendum* in	**Minimum root clearance* in	**Minimum whole depth* in
5.25	16.493	8.247	1.470	11.970	0.065/0.090	4.8381	0.6493	0.3247	0.2067	0.0579	0.4713
5.50	17.278	8.639	1.520	12.520	0.070/0.095	4.6182	0.6803	0.3401	0.2165	0.0598	0.4929
5.75	18.064	9.032	1.560	13.060	0.070/0.095	4.4174	0.7112	0.3556	0.2264	0.0614	0.5142
6.0	18.850	9.425	1.610	13.610	0.070/0.095	4.2333	0.7421	0.3711	0.2362	0.0634	0.5358
6.5	20.420	10.210	1.710	14.710	0.070/0.095	3.9077	0.8040	0.4020	0.2559	0.0673	0.5791
7.0	21.991	10.996	1.820	15.820	0.075/0.100	3.6286	0.8658	0.4239	0.2756	0.0717	0.6228
7.5	23.562	11.781	1.920	16.920	0.075/0.100	3.3867	0.9276	0.4638	0.2953	0.0756	0.6661
8.0	25.133	12.566	2.020	18.020	0.075/0.100	3.1750	0.9895	0.4947	0.3150	0.0795	0.7094
9.0	28.274	14.137	2.240	20.240	0.080/0.105	2.8222	1.1132	0.5566	0.3543	0.0882	0.7968
10.0	31.416	15.708	2.440	22.440	0.080/0.105	2.5400	1.2368	0.6184	0.3937	0.0960	0.8835

*Based on standard tip radius on preshaving hobs and shaper cutters.
Increase whole depth by approximately 0.130 mm to 0.250 mm (0.005 in to 0.010 in) for crown shaving.

2.5.12 Letter symbols for gear dimensions and calculations

a	addendum
b	dedendum
B	backlash
B_n	normal circular backlash
c	clearance
C	centre distance
d	diameter of measuring pin or ball
D	pitch diameter
D_b	base diameter
D_c	contact diameter
D_f	form diameter
D_F	fillet diameter
D_i	minor diameter (internal gears)
D_m	diameter of circle through centre of measuring pins or balls
D_{Me}	measurement over pins or balls (external)
D_{Mi}	measurement between pins or balls (internal)
D_o	outside diameter (O/D)
D_r	rolling or operating pitch diameter
D_R	root diameter
D_s	shaved diameter
F	face width
h_k	working depth
h_t	whole depth
L	lead
LA	total length of line of action
m	module (metric system)
m_F	face contact ratio (helical overlap)
m_n	normal module
m_p	involute contact ratio (involute overlap)
m_t	transverse module
N	number of teeth in gear (N_G) or pinion (N_p)
p	circular pitch
p_b	base pitch
p_n	normal circular pitch
p_t	transverse circular pitch
p_x	axial pitch
P	diametral pitch
P_n	normal diametral pitch

continued

P_t	transverse diametral pitch
SAP	start of active profile
S	circular tooth space
SRP	start of radius profile
S_n	normal circular tooth space
S_t	transverse circular tooth space
t	circular tooth thickness (t_n, t_t etc.)
t_c	chordal tooth thickness (t_{nc}, t_{tc} etc.)
Z	length of contact

Angles

ϕ	pressure angle
ϕ_m	pressure angle to centre of measuring pin or ball
ϕ_n	normal pressure angle
ϕ_r	operating pressure angle (ϕ_{nr}, ϕ_{tr} etc.)
ϕ_t	transverse pressure angle
ϕ_{to}	transverse pressure angle at O/D
ϕ_x	axial pressure angle
ψ	helix angle
ψ_b	base helix angle
ψ_r	operating helix angle
ψ_o	helix angle at O/D
X	crossed axes angle

Notes

(a) The addition of an arc ($\frown$) over the symbol for an angle indicates that the angle is in radians rather than degrees.
(b) Subscripts are used with symbols to differentiate between various diameters and angles and to indicate whether pinion or gear characteristics are involved.

Terminology

Transverse characteristics (subscript t) are taken in the plane of rotation, parallel to the gear face and perpendicular to the axis. *Normal characteristics* (subscript n) are taken from a section of the gear teeth which is normal to the helix at a given diameter.

Axial plane characteristics (subscript x) are in a plane through the teeth and axis of the gear, perpendicular to the gear face.
Start of active profile (*SAP*) is the lowest point of mating gear contact as measured along the line or action in inches or degrees of roll from zero (base diameter).
Contact diameter (D_c) is the diameter through the lowest point of mating gear contact.
Form diameter (D_f) is the diameter through the lowest point on the gear profile where the desired involute tooth form is to start.
Start of radius profile (*SRP*) is the height of the generated root fillet on a gear as measured along the line of action from the base diameter.
Fillet diameter (D_F) is the diameter through the start of radius profile.
Shaved diameter (D_s) is the diameter through the lowest point of contact of the shaving cutter, i.e. the start of the shaved profile of a gear.
Crossed axes angle (X) is the sum or difference of the gear and shaving cutter helix angles, dependent upon the hand of the helix and centre distance. If the hands are opposite, the crossed axes angle will be equal to the difference between the helix angles; if the hands are the same, it will be equal to the sum.

2.5.13 Basic spur gear calculations

To find	in	mm
Pitch diameter D	N/P	mN
Addendum a	$1/P$	Module m (in mm and parts mm)
Standard outside diameter D_o	$D+2a$	$D+2m$
Circular pitch p	π/P	πm
Average backlash per pair B	$0.040/P$	$0.040m$
Root diameter D_R	D_o-2h_t	
Base diameter D_b	$D\cos\phi$	
Standard circular tooth thickness t	$p/2$	

Conversions

Diametral pitch $P = 25.4/m$
Module $m = 25.4/P$
millimetres = inches/0.039 37 = 25.4 inches
inches = 0.039 37 millimetres = millimetres/25.4

2.5.14 Basic helical gear equations

Transverse diametral pitch $P_t = P_n \cos \psi$
Pitch diameter $D = N/P_t$
Addendum a standard $= 1/P_n$
Outside diameter $D_o = D + 2a$
Transverse pressure angle ϕ_t: $\tan \phi_t = \tan \phi_n / \cos \psi$
Base diameter $D_b = D \cos \phi_t$
Lead $L = \pi D \cot \psi = \pi D / \tan \psi$
Normal circular pitch $p_n = \pi / P_n$
Standard normal circular tooth thickness $t_n = p_n/2$
Axial pitch $p_x = \pi/P_n \sin \psi = p_n/\sin \psi = L/N$
Transverse circular pitch $p_t = \pi/P_t = p_n/\cos \psi$

2.5.15 Miscellaneous gear equations

1 Helix angle ψ, when given centre distance is standard:

$$\cos \psi = \frac{N_p + N_G}{2p_n C}$$

2 Operating pitch diameter (pinion), with non-standard centre distance C:

$$D_{rp} = \frac{2CN_p}{N_p + N_G}$$

3 Operating pressure angle ϕ_{rt}, with non-standard centre distance C:

$$\cos \phi_{rt} = \frac{D_{bp} + D_b{}^G}{2C}$$

4 Normal diametral pitch:

$$P_n = P_t \sec \psi$$

5 Helix angle ψ:

$$\cos \psi = \frac{N}{D\ P_n}$$

$$\sin \psi = \frac{\pi\ N}{P_n\ L}$$

At any diameter D_2:

$$\tan \psi_2 = \frac{D_2 \tan \psi_1}{D_1}$$

6 Transverse circular pitch p_{t2} at any diameter D_2:

$$p_{t2} = \frac{\pi\ D_2}{N}$$

7 Involute function of pressure angle (function tables are available):

$$\text{inv}\ \phi = \tan \phi - \phi$$

8 Normal pressure angle (ϕ_n):

$$\tan \phi_n = \tan \phi_t \cos \psi$$

9 Transverse pressure angle ϕ_t at any diameter D_2:

$$\cos \phi_{t2} = \frac{D_b}{D_2}$$

10 Base helix angle ψ_b:

$$\cos \psi_b = \frac{\cos \psi \cos \phi_n}{\cos \phi_t} = \frac{\sin \phi_n}{\sin \phi_t}$$

$$\sin \psi_b = \sin \psi \cos \phi_n$$
$$\tan \psi_b = \tan \psi \cos \phi_t$$

11 Base pitch:

$$p_b = \frac{\pi\ D_b}{N} = p \cos \phi$$

2.5.16 Straight bevel gear nomenclature

2.5.17 Worm and worm wheel nomenclature

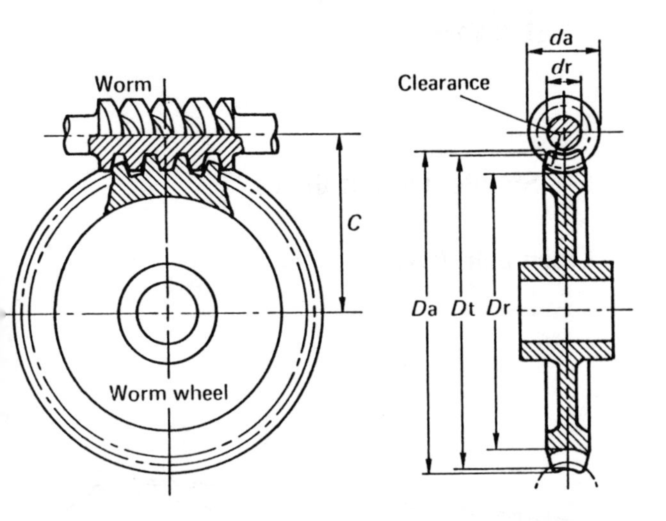

C = centre distance
Dr = worm wheel root diameter
Dt = worm wheel throat diameter
Da = worm wheel tip diameter
da = worm tip diameter
dr = worm root diameter

$$\frac{\text{rev/min worm}}{\text{rev/min worm wheel}} = \frac{\text{number of teeth on worm wheel}}{\text{number of starts on worm}}$$

Example

Calculate the speed of the worm wheel in rev/min, given that the worm rotates at 500 rev/min, that the worm wheel has 50 teeth and that the worm has a two-start helix.

$$\frac{500 \text{ rev/min}}{\text{rev/min worm wheel}} = \frac{50 \text{ teeth}}{2 \text{ starts}}$$

$$\text{rev/min worm wheel} = \frac{500 \times 2}{50} = 20 \text{ rev/min}$$

2.6 Power transmission: belt drives

2.6.1 Simple flat belt drives

Open belt drive

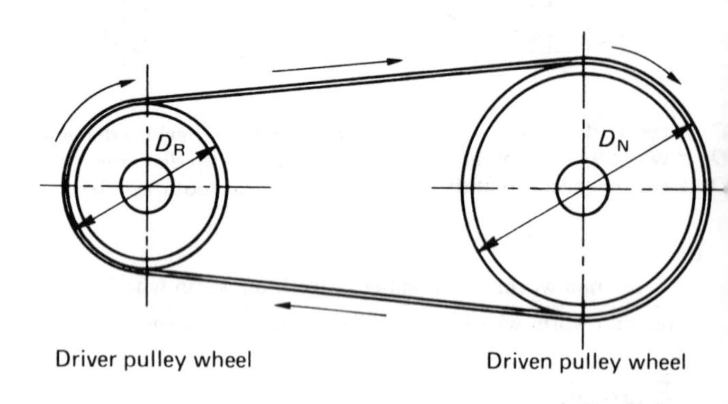

(a) Driver and driven pulley wheels rotate in the same direction.
(b) The relative speed of the pulley wheels is calculated by the expression

$$\frac{\text{rev/min driver}}{\text{rev/min driven}} = \frac{\text{diameter } D_N \text{ of driven}}{\text{diameter } D_R \text{ of driver}}$$

Example
Calculate the speed in rev/min of the driven pulley if the driver rotates at 200 rev/min. Diameter D_R is 500 mm and diameter D_N is 800 mm.

$$\frac{200\text{ rev/min}}{\text{rev/min driven}} = \frac{800\text{ mm}}{500\text{ mm}}$$

$$\text{rev/min driven} = \frac{200 \times 500}{800} = 125\text{ rev/min}$$

Crossed belt drive

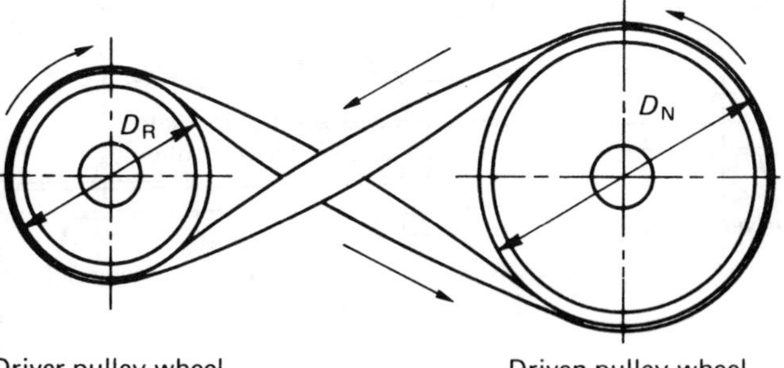

(a) Driver and driven pulley wheels rotate in opposite directions.
(b) Crossed belt drives can only be used with flat section belts (long centre distances) or circular section belts (short centre distances).
(c) The relative speed of the pulley wheels is again calculated by the expression

$$\frac{\text{rev/min driver}}{\text{rev/min driven}} = \frac{\text{diameter } D_N \text{ of driven}}{\text{diameter } D_R \text{ of driver}}$$

Example
The driver pulley rotates at 500 rev/min and is 600 mm in diameter. Calculate the diameter of the driven pulley if it is to rotate at 250 rev/min.

$$\frac{500 \text{ rev/min}}{250 \text{ rev/min}} = \frac{\text{diameter } D_N}{600 \text{ mm}}$$

$$\text{diameter } D_N = \frac{500 \times 60}{250} = 1200 \text{ mm}$$

2.6.2 Compound flat belt drive

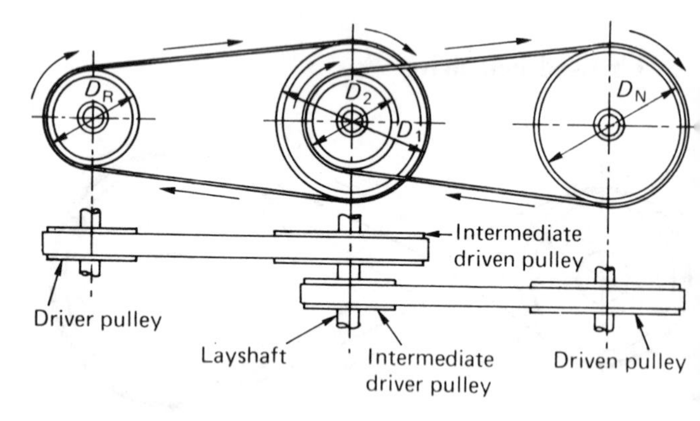

(1) To identify the direction of rotation, the rules for open and crossed belt drives apply (2.6.1).
(2) The relative speeds of the pulley wheels are calculated by the expression

$$\frac{\text{rev/min driver}}{\text{rev/min driven}} = \frac{\text{diameter } D_1}{\text{diameter } D_R} \times \frac{\text{diameter } D_N}{\text{diameter } D_2}$$

Example
Calculate the speed in rev/min of the driven pulley if the driver rotates at 600 rev/min. The diameters of the pulley wheels are: $D_R = 250$ mm. $D_1 = 750$ mm, $D_2 = 500$ mm, $D_N = 1000$ mm.

$$\frac{600 \text{ rev/min}}{\text{rev/min driven}} = \frac{750\,\text{mm}}{250\,\text{mm}} \times \frac{1000\,\text{mm}}{500\,\text{mm}}$$

$$\text{rev/min driven} = \frac{600 \times 250 \times 500}{750 \times 1000} = 100 \text{ rev/min}$$

2.6.3 Typical belt tensioning devices

Swing bed tensioning device

Jockey pulley

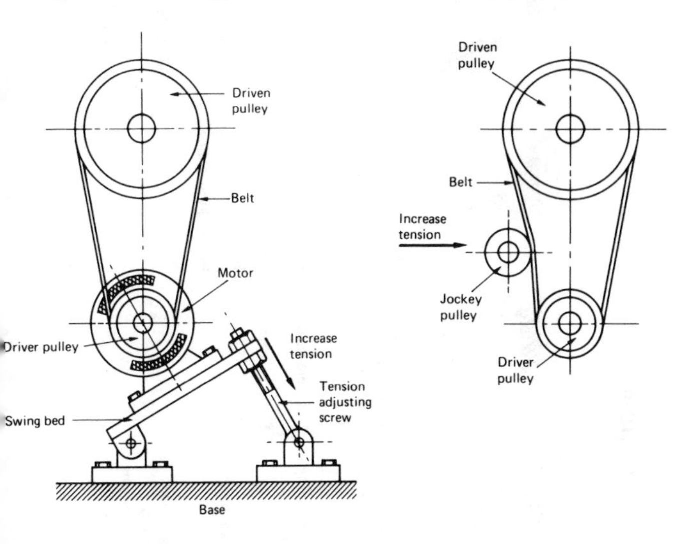

Slide rail tensioning device

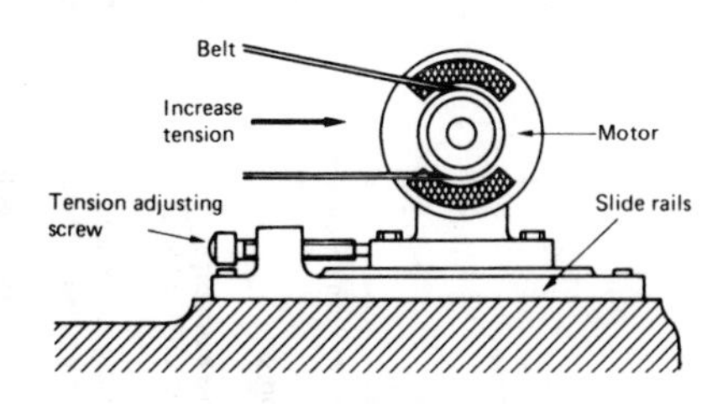

2.6.4 Typical V-belt drive applications

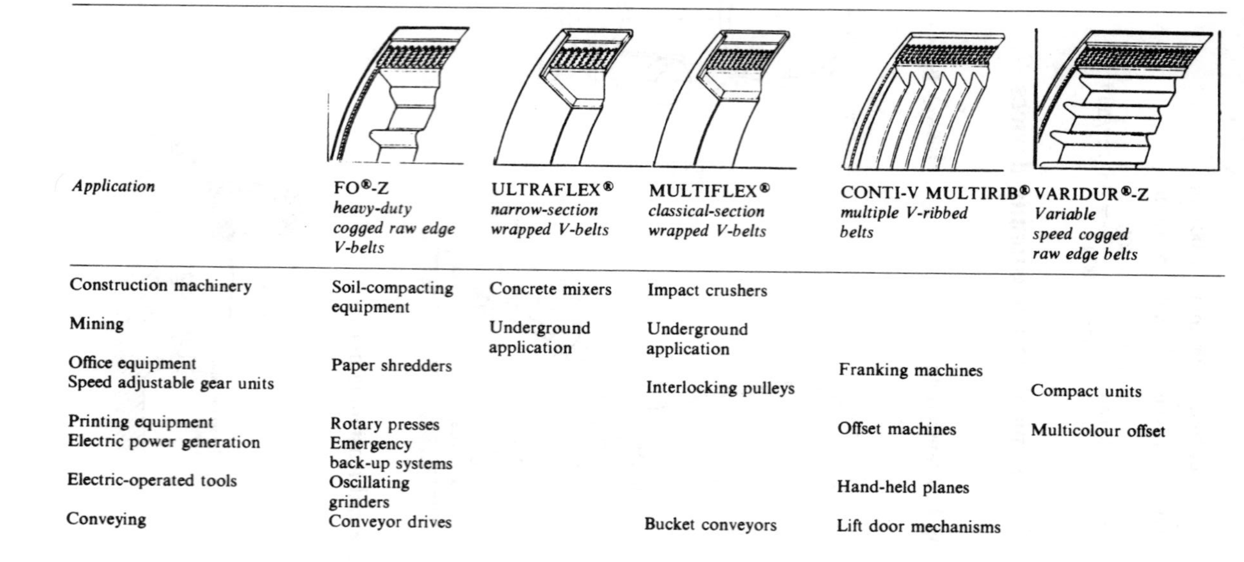

Application	FO®-Z *heavy-duty cogged raw edge V-belts*	ULTRAFLEX® *narrow-section wrapped V-belts*	MULTIFLEX® *classical-section wrapped V-belts*	CONTI-V MULTIRIB® *multiple V-ribbed belts*	VARIDUR®-Z *Variable speed cogged raw edge belts*
Construction machinery	Soil-compacting equipment	Concrete mixers	Impact crushers		
Mining		Underground application	Underground application		
Office equipment	Paper shredders			Franking machines	
Speed adjustable gear units			Interlocking pulleys		Compact units
Printing equipment	Rotary presses			Offset machines	Multicolour offset
Electric power generation	Emergency back-up systems				
Electric-operated tools	Oscillating grinders			Hand-held planes	
Conveying	Conveyor drives		Bucket conveyors	Lift door mechanisms	

Industrial drives	Power transmissions	Power transmissions	Power transmissions		Adjusting pulley sets
Large domestic appliances				Washing machines	
Small domestic appliances	Mixers			Floor polishers	
Woodworking machinery	Planing equipment	Reciprocating saws		Millers	
Rubber and plastics processing	Extruders				
Automotive sector	Auxilliary units			Auxiliary units	
Compressors	Piston compressors				
Agricultural equipment	Blowers	Spreaders	Beet lifters		Threshing cylinders
Motorcycles					Automatic transmission
Paper-making machinery	Drying cylinders				
Pumps	Radial-flow pumps				
Lawn care and cleaning equip.					Lawnmower drives
Textile machinery	Cylindrical dryers				Spoolers
Ventilators	Axial-flow blowers				
Internal combustion engines	Auxiliary units			Auxiliary units	
Metalworking machinery	Lathes			Main spindle drives	Lathes
Crushing/grinding machinery				Shredders	

continued

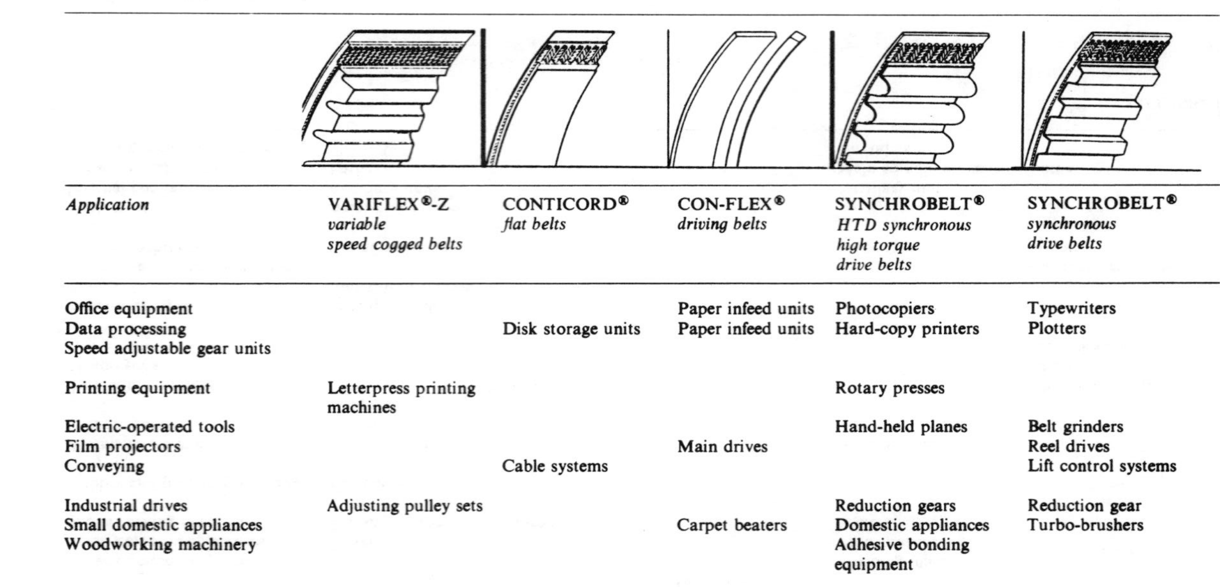

Application	VARIFLEX®-Z *variable speed cogged belts*	CONTICORD® *flat belts*	CON-FLEX® *driving belts*	SYNCHROBELT® *HTD synchronous high torque drive belts*	SYNCHROBELT® *synchronous drive belts*
Office equipment			Paper infeed units	Photocopiers	Typewriters
Data processing		Disk storage units	Paper infeed units	Hard-copy printers	Plotters
Speed adjustable gear units					
Printing equipment	Letterpress printing machines			Rotary presses	
Electric-operated tools				Hand-held planes	Belt grinders
Film projectors			Main drives		Reel drives
Conveying		Cable systems			Lift control systems
Industrial drives	Adjusting pulley sets			Reduction gears	Reduction gear
Small domestic appliances			Carpet beaters	Domestic appliances	Turbo-brushers
Woodworking machinery				Adhesive bonding equipment	

Automotive sector		Camshaft drives	Camshaft drives
Sewing machines			Looper drives
Lawn care and cleaning equip.	Floor cleaners	Cultivators	
Robotics		Positioning drives	Positioning drives
Textile machinery		Weaving machines	
Ventilators		Main drives	
Internal combustion engines		Camshaft drives	Camshaft drives
Packaging machines	Capping machine drives		Counters
Metalworking machinery		Power feed drives	

2.6.5 FO®-Z heavy-duty cogged raw edge V-belts

Belt section	DIN symbol BS/ISO symbol		5 —	6 Y	SPZ SPZ	SPA SPA	SPB SPB	SPC SPC
Top belt width $b_o \approx$		mm	5	6	10	13	16.3	22
Pitch width b_w		mm	4.2	5.3	8.5	11	14	19
Height of belt $h \approx$		mm	3	4	8	9	13	18
Pitch height $h_w \approx$		mm	1.3	1.6	2	2.8	3.5	4.8
Min. pulley pitch diameter $d_{w\ min}$		mm	16	20	50	63	100	160
Max. flexing frequency $f_{B\ max}$		per s	120	120	120	120	120	120
Max. belt speed v_{max}		m/s	50	50	50	50	50	50
Weight per metre		kg/m	0.017	0.027	0.070	0.120	0.180	0.330
Range of pitch length L_w:								
from		mm	171	295	587	592	1250	2000
to		mm	611	865	3550	3550	3550	3550
Length differential value from L_w: $\Delta L = L_w - L_i$		mm	11	15	—	—	—	—

FO®-Z heavy-duty cogged V-belts are manufactured in a raw edge type and supplement the proven range of CONTI® V-belts. They comply in their dimensions as narrow-section V-belts with DIN standard 7753 part 1 and BS 3790 and as standard V-belts with DIN standard 2215 and BS 3790.

2.6.6 ULTRAFLEX® Narrow-section wrapped V-belts

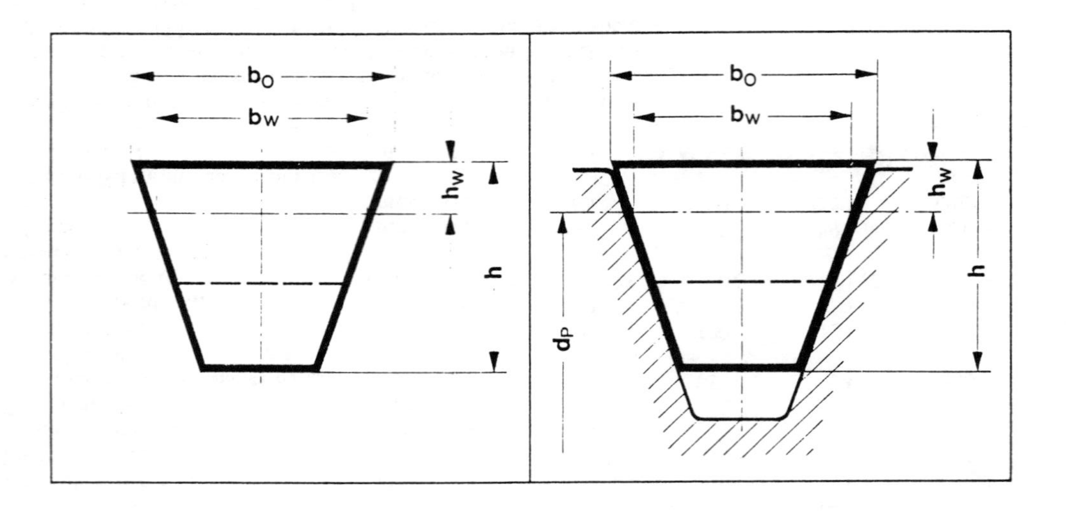

Belt section	DIN symbol BS/ISO symbol	SPZ SPZ	SPA SPA	SPB SPB	SPC SPC	19 —
Top belt width $b_o \approx$	mm	9.7	12.7	16.3	22	18.6
Pitch width b_w	mm	8.5	11	14	19	16
Bottom belt width $b_u \approx$	mm	4	5.6	7.1	9.3	8
Height of belt $h \approx$	mm	8	10	13	18	15
Pitch height $h_w \approx$	mm	2	2.8	3.5	4.8	4
Min. pulley pitch diameter $d_{w\ min}$	mm	63	90	140	224	180
Max. flexing frequency $f_{B\ max}$	per s	100	100	100	100	100
Max. belt speed V_{max}	m/s	40	40	40	40	40
Weight per metre	kg/m	0.070	0.120	0.190	0.360	0.260
Range of pitch length L_w:						
from	mm	512	647	1250	2000	1175
to	mm	3550	4500	8000	12250	5000
Length differential value from L_w: $\Delta L = L_a - L_w$	mm	13	18	22	30	25

ULTRAFLEX® narrow-section wrapped V-belts complying with BS 3790 and DIN standard 7753 part 1 are used in demanding drive systems in all spheres of mechanical engineering. They have high power transmission capacity and economic efficiency coupled with a long service life.

2.6.7 MULTIFLEX® classical-section wrapped V-belts

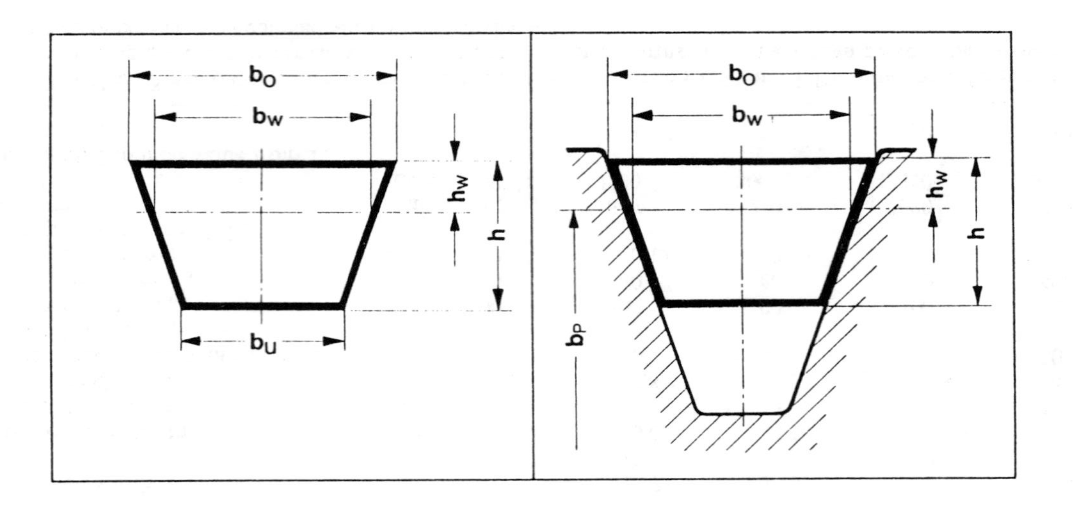

Belt section	DIN symbol BS/ISO symbol		8 —	10 Z	13 A	17 B	20 —	22 C	25 —	32 D	40 E
Top belt width $b_o \approx$		mm	8	10	13	17	20	22	25	32	40
Pitch width b_w		mm	6.7	8.5	11	14	17	19	21	27	32
Bottom belt width $b_u \approx$		mm	4.6	5.9	7.5	9.4	11.4	12.4	14	18.3	22.8
Height of belt $h \approx$		mm	5	6	8	11	12.5	14	16	20	25
Pitch height $h_w \approx$		mm	2	2.5	3.3	4.2	4.8	5.7	6.3	8.1	12
Min. pulley pitch diameter $d_{w\ min}$		mm	40	50	80	125	160	200	250	355	500
Max. flexing frequency $f_{B\ max}$		per s	60	60	60	60	60	60	60	60	60
Max. belt speed V_{max}		m/s	30	30	30	30	30	30	30	30	30
Weight per metre		kg/m	0.040	0.060	0.104	0.190	0.250	0.300	0.400	0.640	1.030
Range of pitch length L_w: from		mm	280	375	400	615	900	1000	1350	2501	3000
to		mm	1500	2500	4000	7100	8000	8500	10000	13460	12500
Length differential value from L_i: $\Delta L = L_w - L_i$		mm	19	22	30	43	48	52	61	75	82

MULTIFLEX® classical-section wrapped V-belts complying with BS 3790 and DIN standard 2215 are designed for all industrial applications from precision engineering to heavy machine construction.

2.6.8 V-belt pulleys complying with BS 3790 and DIN standard 2211 for FO®-Z and ULTRAFLEX® belts. R_z xx refers to surface roughness.

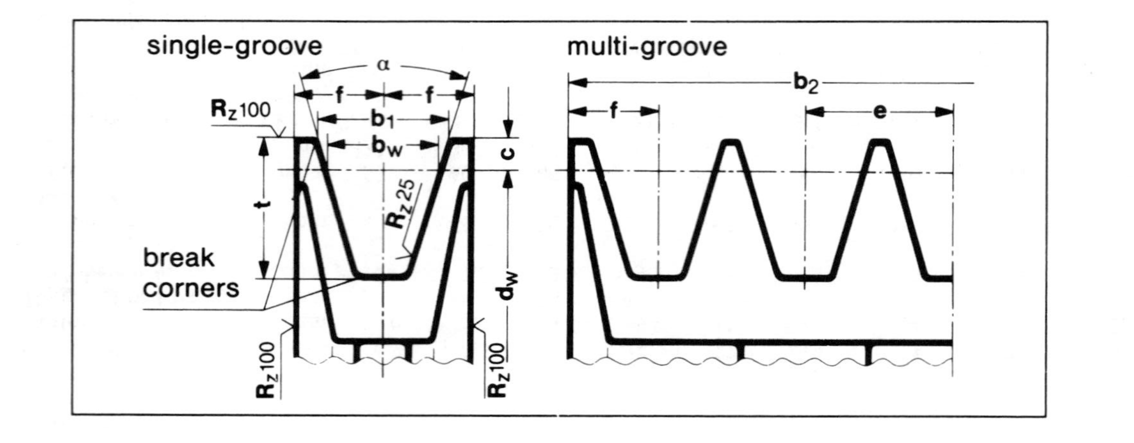

Dimensions in millimetres

Belt section						
To DIN 7753 part 1 and BS 3790:	DIN symbol	SPZ	SPA	SPB	SPC	19
	BS/ISO symbol	SPZ	SPA	SPB	SPC	—
To DIN 2215 and BS 3790:	DIN symbol	10	13	17	22	—
	BS/ISO symbol	Z	A	B	C	—
Pitch width	b_w	8.5	11	14	19	16
Top groove width	$b_1 \approx$	9.7	12.7	16.3	22	18.6
	c	2	2.8	3.5	4.8	4
Groove spacing	e	$12_{\pm 0.3}$	$15_{\pm 0.3}$	$19_{\pm 0.4}$	$25.5_{\pm 0.5}$	$22_{\pm 0.4}$
	f	$8_{\pm 0.6}$	$10_{\pm 0.6}$	$12.5_{\pm 0.8}$	$17_{\pm 1}$	$14.5_{\pm 0.8}$
Groove depth	t	$11^{+0.6}_{0}$	$14^{+0.6}_{0}$	$18^{+0.6}_{0}$	$24^{+0.6}_{0}$	$20^{+0.6}_{0}$
α 34 for pitch diameter	d_w	$\leqslant 80$	$\leqslant 118$	$\leqslant 190$	$\leqslant 315$	$\leqslant 250$
α 38		> 80	> 118	> 190	> 315	> 250
Tolerance for $\alpha = 34° - 38°$		$\pm 1°$	$\pm 1°$	$\pm 1°$	$\pm 0.5°$	$\pm 1°$
Pulley face width b_2 for number of grooves z: $b_2 = (z-1)e + 2f$	1	16	20	25	34	29
	2	28	35	44	59.5	51
	3	40	50	63	85	73
	4	52	65	82	110.5	95
	5	64	80	101	136	117
	6	76	95	120	161.5	139
	7	88	110	139	187	161
	8	100	125	158	212.5	183
	9	112	140	177	238	205
	10	124	155	196	263.5	227
	11	136	170	215	289	249
	12	148	185	234	314.5	271

2.6.9 V-belt pulleys complying with DIN standard 2217 part 1 for FO®-Z and MULTIFLEX® belts

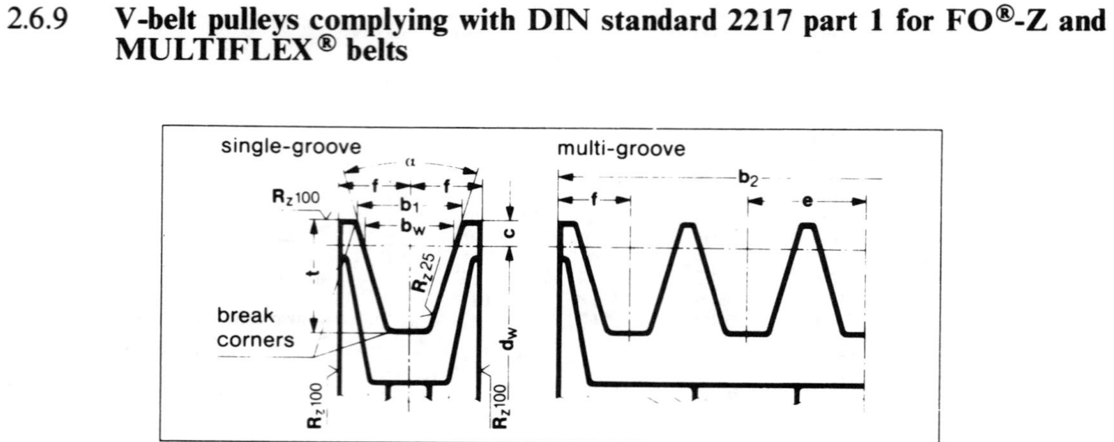

Dimensions in millimetres

Belt section												
To DIN 2215:*	DIN symbol	5	6	(8)	10	13	17	(20)	22	(25)	32	40
	BS/ISO symbol	—	Y	—	Z	A	B	—	C	—	D	E
Alternative section (DIN 2211 part 1) to BS 3790:	BS/ISO symbol	—	—	—	SPZ	SPA	SPB	—	SPC	—	—	—
Pitch width	b_w	4.2	5.3	6.7	8.5	11	14	17	19	21	27	32
Top grove width	$b_1 \approx$	5	6.3	8				20		25	32	40
	c	1.3	1.6	2				5.1		6.3	8.1	12
Groove spacing	e	$6_{\pm 0.3}$	$8_{\pm 0.3}$	$10_{\pm 0.3}$				$23_{\pm 0.4}$		$29_{\pm 0.5}$	$37_{\pm 0.6}$	$44.5_{\pm 0.3}$
	f	$5_{\pm 0.5}$	$6_{\pm 0.5}$	$7_{\pm 0.6}$				$15_{\pm 0.8}$		$19_{\pm 1}$	$24_{\pm 2}$	$29_{\pm 2}$
Groove depth	t	$6^{+0.6}_{0}$	$7^{+0.6}_{0}$	$9^{+0.6}_{0}$				$18^{+0.6}_{0}$		$22^{+0.6}_{0}$	$28^{+0.6}_{0}$	$33^{+0.6}_{0}$
α 32 for pitch diameter	d_w	≦50	≦63	≦75				—		—	—	—
34		—	—	—				≦250		≦355	—	—
36		>50	>63	≧75				—		—	≦500	≦630
38		—	—	—				>250		>355	>500	>630
Tolerance for $\alpha = 32$ 38		±1	±1	±1				±1		≤30′	±30′	±30′
Pulley face width b_2 for number of grooves: $b_2 = (z-1)e + 2$	1	10	12	14				30		38	48	58
	2	16	20	24				53		67	85	102.5
	3	22	28	34				76		96	122	147
	4	28	36	44				99		125	159	191.5
	5	34	44	54				122		154	196	236
	6	40	52	64				145		183	233	280.5
	7		60	74				168		212	270	325
	8			84				191		241	307	369.5
	9							214		270	344	414
	10							237		299	381	458.5
	11							260		328	418	503
	12							283		357	455	547.5

(Columns 10, 13, 17:) Pulleys for narrow-section V-belts (DIN 2211 part 1 and BS 3790) must be used for drives with these sections.

(Column 22:) As columns SPZ SPA SPB

* Sections in brackets should not be used for new constructions.

2.6.10 Deep-groove pulleys

Dimensions in millimetres

Belt section		SPZ	SPA	SPB	SPC	19
To DIN 7753 part 1 and BS 3790:	DIN symbol	SPZ	SPA	SPB	SPC	19
	BS/ISO symbol	SPZ	SPA	SPB	SPC	—
To DIN 2215 and BS 3790:	DIN symbol	10	13	17	22	—
	BS/ISO symbol	Z	A	B	C	—
Pitch width	b_w	8.5	11	14	19	16
Increased groove width $b_1 \approx$	$\alpha = 34°$	11	15	18.9	26.3	22.1
	$\alpha = 38°$	11.3	15.4	19.5	27.3	22.9
	c	4	6.5	8	12	10
Groove spacing	e	$14_{\pm 0.3}$	$18_{\pm 0.3}$	$23_{\pm 0.4}$	$31_{\pm 0.5}$	$27_{\pm 0.5}$
	f	$9_{\pm 0.6}$	$11.5_{\pm 0.6}$	$14.5_{\pm 0.8}$	$20_{\pm 1}$	$17_{\pm 1}$
Increased groove depth	t_{min}	13	18	22.5	31.5	26
α 34° for pitch diameter d_w with belts to DIN 7753 1 and BS 3790		63 to 80	90 to 118	140 to 190	224 to 315	180 to 250
α 38° for pitch diameter d_w with belts to DIN 7753 1 and BS 3790		>80	>118	>190	>315	>250
α 34° for pitch diameter d_w with belts to DIN 2215 and BS 3790		50 to 80	71 to 118	112 to 190	180 to 315	—
α 38° for pitch diameter d_w with belts to DIN 2215 and BS 3790		>80	>118	>190	>315	>250

continued

Section 2.6.10 (*continued*) Dimensions in millimetres

Belt section							
To DIN 7753 part 1 and BS 3790:	DIN symbol		SPZ	SPA	SPB	SPC	19
	BS/ISO symbol		SPZ	SPA	SPB	SPC	—
To DIN 2215 and BS 3790:	DIN symbol		10	13	17	22	—
	BS/ISO symbol		Z	A	B	C	—
Tolerance for $\alpha = 34° - 38°$			$\pm 1°$	$\pm 1°$	$\pm 1°$	$\pm 0.5°$	$\pm 1°$
Pulley face width b_2 for number of grooves z: $b_2 = (z-1)e + 2f$		1	18	23	29	40	34
		2	32	41	52	71	61
		3	46	59	75	102	88
		4	60	77	98	133	115
		5	74	95	121	164	142
		6	88	113	144	195	169
		7	102	131	167	226	196
		8	116	149	190	257	223
		9	130	167	213	288	250
		10	144	185	236	319	277
		11	158	203	259	350	304
		12	172	221	282	381	331

Minimum pulley diameter must be adhered to.
Not to be used for banded V-belts.

Synchronous belt drives: introduction

Synchronous (toothed) belt drives are now widely used in place of traditional, roller chain drives for many applications. Unlike a flat belt or a V-belt the toothed belt cannot slip, therefore it can be used where the rotation of input (driver) and output (driven) elements of a system must always be synchronized.

The main advantages of synchronous belt drives compared with traditional roller chain drives are:

1 Substantially lower cost.
2 Quieter running.
3 Ability to operate in environments which would be hostile to a roller chain drive.
4 No need for lubrication of the drive.
5 The elastomer material from which the belt is made tends to absorb vibrations rather than transmit them.

On the other hand, synchronous belt drives cannot transmit as much power as either chain drives or as V-belt drives.

Synchronous belt drive applications are found where their special properties can be exploited. For example:

1 Office equipment where quiet running and lack of lubrication is important.
2 Food processing machinery where conventional lubrication, necessary with a chain drive, might contaminate the foodstuffs being processed
3 Motor vehicle camshaft drives where synchronous, trouble-free, quiet, lubrication-free, smooth running is required.
4 The coupling of stepper motors and servo-motors to the feed mechanisms of computer controlled machine tools where synchronous, trouble-free, vibration-free, smooth running is required.

The following tables of synchronous-belt data and associated toothed pulley data have been selected to assist in the design of synchronous belt drive systems.

2.6.11 SYNCHROBELT® HTD

Construction

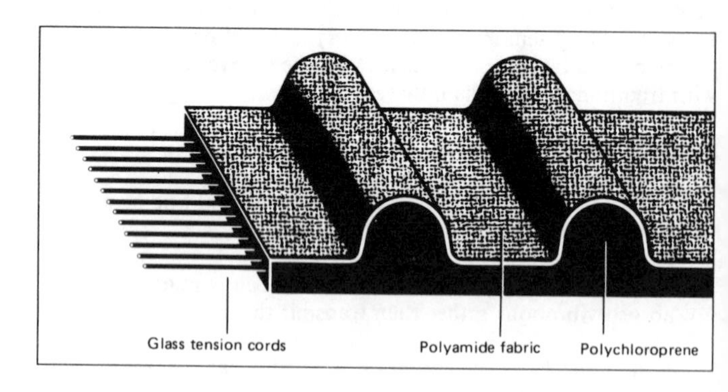

The teeth and the belt top are made from highly loadable polychloroprene-based elastomer compounds. They have excellent adhesion both on the tensile member and on the facing fabric.

A durable protection of the teeth is an essential precondition for a smooth operation and a long service life. This is ensured by the application of particularly abrasion-resistant polyamide fabrics with low friction coefficients.

Synchronous belt drives call for a high degree of length stability and tensile strength. These requirements are optimally met by low-elongation tensile members of glass cord helically wound over the entire belt width. Any longitudinal off-track running will be largely prevented by the use of S/Z tensile cords arranged in pairs.

The belts are also resistant to fatigue failure, temperature change, ageing, deformation and a wide range of environmental conditions.

Designation

SYNCHROBELT® HTD belts are designated by the following data:

Pitch length (mm) The pitch length of the belt is the overall circumference measured on the neutral pitch line. The pitch length is located in the middle of the tensile member. The precise pitch length can only be ascertained on suitable measuring devices (see 2.6.4).
Tooth pitch (mm) The tooth pitch is the linear distance between two adjacent teeth along the pitch line.
Belt width (mm) The belt width and the width designation are identical.

For example, the SYNCHROBELT® HTD 960–8M–50 belt has 960 mm pitch length, 8 mm tooth pitch and 50 mm belt width.
The number of teeth z is a function of pitch length and pitch: $z = L_w/t$

Available belt range

SYNCHROBELT® HTD belts are supplied in four tooth pitch versions:

HTD-3M:	3 mm tooth pitch
HTD-5M:	5 mm tooth pitch
HTD-8M:	8 mm tooth pitch
HTD-14M:	14 mm tooth pitch

The length and width dimensions that can be supplied are shown in 2.6.10. The range of pulleys is illustrated in 2.6.12.

2.6.12 SYNCHROBELT® HTD synchronous (toothed) belts: tooth profiles

Tooth pitch 3 mm

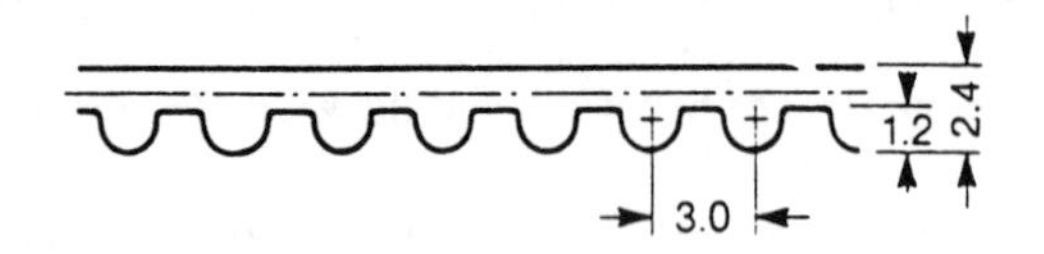

Standard lengths

Designation	*Pitch length L_w* mm	*No. of teeth z*
144-3M	144	48
177-3M	177	59
225-3M	225	75
255-3M	255	85
300-3M	300	100
339-3M	339	113
384-3M	384	128
420-3M	420	140
474-3M	474	158
513-3M	513	171
564-3M	564	188
633-3M	633	211
711-3M	711	237
1125-3M	1125	375

Standard widths: 6, 9, 15 mm; intermediate widths on request.

Tooth pitch 5 mm

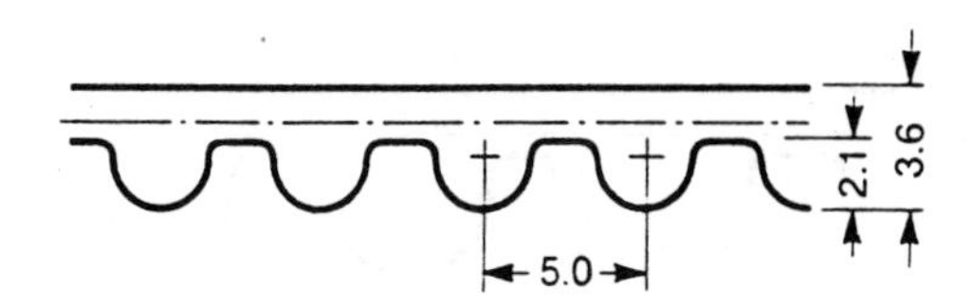

Standard lengths

Designation	*Pitch length L_w* mm	*No. of teeth z*
350-5M	350	70
400-5M	400	80
450-5M	450	90
500-5M	500	100
600-5M	600	120
710-5M	710	142
800-5M	800	160
890-5M	890	178
1000-5M	1000	200
1125-5M	1125	225
1270-5M	1270	254
1500-5M	1500	300

Standard widths: 9, 15, 25 min; intermediate widths on request.

Tooth pitch 8 mm

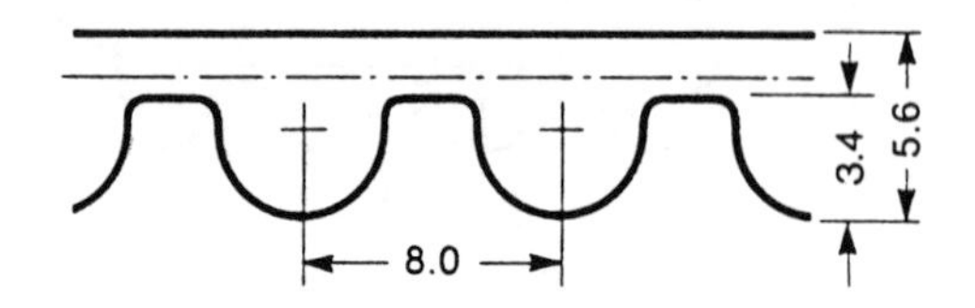

Standard lengths

Designation	*Pitch length L_w* mm	*No. of teeth z*
480-8M	480	60
560-8M	560	70
600-8M	600	75
640-8M	640	80
656-8M	656	82
720-8M	720	90
800-8M	800	100
880-8M	880	110
960-8M	960	120
1040-8M	1040	130
1120-8M	1120	140
1200-8M	1200	150
1280-8M	1280	160
1440-8M	1440	180
1600-8M	1600	200
1760-8M	1760	220
1800-8M	1800	225
2000-8M	2000	250
2400-8M	2400	300
2800-8M	2800	350

Standard widths: 20, 30, 50, 85 mm; intermediate widths on request.

Tooth pitch 14 mm

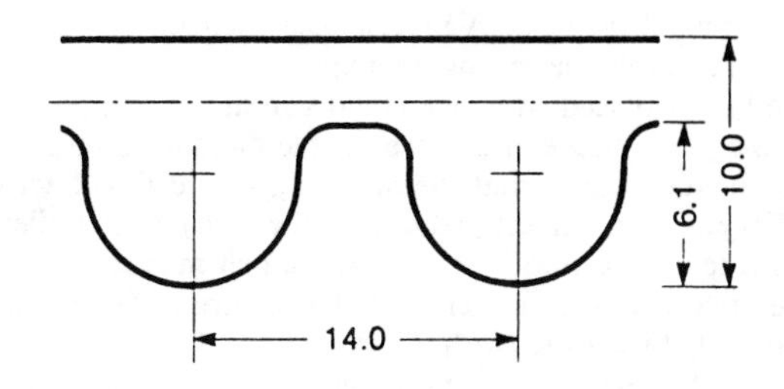

Standard lengths

Designation	*Pitch length* L_w mm	*No. of teeth* z
966-14M	966	69
1190-14M	1190	85
1400-14M	1400	100
1610-14M	1610	115
1778-14M	1778	127
1890-14M	1890	135
2100-14M	2100	150
2310-14M	2310	165
2450-14M	2450	175
2590-14M	2590	185
2800-14M	2800	200
3150-14M	3150	225
3500-14M	3500	250
3850-14M	3850	275
4326-14M	4326	309
4578-14M	4578	327

Standard widths: 40, 55, 85, 115, 170 mm; intermediate widths on request.

2.6.13 Synchronous (toothed) belts: length measurement

The pitch length is decisive for the calculation and application of synchronous drive belts. A precise measurement can only be made on suitable measuring equipment.

The belt is placed over two equal size measuring pulleys with the same pitch diameters. The movable measuring pulley is loaded in such a way that the measuring force F will act on the belt. To ensure a correct position of the belt on the pulleys and a uniform tension on both belt sides, the belt must have completed at least two rotations under load. The centre distance a is then measured between the two pulleys.

The pitch length L_w is double the centre distance a plus the pitch circumference U_w of the test pulleys:

$$L_w = 2a + U_w = 2a + \pi d_w = 2a + zt$$

The test measurement layout is as shown.

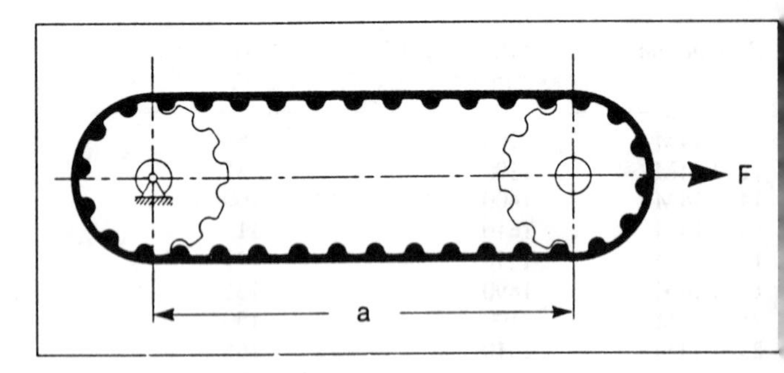

2.6.14 SYNCHROBELT® HTD toothed pulleys: preferred sizes

Tooth pitch 3 mm

Dimensions in millimetres

No. of teeth z	*Pitch dia.* d_w	*Outside dia.* d_a	*Flanged pulley dia.* d_b	*Stock bore dia.* d_v	*Finished bore dia.* $d_{F\,max}$
10	9.55	8.79	12	3	3
12	11.46	10.70	14	3	4
14	13.37	12.61	16	3	6
15	14.32	13.56	16	3	6
16	15.28	14.52	18	3	8
17	16.23	15.47	20	4	8
18	17.19	16.43	20	4	8
19	18.14	17.38	21	4	8
20	19.10	18.34	23	4	10
22	21.01	20.25	25	4	10
24	22.94	22.16	26	4	12
26	24.83	24.07	28	4	14
28	26.74	25.98	30	4	15
30	28.65	27.89	33	6	17
32	30.56	29.80	34	6	19
34	32.47	31.71	36	6	20
36	34.38	33.62	38	6	20
38	36.29	35.53	42	6	25
40	38.20	37.44	42	6	25
44	42.02	41.26	47	8	28
50	47.75	46.99	51	8	32
56	53.48	52.72	59	8	36
62	59.21	58.45	64	8	42
72	68.75	67.99	73	8	50

The relationship between standard belt width and pulley width:

Dimensions in millimetres

Standard belt width b	*Pulley width = toothing width w/o flanged pulleys*	*Toothed width for flanged pulleys*
6	11	≈ 9
9	14	≈ 12
15	20	≈ 18

Tooth pitch 5 mm

Dimensions in millimetres

No. of teeth z	*Pitch dia.* d_w	*Outside dia.* d_a	*Flanged pulley dia.* d_b	*Stock bore dia.* d_v	*Finished bore dia.* $d_{F\ max}$
14	22.28	21.14	26	4	12
15	23.87	22.73	28	4	14
16	25.46	24.32	30	4	14
17	27.06	25.92	32	4	15
18	28.65	27.51	33	6	17
19	30.24	29.10	34	6	18
20	31.83	30.69	36	6	20
22	35.01	33.87	40	6	21
24	38.20	37.06	42	6	25
26	41.38	40.24	45	8	25
28	44.56	43.42	48	8	30
30	47.75	46.61	51	8	32
32	50.93	49.79	55	8	35
34	54.11	52.97	59	8	36
36	57.30	56.16	61	8	38
38	60.48	59.34	64	8	40
40	63.66	62.52	67	8	45
44	70.03	68.89	73	8	50
50	79.58	78.94	85	8	60
56	89.13	87.99	95	8	70
62	98.68	97.54	103	8	75
72	114.59	113.45	118	10	90

Relation between standard belt width and pulley width:

Dimensions in millimetres

Standard belt width b	*Pulley width = toothing width w/o flanged pulleys*	*Toothed width for flanged pulleys*
9	14	≈12
15	20	≈18
25	30	≈28

Tooth pitch 8 mm

Dimensions in millimetres

No. of teeth	Pitch dia. d_w	Outside dia. d_a	Flanged pulley dia. d_b	Stock bore dia. d_v	Finished bore dia. $d_{F\ max}$
22	56.02	54.65	61	8	38
24	61.12	59.75	67	8	45
26	66.21	64.84	75	8	50
28	71.30	70.08	80	8	55
30	76.39	75.13	82	8	60
32	81.49	80.16	86	8	60
34	86.58	85.22	95	8	70
36	91.67	90.30	99	8	75
38	96.77	95.39	103	8	75
40	101.86	100.49	107	10	80
44	112.05	110.67	118	10	90
48	122.23	120.86	127	10	98
56	142.60	141.23	150	10	124
64	162.97	161.60	168	16	138
72	183.35	181.97	189	16	155
80	203.72	202.35	210	20	170
90	229.18	227.81	235	20	190
112	285.21	283.83	292	20	250
144	366.69	365.32	—	30	300
168	427.81	426.44	—	30	350
192	488.92	487.55	—	30	400

Relation between standard belt width and pulley width:

Dimensions in millimetres

Standard belt width b	*Pulley width = toothing width w/o flanged pulleys*	*Toothed width for flanged pulleys*
20	26	≈ 22
30	38	≈ 34
50	58	≈ 54
85	94	≈ 90

Tooth pitch 14 mm

Dimensions in millimetre

No. of teeth z	*Pitch dia.* d_w	*Outside dia.* d_a	*Flanged pulley dia.* d_b	*Stock bore dia.* d_v	*Finished bore dia.* $d_{F\ max}$
28	124.78	122.12	130	10	95
29	129.23	126.57	134	10	100
30	133.69	130.99	138	10	100
32	142.60	139.88	148	10	110
34	151.52	148.79	156	16	120
36	160.43	157.68	166	16	130
40	178.25	175.49	184	16	145
48	213.90	211.11	220	20	180
56	249.55	246.76	254	20	210
64	285.21	282.41	290	20	240
72	320.86	318.06	326	30	260
80	356.51	353.71	362	30	290
90	401.07	398.28	—	30	330
112	499.11	496.32	—	30	420
144	641.71	638.92	—	30	550
192	855.62	852.62	—	30	750

Relation between standard belt width and pulley width:

Dimensions in millimetres

Standard belt width b	*Pulley width = toothing width w/o flanged pulleys*	*Toothed width for flanged pulleys*
40	54	≈ 47
55	70	≈ 63
85	102	≈ 95
115	133	≈ 126
170	187	≈ 180

2.7 Power transmission: shafts

2.7.1 Square and rectangular parallel keys, metric series

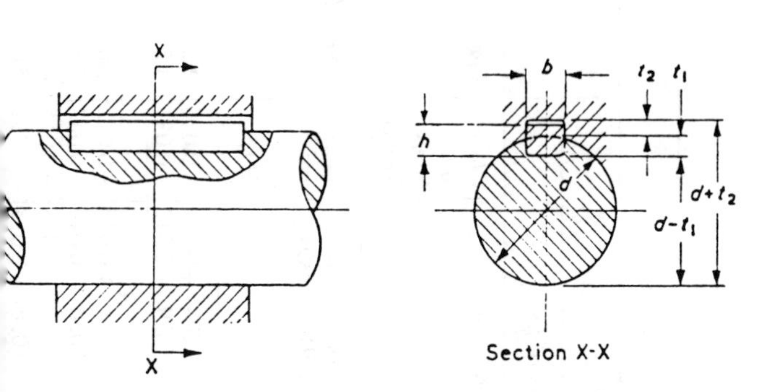

Section X-X

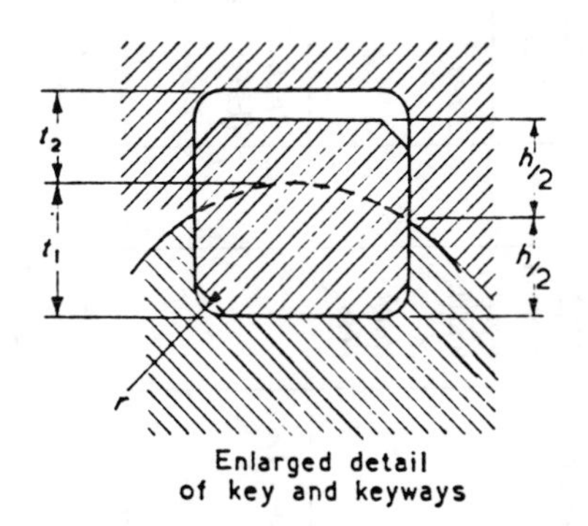

Enlarged detail of key and keyways

continued

Section 2.7.1 (*continued*)

Dimensions in millimetres

Shaft		*Key*	*Keyway*												
Nominal diameter d		(*see* 2.7.2) *section* $b \times h$ *width* × *thick-ness*	*Width b*						*Depth*				*Radius r*	
				Tolerance for class of fit										
				Free		*Normal*		*Close and inter-ference*	*Shaft* t_1		*Hub* t_2			
Over	*Incl.*		*Nom.*	*Shaft* (H9)	*Hub* (D10)	*Shaft* (N9)	*Hub* (Js9)	*Shaft and hub* (P9)	*Nom.*	*Tol.*	*Nom.*	*Tol.*	*Max.*	*Min.*
6	8	2 × 2	2	+0.025	+0.060	−0.004	+0.012	−0.006	1.2		1.0		0.16	0.08
8	10	3 × 3	3	0	+0.020	−0.029	−0.012	−0.031	1.8		1.4		0.16	0.08
10	12	4 × 4	4						2.5	+0.1	1.8	+0.1	0.16	0.08
12	17	5 × 5	5	+0.030	+0.078	0	+0.015	−0.012	3.0	0	2.3	0	0.25	0.16
17	22	6 × 6	6	0	+0.080	−0.030	−0.015	−0.042	3.5		2.8		0.25	0.16
22	30	8 × 7	8	+0.036	+0.095	0	+0.018	−0.015	4.0	+0.2	3.3	+0.2	0.25	0.16
30	38	10 × 8	10	0	+0.040	−0.036	−0.018	−0.051	5.0	0	3.3	0	0.40	0.25

38	44	12 × 8	12						5.0		3.3		0.40	0.25
44	50	14 × 9	14	+0.043	+0.120	0	+0.021	−0.018	5.5		3.8		0.40	0.25
50	58	16 × 10	16	0	+0.050	−0.043	−0.021	−0.061	6.0	+0.2	4.3	+0.2	0.40	0.25
58	65	18 × 11	18						7.0	0	4.4	0	0.40	0.25
65	75	20 × 12	20						7.5		4.9		0.60	0.40
75	85	22 × 14	22	+0.052	+0.149	0	+0.026	−0.022	9.0		5.4		0.60	0.40
85	95	25 × 14	25	0	+0.065	−0.052	−0.026	−0.074	9.0		5.4		0.60	0.40
95	110	28 × 16	28						10.0		6.4		0.60	0.40
110	130	32 × 18	32						11.0		7.4		0.60	0.40
130	150	36 × 20	36	+0.062	+0.180	0	+0.031	−0.025	12.0		8.4		1.00	0.70
150	170	40 × 22	40	0	+0.080	−0.062	−0.031	−0.088	13.0	+0.3	9.4	+0.3	1.00	0.70
170	200	45 × 25	45						13.0	0	10.4	0	1.00	0.70

For full range and further information see BS 4235 : Pt 1 : 1972.

2.7.2 Dimensions and tolerances for square and rectangular parallel keys

Form A

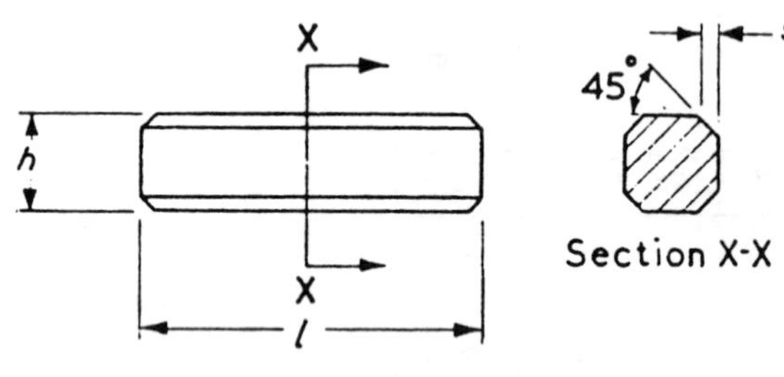

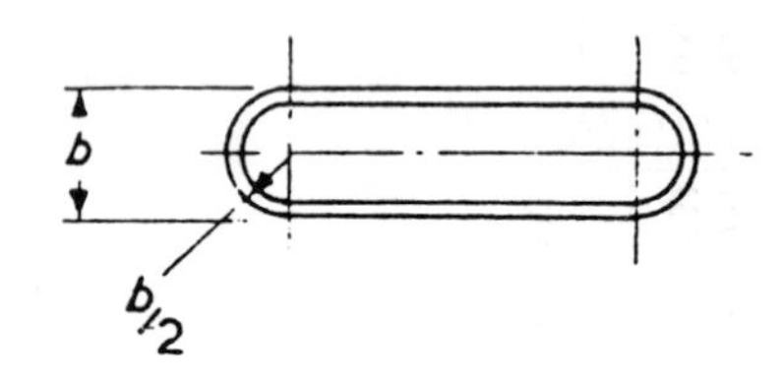

Form B

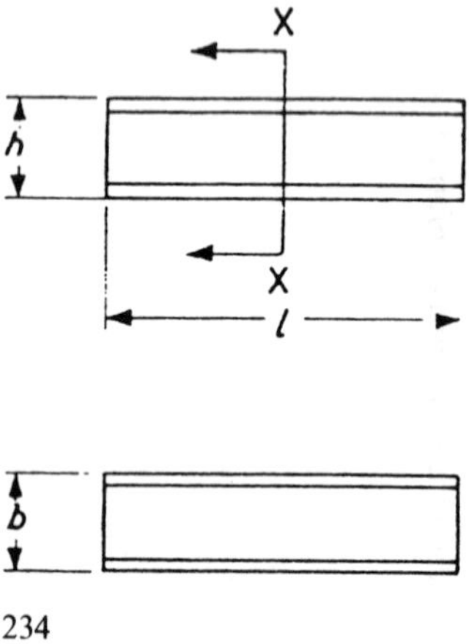

Form C

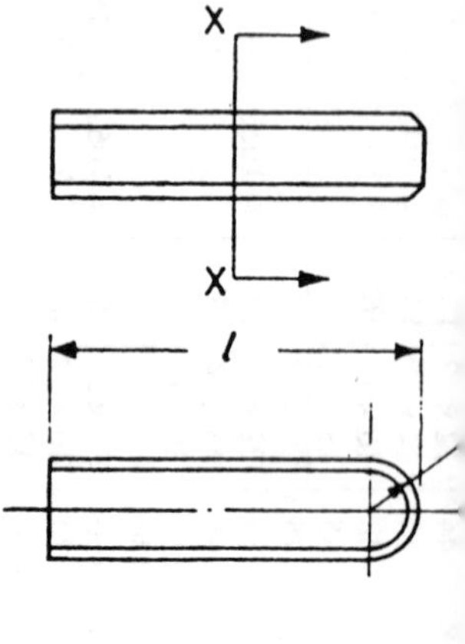

Dimensions in millimetres

Width b		*Thickness h*		*Chamfer s*		*Range of lengths l**	
Nom.	*Tol.* (h9)	*Nom.*	*Tol.* (h9)	*Min.*	*Max.*	*From*	*Incl.*
2	0	2	0	0.16	0.25	6	20
3	−0.025	3	−0.025	0.16	0.25	6	36
4	0	4	0	0.16	0.25	8	45
5	−0.030	5	−0.030	0.25	0.40	10	56
6		6		0.25	0.40	14	70
8	0	7	Tol. (h11)	0.25	0.40	18	90
10	−0.036	8	0	0.40	0.60	22	110
12		8	−0.090	0.40	0.60	28	140
14	0	9		0.40	0.60	36	160
16	−0.043	10		0.40	0.60	45	180
18		11		0.40	0.60	50	200
20		12		0.60	0.80	56	220
22	0	14	0	0.60	0.80	63	250
25	−0.052	14	−0.110	0.60	0.80	70	280
28		16		0.60	0.80	80	320
32		18		0.60	0.80	90	360
36	0	20		1.00	1.20	100	400
40	−0.062	22	0	1.00	1.20	—	—
45		25	−0.130	1.00	1.20	—	—
50		28		1.00	1.20	—	—
56		32		1.60	2.00	—	—
63	0	32		1.60	2.00	—	—
70	−0.074	36	0	1.60	2.00	—	—
80		40	−0.160	2.50	3.00	—	—
90	0	45		2.50	3.00	—	—
100	−0.087	50		2.50	3.00	—	—

*For preferred sizes see BS 4235 : Table 9.
For full range and further information see BS 4235 : Pt 1 : 1972.

2.7.3 Square and rectangular taper keys, metric series

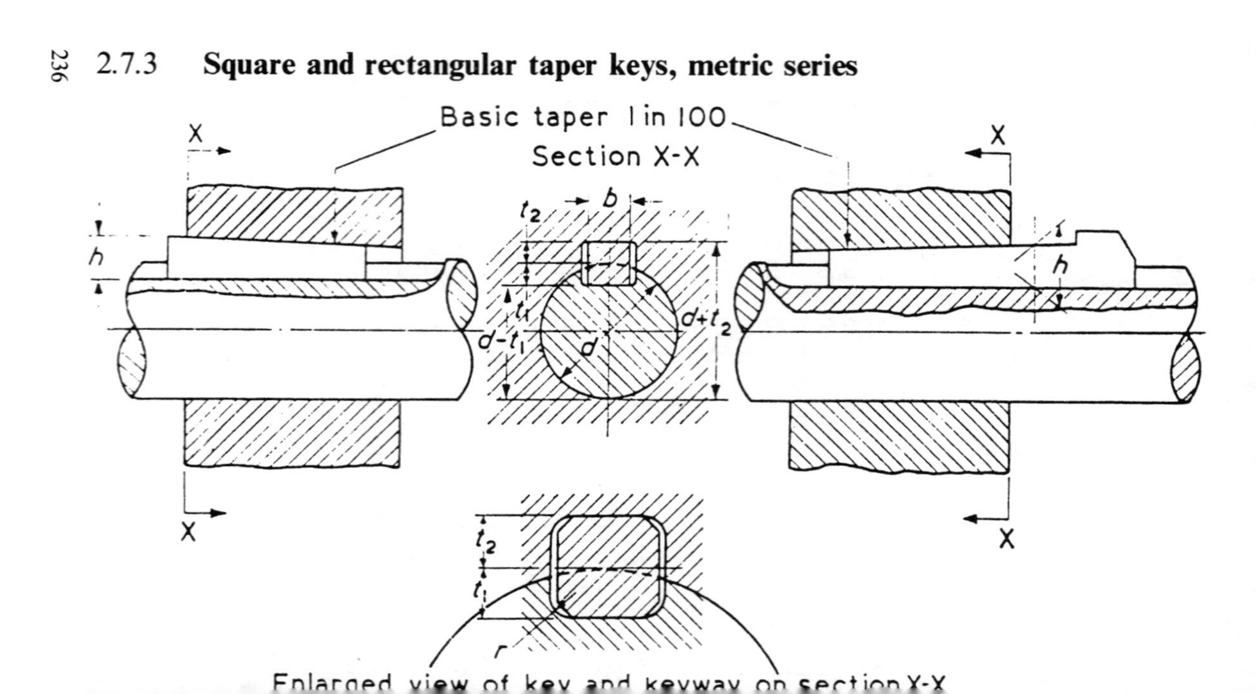

Dimensions in millimetres

Shaft		Key	Keyway							
Nominal diameter d		Section $b \times h$ width × thickness	Width b, shaft and hub		Depth				Radius r	
					Shaft t_1		Hub t_2			
Over	Incl.		Nom.	Tol. (D10)	Nom.	Tol.	Nom.	Tol.	Max.	Min.
6	8	2 × 2	2	+0.060	1.2		0.5		0.16	0.08
8	10	3 × 3	3	+0.020	1.8	+0.1	0.9	+0.1	0.16	0.08
10	12	4 × 4	4	+0.078	2.5	0	1.2	0	0.16	0.08
12	17	5 × 5	5	+0.030	3.0		1.7		0.25	0.16
17	22	6 × 6	6		3.5		2.2		0.25	0.16
22	30	8 × 7	8	+0.098	4.0		2.4		0.25	0.16
30	38	10 × 8	10	+0.040	5.0		2.4		0.40	0.25
38	44	12 × 8	12		5.0		2.4		0.40	0.25
44	50	14 × 9	14	+0.120	5.5		2.9		0.40	0.25
50	58	16 × 10	16	+0.050	6.0	+0.2	3.4	+0.2	0.40	0.25
58	65	18 × 11	18		7.0	0	3.4	0	0.40	0.25
65	75	20 × 12	20		7.5		3.9		0.60	0.40
75	85	22 × 14	22	+0.149	9.0		4.4		0.60	0.40
85	95	25 × 14	25	+0.065	9.0		4.4		0.60	0.40

continued

Section 2.7.3 (*continued*)

Dimensions in millimetres

Shaft		*Key*	*Keyway*							
Nominal diameter d		*Section b × h width × thickness*	*Width b, shaft and hub*		*Depth*				*Radius r*	
					Shaft t_1		*Hub t_2*			
Over	*Incl.*		*Nom.*	*Tol.* (D10)	*Nom.*	*Tol.*	*Nom.*	*Tol.*	*Max.*	*Min.*
95	110	28 × 16	28	+0.149 +0.065	10.0	+0.2	5.4	+0.2	0.60	0.40
110	130	32 × 18	32		11.0	0	6.4	0	0.60	0.70
130	150	36 × 20	36	+0.180	12.0		7.1		1.00	0.70
150	170	40 × 22	40	+0.080	13.0		8.1		1.00	0.70
170	200	45 × 25	45		15.0		9.1		1.00	0.70
200	230	50 × 28	50		17.0	+0.3	10.1	+0.3	1.00	0.70
230	260	56 × 32	56		20.0	0	11.1	0	1.60	1.20
260	290	63 × 32	63	+0.220	20.0		11.1		1.60	1.20
290	330	70 × 36	70	+0.120	22.0		13.1		1.60	1.20
330	380	80 × 40	80		25.0		14.1		2.50	2.00
380	440	90 × 45	90	+0.260	28.0		16.1		2.50	2.00
440	500	100 × 50	100	+0.120	31.0		18.1		2.50	2.00

For full range and further information see BS4235 : Pt 1 : 1972

2.7.4 Dimensions and tolerances for square and rectangular taper keys

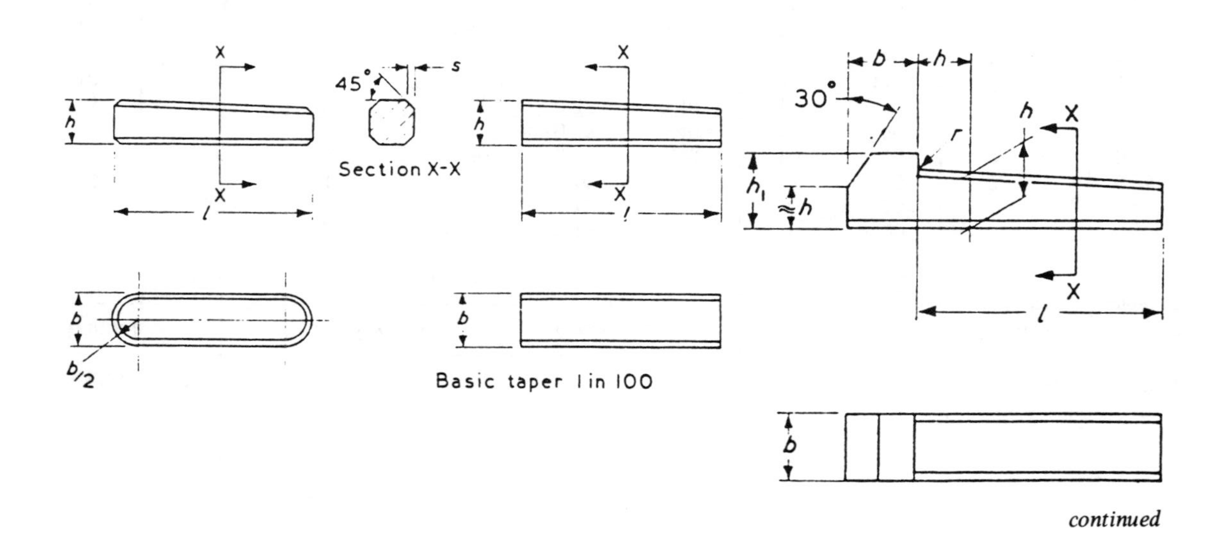

continued

Section 2.7.4 (*continued*)

Dimensions in millimetres

Width b		*Thickness h*		*Chamfer s*		*Length l**		*Gib-head nom' h_1*	*Radius nom. r*
Nom.	*Tol.* (h9)	*Nom.*	*Tol.* (h9)	*Min.*	*Max.*	*From*	*Incl.*		
2	0	2	0	0.16	0.25	6	20	—	—
3	−0.025	3	−0.025	0.16	0.25	6	36	—	—
4	0	4	0	0.16	0.25	8	45	7	0.25
5	−0.030	5	−0.030	0.25	0.40	10	56	8	0.25
6		6		0.25	0.40	14	70	10	0.25
8	0	7		0.25	0.40	18	90	11	1.5
10	−0.036	8	Tol. (h11)	0.40	0.60	22	110	12	1.5
12		8	0	0.40	0.60	28	140	12	1.5
14	0	9	−0.090	0.40	0.60	36	160	14	1.5
16	−0.043	10		0.40	0.60	45	180	16	1.5
18		11		0.40	0.60	50	200	18	1.5
20		12		0.60	0.80	56	220	20	1.5
22	0	14	0	0.60	0.80	63	250	22	1.5
25	−0.052	14	−0.110	0.60	0.80	70	280	22	1.5

28		16		0.60	0.80	80	320	25	1.5
32		18		0.60	0.80	90	360	28	1.5
36	0	20		1.00	1.20	100	400	32	1.5
40	−0.062	22	0	1.00	1.20	—	—	36	1.5
45		25	−0.130	1.00	1.20	—	—	40	1.5
50		28		1.00	1.20	—	—	45	1.5
56		32		1.60	2.00	—	—	50	1.5
63	0	32		1.60	2.00	—	—	50	1.5
70	−0.074	36	0	1.60	2.00	—	—	56	1.5
80		40	−0.160	2.50	3.00	—	—	63	1.5
90	0	45		2.50	3.00	—	—	70	1.5
100	−0.087	50		2.50	3.00	—	—	80	1.5

*For preferred lengths see BS 4235 : Pt 1 : Table 9.
For full range and further information see BS 4235 : Pt 1 : 1972..

2.7.5 Woodruff keys and keyways, metric series

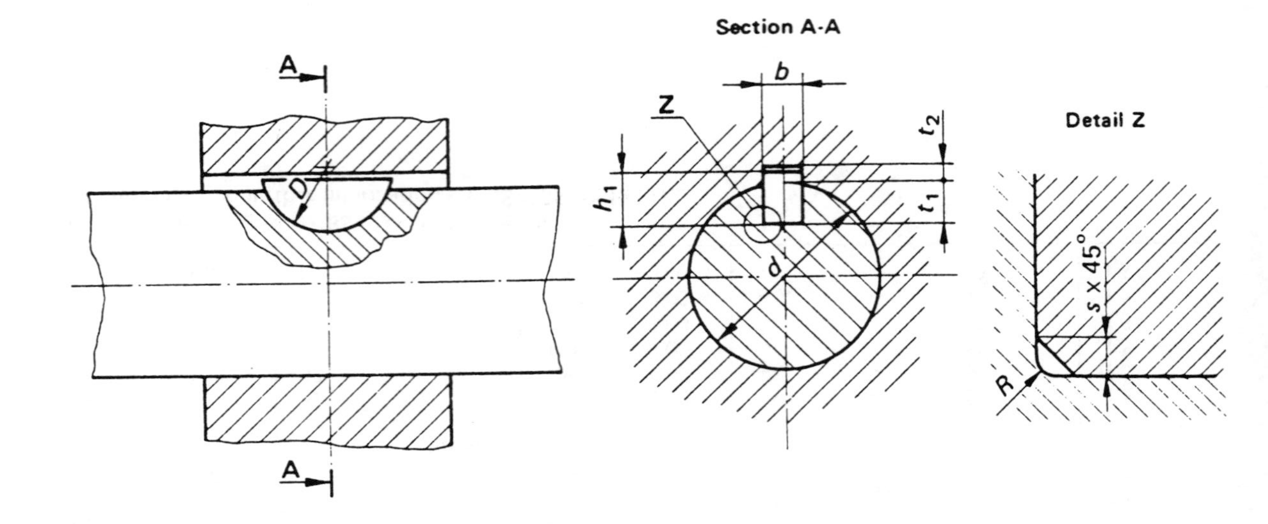

Key size of normal for $b \times h_1 \times D$ or equivalent Whitney form	Width *b*				Depth				Radius R	
	Nom.	Tolerance			Shaft t_1		Hub t_2			
		Normal fit		Close fit						
		Shaft (N9)	Hub (Js9)	Shaft and hub (P9)	Nom.	Tol.	Nom.	Tol.	Max.	Min.
1.0 × 1.4 × 4	1.0				1.0		0.6		0.16	0.08
1.5 × 2.6 × 7	1.5				2.0	+0.1	0.8		0.16	0.08
2.0 × 2.6 × 7	2.0	−0.004	+0.012	−0.006	1.8	0	1.0		0.16	0.08
2.0 × 3.7 × 10	2.0	−0.029	−0.012	−0.031	2.9		1.0		0.16	0.08
2.5 × 3.7 × 10	2.5				2.7		1.2	+0.1	0.16	0.08
3.0 × 5.0 × 13	3.0				3.8		1.4	0	0.16	0.08
3.0 × 6.5 × 16	3.0				5.3		1.4		0.16	0.08
4.0 × 6.5 × 16	4.0				5.0	+0.2	1.8		0.25	0.16
4.0 × 7.5 × 19	4.0				6.0	0	1.8		0.25	0.16
5.0 × 6.5 × 16	5.0				4.5		2.3		0.25	0.16
5.0 × 7.5 × 19	5.0	0	+0.015	−0.012	5.5		2.3		0.25	0.16
5.0 × 9.0 × 22	5.0	−0.030	−0.015	−0.042	7.0		2.3		0.25	0.16
6.0 × 9.0 × 22	6.0				6.5	+0.3	2.8		0.25	0.16
6.0 × 11.0 × 28	6.0				7.5	0	2.8	+0.2	0.25	0.16
8.0 × 11.0 × 28	8.0	0	+0.018	−0.015	8.0		3.3	0	0.40	0.25
10.0 × 13.0 × 32	10.0	−0.036	−0.018	−0.051	10.0		3.3		0.40	0.25

For further information see BS 4235 : Pt 2 : 1977.

2.7.6 Dimensions and tolerances for Woodruff keys

Normal form

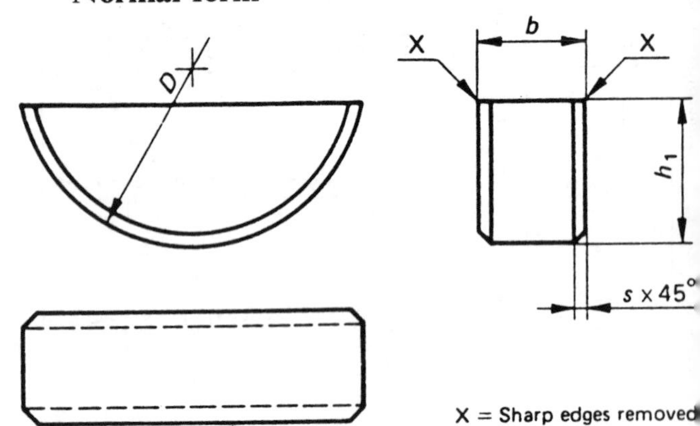

Whitney form

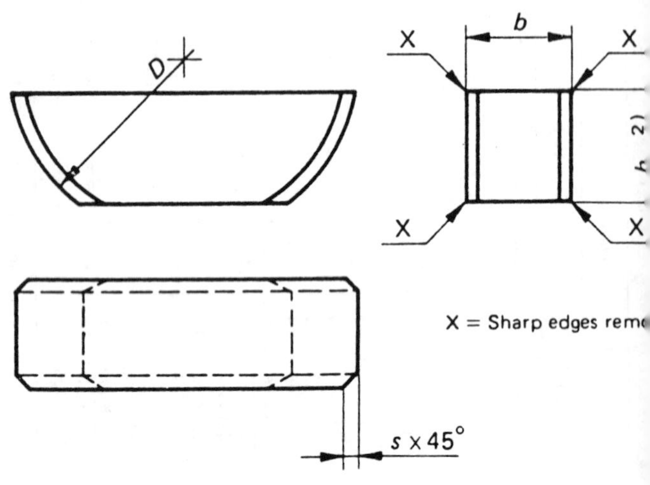

Dimensions in millimetres

Width b		Height h_1		Diameter D		Chamfer s	
Nom.	*Tol.* (h9)	*Nom.*	*Tol.* (h11)	*Nom.*	*Tol.* (h12)	*Min.*	*Max.*
					0		
1.0		1.4	0	4	−0.120	0.16	0.25
1.5		2.6	−0.060	7		0.16	0.25
2.0	0	2.6		7	0	0.16	0.25
2.0	−0.025	3.7	0	10	−0.150	0.16	0.25
2.5		3.7	−0.075	10		0.16	0.25
3.0		5.0		13	0	0.16	0.25
3.0		6.5		16	−0.180	0.16	0.25
4.0		6.5		16		0.25	0.40
4.0		7.5		19	0	0.25	0.40
					−0.210		
					0		
5.0		6.5	0	16	−0.180	0.25	0.40
5.0	0	7.5	−0.090	19		0.25	0.40
5.0	−0.030	9.0		22	0	0.25	0.40
6.0		9.0		22	−0.210	0.25	0.40
6.0		10.0		25		0.25	0.40
8.0	0	11.0	0	28		0.40	0.60
10.0	−0.036	13.0	−0.110	32	0	0.40	0.60
					−0.250		

*A tolerance closer than h9 may be adopted subject to agreement between interested parties.
For further information see BS 4235 : Pt 2 : 1977.

Note

The Whitney form should only be adopted by agreement between the interested parties. In this case h_2 of the Whitney form key shall equal 0.8 times the height h_1 of the normal form Woodruff key, i.e. $h_2 = 0.8\, h_1$. The calculated values shall be rounded off to the nearest 0.1 mm.

2.7.7 Shaft ends types: general relationships

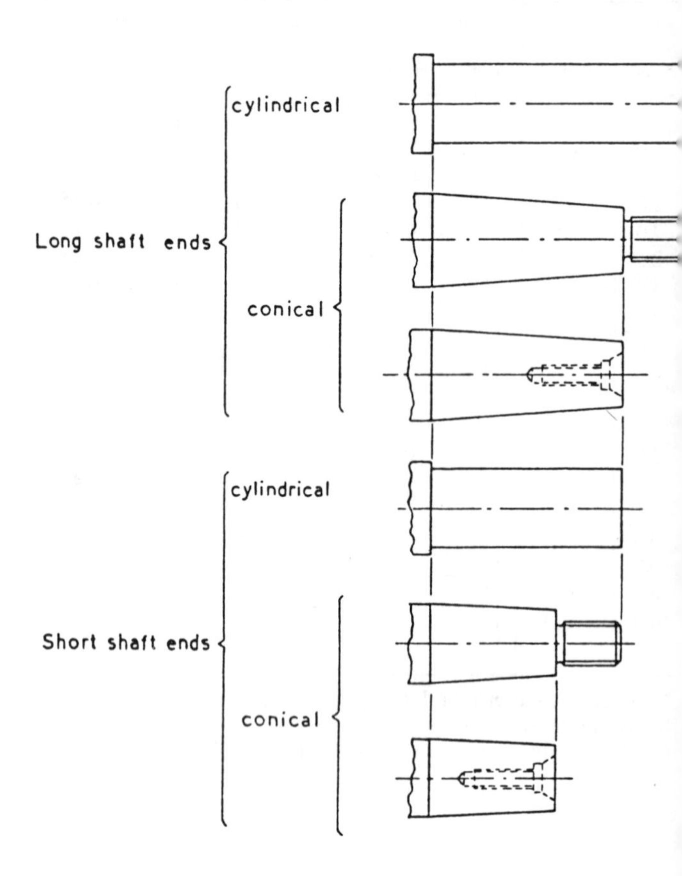

2.7.8 Dimensions and tolerances of cylindrical shaft ends, long and short series

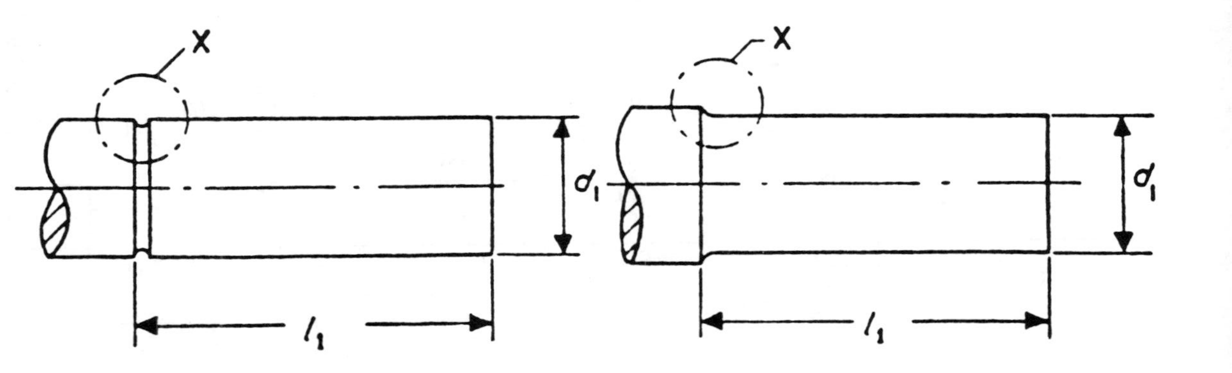

Detail x: undercut grooves for tool relief and blendina radii are still under consideration in ISO. Details are not yet available.

Section 2.7.8 (*continued*)

Dimensions in millimetres

Diameter d_1 Nom.	Diameter d_1 Tol.	Lengths l_1 Long series	Lengths l_1 Short series
6	j6 $^{+0.006}_{-0.002}$	16	—
7	j6 $^{+0.007}_{-0.002}$		
8		20	—
9			
10		23	20*
11	j6 $^{+0.008}_{-0.003}$		
12		30	25*
14			
16		40	28
18			
19	j6 $^{+0.009}_{-0.004}$		
20		50	36
22			
24			
25		60	42
28			

Diameter d_1 Nom.	Diameter d_1 Tol.	Lengths l_1 Long series	Lengths l_1 Short series
100	m6 $^{+0.035}_{+0.013}$	210	165
110			
120			
125	m6 $^{+0.040}_{+0.015}$		
130		250	200
140			
150			
160			
170			
180			
190	m6 $^{+0.046}_{+0.017}$	300	240
200			
220			
240		350	280
250			
260			

30		80	58
32	k6 $^{+0.018}_{+0.002}$		
35			
38			
40		110	82
42			
45			
48			
50			
55	m6 $^{+0.030}_{+0.011}$		
56			
60		140	105
63			
65			
70			
71			
75			
80		170	130
85	m6 $^{+0.035}_{+0.013}$		
90			
95			

280	m6 $^{[illegible]}_{+0.020}$	410	330
300			
320	m6 $^{+0.057}_{+0.021}$		
340		550	450
360			
380			
400		650	540
420	m6 $^{+0.063}_{+0.023}$		
440			
450			
460			
480			
500			
530	m6 $^{+0.070}_{+0.026}$	800	680
560			
600			
630			

*The dimensions thus indicated are not in agreement with the related dimensions of long series conical shaft ends: see BS 4506 Table 2 and Clause 2.

2.7.9 Dimensions of conical shaft ends with parallel keys, long series

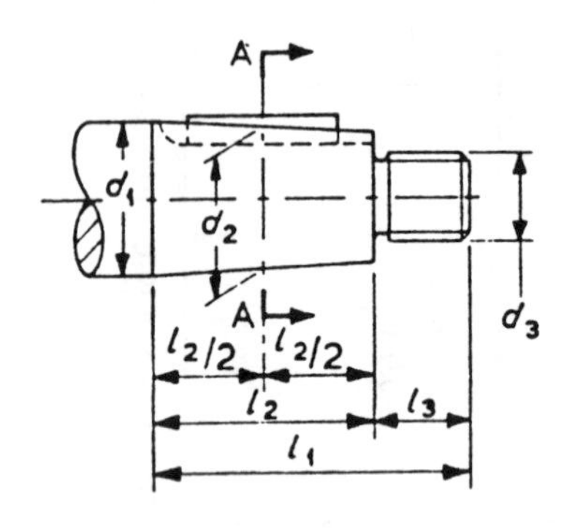

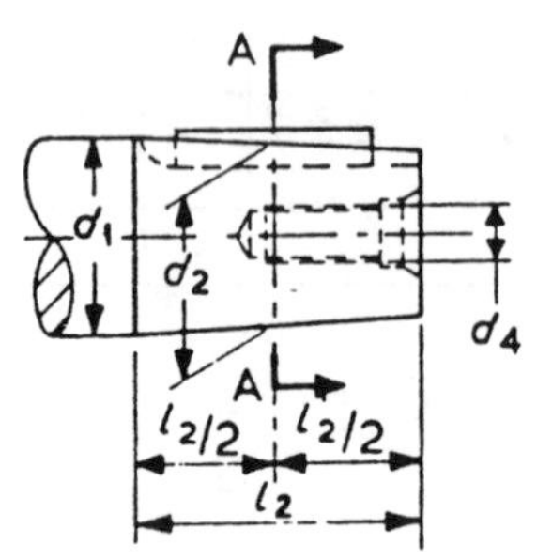

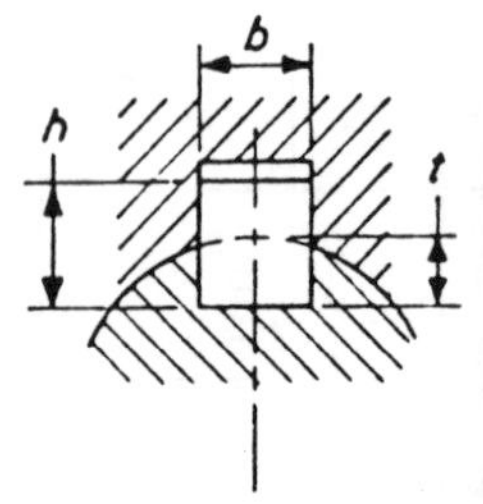

Part view enlarged at Sections A - A

Keyway may have forms other than shown.
Conicity of 1 : 10 corresponds to $(d_1 - d_2)/(l_2/2) = 1/10$.

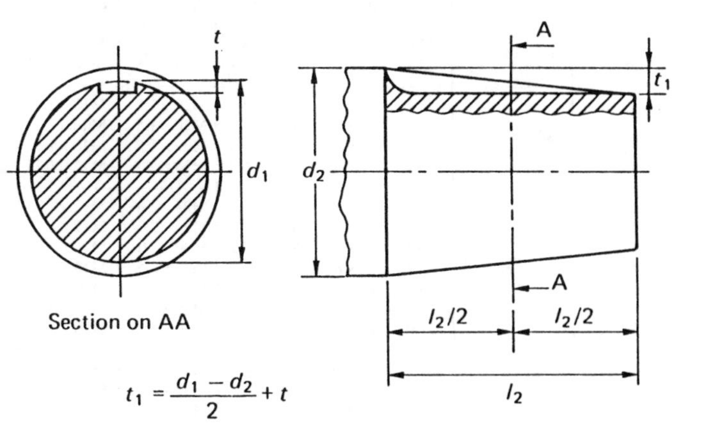

Dimensions in millimetres

Diameter	Length			Key and keyway				External thread	Internal thread
d_1	l_1	l_2	l_3	d_2	$b \times h$	t	t_1	d_3	d_4
6	16	10	6	5.5	—	—	—	M 4×0.7	—
7				6.5	—	—	—	M 4×0.7	—
8	20	12	8	7.4	—	—	—	M 6×1	—
9				8.4	—	—	—	M 6×1	—
10	23	15*	8	9.25	—	—	—	M 6×1	—
11				10.25	2×2	1.2	1.6	M 6×1	—
12	30	18*	12	11.1	2×2	1.2	1.7	M 8×1	M 4×0.7
14				13.1	3×3	1.8	2.3	M 8×1	M 4×0.7
16				14.6	3×3	1.8	2.5	M10×1.25	M 4×0.7
18	40	28	12	16.6	4×4	2.5	3.2	M10×1.25	M 5×0.8
19				17.6	4×4	2.5	3.2	M10×1.25	M 5×0.8
20				18.2	4×4	2.5	3.4	M12×1.25	M 6×1
22	50	36	14	20.2	4×4	2.5	3.4	M12×1.25	M 6×1
24				22.2	5×5	3.0	3.9	M12×1.25	M 6×1

continued

Section 2.7.9 (*continued*)

Diameter	*Length*			*Key and keyway*				*External thread*	*Internal thread*
d_1	l_1	l_2	l_3	d_2	$b \times h$	t	t_1	d_3	d_4
25	60	42	18	22.9	5 × 5	3.0	4.1	M16 × 1.5	M 8 × 1.25
28				25.9	5 × 5	3.0	4.1	M16 × 1.5	M 8 × 1.25
30	80	58	22	27.1	5 × 5	3.0	4.5	M20 × 1.5	M10 × 1.5
32				29.1	6 × 6	3.5	5.0	M20 × 1.5	M10 × 1.5
35				32.1	6 × 6	3.5	5.0	M20 × 1.5	M10 × 1.5
38				35.1	6 × 6	3.5	5.0	M24 × 2.0	M12 × 1.75
40	110	82	28	35.9	10 × 8	5.0	7.1	M24 × 2.0	M12 × 1.75
42				37.9	10 × 8	5.0	7.1	M24 × 2.0	M12 × 1.75
45				40.9	12 × 8	5.0	7.1	M30 × 2.0	M16 × 2.0
48				43.9	12 × 8	5.0	7.1	M30 × 2.5	M16 × 2.0
50				45.9	12 × 8	5.0	7.1	M36 × 3.0	M16 × 2.0
55				50.9	14 × 9	5.5	7.6	M36 × 3.0	M20 × 2.5
56				51.9	14 × 9	5.5	7.6	M36 × 3.0	M20 × 2.5
60	140	105	35	54.75	16 × 10	6.0	8.6	M42 × 3.0	M20 × 2.5
63				57.75	16 × 10	6.0	8.6	M42 × 3.0	M20 × 2.5
65				59.75	16 × 10	6.0	8.6	M42 × 3.0	M20 × 2.5
70				64.75	18 × 11	7.0	9.6	M48 × 3.0	M24 × 3.0
71				65.75	18 × 11	7.0	9.6	M48 × 3.0	M24 × 3.0
75				69.75	18 × 11	7.0	9.6	M48 × 3.0	M24 × 3.0
80	170	130	40	73.50	20 × 12	7.5	10.8	M56 × 4.0	M30 × 3.5
85				78.50	20 × 12	7.5	10.8	M56 × 4.0	M30 × 3.5
90				83.50	22 × 14	9.0	12.3	M64 × 4.0	M30 × 3.5
95				88.50	22 × 14	9.0	12.3	M64 × 4.0	M36 × 4.0
100	210	165	45	91.75	25 × 14	9.0	13.1	M72 × 4.0	M36 × 4.0
110				101.75	25 × 14	9.0	13.1	M80 × 4.0	M42 × 4.5
120				111.75	28 × 16	10.0	14.1	M90 × 4.0	M42 × 4.5
125				116.75	28 × 16	10.0	14.1	M90 × 4.0	M48 × 5.0
130	250	200	50	120.0	28 × 16	10.0	15.0	M100 × 4.0	—
140				130.0	32 × 18	11.0	16.0	M100 × 4.0	—
150				140.0	32 × 18	11.0	16.0	M110 × 4.0	—
160	300	240	60	148.0	36 × 20	12.0	18.0	M125 × 4.0	—
170				158.0	36 × 20	12.0	18.0	M125 × 4.0	—
180				168.0	40 × 22	13.0	19.0	M140 × 6.0	—
190	350	280	70	176.0	40 × 22	13.0	20.0	M140 × 6.0	—
200				186.0	40 × 22	13.0	20.0	M160 × 6.0	—
220				206.0	45 × 25	15.0	22.0	M160 × 6.0	—

*The dimensions thus indicated are not in agreement with the related dimensions for long series conical shaft ends. See BS 4506 : Table 2 and Clause 2.
For further information see BS 4506.

2.7.10 Dimensions of conical shaft ends with diameters above 220 mm with the keyway parallel to the shaft surface, long series

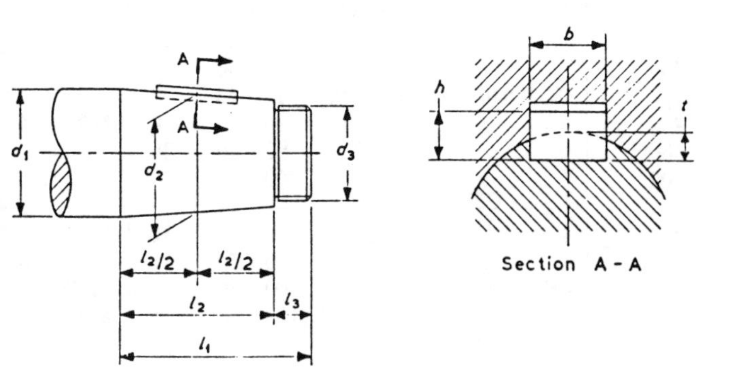

Conicity of 1 : 10 corresponds to $(d_1 - d_2)/(l_2/2) = 1/10$.

Dimensions in millimetres

Diameter	*Length*			*Key and keyway*			*External thread*
d_1	l_1	l_2	l_3	d_2	$b \times h$	t	d_3
240	410	330	80	223.5	50 × 28	17	M180 × 6
250				233.5	50 × 28	17	M180 × 6
260				243.5	50 × 28	17	M200 × 6
280	470	380	90	261.0	56 × 32	20	M220 × 6
300				281.0	63 × 32	20	M220 × 6
320				301.0	63 × 32	20	M250 × 6
340	550	450	100	317.5	70 × 36	22	M280 × 6
360				337.5	70 × 36	22	M280 × 6
380				357.5	70 × 36	22	M300 × 6

continued

Diameter	*Length*			*Key and keyway*			*External thread*
d_1	l_1	l_2	l_3	d_2	$b \times h$	t	d_3
400				373.0	80 × 40	25	M320 × 6
420				393.0	80 × 40	25	M320 × 6
440				413.0	80 × 40	25	M350 × 6
450	650	540	110	423.0	90 × 45	28	M350 × 6
460				433.0	90 × 45	28	M380 × 6
480				453.0	90 × 45	28	M380 × 6
500				473.0	90 × 45	28	M420 × 6
530				496.0	100 × 50	31	M420 × 6
560				526.0	100 × 50	31	M450 × 6
600	800	680	120	566.0	100 × 50	31	M500 × 6
630				596.0	100 × 50	31	M550 × 6

For further information see BS 4506.

2.7.11 Dimensions of conical shaft ends with parallel keys, short series

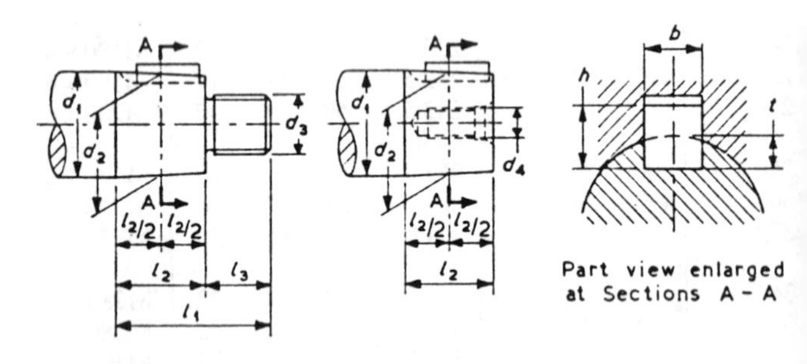

Keyway may have forms other than shown.
Conicity of 1 : 10 corresponds to $(d_1 - d_2)/(l_2/2) = 1/10$.

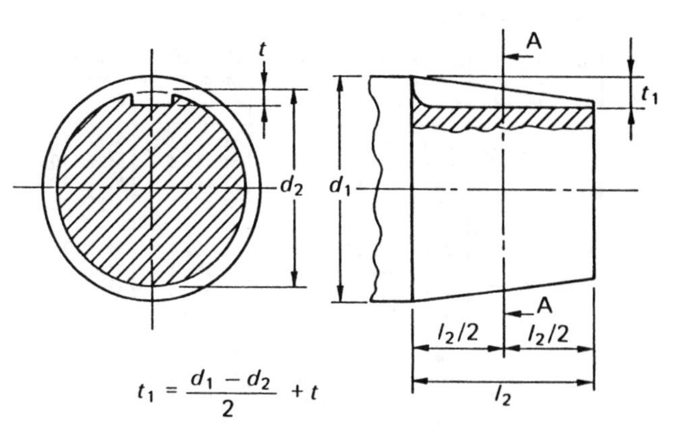

Dimensions in millimetres

Diameter	Length			Key and key way				External thread	Internal thread
d_1	l_1	l_2	l_3	d_2	$b \times h$	t	t_1	d_3	d_4
16				15.2	3 × 3	1.8		M 10 × 1.25	M 4 × 0.7
18	28	16	12	17.2	4 × 4	2.5		M 10 × 1.25	M 5 × 0.8
19				18.2	4 × 4	2.5		M 10 × 1.25	M 5 × 0.8
20				18.9	4 × 4	2.5		M 12 × 1.25	M 6 × 1.0
22	36	22	14	20.9	4 × 4	2.5		M 12 × 1.25	M 6 × 1.0
24				22.9	5 × 5	3.0		M 12 × 1.25	M 6 × 1.0
25	42	24	18	23.8	5 × 5	3.0		M 16 × 1.5	M 8 × 1.25
28				26.8	5 × 5	3.0		M 16 × 1.5	M 8 × 1.25
30				28.2	5 × 5	3.0		M 20 × 1.5	M10 × 1.5
32	58	36	22	30.2	6 × 6	3.5		M 20 × 1.5	M10 × 1.5
35				33.2	6 × 6	3.5		M 20 × 1.5	M10 × 1.5
38				36.2	6 × 6	3.5		M 24 × 2.0	M12 × 1.75
40				37.3	10 × 8	5.0		M 24 × 2	M12 × 1.75
42				39.3	10 × 8	5.0		M 24 × 2	M12 × 1.75
45				42.3	12 × 8	5.0		M 30 × 2	M16 × 2.0
48	82	54	28	45.3	12 × 8	5.0		M 30 × 2	M16 × 2.0
50				47.3	12 × 8	5.0		M 36 × 3	M16 × 2.0
55				52.3	14 × 9	5.5		M 36 × 3	M20 × 2.5
56				53.3	14 × 9	5.5		M 36 × 3	M20 × 2.5
60				56.5	16 × 10	6.0		M 42 × 3	M20 × 2.5
63				59.5	16 × 10	6.0		M 42 × 3	M20 × 2.5

continued

Diameter	*Length*			*Key and key way*				*External thread*	*Internal thread*
d_1	l_1	l_2	l_3	d_2	$b \times h$	t	t_1	d_3	d_4
65	105	70	35	61.5	16 × 10	6.0		M 42 × 3	M20 × 2.5
70				66.5	18 × 11	7.0		M 48 × 3	M24 × 3.0
71				67.5	18 × 11	7.0		M 48 × 3	M24 × 3.0
75				71.5	18 × 11	7.0		M 48 × 3	M24 × 3.0
80	130	90	40	75.5	20 × 12	7.5		M 56 × 4	M30 × 3.5
85				80.5	20 × 12	7.5		M 56 × 4	M30 × 3.5
90				85.5	22 × 14	9.0		M 64 × 4	M30 × 3.5
95				90.5	22 × 14	9.0		M 64 × 4	M36 × 4.0
100	165	120	45	94.0	25 × 14	9.0		M 72 × 4	M36 × 4.0
110				104.0	25 × 14	9.0		M 80 × 4	M42 × 4.5
120				114.0	28 × 16	10.0		M 90 × 4	M42 × 4.5
125				119.0	28 × 16	10.0		M 90 × 4	M48 × 5.0
130	200	150	50	122.5	28 × 16	10.0		M100 × 4	—
140				132.5	32 × 18	11.0		M100 × 4	—
150				142.5	32 × 18	11.0		M110 × 4	—
160	240	180	60	151.0	36 × 20	12.0		M125 × 4	—
170				161.0	36 × 20	12.0		M125 × 4	—
180				171.0	40 × 22	13.0		M140 × 6	—
190	280	210	70	179.5	40 × 22	13.0		M140 × 6	—
200				189.5	40 × 22	13.0		M160 × 6	—
220				209.5	45 × 25	15.0		M160 × 6	—

For further information see BS 4506.

2.7.12

Transmissible torque values

Shaft end diameter d_1 mm	*Transmissible torque T N m*		
	(a)	(b)	(c)
6		0.307	0.145
7		0.53	0.25
8		0.85	0.4
9		1.25	0.6
10		1.85	0.875
11		2.58	1.22
12		3.55	1.65
14		6.00	2.8

Shaft end diameter d_1 mm	Transmissible torque T N m		
	(a)	(b)	(c)
6		9.75	4.5
8		14.5	6.7
9		17.5	8.25
0		21.2	9.75
2		29.0	13.6
4		40.0	18.5
5		46.2	21.2
8		69.0	31.5
0	206	87.5	40.0
2	250	109.0	50.0
5	325	150.0	69.0
3	425	200.0	92.5
0	487	236.0	112
2	560	280	132
5	710	355	170
8	850	450	212
0	950	515	243
5	1280	730	345
6	1360	775	355
[illegible]	1650	975	462
3	1900	1150	545
5	2120	1280	600
[illegible]	2650	1700	800
[illegible]	2780	1800	825
5	3250	2120	1000
[illegible]	3870	2650	1250
5	4750	3350	1550
[illegible]	5600	4120	1900
[illegible]	6500	4870	2300
[illegible]	7750	5800	2720
[illegible]	10 300	8250	3870

Shaft end diameter d_1 mm	Transmissible torque T N m		
	(a)	(b)	(c)
120	13 700	11 200	5150
125	15 000	12 800	6000
130	17 000	14 500	
140	21 200	19 000	
150	25 800	24 300	
160	31 500	30 700	
170	37 500	37 500	
180	45 000		
190	53 000		
200	61 500		
220	82 500		
240	106 000		
250	118 000		
260	136 000		
280	170 000		
300	206 000		
320	250 000		
340	300 000		
360	355 000		
380	425 000		
400	487 000		
420	560 000		
440	650 000		
450	690 000		
460	750 000		
480	850 000		
500	950 000		
530	1 150 000		
560	1 360 000		
600	1 650 000		
630	1 900 000		

The values of transmissible torque have been calculated from the following formulae and rounded off to the values of the R80 (preferred numbers) series:

(a) Transmission of pure torque: $T = 2.45166\pi \times 10^{-3} \times d_1^{\,3}$ N m.

(b) Transmission of a known torque associated with a bending moment of a known magnitude: $T = 58.8399 \times 10^{-5} \times d_1^{3.5}$ N m.

(c) Transmission of a known torque associated with an undetermined bending moment: $T = 27.45862 \times 10^{-5} \times d_1^{3.5}$ N m.

These three formulae assume use of a steel with a tensile strength of 490 to 590 N/mm². These values are intended to provide a rapid comparison between shafts of different sizes and *not* as fundamental design criteria. Steady torque conditions are assumed.

2.7.13 Straight-sided splines for cylindrical shafts, metric

Designation: nominal dimensions

The profile of a splined shaft or hub is designated by stating, in the following order:

The number of splines N
The minor diameter d
The outside diameter D.

For example, shaft (or hub) 6 × 23 × 26.

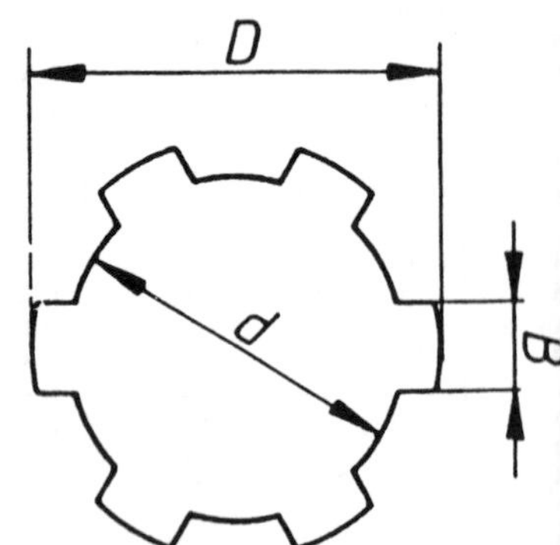

d	Light series				Medium series			
mm	Designation	N	D mm	B mm	Designation	N	D mm	B mm
11					6 × 11 × 14	6	14	3
13					6 × 13 × 16	6	16	3.5
16					6 × 16 × 20	6	20	4
18					6 × 18 × 22	6	22	5

21					6 × 21 × 25	6	25	5
23	6 × 23 × 26	6	26	6	6 × 23 × 28	6	28	6
26	6 × 26 × 30	6	30	6	6 × 26 × 32	6	32	6
28	6 × 28 × 32	6	32	7	6 × 28 × 34	6	34	7
32	8 × 32 × 36	8	36	6	8 × 32 × 38	8	38	6
36	8 × 36 × 40	8	40	7	8 × 36 × 42	8	42	7
42	8 × 42 × 46	8	46	8	8 × 42 × 48	8	48	8
46	8 × 46 × 50	8	50	9	8 × 46 × 54	8	54	9
52	8 × 52 × 58	8	58	10	8 × 52 × 60	8	60	10
56	8 × 56 × 62	8	62	10	8 × 56 × 65	8	65	10
62	8 × 62 × 68	8	68	12	8 × 62 × 72	8	72	12
72	10 × 72 × 78	10	78	12	10 × 72 × 82	10	82	12
82	10 × 82 × 88	10	88	12	10 × 82 × 92	10	92	12
92	10 × 92 × 98	10	98	14	10 × 92 × 102	10	102	14
02	10 × 102 × 108	10	108	16	10 × 102 × 112	10	112	16
12	10 × 112 × 120	10	120	18	10 × 112 × 125	10	125	18

Tolerances on holes and shafts

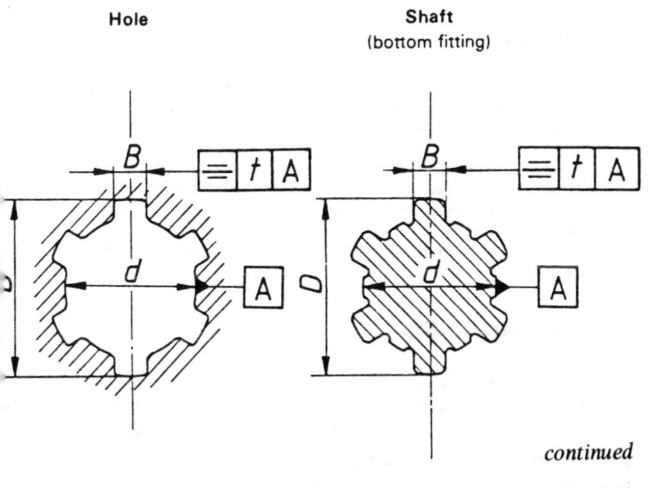

continued

Tolerances on hole						*Tolerances on shaft*			*Mounting type*
Not treated after broaching			*Treated after broaching*						
B	*D*	*d*	*B*	*D*	*d*	*B*	*D*	*d*	
H9	H10	H7	H11	H10	H7	d10	a11	f7	Sliding
						f9	a11	g7	Close sliding
						h10	a11	h7	Fixed

Tolerances on symmetry

Dimensions in millimetr

Spline width *B*	3	3.5 4 5 6	7 8 9 10	12 14 16 18
Tolerance of symmetry *t*	0.010 (IT7)	0.012 (IT7)	0.015 (IT7)	0.018 (IT7)

The tolerance specified on *B* includes the index variation (and the symmetry variation

Notes

(a) With certain milling cutters, it is possible for special applications to produce splines without bottom tool clearance with a very reduced fillet radius between the spline side and the minor diameter *d* (for example, milling cutters with fixed working positions).
(b) The dimensional tolerances on holes and shafts relate to entirely finished workpieces (shafts and hubs). Tooling should therefore be different for untreated workpieces, or workpieces treated before machining and for workpieces treated after machining.
(c) For further information on straight sided splines and gauges for checking such splines see BS 5686 : 1986.

Involute splines

These have a similar profile to spur gear teeth. They have a much greater root strength than straight sided splines and can b produced on gear cutting machines with standard gear tooth cutters. However, their geometry and checking is much more complex than for straight sided splines and is beyond the scope of this book. See BS 3550 (inch units) and BS 6186 (metric units)

2.7.14 Self-holding Morse and metric 5% tapers

Self-holding shanks with tang and socket

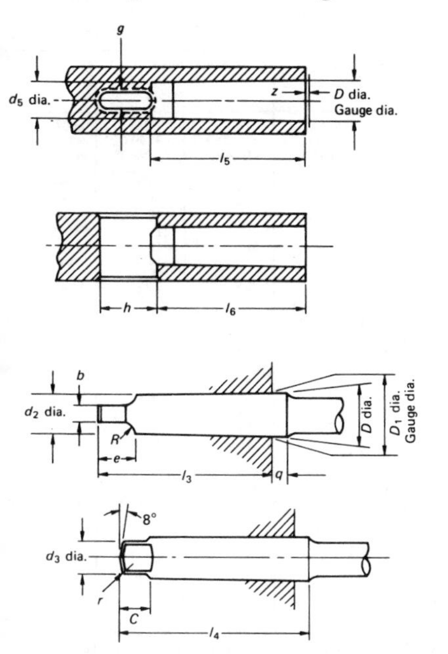

Self-holding shanks with tapped end and socket

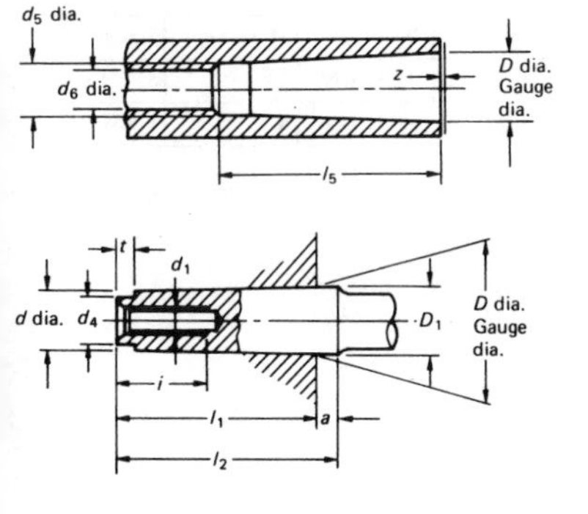

2.7.15 General dimensions of self-holding Mor and metric 5% taper shanks and socket

Dimensions in millimetres

Designation (see 2.7.14)		Metric taper 4	Metric taper 6	Morse taper 0	Morse taper 1	Morse taper 2	Morse taper 3
Taper	Dimensions	1 : 20 = 0.05		0.6246 : 12 = 1 : 19.212 = 0.05205	0.59858 : 12 = 1 : 20.047 = 0.04988	0.59941 : 12 = 1 : 20.020 = 0.04995	0.60235 : 12 = 1 : 19.922 = 0.05020
External taper	D	4	6	9.045	12.065	17.780	23.825
	a	2	3	3	3.5	5	5
	D_1*	4.1	6.2	9.2	12.2	18	24.1
	d*.	2.9	4.4	6.4	9.4	14.6	19.8
	d_1†	—	—	—	M6	M10	M12
	d_2*	—	—	6.1	9	14	19.1
	d_3 max.	—	—	6	8.7	13.5	18.5
	d_4 max.	2.5	4	6	9	14	19
	l_1 max.	23	32	50	53.5	64	81
	l_2 max.	25	35	53	57	69	86
	l_3 max.	—	—	56.5	62	75	94
	l_4 max.	—	—	59.5	65.5	80	99
	b(h13)	—	—	3.9	5.2	6.3	7.9
	c‡	—	—	6.5	8.5	10	13
	e max.	—	—	10.5	13.5	16	20
	i min.	—	—	—	16	24	28
	R max.	—	—	4	5	6	7
	r	—	—	1	1.2	1.6	2
	t max.	2	3	4	5	5	7
Internal taper	d_5(H11)	3	4.6	6.7	9.7	14.9	20.2
	d_6	—	—	—	7	11.5	14
	l_5 min.	25	34	52	56	67	84
	l_6	21	29	49	52	62	78
	g(A13)	2.2	3.2	3.9	5.2	6.3	7.9
	h	8	12	15	19	22	27
	z§	0.5	0.5	1	1	1	1

* D_1 and d or d_2. Approximate values given for guidance. (The actual values result from the actual values of a and l_1 or l_3 respectively, taking into account the taper and the basic size D.)

† d_1 = thread diameter: either a metric thread M with standard pitch or, during the transition period and only if expressly stated, a UNC thread (see below). In every case, the appropriate symbol M or UNC should be marked on the component.

Morse taper	*Thread*	*Morse taper*	*Thread*	*Morse taper*	*Thread*
1	1 4-20 UNC	3	1/2-13 UNC	5	5 8-11 UNC
2	3 8-16 UNC	4	5.8-11 UNC	6	1-8 UNC

Dimensions in millimetres

Morse taper			*Non-preferred*	*Metric taper*				
4	5	6	7	80	100	120	160	200
0.62326 : 12 = 1 : 19.254 = 0.05194	0.63151 : 12 = 1 : 19.002 = 0.05263	0.62565 : 12 = 1 : 19.180 = 0.05214	0.6240 : 12 = 1 : 19.248 = 0.05200	1 : 20 = 0.05				
31.267	44.399	63.348	83.058	80	100	120	160	200
6.5	6.5	8	9.5	8	10	12	16	20
31.6	44.7	63.8	83.6	80.4	100.5	120.6	160.8	201
25.9	37.6	53.9	69.85	70.2	88.4	106.6	143	179.4
M16	M20	M24	M30	M30	M36	M36	M48	M48
25.2	36.5	52.4	68.2	69	87	105	141	177
24.5	35.7	51	66.7	67	85	102	138	174
25	35.7	51	66.7	67	85	102	138	174
102.5	129.5	182	254	196	232	268	340	412
109	136	190	263.5	204	242	280	356	432
117.5	149.5	210	286	220	260	300	380	460
124	156	218	295.5	228	270	312	396	480
11.9	15.9	19	28.6	26	32	38	50	62
16	19	27	35	24	28	32	40	48
24	29	40	54	48	58	68	88	108
32	40	50	60	65	80	80	100	100
8	10	13	19	24	30	36	48	60
2.5	3	4	5	5	5	6	8	10
9	10	16	20	24	30	36	48	60
26.5	38.2	54.6	71	71.5	90	108.5	145.5	182.5
18	23	27	34	33	39	39	52	52
107	135	188	257	202	240	276	350	424
98	125	177	241	186	220	254	321	388
11.9	15.9	19	28.6	26	32	38	50	62
32	38	47	67	52	60	70	90	110
1.5	1.5	2	2	2	2	2	3	3

‡ It is permissible to increase the length c over which the tenon is turned to diameter d_3, but without exceeding e.

§ Z = maximum permissible deviation, outwards only, of the position of the gauge plane D from the nominal position of coincidence with the leading face.

For further information see BS 1660.

2.7.16 Tolerances on self-holding Morse taper shanks and sockets

Dimensions in millimetres

Dimension	*Class of fit*	*max.*	*min.*	*max.*	*min.*	*max.*	*min.*	*max.*	*min.*	*max.*	*min.*	*max.*	*min.*	*max.*	*min.*	*max.*	*min.*
Morse: designation		0		1		2		3		4		5		6		7	
b	h13	3.900	3.720	5.200	5.020	6.300	6.080	7.900	7.680	11.900	11.630	15.900	15.630	19.000	18.670	28.600	28.270
d_5	H11	6.790	6.700	9.790	9.700	15.010	14.900	20.330	20.200	26.630	26.500	38.360	38.200	54.790	54.600	71.190	71.000
g	A13	4.350	4.170	5.650	5.470	6.800	6.580	8.400	8.180	12.460	12.190	16.460	16.190	19.630	19.300	29.230	28.900
Metric: designation		4		6		80		100		120		160		200		—	
b	h13	—	—	—	—	26.000	25.470	32.000	31.610	38.000	37.610	50.000	49.540	62.000	61.540	—	—
d_5	H11	3.060	3.000	4.675	4.600	71.690	71.500	90.220	90.000	108.720	108.500	145.750	145.500	182.790	182.500	—	—
g	A13	2.610	2.470	3.650	3.470	26.630	26.300	32.700	32.310	38.700	38.310	50.780	50.320	62.800	62.340	—	—

Tolerances on taper:

Shanks The rate of taper on taper shanks shall always be *nominal to fast*. The tolerance shall be +0.010 mm on diameter per 100 mm of length.
Sockets The rate of taper on taper sockets shall always be *nominal to slow*. The tolerance shall be −0.010 mm on diameter per 100 mm of length.
Symmetry of tang with shank This is to be within: 0.1 FIM (full indicator movement) for no. 0 to no. 5 Morse; 0.12 FIM for no. 6 and no. 7 Morse and for all metric 5% sizes.
Symmetry of slot with axis of taper bore This is to be within: 0.1 FIM for no. 0 to no. 5 Morse; 0.12 FIM for nos 6 and 7 Morse, and for all metric 5% sizes.

For further information see BS 1660.

2.7.17 Spindle noses with self-release 7/24 tapers

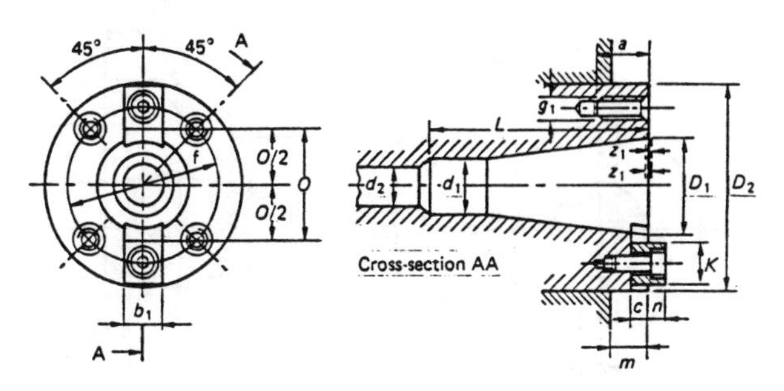

Rate of taper = 7 : 24 = 1 : 3.428 571 = 0.291 667.

Dimensions are in millimetres

Designation	30	40	45	50	(55)	60
D_1	31.750	44.450	57.150	69.850	88.900	107.950
D_2(h5)*	69.832	88.882	101.6	128.570	152.4	221.440
d_1(H12)*	17.4	25.3	32.4	39.6	50.4	60.2
d_2 min.	17	17	21	27	27	35
L min.	73	100	120	140	178	220
g_1	M10	M12	M12	M16	M20	M20
a min.	16	20	20	25	30	30
f†	54	66.7	80	101.6	120.6	177.8
m min.	12.5	16	18	19	25	38
n max.	8	8	9.5	12.5	12.5	12.5
$O/2$ min.	16.5	23	30	36	48	61
b_1‡	15.9	15.9	19	25.4	25.4	25.4
c min.	8	8	9.5	12.5	12.5	12.5
K max.	16.5	19.5	19.5	26.5	26.5	45.4
Z_1§	0.4	0.4	0.4	0.4	0.4	0.4
v‡	±0.03	±0.03	±0.03	±0.04	±0.04	±0.04
Screw for tenon key	M6 × 16	M6 × 16	M8 × 20	M10 × 25	M10 × 25	M10 × 25

* For tolerances, see BS 1660 Table 9.
† Tolerance on the position of fixing holes (maximum radial deviation from their theoretical position): nos 30, 40 and 45, 0.075 mm; nos 50, 55 and 60, 0.100 mm.
‡ M6/h5 fit for the assembly of the tenon in the slot. The dimension v corresponds to the permissible eccentricity of the tenon b_1; it is the distance between the mid-plane of the tenon and the spindle nose axis.
§ Z_1 = maximum permissible deviation, on either side of the leading face, of the position of the gauge plane D_1 from the nominal position of coincidence with the leading face.
Note: (55) taper is non-preferred.
For further information see BS 1660.

2.7.18 Self-release 7/24 taper shanks

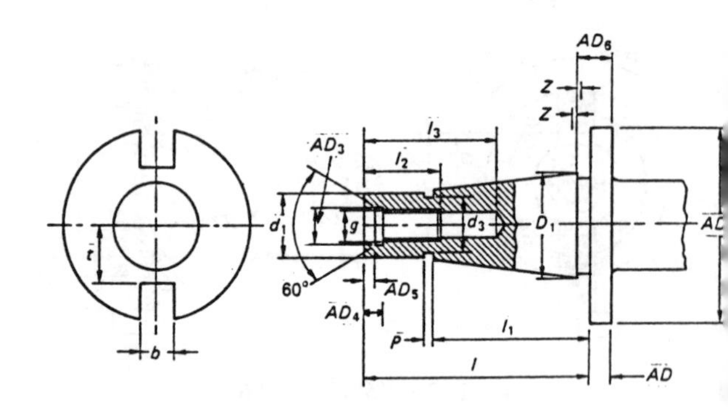

Rate of taper = 7 : 24 = 1 : 3.428 571 = 0.291 667.

Dimensions in millimetre

Designation	30	40	45	50	(55)	60
D_1	31.750	44.450	57.150	69.850	88.900	107.950
d_1(a10)*	17.4	25.3	32.4	39.6	50.4	60.2
l max.	70	95	110	130	168	210
l_1	50	67	86	105	135	165
AD_1	8	10	10	12	14	16
AD_2	50	63	80	100	130	160
g†	M12	M16	M20	M24	M24	M30
AD_3	13	17	21	26	26	32
AD_4	6	8	10	11	11	14
AD_5	4.5	5	5	6.5	6.5	8
l_2	24	30	38	45	45	56
l_3 min.	50	70	70	90	90	110 or 160 ¶
d_3	16.5	24	30	38	48	58
b(H12)*	16.1	16.1	19.3	25.7	25.7	25.7
t max.	16.2	22.5	29	35.3	45	60
p	3	5	6	8	9	10
z‡	0.4	0.4	0.4	0.4	0.4	0.4
w§	±0.06	±0.06	±0.06	±0.10	±0.10	±0.10
AD_6 ‖ ±0.1	9.6	11.6	13.2	15.2	17.2	19.2

* For tolerances, see BS 1660 Table 10.
† Alternative threads permissible during transition period; see BS 1660 Clause 4.2.
‡ z = maximum permissible deviation, on either side of the end of the taper, of the position of the gauge plane D_1 from the nominal position, of coincidence with the end of the taper.

§The dimension w corresponds to the permissible eccentricity of the slot b: it is the distance between the mid-plane of the slot and the tool shank axis.
||Dimension AD_6 is only vital when use is required in quick change systems.
¶The alternative value of 160 mm allows for the use of reducing sockets.
Note: (55) taper is non-preferred.
For further information, see BS 1660.

Part 3 Engineering Materials

3.1 Mechanical properties

3.1.1 Tensile strength

This is the ability of a material to withstand tensile (stretching) loads without rupture occurring. The material is in tension.

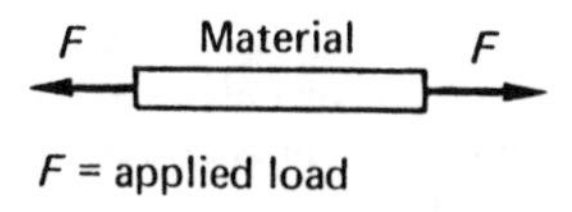

3.1.2 Compressive strength

This is the ability of a material to withstand compressive (squeezing) loads without being crushed or broken. The material is in compression.

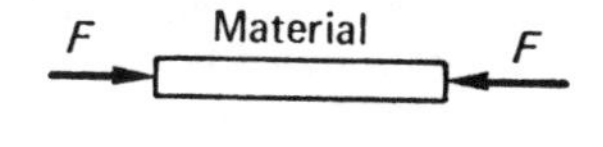

3.1.3 Shear strength

This is the ability of a material to withstand offset or transverse loads without rupture occurring. The rivet connecting the two bars shown is in *shear* whilst the bars themselves are in *tension.* Note that the rivet would still be in *shear* if the bars were in *compression.*

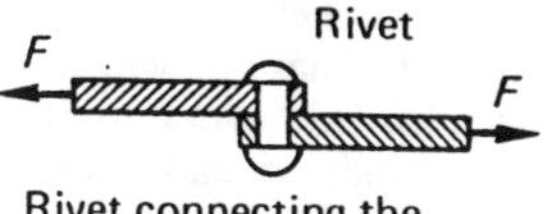

Rivet connecting the two bars is resisting shear

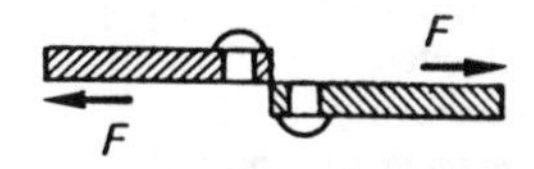

Rivet connecting the two bars has failed in shear

3.1.4 Toughness: impact resistance

This is the ability of a material to resist shatter. If a material shatters it is brittle (e.g. glass). If it fails to shatter when subjected to an impact load it is tough (e.g. rubber). Toughness should not be confused with strength. Any material in which the spread of surface cracks does not occur or only occurs to a limited extent is said to be tough.

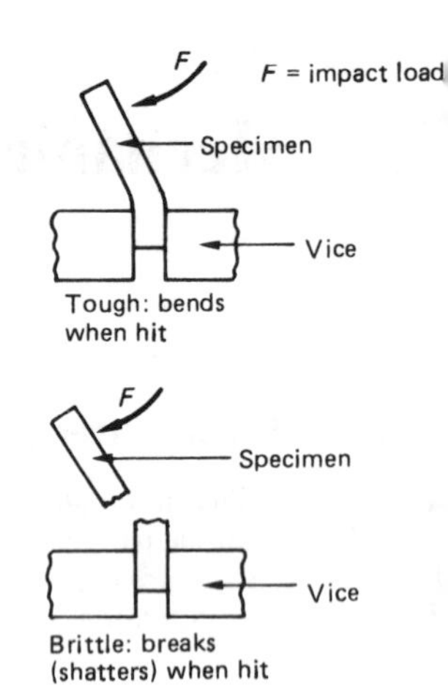

3.1.5 Elasticity

This is the ability of a material to deform under load and return to its original size and shape when the load is removed. Such a material would be required to make the spring shown.

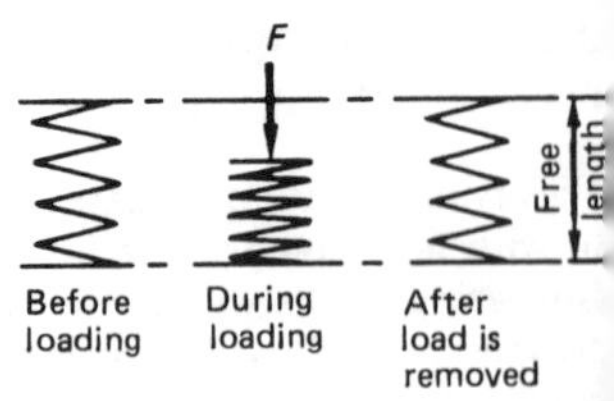

3.1.6 Plasticity

This property is the exact opposite of elasticity. It is the state of a material which has been loaded beyond its elastic state. Under a load beyond that required to cause elastic deformation (the elastic limit) a material possessing the property of plasticity deforms permanently. It takes a *permanent set* and will not recover when the load is removed.

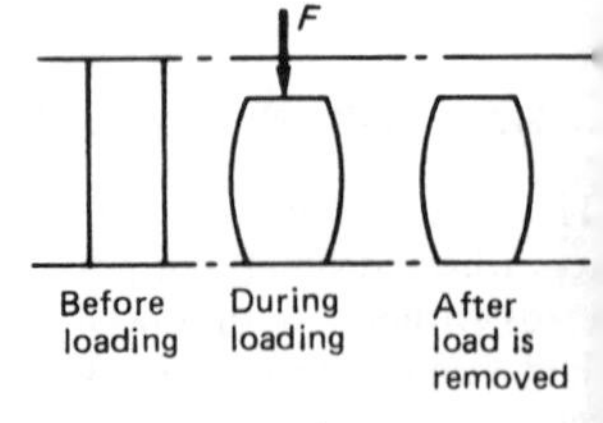

3.1.7 Ductility

This is the term used when plastic deformation occurs as the result of applying a *tensile load*. A *ductile* material combines the properties of plasticity and tenacity (tensile strength) so that it can be stretched or drawn to shape and will retain that shape when the deforming force is removed. For example, in wire drawing the wire is reduced in diameter by drawing it through a die.

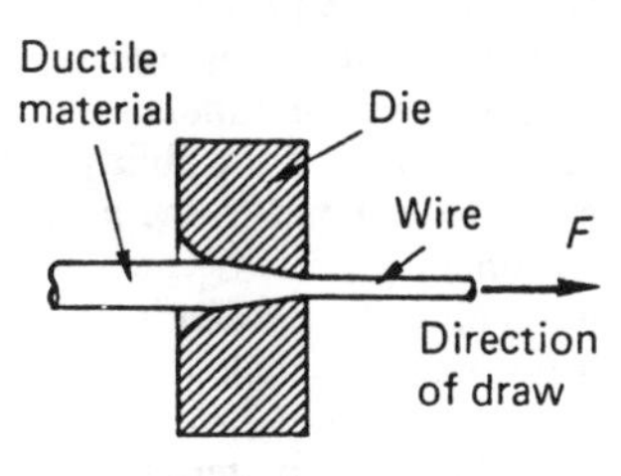

F = applied load (tensile)

3.1.8 Malleability

This is the term used when plastic deformation occurs as the result of applying a *compressive load*. A *malleable* material combines the properties of plasticity and compressibility, so that it can be squeezed to shape by such processes as forging, rolling and rivet heading.

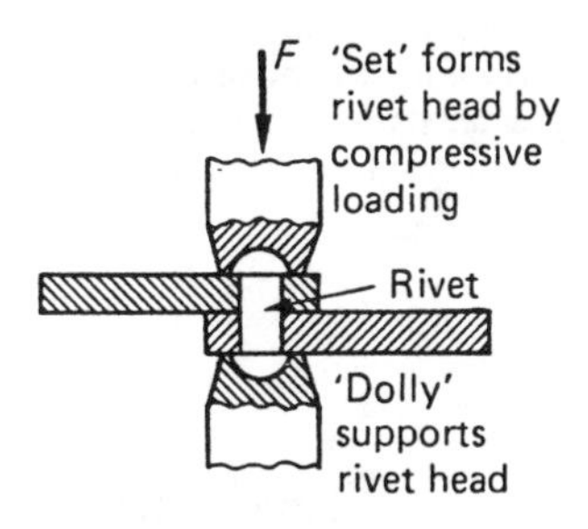

F = applied load (compressive)

3.1.9 Hardness

This is the ability of a material to withstand scratching (abrasion) or indentation by another hard body. It is an indication of the wear resistance of a material.

Processes which increase the hardness of materials also increase their tensile strength. At the same time the toughness of

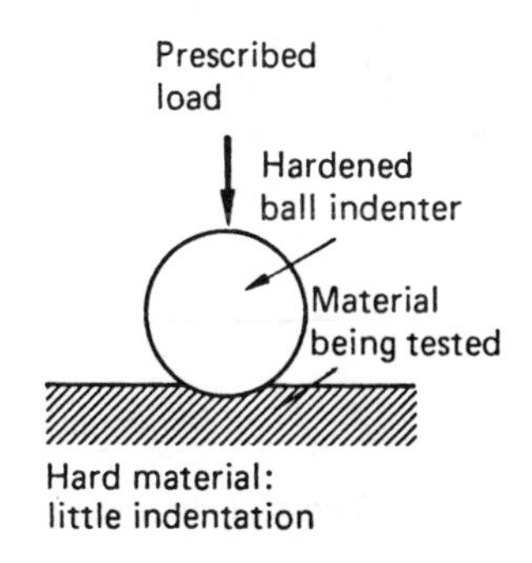

Hard material: little indentation

the material is reduced as it becomes more brittle.

Hardenability must not be confused with hardness. Hardenability is the ability of a metal to respond to the heat treatment process of quench hardening. To harden it, the hot metal must be chilled at a rate in excess of its *critical cooling rate.* Since any material cools more quickly at the surface than at the centre there is a limit to the size of bar which can cool quickly enough at its centre to achieve uniform hardness throughout. This is the *ruling section* for the material. The greater its hardenability the greater will be its ruling section.

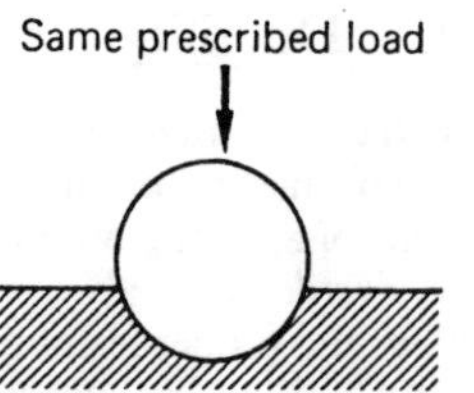

3.1.10 Tensile test

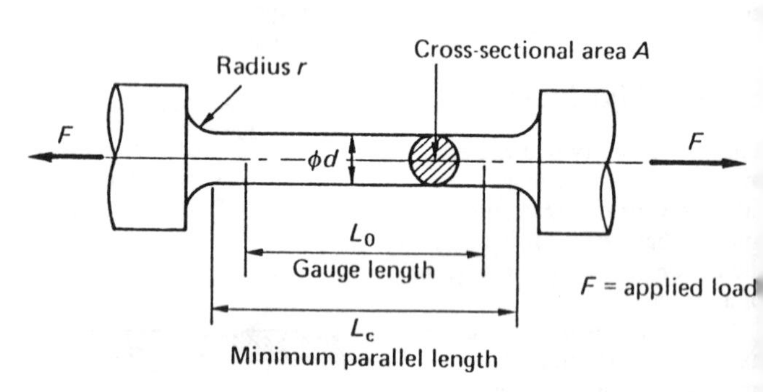

Typical cylindrical tensile test specimen (BS 18)

The tensile test is widely used for determining the strength and ductility of a material. The test involves loading a standard specimen axially as shown. The load is increased at a constant rate mechanically or hydraulically. The specimen increases in length until it finally fractures. During the test the specimen is gripped at each end to ensure simple uniaxial loading and freedom of bending. The extension is measured from the *gauge length*. The mid-portion of the specimen is reduced in diameter as shown to ensure fracture occurs within the gauge length.

The results of the test are plotted as shown in 3.1.11; it is usual to plot the applied load vertically and the resulting extension horizontally. Alternatively, stress and strain may be plotted with the stress vertical and the resulting strain horizontal. For a given specimen similar curves would be produced. The stress and strain relations are

$$\text{stress} = \frac{\text{load}}{\text{original cross-sectional area}}$$

$$\text{strain} = \frac{\text{increase in length under load}}{\text{original length}}$$

Proportional specimens (BS 18) are given by the relationship $L_0 = 5.65\sqrt{A}$. Since $A = \pi d^2/4$, then $\sqrt{A} = d\sqrt{(\pi)}/2 = 0.886d$. Thus $L_0 = 5.65 \times 0.886d \approx 5d$. Hence a specimen of 10 mm diameter will have a gauge length of 50 mm.

3.1.11 Interpretation of a tensile test: material showing a yield point

The curve shown is typical for a ductile material with a pronounced yield point, e.g. annealed low carbon steel.

The initial part of the plot from O to A is linear since the material is behaving in an elastic manner (Hooke's law). If the load is released at any point between O and A the specimen will return to its original length. The steeper the slope of OA the more rigid (stiffer) will be the material. The point A is called the *limit of proportionality*.

At the point A some materials may undergo a sudden extension without a corresponding increase in load. This is called the *yield point*, and the yield stress at this point is calculated by dividing the load at yield by the original cross-sectional area.

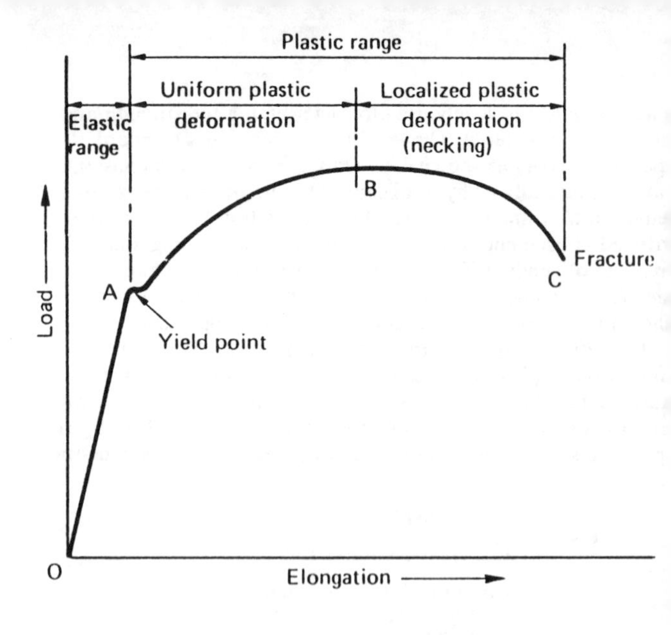

Beyond the yield point A the plot ceases to be linear since the material is behaving in a plastic manner. If the load is released a any point in the plastic range, the elastic strain is recovered but the plastic element of the deformation is maintained and the material will have undergone permanent extension. That is, it ha taken a *permanent set*.

Beyond the point B the material extends with a reducing load. However, since there is a local reduction in cross-sectional area (necking) the stress (load/area) is actually increasing up to the breaking point. The stress calculated at the point B is called the *maximum tensile stress* (or just *tensile strength*) of the material.

The *ductility* of the material is calculated by reassembling the broken specimen and measuring the increase in gauge length. Then

$$\text{elongation } \% = \frac{\text{increase in length}}{\text{original length}} \times 100$$

3.1.12 Interpretation of a tensile test: proof stress

Many materials do not show a marked yield point, and an offset yield stress or *proof stress* is specified instead. This is the stress required to produce a specified amount of plastic deformation.

A line BC is drawn parallel to the elastic part of the plot OA so as to cut the load/elongation curve at C. The offset is specified (usually 0.1 or 0.2% of the gauge length).

The offset yield stress (proof stress) is calculated by taking the load F_1 at C and dividing it by the original cross-sectional area of the specimen A_0. The material will have fulfilled its specification if, after the proof stress has been applied for 15 seconds and removed, its permanent set is not greater than the specified offset.

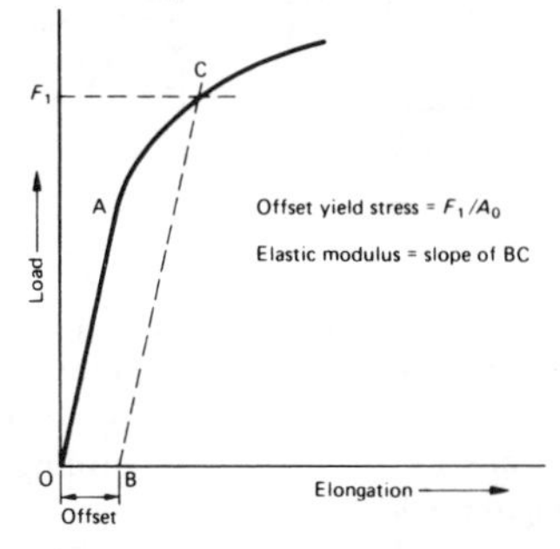

3.1.13 Interpretation of a tensile test: secant modulus

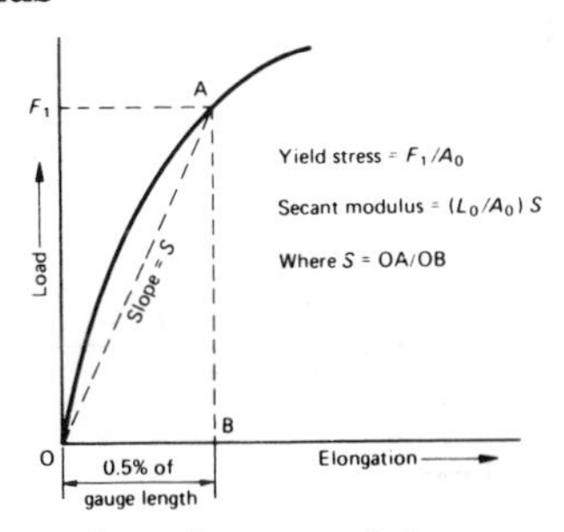

Some highly ductile metals such as annealed copper and certain polymers do not show a linear region on the tensile test plot, and therefore the offset yield stress (proof stress) cannot be determined.

In these cases an appropriate extension is specified (typically 0.5% of gauge length) and the yield stress is specified as the load to produce a total extension of 0.5% of gauge length divided by the original cross-section area A_0.

In place of an elastic modulus the *secant modulus* is used to determine the elasticity of the material.

3.1.14 Impact testing for toughness: Izod test

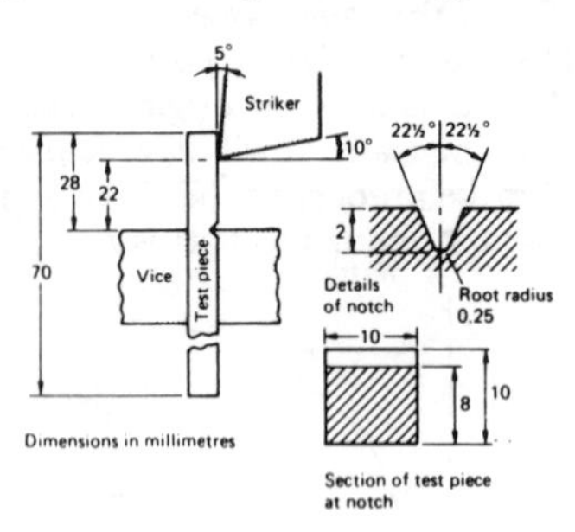

In the Izod impact test a 10 mm square notched test piece is used. It is supported as a *cantilever* in the vice of the testing machine and struck with a kinetic energy of 162.72 J at a velocity of 3.8 m/s. The energy absorbed in deforming or breaking the test piece is its toughness factor.

3.1.15 Impact testing for toughness: Charpy test

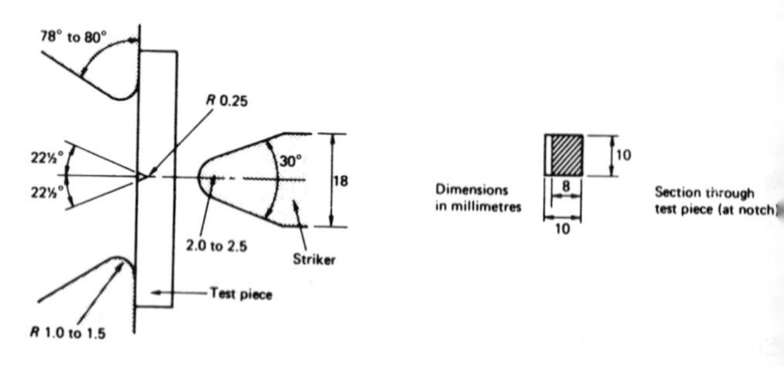

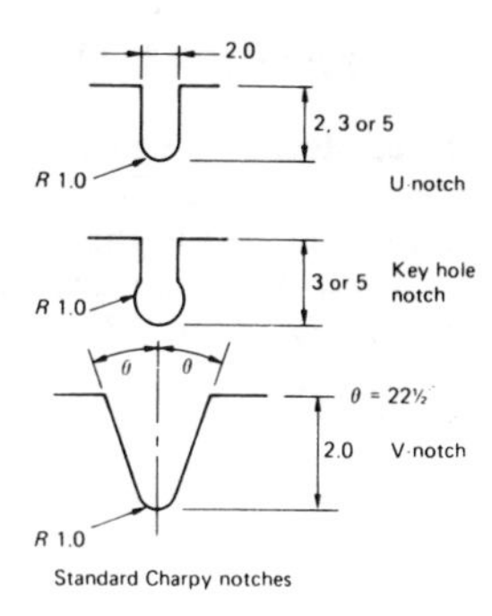

Standard Charpy notches

In the Charpy impact test a 10 mm square specimen is supported as *beam* and struck with a kinetic energy of 298.3 J at a velocity of 5 m/s. The energy absorbed in bending or breaking the test piece is its toughness factor.

3.1.16 Interpretation of impact test results

Brittle metals There is a clean break with little reduction in cross-sectional area. The fractured surfaces show a granular structure.
Ductile metals The fracture is rough and fibrous. In very ductile metals the fracture may not be complete: the test piece bends over and only shows slight tearing from the notch. There will also be some reduction in cross-sectional area at the point of fracture or bending.
Brittle polymers There is a clean break showing smooth, glassy fractured surfaces with some splintering.
Ductile polymers There is no distinctive appearance to fracture if one occurs at all. There will be a considerable reduction in cross-sectional area and some tearing at the notch.
Crack spread Since the Izod and Charpy tests both use notched test pieces, useful information can be obtained regarding the resistance of a material to the spread of a crack. Such a crack may originate from a point of stress concentration and indicates the need to avoid sharp corners, undercuts, sudden changes in sections and machining marks.

3.1.17 Brinell hardness test

In this test a hardened steel ball is pressed into the surface of the test piece using a prescribed load. The combination of load and ball diameter have to be related to the material under test to avoid errors of distortion. The test piece hardness should be limited to $H_B = 500$, otherwise the ball indenter will tend to flatten and introduce errors.

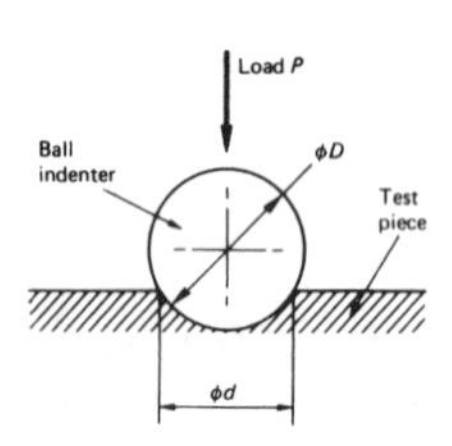

$$\frac{P}{D^2} = k$$

where P = load (kg)
D = diameter of indenter (mm)
k = 30 for ferrous metals
= 10 for copper and copper alloys
= 5 for aluminium and aluminium alloys
= 1 for lead, tin, white bearing metals

hardness number H_B

$$= \frac{\text{load}}{\text{spherical area of indentation}}$$

$$= \frac{P}{\pi(D/2)[D - \sqrt{(D^2 - d^2)}]}$$

3.1.18 Vickers hardness test

In this test a diamond indenter is used in the form of a square-based pyramid with an angle of 136° between facets. Since diamond has a hardness of 6000 H_B, this test can be used for testing very hard materials. Only one size of indenter is used and the load is varied. Standard loads are 5, 10, 20, 30, 50 and 100 kg. It is necessary to state the test load when specifying a Vickers hardness number (e.g. $HD(50)=200$).

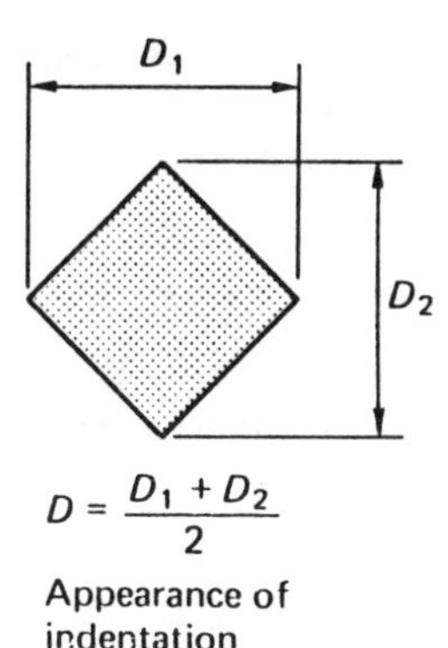

$$D = \frac{D_1 + D_2}{2}$$

Appearance of indentation

hardness value $H_D = 1.844\frac{P}{D^2}$

where P = load (kg)
D = diagonal length of indentation (average)

3.1.19 Rockwell hardness test

This test uses either a hard steel ball for softer materials or a 120° diamond cone indenter for harder materials. The test compares the differences in depth of penetration between a minor initial load (98N) and a major additional load. The result of the test is read directly from the machine scale.

$$H_R = E - e$$

where E = a constant dependent upon indenter used
e = the permanent *increase* in penetration due to the application of an additional major load

Scale	*Indenter*	*Additional force* kN	*Applications*
A	120° diamond cone	0.59	Sheet steel; shallow case-hardened components
B	Ball, ϕ 1.588 mm	0.98	Copper alloys; aluminium alloys;

continued

Scale	*Indenter*	*Additional force* kN	*Applications*
			annealed low carbon steels
C	128° diamond cone	1.47	Most widely used range; hardened steels; cast irons; deep case-hardened components
D	120° diamond cone	0.98	Thin but hard steel; medium depth case-hardened components
E	Ball, ϕ 3.175 mm	0.98	Cast iron; aluminium alloys, magnesium alloys; bearing metals
F	Ball, ϕ 1.588 mm	0.59	Annealed copper alloys; thin soft sheet metals
G	Ball, ϕ 1.588 mm	1.47	Malleable cast irons; phosphor bronze; gunmetals; cupro-nickel alloys etc.
H	Ball, ϕ 3.175 mm	0.59	Soft materials; high ferritic alloys; aluminium; lead; zinc
K	Ball, ϕ 3.175 mm	1.47	Aluminium and magnesium alloys
L	Ball, ϕ 6.350 mm	0.59	Thermoplastics
M	Ball, ϕ 6.350 mm	0.98	Thermoplastics
P	Ball, ϕ 6.350 mm	1.47	Thermosetting plastics
R	Ball, ϕ 12.70 mm	0.59	Very soft plastics and rubbers
S	Ball, ϕ 12.70 mm	0.98	—
V	Ball, ϕ 12.70 mm	1.47	—

3.1.20 **Rockwell superficial hardness test**

In this test the initial force is reduced from 98 N to 29.4 N and the additional (major) force is also reduced. This range of tests is used when measuring the hardness of thin sheets and foils.

Scale	*Indenter*	*Additional force* **kN**
15-N	120° diamond cone	0.14
30-N	120° diamond cone	0.29
45-N	120° diamond cone	0.44
15-T	Ball, ϕ1.588 mm	0.14
30-T	Ball, ϕ 1.588 mm	0.29
45-T	Ball, ϕ 1.588 mm	0.44

3.1.21 Comparative hardness scales

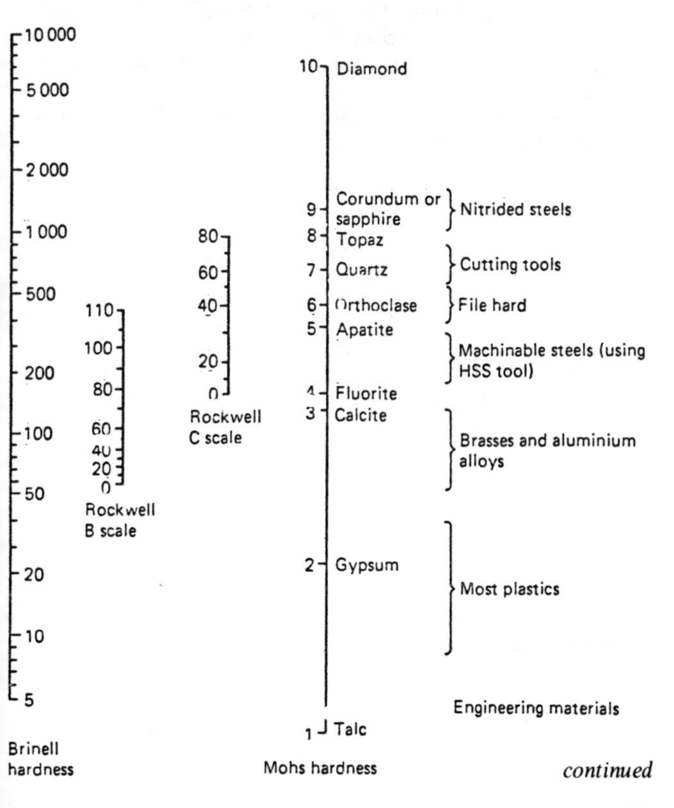

continued

Tables and charts showing comparative hardness figures for various methods of testing should be treated with caution since the tests are carried out under different conditions. For example:

(a) The relatively large diameter ball indenter of the Brinell test and some Rockwell tests displaces the metal of the test piece by plastic flow.
(b) The sharp edged and sharply pointed diamond pyramid of the Vickers test tends to cut its way into the test piece by shear.
(c) The Rockwell test uses yet another form of indenter, namely a 120° diamond cone. This test also compares the increase in depth of penetration when the load is increased, whereas in (a) and (b) the area of indentation is measured for a single stated load.
(d) The Scleroscope is a dynamic test, measuring hardness as a function of resilience.

3.2 Ferrous metals and alloys

3.2.1 Ferrous metals: plain carbon steels

Ferrous metals are based upon the metallic element *iron* (Latin *ferrum*=iron). The iron is associated with carbon, either as a solid solution or as the chemical compound iron carbide (cementite). In the case of cast irons, some the carbon may be uncombined (free) in the form of flake graphite. In addition to carbon, other elements may also be present. These may be *impurities* such as sulphur and phosphorus which weaken the metal and are kept to a minimum. *Alloying elements* are added to enhance the performance of the metal, e.g. chromium and nickel.

Plain carbon steels consist mainly of iron and carbon and are the simplest of the ferrous metals. Some manganese will also be present to neutralize the deleterious effects of the sulphur and to enhance the grain structure. It is not present in sufficient quantity to be considered as an alloying element.

The amount of carbon present affects the properties of the steel, as shown in 3.2.3. The maximum amount of carbon which can remain combined with the iron at all temperatures is 1.7%. In practice an upper limit of 1.2 to 1.4% is set to ensure a margin of safety. A steel, by definition, must contain *no* free carbon.

Low carbon steels

These have a carbon content 0.1 to 0.3% plus impurities, plus some manganese to neutralize the effect of any sulphur content left over from the extraction process. Such steels cannot be directly hardened by heat treatment, but they can be readily carburized and case-hardened. The lower carbon steels in this category are used for steel sheets for pressing out such components as motor car body panels as they have a high ductility. The lower carbon steels in this category are also made into drawn wire rod and tube. The higher carbon steels in this category are stiffer and less ductile and are used for general workshop bars, plates and girders. Low carbon steels are substantially stronger than wrought-iron which is no longer considered to be a structural material.

Medium carbon steels

(a) Carbon content 0.3 to 0.5%. Such steels can be toughened by heat treatment (heating to red heat and quenching – rapid cooling – in water). They are used for crankshaft and axle forgings where cost is important and the service requirements do not warrant stronger but more expensive alloy steels.
(b) Carbon content 0.5 to 0.8%. These are used for vehicle leaf springs and garden tools. Such steels can be quench hardened by heat treatment as above.

High carbon steels

All high carbon steels can be hardened to a high degree of hardness by heating to a dull red heat and quenching. The hardness and application depend upon the carbon content and the degree of tempering after hardening.

(a) Carbon content 0.8 to 1.0%; used for coil springs and wood chisels
(b) Carbon content 1.0 to 1.2%; used for files, drills, taps and dies
(c) Carbon content 1.2 to 1.4%; used for fine edge tools (knives, etc.).

3.2.2 Properties and uses of some plain carbon steels

Type of steel	Relevant specification	Typical compositions %	Heat treatment	Typical mechanical properties					Uses
				Yield point N/mm²	Tensile strength N/mm²	Elong. %	Impact J	Hardness (Brinell)	
Low carbon steel	BS 970.040A10	0.10 C 0.40 Mn	No heat treatment (except process annealing to remove the effects of coldwork)	—	300	28	—	—	Lightly stressed parts produced by cold forming processes, e.g. deep drawing and pressing
Structural steels	BS 15 BS 968	0.20 C 0.20 C 1.50 Mn	No heat treatment No heat treatment	240 350	450 525	25 20	—	—	General structural steel; high tensile structural steel for bridges and general building construction fusion welding quality
Casting steel	BS 1504 161B	0.30 C	No heat treatment other than 'annealing' to refine grain	265	500	18	20	150	Castings for a wide range of engineering purposes where medium strength and good machinability are required
Constructional steels (medium carbon)	BS 970:080M40	0.40 C 0.80 Mn	Harden by quenching from 830 860°C. Temper at a suitable temperature between 550 and 660°C	500	700	20	55	200	Axles crankshafts, spindles etc. under medium stress

continued

Section 3.2.2 (*continued*)

Type of steel	Relevant specification	Typical compositions %	Heat treatment	Typical mechanical properties: Yield point N/mm²	Tensile strength N/mm²	Elong. %	Impact J	Hardness (Brinell)	Uses
	BS 970:070M55	0.55 C 0.70 Mn	Harden by quenching from 810–840°C.; Temper at a suitable temperature between 550 and 660°C	550	750	14		250	Gears, cylinders and machine tool parts requiring resistance to wear
Tool steels (High carbon)		0.70 C 0.35 Mn	Heat slowly to 790–810°C and quench in water or brine. Temper at 150–300°C					780	Hand chisels, cold sets, mason's tools, smith's tools, screwdriver blades, stamping dies, keys, cropping blades, miner's drills, paper knives
	BS 4659 BW1A	0.90 C 0.35 Mn	Heat slowly to 760–780°C and quench in water or brine. Temper at 200–300°C					800	Press tools; punches; dies; cold-heading, minting and embossing dies; shear blades; woodworking tools; lathe centres; draw plates
	BS 4659:BW1B	1.00 C 0.35 Mn	Heat slowly to 770–790°C and quench in water or brine. Temper at 150–350°C					800	Taps; screwing dies; twist drills; reamers; counter sinks; blanking tools; embossing, engraving, minting, drawing, needle and paper dies; shear blades, knives; press tools; centre punches; woodworking cutters; straight edges; gouges; pneumatic chisels; wedges
	BS 4659:BW1C	1.20 C 0.35 Mn	Heat slowly to 760–780°C and quench in water or brine.					800	Engraving tools; files; surgical instruments; taps; screwing tools

3.2.3 Effect of carbon content on the composition, properties and uses of plain carbon steels

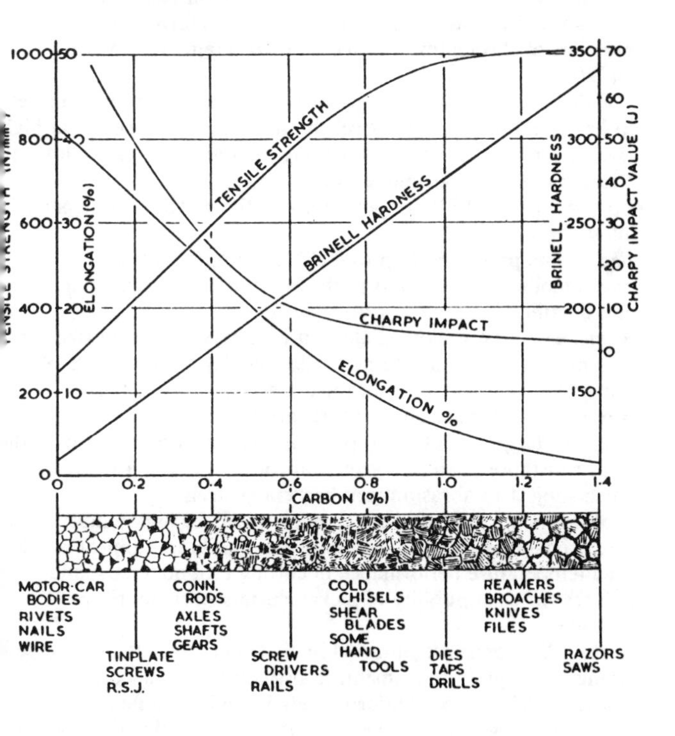

3.2.4 Ferrous metals: alloying elements

Alloy steels are carbon steels containing less than 1% carbon but to which other metals have been added in sufficient quantities to alter the properties of the steel significantly. The more important alloying elements are as follows:

Aluminium Up to 1% aluminium in alloy steels enables them to be given a hard, wear-resistant skin by the process of *nitriding*.

Chromium The presence of small amounts of chromium stabilizes the formation of hard carbides. This improves the response of the steel to heat treatment. The presence of large amounts of chromium improves the corrosion resistance and heat resistance of the steel (e.g. stainless steel). Unfortunately, the presence of chromium in a steel leads to grain growth (see *nickel*).

Cobalt Cobalt induces sluggishness into the response of a steel to heat treatment. In tool steels it allows them to operate at high level temperatures without softening. It is an important alloying element in some high speed steels.

Copper Up to 0.5% copper improves the corrosion resistance of alloy steels.

Lead The presence of up to 0.2% lead improves the machinability of steels, but at the expense of reduced strength and ductility.

Manganese This alloying element is always present in steels up to a maximum of 1.5% to neutralize the deleterious effects of impurities carried over from the extraction process. It also promotes the formation of stable carbides in quench-hardened steels. In larger quantities (up to 12.5%) manganese improves the wear resistance of steels by spontaneously forming a hard skin when subject to abrasion (self-hardening steels).

Molybdenum This alloying element raises the high temperature creep resistance of steels; stabilizes their carbides; improves the high temperature performance of cutting tool materials; and reduces the susceptibility of nickel-chrome steels to 'temper brittleness'.

Nickel The presence of nickel in alloy steels results in increased strength and grain refinement. It also improves the corrosion resistance of the steel. Unfortunately it tends to soften the steel by graphitizing any carbides present. Since nickel and chromium have opposite properties they are frequently combined together (nickel-chrome steels). Their advantages are complementary, whilst their undesirable effects are cancelled out.

Phosphorus This is a residual element from the extraction process. It causes weakness in the steel, and usually care is taken to reduce its presence to below 0.05%. Nevertheless, it can improve machinability by acting as an internal lubricant. In larger quantities it also improves the fluidity of cast steels and cast irons.

Silicon The presence of up to 0.3% silicon improves the fluidity of casting steels and cast irons without the weakening effects of phosphorus. Up to 1% silicon improves the heat resistance of steels. Unfortunately, like nickel, it is a powerful graphitizer and is never added in large quantities to high carbon steels. It is used to enhance the magnetic properties of 'soft' magnetic materials as used for transformer laminations and the stampings for electric motor stators and rotors.

Sulphur This is also a residual element from the extraction process. Its presence greatly weakens steel, and every effort is made to refine it out; in addition, manganese is always present in steels to nullify the effects of any residual sulphur. Nevertheless, sulphur is sometimes deliberately added to low carbon steels to improve their machinability where a reduction in component strength can be tolerated (sulphurized free-cutting steels).

Tungsten The presence of tungsten in alloy steels promotes the formation of very hard carbides and, like cobalt, induces sluggishness into the response of the steel to heat treatment. This enables tungsten steels (high speed steels) to retain their hardness at high temperatures. Tungsten alloys form the bases of high duty tool and die steels.

Vanadium This element enhances the effects of the other alloying elements present and has many and varied effects on alloy steels:

(a) Its presence promotes the formation of hard carbides.
(b) It stabilizes the *martensite* in quench-hardened steels and thus improves hardenability and increases the limiting ruling section of the steel.
(c) It reduces grain growths during heat treatment and hot working processes.
(d) It enhances the 'hot hardness' of tool steels and die steels.
(e) It improves the fatigue resistance of steels.

3.2.5 Low alloy constructional steels

Type of steel	Relevant spec'n. BS 970	Composition %	Condition	Mechanical properties: Yield stress N/mm^2	Tensile stress N/mm^2	Elongation %	Izod J	Heat treatment	Uses
Low manganese	150M28	0.28 C 1.50 Mn	Normalized	355	587	20	—	Oil-quench from 860°C (water-quench for sections over 38 mm diameter). Temper as required	Automobile axles, crankshafts, connecting rods etc. where a relatively cheap steel is required
Nickel-manganese	503M40	0.40 C 0.90 Mn 1.00 Ni	Quenched and tempered at 600°C	494	695	25	91	Oil-quench from 850°C; temper between 550 and 660°C and cool in oil or air	Crankshafts, axles, connecting rods; other parts in the automobile industry and in general engineering
Manganese-molybdenum	608M38	0.38 C 1.50 Mn 0.50 Mo	28.5 mm bar, o.q. and tempered at 600°C	1000	1130	19	70	Oil-quench from 830–850°C; temper between 550 and 650°C and cool in oil or air	A substitute for the more highly alloyed nickel-chrome-molybdenum steels
Nickel-chromium	653M31	0.31 C 0.60 Mn 3.00 Ni 1.00 Cr	28.5 mm bar, o.q. and tempered at 600°C	819	927	23	104	Oil-quench from 820–840°C; temper between 550 and 650°C. Cool in oil to avoid 'temper brittleness'	Highly stressed parts in automobile and general engineering, e.g. differential shafts, stub axles, connecting rods, high tensile studs, pinion shafts

Nickel-chromium-molybdenum	817M40	0.40 C 0.55 Mn 1.50 Ni 1.20 Cr 0.30 Mo	O.q. and tempered at 200°C	—	2010	14	27	Oil-quench from 830–850°C; 'light temper' 180–200°C; 'full temper' 550–650°C; cool in oil or air	Differential shafts, crankshafts and other highly stressed parts where fatigue and shock resistance are important; in the 'light tempered' condition it is suitable for automobile gears; can be surface hardened by nitriding
			O.q. and tempered at 600°C	988	1080	22	69		
	835M30	0.30 C 0.55 Mn 4.25 Ni 1.25 Cr 0.30 Mo	Air-hardened and tempered at 200°C	1470	1700	14	35	Air-harden from 820–840°C; temper at 150–200°C and cool in air	An air-hardening steel for aero-engine connecting rods, valve mechanisms, gears, differential shafts and other highly stressed parts; suitable for surface hardening by cyanide or carburizing
Manganese-nickel-chromium-molybdenum	945M38	0.38 C 1.40 Mn 0.75 Ni 0.50 Cr 0.20 Mo	28.5 mm bar, o.q. from 850°C and tempered at 600°C	958	1040	21	85	Oil-quench from 830–850°C; temper at 550–660°C, and cool in air	Automobile and genera! engineering components requiring a tensile strength of 700 to 1000 N/mm^2

3.2.6 Alloy tool and die steels

Type of steel	*Relevant specification*	*Composition %*	*Heat treatment*	*Uses*
'60' carbon-chromium	BS 970 : 526M60	0.60 C 0.65 Mn 0.65 Cr	Oil-quench from 800–850°C. Temper: (a) For cold-working tools at 200–300°C (b) For hot-working tools at 400–600°	Blacksmith's and boilermaker's chisels and other tools; mason's and miner's tools; vice jaws; hot stamping and forging dies
1% carbon chromium	BS 970 : 534A99	1.00 C 0.45 Mn 1.40 Cr	Oil-quench from 810°C; temper at 150°C	Ball and roller bearings; instrument pivots; cams; small rolls
High carbon, high chromium	BS 4659 : BD3	2.10 C 0.30 Mn 12.50 Cr	Heat slowly to 750–800°C and then raise to 960–990°C. Oil-quench (small sections can be air cooled). Temper at 150–400°C for 30–60 minutes	Blanking punches, dies and shear blades for hard, thin materials; dies for moulding abrasive powders, e.g. ceramics; master gauges; thread rolling dies
¼% vanadium	—	1.00 C 0.25 Mn 0.20 V	Water-quench from 850°C; temper as required	Cold drawing dies etc.
4% vanadium	—	1.40 C 0.40 Mn 0.40 Cr 0.40 Mo 3.60 V	Water-quench from 770°C; temper at 150–300°C	Cold heading dies etc.

Hot working die steel	BS 4659 : BH12	0.35 C 1.00 Si 5.00 Cr 1.50 Mo 0.40 V 1.35 W	Pre-heat to 800°C, soak and then heat quickly to 1020°C and air cool. Temper at 540–620°C for 1½ hours	Extrusion dies, mandrels and noses for aluminium and copper alloys; hot forming, piercing, gripping and heading tools; brass forging and hot pressing dies
High speed steels 18% tungsten	BS 4659 : BT1	0.75 C 4.25 Cr 18.00 W 1.20 V	Quench in oil or air blast from 1290–1310°C. Double temper at 565°C for 1 hour	Lathe, planar and shaping tools; millers and gear cutters; reamers; broaches; taps; dies; drills; hacksaw blades; bandsaws; roller bearings at high temperatures (gas turbines)
12% cobalt	BS 4659 : BT6	0.80 C 4.75 Cr 22.0 W 1.50 V 0.50 Mo 12.0 Co	Quench in oil or air blast from 1300–1320°C. Double temper at 565°C for 1 hour	Lathe, planing and shaping tools, milling cutters, twist drills etc. for exceptionally hard materials; has maximum red hardness and toughness; suitable for severest machining duties, e.g. manganese steels and high tensile steels, close-grained cast irons
Molybdenum '562'	BS 4659 : BM2	0.83 C 4.25 Cr 6.50 W 1.90 V 5.00 Mo	Quench in oil or air blast from 1250°C. Double temper at 565°C for 1 hour	Roughly equivalent to the standard 18–4–1 tungsten high speed steel but tougher; drills, reamers, taps, milling cutters, punches, threading dies, cold forging dies
9% Mo–8% Co	BS 4659 : BM42	1.00 C 3.75 Cr 1.65 W 1.10 V 9.50 Mo 8.25 Co	Quench in oil or air blast from 1180–1210°C. Triple temper at 530°C for 1 hour	Similar uses to the 12% Co–22% W high speed steel

Note: BS 4659 coding is based upon that of the American AISI coding except that the BSI coding has the prefix letter B.

3.2.7 Stainless and heat resisting steels

				Typical mechanical properties					
Type of steel	*Relevant specification*	*Composition* %	*Condition*	*Yield stress* N/mm^2	*Tensile strength* N/mm^2	*Elongation* %	*Hardness (Brinell)*	*Heat treatment*	*Uses*
Stainless iron (ferritic)	BS 970 : 403S17	0.04 C 0.45 Mn 14.00 Cr	Soft	340	510	31	—	Non-hardenable except by cold work	Wide range of domestic articles, forks, spoons; can be spun, drawn and pressed
Cutlery steel (martensitic)	BS 970 : 420S45	0.30 C 0.50 Mn 13.00 Cr	Cutlery temper Spring temper	— —	1670 1470	— —	534 450	Water- or oil-quench (or air-cool) from 950–1000°C. Temper: for cutlery, at 150–180°C; for springs, at 400–450°C	Cutlery and sharp-edged tools requiring corrosion resistance; circlips etc; approximately pearlitic in structure when normalized

18/8 stainless (austenitic)	BS 970 : 302S25	0.05 C 0.80 Mn 8.50 Ni 18.00 Cr	Softened	278	618	50	170	Non-hardening except by cold-work. (Cool quickly from 1050°C to retain carbon in solid solution)	Particularly suitable for domestic and decorative purposes; an austenitic steel
			Cold-rolled	803	896	30	—		
18/8 stainless (weld decay proofed)	BS 970 : 321S20	0.05 C 0.80 Mn 8.50 Ni 18.00 Cr 1.60 Ti	Softened	278	649	45	180	Non-hardening except by cold-work. (Cool quickly from 1050°C to retain carbon in solid solution)	A weld decay proofed steel (fabrication by welding can be safely employed); used extensively in nitric acid plant and similar chemical processes
			Cold-rolled	402	803	30	225		

3.2.8 Interpretation of BS 970 : *Wrought steels*

The random En numbers of the original BS 970 were changed in 1972 to a logical and informative six symbol code for each grade of steel. The code is built up as follows:

(a) The first three symbols are a number code indicating the type of steel:
   000 to 199 Carbon and carbon-manganese steels. The numbers represent the manganese content × 100.
   200 to 240 Free cutting steels. The second and third numbers indicate the sulphur content × 100.
   250 Silicon-manganese valve steels.
   300 to 499 Stainless and heat resisting steels.
   500 to 999 Alloy steels.
(b) The fourth symbol is a letter code:
   A The steel is supplied to a chemical composition determined by chemical analysis of a batch sample.
   H The steel is supplied to a hardenability specification.
   M The steel is supplied to a mechanical property specification.
   S The material is a stainless steel.
(c) The fifth and sixth symbol is a number code indicating the mean carbon content. The code is the actual mean carbon content × 100 (e.g. a steel of carbon content 0.04% would have a code of 04).

The following are examples of the BS 970 six figure code:

070M30 A plain carbon steel with a composition of 0.3% carbon and 0.7% manganese. The symbol M indicates that the steel has to meet a prescribed mechanical property specification.

230M07 A low carbon, free cutting steel with a composition of 0.07% carbon and 0.30% sulphur. Again, the letter M indicates that the steel has to meet a prescribed mechanical property specification.

070A26 A plain carbon steel with a composition of 0.26% carbon and 0.7% manganese. However, the symbol A indicates that the steel must meet a prescribed chemical composition specification.

Unfortunately, for alloy steels coded between 500 and 999 the logicality of the first three digits breaks down (see tables following).

In addition to the six symbol grading code, a *condition code* is applied. This code letter indicates the tensile strength range for a given steel after heat treatment (see tables following).

The final factor to be considered in the coding of wrought steels is the *limiting ruling section.* As explained in 3.1.9, this is the maximum diameter bar of given composition which, after appropriate heat treatment, will attain its specified mechanical properties.

For example, a plain carbon steel bar of composition 070M55 can attain condition R after heat treatment providing it is not greater than 100 mm in diameter. However, if it is to attain condition S, then the maximum diameter must be limited to 63 mm. In the first example the limiting ruling section is 100 mm in diameter, and in the second example the limiting ruling section is 63 mm in diameter.

British standard 970 : *Wrought steels* is published in six parts:

BS970 : Part 1 : 1972	Carbon and carbon-manganese steels including free cutting steels. Typical examples are listed in the following tables.
BS970 : Part 2 : 1970	Direct hardening alloy steels, including nitriding steels
BS970 : Part 3 : 1971	Case-hardening steels
BS970 : Part 4 : 1970	Stainless, heat resisting and valve steels
BS970 : Part 5 : 1972	Spring steels for hot formed springs
BS970 : Part 6 : 1973	SI metric values for use with BS970 : Parts 1 to 5 inclusive

Code letter/strength relationship

Condition code letter	*Tensile strength* (MPa) min.	max.
P	550	700
Q	620	770
R	700	850
S	770	930
T	850	1000
U	930	1080
V	1000	1150
W	1080	1240
X	1150	1300
Y	1240	1400
Z	1540	—

The condition code letter is applied in brackets after the six symbol code: for example, 150M19 (R), limiting ruling section 29 mm in diameter.

Carbon and carbon manganese steels: derived from BS 970 : Pt 1

Heat treatment condition symbol	*P*					*Q*					*R*					*S*					*T*				
Tensile strength range R_m (MPa)	550–700					620–770					690–850					770–930					850–1000				
Brinell hardness number range H_B	152–207					179–229					201–255					223–277					248–302				
Steel	LRS	R_e	A	I	$R_{p0.2}$	LRS	R_e	A	I	$R_{p0.2}$	LRS	R_e	A	I	$R_{p0.2}$	LRS	R_e	A	I	$R_{p0.2}$	LRS	R_e	A	I	$R_{p0.2}$
070M20	19	355	20	41	340	—	—	—	—	—	—	—	—	—	—	—	—	—	—	—	—	—	—	—	—
070M26	29	355	20	41	325	13	415	16	34	400	—	—	—	—	—	—	—	—	—	—	—	—	—	—	—
080M30	63	340	18	34	310	19	415	16	34	400	—	—	—	—	—	—	—	—	—	—	—	—	—	—	—
080M36		—	—	—	—	29	400	16	34	370	13	465	16	34	450	—	—	—	—	—	—	—	—	—	—
080M40	—	—	—	—	—	63	385	16	34	355	19	465	16	34	450	—	—	—	—	—	—	—	—	—	—
080M46	—	—	—	—	—	100	370	16	—	340	29	450	16	—	415	13	525	14	—	510	—	—	—	—	—
080M50		—	—	—	—	—	—	—	—	—	63	430	14	—	400	29	495	14	—	465	13	570	12	—	555
070M55		—	—	—	—	—	—	—	—	—	100	415	14	—	385	63	480	14	—	450	19	570	12	—	555
120M19	100	355	18	28	325	29	450	16	47	415	19	510	16	34	495	—	—	—	—	—	—	—	—	—	—
150M19	150	340	18	27	310	63	430	16	54	400	29	510	16	41	480	—	—	—	—	—	—	—	—	—	—
120M28		—	—	—	—	100	415	16	41	385	29	510	16	34	480	—	—	—	—	—	—	—	—	—	—
150M28			—	—	—	150	400	16	47	370	63	480	16	41	450	13	510	16	34	555	—	—	—	—	—
120M36			—	—	—	100	415	18	41	385	29	510	16	34	480	19	570	14	34	555	—	—	—	—	—
150M36	—	—	—	—	—	150	400	18	47	370	63	480	16	41	450	29	555	14	41	525	13	635	12	34	620
216M28	63	355	20	34	325	19	430	18	41	415	—	—	—	—	—	—	—	—	—	—	—	—	—	—	—
212M36	100	340	20	34	310	63	400	18	47	370	13	495	16	54	480	—	—	—	—	—	—	—	—	—	—
225M36	—	—	—	—	—	63	400	18	34	370	29	480	16	34	450	—	—	—	—	—	—	—	—	—	—
216M36	100	340	20	34	310	63	400	18	34	370	29	480	16	34	450	—	—	—	—	—	—	—	—	—	—
212M44		—	—	—	—	100	400	18	34	370	63	465	16	34	430	13	540	14	27	525		—	—	—	—
225M44	—	—	—	—	—	—	—	—	—	—	100	450	16	34	415	29	525	14	27	495	13	600	12	27	585

LRS = limiting ruling section A = elongation (%) $R_{p0.2}$ = 0.2% proof stress (MPa) R_e = yield stress (MPa) I = Izod impact value (J)

Direct hardening alloy steels: derived from BS 970 : Pt 2

Heat treatment condition symbol	*R*					*S*					*T*					*U*					*V*				
Tensile strength range R_m (MPa)	690–850					770–930					850–860					930–1080					1000–1160				
Brinell hardness number range H_B	201–255					223–277					248–302					269–331					293–352				
Steel	LRS	R_e	A	I	$R_{p0.2}$	LRS	R_e	A	I	$R_{p0.2}$	LRS	R_e	A	I	$R_{p0.2}$	LRS	R_e	A	I	$R_{p0.2}$	LRS	R_e	A	I	$R_{p0.2}$
530M40	100	530	17	54	510	63	585	12	54	570	29	680	13	54	665	—	—	—	—	—	—	—	—	—	—
605M30	150	530	17	54	510	100	585	15	54	570	63	680	13	54	665	29	755	12	47	740	19	850	12	—	835
605M36	250	490	15	34	480	100	585	15	54	570	63	680	13	54	665	29	755	12	47	740	19	850	12	47	835
	150	530	17	54	510	—	—	—	—	—	—	—	—	—	—	—	—	—	—	—	—	—	—	—	—
606M36	100	530	15	54	510	63	585	13	47	570	29	680	11	40	665	—	—	—	—	—	—	—	—	—	—
608M38	250	490	15	40	480	250	555	13	34	540	—	—	—	—	—	—	—	—	—	—	—	—	—	—	—
	150	530	17	54	510	150	585	15	54	570	100	680	13	54	665	63	755	12	47	740	29	850	12	47	835
640M40	150	530	17	54	510	100	585	15	54	570	63	680	13	54	665	29	755	12	47	740	—	—	—	—	—
653M31	—	—	—	—	—	150	585	15	54	570	100	680	13	54	665	63	755	12	47	740	—	—	—	—	—
708M40	150	530	17	54	510	100	585	15	54	570	63	680	13	54	665	29	755	12	47	740	—	—	—	—	—
709M40	250	490	15	34	480	250	555	13	27	540	—	—	—	—	—	—	—	—	—	—	—	—	—	—	—
	—	—	—	—	—	150	585	15	54	570	100	680	13	54	665	63	755	12	47	740	29	850	12	47	835
722M24*	—	—	—	—	—	—	—	—	—	—	250	650	13	40	635	150	755	12	47	740	—	—	—	—	—
	—	—	—	—	—	—	—	—	—	—	150	680	13	54	665	—	—	—	—	—	—	—	—	—	—

Composition (%) *Steel*	Carbon (C)	Silicon (Si)	Manganese (Mn)	Nickel (Ni)	Chromium (Cr)	Molybdenum (Mo)	Others
530M40	0.36–0.44	0.10–0.35	0.60–0.90	0.90–1.20	—	—	—
605M30	0.26–0.34	0.10–0.35	1.30–1.70	—	—	0.22–0.32	—
605M36	0.32–0.40	0.10–0.35	1.30–1.70	—	—	0.22–0.32	—
606M36	0.32–0.40	0.25 max.	1.30–1.70	—	—	0.22–0.32	sulphur 0.15–0.25
608M38	0.32–0.40	0.10–0.35	1.30–1.70	—	—	0.40–0.55	—
640M40	0.36–0.44	0.10–0.25	0.60–0.90	1.10–1.50	0.50–0.80	—	—
653M31	0.27–0.35	0.10–0.35	0.45–0.70	2.75–3.25	0.90–1.20	—	—
708M40	0.36–0.44	0.10–0.35	0.70–1.00	—	0.90–1.20	0.15–0.26	—
709M40	0.36–0.44	0.10–0.35	0.70–1.00	—	0.90–1.20	0.25–0.35	—
722M24*	0.20–0.28	0.10–0.35	0.45–0.70	—	3.00–3.50	0.45–0.65	—

* Nitriding alloy R_e = yield stress (MPa) I = Izod impact value (J) LRS = limiting ruling section (min) A = elongation (%) $R_{p0.2}$ = 0.2% proof stress

3.2.9 Grey cast irons

Cast iron is the name given to those ferrous metals containing more than 1.7% carbon. Since the maximum amount of carbon which can be held in solid solution as austenite (γ phase) is 1.7%, there will be excess carbon in all cast irons. This can be either taken up by the iron as cementite (combined carbon) or precipitated out as free carbon in the form of graphite flakes (uncombined carbon).

Slow cooling results in coarse gains of ferrite and large flakes of graphite.
More rapid cooling results in both ferrite and pearlite being present together with finer and more uniformly dispersed flakes of graphite. This results in a stronger, tougher and harder cast iron.
Rapid cooling results in very fine flake graphite dispersed throughout a matrix of pearlite. This results in a further increase in strength and hardness.

It is the grey appearance of the freshly fractured surface of cast iron, resulting from the flake graphite, that gives ferritic and pearlite cast irons the name *grey cast irons.*

Very rapid cooling and a reduction in silicon content results in all the carbon remaining combined as pearlite and cementite. Since no grey carbon is visible in the fractured surface, such cast iron is referred to as *white cast iron.* It is too hard and brittle to be of immediate use, but white iron castings are used as a basis for the malleable cast irons (see 3.2.10).

As well as iron and carbon the following elements are also present in cast irons:

Silicon This softens the cast iron by promoting the formation of uncombined carbon (graphite) at the expense of combined carbon (cementite). The silicon content is increased in small castings, which tend to cool rapidly, to promote the formation of ferrite and pearlite and prevent the formation of excess cementite.
Phosphorus This is a residual impurity from the extraction process. Its presence causes embrittlement and hardness. However, its presence is desirable in complex, decorative castings, where strength and shock resistance is relatively unimportant, as it increases the fluidity of molten iron.

Sulphur This is also a residual impurity. It stabilizes the cementite and prevents the formation of flake graphite, thus hardening the iron. The presence of iron sulphide (FeS) causes embrittlement.

Manganese This is added in small quantities to neutralize the effects of the sulphur. It also refines the grain of the cast iron and so increases its strength. Since excess manganese stabilizes the cementite and promotes hardness, the manganese content must be balanced with the silicon content.

A typical composition for a grey cast iron could be as follows (see also 3.2.13):

Carbon	3.3%
Silicon	1.5%
Manganese	0.75%
Sulphur	0.05%
Phosphorus	0.5%
Iron	remainder

British standard 1452

BS 1452 specifies the requirements of seven grades of grey cast iron. Unlike earlier standards it does not specify the composition or its processing in the foundry. BS 1452 specifies the properties, test conditions and quality control of the castings. How these are attained are left to the foundry in consultation with the customer. In addition the customer may specify or require:

(a) A mutually agreed chemical composition
(b) Casting tolerances, machining locations
(c) Test bars and/or test certificates
(d) Whether testing and inspection is to be carried out in the presence of the customer's representative
(e) Any other requirement such as hardness tests and their locations, non-destructive tests, and quality assurance.

The main properties of grey cast irons as specified in BS 1452 are given in the table on page 306. Note that for grey cast iron, hardness is not related to tensile strength but varies with casting section thickness and materials composition.

Section 3.2.9 (*continued*)
Grey cast irons

Grade	*UTS*	*0.1% proof stress*	*Compressive strength*	*0.1% Compressive proof stress*	*Shear strength*	*Modulus of elasticity*		*Modulus of rigidity*
						Tension	*Comp*	
	MPa	MPa	MPa	MPa	MPa	GPa	GPa	GPa
150	150	98	600	195	173	100	100	40
180	180	117	672	234	207	109	109	44
220	220	143	768	286	253	120	120	48
260	260	169	864	338	299	128	128	51
300	300	195	960	390	345	135	135	54
350	350	228	1080	455	403	140	140	56
400	400	260	1200	520	460	145	145	58

.2.10 Malleable cast irons

Blackheart process

/hite iron castings are heated out of contact with air at 850°C
950°C for 50 to 170 hours, depending upon the mass and the
iickness of the castings. Cementite breaks down into small
osettes of free graphite dispersed throughout a matrix of ferrite.
his results in an increase in malleability, ductility, tensile
rength and toughness.

Whiteheart process

/hite iron castings are heated in contact with an oxidizing
edium at about 1000°C for 70 to 100 hours, depending upon
e mass and the thickness of the castings. The carbon is drawn
ut of the castings and oxidized, leaving the castings with a
rritic structure at the surface and a pearlitic structure near the
ntre of the casting. There will be some residual rosettes of free
raphite. Whiteheart castings behave more like steel castings but
ave the advantage of a much lower melting point and greater
uidity at the time of casting.

Pearlitic process

his is similar to the blackheart process but is accompanied by
pid cooling. This prevents the formation of ferrite and flake
aphite and instead, results in some rosettes of graphite
ispersed throughout a matrix of pearlite. This results in castings
hich are harder, tougher and with a higher tensile strength, but
ith reduced malleability and ductility.

Type of cast iron	Condition	Properties			Applications
		UTS MPa	Elong. %	Hardness H_B	
Blackheart malleable	Annealed	300–350	6–12	150 max.	Wheel hubs, brake drums, conduit fittings, control levels ar pedals
Whiteheart malleable	Annealed	340–480	3–15	230 max.	Wheel hubs, bicycle and mot cycle frame fittings; gas, water, and stean pipe fittings
Pearlitic malleable	Normalized	450–700	3–6	150–290	Gears, coupling camshafts, axle housings, differential housings and components

British Standard 6681

BS 6681 specifies the requirements of malleable cast irons. The type of cast iron is indicated by the initial letter of the process thus:

W whiteheart malleable cast iron
B blackheart malleable cast iron
P pearlitic malleable cast iron.

This initial letter is followed by a two figure code designating tl minimum tensile strength in MPa of a 12 mm diameter test piec The test result is divided by ten to give the code. Finally, there are two figures representing the minimum elongation percentag on the specified gauge length.

Thus a complete designation for a malleable cast iron could t W35-04: this is a whiteheart malleable cast iron with a minimu tensile strength of 350 MPa on a 12 mm diameter test piece, an a minimum elongation of 4%.

As for grey irons, the specification is not concerned with the composition of the iron except for stating that the phosphorus content shall not exceed 0.12%. The composition and manufacturing processes are left to the discretion of the foundry in consultation with the customer.

The melt and the castings made from it will have satisfied the requirements of BS 6681 providing the test results and general quality of the castings meet the specifications laid down therein.

3.2.11 Spheroidal graphite cast irons

Spheroidal graphite cast iron is also known as nodular cast iron, ductile cast iron, high duty cast iron etc.

The addition of magnesium or cerium to molten grey cast iron prevents the formation of flake graphite upon cooling and solidification. Instead, the uncombined carbon is distributed as fine spheroids throughout the mass of the casting. This results in a more homogeneous structure having greater strength and ductility and less susceptibility to fatigue failure.

British standard 2789: *Spheroidal graphite cast irons*

BS 2789 specifies the requirements for spheroidal or nodular graphite cast irons. Again, the standard does not specify the chemical composition of the iron, its method of manufacture or any subsequent heat treatment. The standard is solely concerned with the properties, testing and quality control of the finished castings. How this is attained is left to the discretion of the foundry in consultation with the customer. It is a very comprehensive standard and it is only possible to review briefly some of its more important points within the scope of this chapter. The standard itself should be consulted for more detailed study.

This revised standard includes requirements for tensile strength, elongation, 0.2% proof stress and, for two grades of iron, resistance to impact. The standard covers the majority of commercial applications and includes the requirements for a total of nine grades of iron including two new grades: 900/2, which increases the range of mechanical properties available to designers; and 450/10, which has a higher proof stress to tensile stress ratio than the previous grades. The grades specified are:

900/2	This grade has a tempered martensitic structure.
800/2 700/2 600/3	These grades have a mainly pearlitic matrix, characterized by high tensile strength but at the expense of lower ductility and resistance to impact.
500/7 450/10	These intermediate grades have ferritic/pearlitic matrices combining strength with reasonable ductility and impact strength.
420/12	This grade has a mainly ferritic matrix of moderately high tensile strength, but with subsequent ductility and impact resistance.
400/18 350/20	These grades have wholly ferritic matrices with even greater ductility and even higher resistance to impact.

To interpret these grades, the first three figures indicate the minimum tensile strength in MPa and the final figure (after the / indicates the minimum elongation percentage. The addition of the letter L followed by a number in the case of 400/18L20 and 350/22L40 indicates that the impact strength must be attained at low temperatures, that is at −20°C and −40°C respectively.

The standard specifies the shape and dimensions of test pieces for tensile testing and it also specifies how the test bars are derived, that is whether they are cast separately or whether they are cast on to the main casting or on to a runner bar. If they are 'cast on', then they must not be separated from the main casting until they have cooled below 500°C.

Properties and uses of some typical spheroidal graphite cast irons

Type of cast iron	Grade	Properties				Applications
		UTS MPa	*0.2% Proof stress*	*Elong.* %	*Hardness* H_B	
Ferritic	350/22	350–420	220–270	12–22	160–212	Water main pipes, hydraulic cylinder and valve bodies, machine vice handles
Ferritic/pearlitic	450/10 to 600/3	450–600	320–370	3–10	160–269	
Pearlitic	700/2	700–800	420–480	2	229–352	These grades will surface harden and can replace steel forgings for such stressed applications as automobile engine camshafts and crankshafts
Martensitic	900/2	900	600	2	302–359	

3.2.12 Alloy cast irons

The alloying elements in cast irons are similar to those in alloy steels:

Nickel is used for grain refinement, to add strength, and to promote the formation of free graphite. Thus it toughens the casting.
Chromium stabilizes the combined carbon (cementite) present and thus increases the hardness and wear resistance of the casting. It also improves the corrosion resistance of the casting, particularly at elevated temperatures. As in alloy steels, nickel and chromium tend to be used together. This is because they have certain disadvantages when used separately which tend to offset their advantages. However, when used together the disadvantages are overcome whilst the advantages are retained.
Copper is used very sparingly as it is only slightly soluble in iron However, it is useful in reducing the effects of atmospheric corrosion.
Vanadium is used in heat resisting castings as it stabilizes the carbides and reduces their tendency to decompose at high temperatures.
Molybdenum dissolves in the ferrite and, when used in small amounts (0.5%), it improves the impact strength of the casting. It also prevents 'decay' at high temperatures in castings containing nickel and chromium. When molybdenum is added in larger amounts it forms double carbides, increases the hardness of castings with thick sections, and also promotes uniformity of the microstructure.

Martensitic cast irons contain between 4 and 6% nickel and approximately 1% chromium, for example Ni-hard cast iron. This is naturally martensitic in the cast state but, unlike alloys with rather less nickel and chromium, it does not need to be quench-hardened, thus reducing the possibility of cracking and distortion. It is used for components which need to resist abrasion. It can only be machined by grinding.
Austenitic cast irons contain between 11 and 20% nickel and up to 5% chromium. These alloys are corrosion resistant, heat resistant, tough, and non-magnetic.

Since the melting temperatures of alloy cast irons can be substantially higher than those for common grey cast irons, care must be taken in the selection of moulding sands and the preparation of the surfaces of the moulds. Increased venting of the moulds is also required as the higher temperatures cause more rapid generation of steam and gases. The furnace and crucible linings must also be suitable for the higher temperatures and the inevitable increase in maintenance costs is also a significant factor when working with high alloy cast irons.

The *growth* of cast irons is caused by the breakdown of pearlitic cementite into ferrite and graphite at approximately 700°C. This causes an increase in volume. This increase in volume is further aggravated by hot gases penetrating the graphite cavities and oxidizing the ferrite grains. This volumetric growth causes warping and the setting up of internal stresses leading to cracking, particularly at the surface. Therefore, where castings are called upon to operate at elevated temperatures, alloy cast irons should be used. A low cost alloy is Silal which contains 5% silicon and a relatively low carbon content. The low carbon content results in a structure which is composed entirely of ferrite and graphite with no cementite present. Unfortunately Silal is rather brittle because of the high silicon content. A more expensive alloy is Nicrosilal. This is an austenitic nickel-chromium alloy which is much superior in all respects for use at elevated temperatures.

Three typical alloy cast irons are listed in 3.2.13 together with their properties, composition and some uses.

3.2.13 Composition, properties and uses of some cast irons

		Representative mechanical properties		
Type of iron	*Composition* %	*Tensile strength* N/mm^2	*Hardness (Brinell)*	*Uses*
Grey iron	3.30 C 1.90 Si 0.65 Mn 0.10 S 0.15 P	Strengths vary with sectional thickness but are generally in the range 150–350 N/mm^2	—	Motor vehicle brake drums

continued

Type of iron	Composition %	Representative mechanical properties: Tensile strength N/mm²	Representative mechanical properties: Hardness (Brinell)	Uses
Grey iron	3.25 C 2.25 Si 0.65 Mn 0.10 S 0.15 P	Strengths vary with sectional thickness but are generally in the range 150–350 N/mm² (applies to all three grey iron types)	—	Motor vehicle cylinders and pistons
Grey iron	3.25 C 1.25 Si 0.50 Mn 0.10 S 0.35 P		—	Heavy machine castings
Phosphoric grey iron	3.60 C 1.75 Si 0.50 Mn 0.10 S 0.80 P		—	Light and medium water pipes
Chromidium	3.20 C 2.10 Si 0.80 Mn 0.05 S 0.17 P 0.32 Cr	275	230	Cylinder blocks, brake drums, clutch casings etc.
Wear and shock resistant	2.90 C 2.10 Si 0.70 Mn 0.05 S 0.10 P 1.75 Ni 0.10 Cr 0.80 Mo 0.15Cu	450	300	Crankshafts for diesel and petrol engines (good strength, shock resistance and vibration damping capacity)
Ni-resist	2.90 C 2.10 Si 1.00 Mn 0.05 S 0.10 P 15.00 Ni 2.00 Cr 6.00 Cu	215	130	Pump castings handling concentrated chloride solutions; an austenitic corrosion resistant alloy

3.3 Non-ferrous metals and alloys

3.3.1 Non-ferrous metals and alloys

Non-ferrous metals are all the known metals other than iron. Few of these metals are used in the pure state by engineers because of their relatively low strengths; two notable exceptions are copper and aluminium. Mostly they are used as the bases and alloying elements in both ferrous and non-ferrous alloys. Some non-ferrous metals are used for corrosion resistant coatings, e.g. galvanized iron (zinc coated, low carbon steel) and tinplate (tin coated, low carbon steel).

It is not possible within the scope of this book to consider the composition and properties of the very large range of non-ferrous materials available. The following sections are, therefore, only an introduction to the composition and properties of some of the more widely used non-ferrous metals and alloys. For further information the wide range of British Standards relating to non-ferrous metals and alloys should be consulted, as should the comprehensive manuals published by the metal manufacturers and their trade associations (e.g. Copper Development Association).

Only a limited number of non-ferrous alloys can be hardened by heat treatment. The majority can only be *work-hardened* by processing (e.g. cold rolling). Thus the *condition* of the metal, as the result of processing, has an important effect upon its properties, as will be shown in the following sections.

Other notable non-ferrous alloys, which are not included in this section, but which should be considered are

Magnesium (Elektron): used for ultra-lightweight castings
Nickel alloys (Nimonic): high temperature resistant alloys, used in jet engines and gas-turbines
Zinc based alloys (Mazak): used for pressure die-casting alloys.

3.3.2 High copper content alloys

Silver copper

The addition of 0.1% silver to high conductivity copper raises t
annealing temperature by 150°C with minimal loss of
conductivity. This avoids hard drawn copper components
softening when conductors are being soldered to them.

Cadmium copper

Like silver, cadmium has little effect upon the conductivity of th
copper. Cadmium strengthens, toughens, and raises the temperin
temperature of copper. Cadmium copper is widely used for
medium and low voltage overhead conductors, overhead
telephone and telegraph wires, and the overhead conductors for
electrified railways. In the annealed condition it has high
flexibility and is used for aircraft wiring where its ability to
withstand vibration without failing in fatigue is an important
safety factor.

Chromium copper

A typical alloy contains 0.5% chromium. It is one of the few
non-ferrous alloys which can be heat treated. Thus it can be
manipulated and machined in the ductile condition and
subsequently hardened and strengthened by heating to 500°C fo
approximately 2 hours. It has a relatively low conductivity
compared with silver copper and cadmium copper.

Tellurium copper

The addition of 0.5% tellurium makes the copper as machineabl
as free-cutting brass whilst retaining its high conductivity. It als
improves the very high corrosion resistance of copper. Tellurium
copper is widely used in electrical machines and switchgear in
hostile environments such as mines, quarries and chemical plant
The addition of traces nickel and silicon makes tellurium copper
heat treatable, but with some loss of conductivity.

Beryllium copper

This is used where mechanical rather than electrical properties are required. Beryllium copper is softened by heating it to 800°C and quenching it in water. In this condition it is soft and ductile and capable of being extensively cold worked. It can be hardened by reheating to 300°C to 320°C for upwards of 2 hours. The resulting mechanical properties will depend upon the extent of the processing (cold working) received prior to reheating. Beryllium copper is widely used for instrument springs, flexible metal bellows and corrugated diaphragms for aneroid barometers and altimeters, and for the Bourdon tubes in pressure gauges. Hand tools made from beryllium copper are almost as strong as those made from steel, but will not strike sparks from other metals or from flint stones. Thus tools made from beryllium are used where there is a high risk of explosion, for example mines, oil refineries, oil rigs and chemical plants.

3.3.3 Wrought copper and copper alloys: condition code

O — material in the annealed condition (soft)
M — material in the 'as manufactured' condition
¼H — material with quarter-hard temper (due to cold working)
½H — material with half-hard temper
H — material with fully-hard temper
EH — material with extra-hard temper
SH — material with spring-hard temper
ESH — material with extra-spring-hard temper.

The above are listed in order of ascending hardness.

Materials which have acquired a hard temper due to cold working can have their hardness reduced and their ductility increased by heat treatment (e.g. annealing or solution treatment).

For further information see BS 2870. See also 3.3.16 and 3.3.21.

3.3.4 Copper sheet, strip and foil

Designation	*Material*	*Copper Including silver %*	*Tin %*	*Lead %*	*Iron %*	*Nickel %*	*Arsenic %*	*Antimony %*	*Bismuth %*	*Phosphorus %*	*Oxygen %*	*Selenium %*	*Tellurium %*	*Total impurities %*	*Complies with or falls within ISO*
C101	Electrolytic tough pitch high conductivity copper	**99.90** (min.)	—	0.005	—	—	—	—	0.001	—	—	—	—	0.03 (excl. oxygen and silver)	Cu-ETP (ISO 1337)
C102	Fine refined tough pitch high conductivity copper	**99.90** (min.)	—	0.005	—	—	—	—	0.0025	—	—	—	—	0.04 (excl. oxygen and silver)	Cu-FRHC (ISO 1337)
C103	Oxygen free high conductivity copper	**99.95**	—	0.005	—	—	—	—	0.001	—	—	—	—	(excl. oxygen and silver)	Cu-OF (ISO 1337)
C104	Tough pitch non-arsenical copper	**99.85**	0.01	0.01	0.01	0.05	0.02	0.005	0.003	—	0.10	0.02	0.01	0.05 (excl. nickel, oxygen and silver)	Cu-FRTP (ISO 1337)
C106	Phosphorus deoxidized non-arsenical copper	**99.85**	0.01	0.01	0.03	0.10	0.05	0.01	0.003	**0.013/ 0.050**	—	Se + Te 0.20	0.01	0.06 (excl. silver, arsenic, nickel and phosphorus)	Cu-DHP (ISO 1337)

These properties are common to C101, C102, C103, C104 and C106 as listed above

Condition	Thickness		Tensile strength		Elongation on 50 mm (min.) %	Hardness HV	Bend test			
							Transverse bend		Longitudinal bend	
	Over mm	Up to and including mm	Up to and including 450 mm wide (min.) N/mm²	Over 450 mm wide (min.) n/mm²			Angle degrees	Radius	Angle degrees	Radius
O	0.5	10.0	210	210	35	55 (max.)	180	close	180	close
M	3.0	10.0	210	210	35	65 (max.)	180	close	180	close
½H	0.5	2.0	240	240	10	70/95	180	*t*	180	*t*
	2.0	10.0	240	240	15	70/95	180	*t*	180	*t*
	0.5	2.0	310	280	—	90 *min.*	90	*t*	90	*t*
H	2.0	10.0	290	280	—	—	—	—	—	—

Based upon BS 2870 : 1980, which should be consulted for full information.
For essential alloying elements, limits are in **bold type**. Unless otherwise stated, figures in total impurities column include those in lighter type. Unless otherwise indicated, all limits are maxima.
Note: $N/mm^2 = MPa$.

3.3.5(a) Brass sheet, strip and foil: binary alloys of copper and zinc

Designation	Material	Copper %	Lead %	Iron %	Zinc %	Total impurities %	Condition	Thickness: Over mm	Thickness: Up to and including mm	Tensile strength: Up to and including 450 mm wide (min.) N/mm²	Tensile strength: Over 450 mm wide (min.) N/mm²
CZ125	Cap copper	**95.0/98.0**	0.02	0.05	**Rem.**	0.025	O	—	10	—	—
CZ101	90/10	**89.0/91.0**	0.05	0.10	**Rem.**	0.40	O	—	10.0	245	245
							½H	—	3.5	310	380
	Brass						½H	3.5	10.0		
							H	—	10.0	350	325
CZ102	85/15 Brass	**84.0/86.0**	0.05	0.10	**Rem.**	0.40	O	—	10.0	245	245
							½H	—	3.5	325	295
							½H	3.5	10.0		
							H	—	10.0	370	340
CZ103	80/20 brass	**79.0/81.0**	0.05	0.10	**Rem.**	0.40	O	—	10.0	265	265
							½H	—	3.5	340	310
							½H	3.5	10.0		
							H	—	10.0	400	370

Further properties for the materials listed above

Designation	Elongation on 50 mm	Vickers hardness HV				Bend test				Complies with or falls within ISO
		Up to and including 450 mm wide		Over 450 mm wide		Transverse bend		Longitudinal bend		
	min. %	min.	max.	min.	max.	Angle degree	Radius	Angle degree	Radius	
CZ125	—	—	75	—	75	180	close	180	close	—
CZ101	35	—	75	—	75	180	close	180	close	ISO 426/1 Cu Zn 10
	7	95	—	85	—	180	close	180	close	
						180	*t*	180	*t*	
	3	110	—	100	—	90	2*t*	90	*t*	
CZ102	35	—	75	—	75	180	close	180	close	ISO 426/1 CuZn 15
	7	95	—	85	—	180	close	180	close	
						180	*t*	180	*t*	
	3	110	—	100	—	90	2*t*	90	*t*	
CZ103	40	—	80	—	80	180	close	180	close	ISO 426/1 Cu Zn 20
	10	95	—	85	—	180	close	180	close	
						180	*t*	180	*t*	
	5	120	—	110	—	90	2*t*	90	*t*	

3.3.5(b) Brass sheets, strip and foil: binary alloys of copper and zinc

Designation	Material	Copper %	Lead %	Iron %	Zinc %	Total impurities %	Condition	Thickness Over mm	Thickness Up to and including mm	Tensile strength Up to and including 450 mm wide (min.) N/mm²	Tensile strength Over 450 mm wide (min.) N/mm²
CZ106	70/30 Cartridge brass	**68.5/71.5**	0.05	0.05	**Rem.**	0.30	O	—	10.0	280	280
							$\frac{1}{4}$H	—	10.0	325	325
							$\frac{1}{2}$H	—	3.5	350	340
							$\frac{1}{2}$H	3.5	10.0		
							H	—	10.0	415	385
CZ107	2/1 brass	**64.0/67.0**	0.10	0.10	**Rem.**	0.40	O	—	10.0	280	280
							$\frac{1}{4}$H	—	10.0	340	325
							$\frac{1}{2}$H	—	3.5	385	350
							$\frac{1}{2}$H	3.5	10.0		
							H	—	10.0	460	415
							EH	—	10.0	525	—
CZ108	Common brass	**62.0/65.0**	0.30	0.20	**Rem.**	0.50 (excl. lead)	O	—	10.0	280	280
							$\frac{1}{4}$H	—	10.0	340	325
							$\frac{1}{2}$H	—	3.5	358	350
							$\frac{1}{2}$H	3.5	10.0		
							H	—	10.0	460	415
							EH	—	10.0	525	—

Further properties for the materials listed above

Designation	Elongation on 50 mm	Vickers hardness HV				Bend test				Complies with or falls within ISO
		Up to and including 450 mm wide		*Over 450 mm wide*		*Transverse bend*		*Longitudinal bend*		
	min. %	*min.*	*max.*	*min.*	*max.*	*Angle* degree	*Radius*	*Angle* degree	*Radius*	
CZ106	50	—	80	—	80	180	close	180	close	ISO 426/1 Cu Zn 30
	35	75	—	75	—	180	close	180	close	
	20	100	—	95	—	{ 180	close	180	close	
						{ 180	*t*	180	*t*	
	5	125	—	120	—	90	2*t*	90	*t*	
CZ107	40	—	80	—	80	180	close	180	close	ISO 426/1 Cu Zn 33
	30	75	—	75	—	180	close	180	close	
	15	110	—	100	—	{ 180	close	180	close	
						{ 180	*t*	180	*t*	
	5	135	—	125	—	90	2*t*	90	*t*	
	—	165	—	—	—	—		90	2*t*	
CZ108		1	2	3	4	5	6	7	8	ISO 426/1 Cu Zn 37

Based upon BS 2870 : 1980, which should be consulted for full information.
For essential alloying elements, limits are in **bold type**. Unless otherwise stated, figures in total impurities column include those in lighter type. Unless otherwise indicated, all limits are maxima.
Note: $N/mm^2 = MPa$.

3.3.6 Brass sheet, strip and foil: special alloys and leaded brasses

Designation	*Material*	*Copper* %	*Tin* %	*Lead* %	*Iron* %	*Zinc* %	*Aluminium* %	*Arsenic* %	*Total impurities* %	*Condition*	*Thickness up to and including* mm
CZ110	Aluminium brass	**76.0/78.0**	—	**0.04**	**0.06**	**Rem.**	**1.80/2.30**	**0.02/0.05**	0.30	M O	10.0 10.0
CZ112	Naval brass	**61.0/63.5**	**1.0/1.4**	—	—	**Rem.**	—	—	0.75	Mor O H	10.0 10.0
CZ118	Leaded brass 64% Cu 1% Pb	**63.0/66.0**	—	**0.75/1.5**	—	**Rem.**	—	—	0.30	½H H EH	6.0 6.0 6.0
CZ119	Leaded brass 62% Cu 2% Pb	**61.0/64.0**	—	**1.0/2.5**	—	**Rem.**	—	—	0.30	½H H EH	6.0 6.0 6.0
CZ120	Leaded brass 59% Cu 2% Pb	**58.0/60.0**	—	**1.5/2.5**	—	**Rem.**	—	—	0.30	½ H EH	6.0 6.0 6.0
CZ123	60/40 low lead brass: stamping brass	**59.0/62.0**	—	**0.3/0.8**	—	**Rem.**	—	—	0.30	M	10.0

Properties for the materials listed above

Designation	*Tensile strength (min.)*	*Elongation on 50 mm*	*Vickers hardness HV*		*Bend test*				*Complies with or falls within ISO*
					Transverse bend		*Longitudinal bend*		
	N/mm²	*(min.)* %	*min.*	*max.*	*Angle* degrees	*Radius*	*Angle* degrees	*Radius*	
CZ110	340	45	—	—	—	—	—	—	ISO 462/2
	310	50	—	80	180	close	180	close	Cu Zn 20/Al2
CZ112	340	25	—	—	180	*t*	180	*t*	—
	400	20	—	—	—	—	90	*t*	
CZ118	370	10	110	140	—	—	—	—	
	430	5	140	165	—	—	—	—	—
	510	3	165	190	—	—	—	—	
CZ119	370	10	110	140	—	—	—	—	
	430	5	140	165	—	—	—	—	—
	510	3	165	190	—	—	—	—	
CZ120	—	10	110	140	—	—	—	—	ISO 426/2
	510	5	140	165	—	—	—	—	Cu Zn 39/Pb 2
	575	3	165	190	—	—	—	—	
CZ123									ISO 426/2
	370	—	20	—	—	—	—	—	Cu Zn 40/Pb

Based upon BS 2870 : 1980, which should be consulted for full information.
For essential alloying elements, limits are in **bold type**. Unless otherwise stated, figures in total impurities column include those in lighter type. Unless otherwise indicated all limits are maxima.
Note: N/mm^2 = MPa.

3.3.7 Phosphor bronze sheet, strip and foil

Designation	*Material*	*Copper* %	*Tin* %	*Lead* %	*Phosphorus* %	*Zinc* %	*Total impurities* %	*Condition*	*Thickness up to and including* mm	*Tensile strength* *Up to and including 450 mm wide (min.)* N/mm²	*Tensile strength* *Over 450 mm wide (min.)* N/mm²
PB101	4% phosphor bronze (copper-tin-phosphorus)	**Rem.**	**3.5/4.5**	0.2	**0.02/0.40**	0.30	0.50	O	10.0	295	259
								$\frac{1}{4}$H	10.0	340	340
								$\frac{1}{2}$H	10.0	430	400
								H	6.0	510	495
								EH	6.0	620	—
PB102	5% phosphor bronze (copper-tin-phosphorus)	**Rem.**	**4.5/5.5**	0.02	**0.02/0.40**	0.30	0.50	O	10.0	310	310
								$\frac{1}{4}$H	10.0	350	350
								$\frac{1}{2}$H	10.0	495	460
								H	6.0	570	525
								EH	6.0	645	—
								SH	0.9	—	—
PB103	7% phosphor bronze (copper-tin-phosphorus)	**Rem.**	**5.5/7.5**	0.02	**0.02/0.40**	0.30	0.50	O	10.0	340	340
								$\frac{1}{4}$H	10.0	385	385
								$\frac{1}{2}$H	10.0	525	460
								H	6.0	620	540
								EH	6.0	695	—
								SH	0.9	—	—
								ESH	0.6	—	—

Designation	0.2% proof stress		Elongation on 50 mm	Vickers hardness HV				Bend test				Complies with or falls within ISO
	Up to and including 450 mm wide	Over 450 mm wide		Up to and including 450 mm wide		Over 450 mm wide		Transverse bend		Longitudinal bend		
	(min.) N mm^2	(min.) N MM^2	%	min.	max.	min.	max.	Angle degrees	Radius	Angle degrees	Radius	
PB101	—	—	40	—	80	—	80	180	close	180	close	ISO 427 Cu Sn 4
	125	125	30	100	—	100	—	180	close	180	close	
	390	340	8	150	—	130	—	90	*t*	180	*t*	
	480	435	4	180	—	150	—	—	—	90	*t*	
	580	—	—	180	—	—	—	—	—	90	*t*	
PB102	—	—	45	—	85	—	85	180	close	180	close	
	140	140	35	110	—	110	—	180	close	180	close	
	420	385	10	160	—	140	—	90	*t*	180	*t*	ISO 427 Cu Sn 4
	520	480	4	180	—	160	—	—	—	90	*t*	
	615	—	—	200	—	—	—	—	—	90	*t*	
	—	—	—	215	200	—	—	—	—	90	*t*	
PB103	—	—	50	—	90	—	90	180	close	180	close	
	200	200	40	115	—	115	—	180	close	180	close	
	440	380	12	170	—	150	—	90	*t*	180	*t*	ISO 427 Cu Sn 6
	550	480	6	200	—	165	—	—	—	90	*t*	
	650	—	—	215	—	—	—	—	—	90	*t*	
	—	—	—	220*	240*	—	—	—	—	90	*t*	
		—	—	220*	—	—	—	—	—	—	—	

* Up to 150 mm wide only.

Based upon BS 2870 : 1980, which should be consulted for full information.

For essential alloying elements, limits are in **bold type**. Unless otherwise stated, figures in total impurities column include those in lighter type. Unless otherwise indicated, all limits are maxima.

Note: N mm^2 = MPa.

Aluminium bronze alloys – introduction to Table 3.3.8

Despite their name, these are *copper* based alloys containing up to 10 per cent (nominal) aluminium. They combine relatively high strength with excellent corrosion resistance at high temperatures. These alloys can be grouped into two categories.

Single-phase alloys
The single phase, or α-alloys, contain up to 5 per cent aluminium. They are highly ductile and corrosion resistant. Because the colour of the α-alloys resembles 18 carat gold, this alloy is widely used in the manufacture of costume jewelry. This range of alloys are also widely used in engineering, particularly for pipe work where corrosion resistance at high temperatures is required.

Duplex-phase alloys
These alloys contain approximately 10 per cent aluminium and can be heat treated in a similar manner to plain carbon steels. Heating followed by slow cooling anneals this alloy giving a primary α-phase (analogous to ferrite) in a eutectoid matrix of $\alpha+\gamma_2$ (analogous to pearlite). This results in the alloy becoming relatively soft and ductile. Heating followed by rapid cooling (quenching) produces a hard β' structure (analogous to martensite). An example of the composition and properties of a typical duplex-phase alloy is given in the following table.

The duplex phase alloys are also used for both sand- and die-casting where high strength combined with corrosion resistance and pressure tightness is required. However, these alloys are not easy to cast as the aluminium content tends to oxidize at their relatively high melting temperatures. Special precautions have to be taken to overcome this difficulty and these increase the cost of the process.

3.3.8 Aluminium bronze sheet, strip and foil

Designation	*Material*	*Copper* %	*Tin* %	*Lead* %	*Iron* %	*Nickel* %	*Zinc* %	*Aluminium* %	*Silicon* %
CA104	10% aluminium bronze (copper-aluminium-nickel-iron)	**Rem.**	0.10	0.05	**4.0/6.0**	**4.0/6.0**	0.40	**8.5/11.0**	0.10

Table continued from above

Manganese %	*Magnesium* %	*Total impurities* %	*Condition*	*Size up to and including* mm	*Tensile strength (min.)* N/mm²	*0.2% proof stress (min.)* N/mm²	*Elongation on 50 mm (min.)* %	*Complies with or falls within ISO*
0.50	0.05	0.05 (excl. Mn)	M	10	700	380	10	ISO 428 Cu Al 10 Fe 5 Ni 5

Based upon BS 2870 : 1980, which should be consulted for full information.
For essential alloying elements, limits are in **bold type**. Unless otherwise stated, figures in total impurities column include those in lighter type. Unless otherwise indicated, all limits are maxima.
Note: $N/mm^2 = MPa$.

3.3.9 Copper-nickel (cupro-nickel) sheet, strip and foil

Designation	*Material*	*Copper* %	*Zinc* %	*Lead* %	*Iron* %	*Nickel* %	*Manganese* %	*Sulphur* %	*Carbon* %	*Total impurities* %	*Condition*
CN102	90/10 copper-nickel-iron	**Rem.**	—	0.01	**1.00/ 2.00**	**10.0/ 11.0**	**0.50/ 1.00**	0.05	0.05	0.30	**M** **O**
CN104	80/20 copper-nickel	**79.0/ 81.0**	—	0.01	0.30	**19.0/ 21.0**	**0.05/ 0.50**	0.02	0.05	0.10	**O** **O**
CN105	75/25 copper-nickel	**Rem.**	0.20	—	0.30	**24.0/ 26.0**	**0.05/ 0.40**	0.02	0.05	0.35	**O** **O** **H**
CN107	70/30 copper-nickel-iron	**Rem.**	—	0.01	**0.40/ 1.00**	**30.0/ 32.0**	**0.05/ 1.50**	0.08	0.06	0.30	**O** **O**

Table continued from above

Designation	Thickness		Tensile strength	Elongation on 50 mm	Bend test: longitudinal and transverse bend		Vickers hardness HV	Complies with or falls within ISO
	Over	*Up to and including*			*Angle*	*Radius*		
	mm	(min.) mm	(min.) N/mm^2	%	degrees			
CN102	—	10.0	310	30	—	—	90 (max.)	ISO 429 Cu Ni 10 Fe 1 Mn
	—	10.0	280	40	—	—		
CN104	0.6	2.0	310	35	180	close	—	ISO 429 Cu Ni 20
	2.0	10.0	310	38	180	close		
CN105	0.6	2.0	340	30	180	close	—	ISO 429 Cu Ni 25
	2.0	10.0	340	35	180	close	—	
	0.6	10.0	—	—	—	—	155 (min.)	
CN107	0.6	2.0	370	30	180	close	—	ISO 429 Cu Ni 30 Mn 1 Fe
	2.0	10.0	370	35	180	close	—	

Based upon BS 2870 : 1980, which should be consulted for full information.
For essential alloying elements, limits are in **bold type**. Unless otherwise stated, figures in total impurities column include those in lighter type. Unless otherwise indicated, all limits are maxima.
Note: $N/mm^2 = MPa$.

3.3.10 Nickel-silver sheet, strip and foil

Designation	*Material*	*Copper* %	*Lead* %	*Iron* %	*Nickel* %	*Zinc* %	*Manganese* %	*Total impurities* %	*Condition*
NS103	10% nickel silver copper-nickel -zinc)	**60.0/65.0**	0.04	0.25	**9.0/11.0**	**Rem.**	**0.05/0.30**	0.50	O ½H H EH
NS104*	12% nickel silver (copper-nickel -zinc)	**60.0/65.0**	0.04	0.25	**11.0/13.0**	**Rem.**	**0.05/0.30**	0.50	O ½H H EH
NS105	15% nickel silver (copper-nickel -zinc)	**60.0/65.0**	0.04	0.30	**14.0/16.0**	**Rem.**	**0.05/0.50**	0.50	O ½H H EH
NS106	18% nickel silver (copper-nickel -zinc)	**60.0/65.0**	0.03	0.30	**17.0/19.0**	**Rem.**	**0.05/0.50**	0.50	O ½H H EH
NS107*	18% nickel silver (copper-nickel -zinc)	**54.0/56.0**	0.03	0.30	**17.0/19.0**	**Rem.**	**0.05/0.35**	0.50	—
NS111	Lead 10% nickel silver (copper-nickel -zinc-lead)	**58.0/63.0**	**1.0/ 2.0**	—	**9.0/11.0**	**Rem.**	**0.10/0.50**	0.50	O ½H H

Designation	Bend test				Vickers hardness HV		Thickness up to and including	Complies with or falls within ISO
	Transverse bend		Longitudinal bend					
	Angle degrees	Radius	Angle degrees	Radius	min.	max.	mm	
NS103	180	t	180	t	—	100	10.0	—
	180	t	180	t	125	—	10.0	
	90	t	90	t	160	—	10.0	
	—	—	90	t	185	—	10.0	
NS104*	180	t	180	t	—	100	10.0	—
	180	t	180	t	130	—	10.0	
	90	t	90	t	160	—	10.0	
	—	—	90	t	190	—	10.0	
NS105	180	t	180	t	—	105	10.0	—
	180	t	180	t	135	—	10.0	
	90	t	90	t	165	—	10.0	
	—	—	90	t	195	—	10.0	
NS106	180	t	180	t	—	110	10.0	ISO 430 Cu Ni 18 Zn 20
	180	t	180	t	135	—	10.0	
	90	t	90	t	170	—	10.0	
	—	—	90	t	200	—	10.0	
NS107*	—	—	—	—	—	—	—	ISO 430 Cu Ni 18 Zn 27
NS111	—	—	—	—	—	100	—	—
	—	—	—	—	150	180	—	
	—	—	—	—	160	—	—	

* For special requirements relevant to particular applications, see BS 2870 : 1980 Section 4.
Based upon BS 2870 : 1980, which should be consulted for full information.
For essential alloying elements, limits are in **bold type**. Unless otherwise stated, figures in total impurities column include those in lighter type. Unless otherwise indicated, all limits are maxima.

3.3.11 Miscellaneous wrought copper alloys

Designation[*‡]	C105	C107	C108	C109	CZ109	CZ111	CZ114	CZ115	CZ122	CZ127	CZ132
Material	Tough pitch arsenical copper	Phosphorus deoxidized arsenical copper	Cadmium copper	Tellurium copper	Lead-free 60/40 brass	Admiralty brass	High tensile brass	High tensile brass (soldering quality)	Leaded brass 58% Cu 2% Pb	Aluminium -nickel -silicon brass	Dezincification resistant brass
Availability‡	P	P, T	W, P	RS	FS, RS	T	FS RS	FS RS	FS RS	T	FS RS
Copper (%)	**99.20 (min)**	**99.20 (min)**	**Rem**	**Rem**	**59.0/62.0**	**70.0/73.0**	**56.0/60.0**	**56.0/59.0**	**56.5/60.0**	**81.0/86.0**	**Rem**
Tin (%)	0.03	0.01	—	—	—	**1.0/1.5**	**0.2/1.0**	**0.6/1.1**	—	0.10	0.20
Lead (%)	0.02	0.01	—	—	0.10	0.7	**0.5/1.5**	**0.5/1.5**	**1.0/2.5**	0.05	**1.7/2.8**
Iron (%)	0.02	0.03	—	—	—	0.6	**0.5/1.2**	**0.5/1.2**	0.30	0.25	0.30
Nickel (%)	0.15	0.15	—	—	—	—	—	—	—	**0.80/1.40**	**35.0/37.0**
Zinc (%)	—	—	—	—	**Rem**	**Rem**	**Rem**	**Rem**	**Rem**	**Rem**	**0.08/0.15**
Arsenic (%)	**0.3/0.5**	**0.3/0.5**	—	—	—	**0.02/0.06**	—	—	—	—	—
Antimony (%)	0.01	0.01	—	—	0.021	—	0.020	—	0.020	—	—
Aluminium (%)	—	—	—	—	—	—	1.5	0.2	—	**0.70/1.20**	—
Bismuth (%)	0.005	0.003	—	—	—	—	—	—	—	—	—
Cadmium (%)	—	—	**0.5/1.2**	—	—	—	—	—	—	—	—
Manganese (%)	—	—	—	—	—	—	**0.3/2.0**	**0.3/2.0**	—	0.10	—
Sulphur	—	—	—	—	—	—	—	—	—	—	—

Silicon (%)	—	—	—	—	—	—	—	—	—	**0.80/1.30**	—
Oxygen (%)	**0.70**	—	—	—	—	—	—	—	—	—	—
Phosphorus (%)	—	**0.013/0.050**	—	—	—	—	—	—	—	—	—
Tellurium (%)	Se + Te 0.03	0.010 Se + Te 0.20	—	**0.3/0.7**	—	—	—	—	—	—	—
Total impurities (%)	—	0.07 (excl. silver, arsenic, nickel, phosphorus	0.05	—	0.30 (excl. lead)	0.30	0.50	0.50	0.75	0.50 (excl. tin, lead, iron, manganese)	0.60

* These alloys are not included in BS 2870, except in appendix A, but are available in other product forms and other BS specifications.

† Oxygen-free high conductivity copper for special applications (C110) is found in BS 1433, BS 1977, BS 3839 and BS 4608. This material is used for conductors in electrical and electronic applications.

‡ Availability: T = tube, FS = forging stock, W = wire, RS = rods, sections, P = plate.

For essential alloying elements, limits are in **bold type**. Unless otherwise stated, figures in total impurities column include those in lighter type. Unless otherwise indicated all limits are maxima.

Section 3.3.11 (*continued*)

*Designation**	CA 102	C 105	CN 101	CN 108	NS 101	NS 102	NS 109	NS 112	CS 101
Material	7% Aluminium bronze	10% Aluminium bronze	95/5 Copper-nickel-iron	66/30/2/2 Copper-nickel-iron-manganese	Leaded 10% nickel brass	Leaded 14% nickel brass	25% nickel silver	15% leaded nickel silver (Cu-Ni-Zn-Pb)	Silicon bronze (Cu Si)
Availability†	T, P	P	P	T	FS RS	RS	W	RS	FS, W, RS, P
Copper (%)	**Rem**	**78.0/85.0**	**Rem**	**Rem**	**44.0/47.0**	**34.0/42.0**	**55.0/60.0**	**60.0/63.0**	**Rem**
Tin (%)	—	0.10	0.01	—	—	—	—	—	—
Lead (%)	—	0.05	0.01	—	**1.0/2.5**	**1.0/2.25**	0.025	0.5/1.0	—
Iron (%)	Ni + Fe + Mn **1.0/2.5** (optional) but between these limits	**1.5/3.5**	**1.05/1.35**	**1.7/2.3**	0.4	0.3	0.3	—	0.25
Nickel (%)	—	**4.0/7.0**	**5.0/6.0**	**29.0/32.0**	**9.0/11.0**	**13.0/15.0**	**24.0/26.0**	**14.0/16.0**	—
Zinc (%)	—	0.40	—	—	**Rem**	**Rem**	**Rem**	**Rem**	—
Arsenic (%)	—	—	0.05	—	—	—	—	—	—
Antimony (%)	—	—	0.01	—	—	—	—	—	—
Aluminium (%)	**6.0/7.5**	**8.5/10.5**	—	—	—	—	—	—	—
Silicon (%)	—	0.15	0.05	—	—	—	—	—	**3.15/3.25**

Magnesium (%)		0.05	—	—	—	—	—	—	—
Manganese (%)	see iron & nickel	**0.5/2.0**	**0.3/0.8**	**1.5/2.5**	**0.2/0.5**	**1.5/3.0**	**0.05/0.75**	**0.1/0.5**	**0.75/1.25**
Sulphur (%)	—	—	0.05	—	—	—	—	—	—
Carbon (%)	—	—	0.05	—	—	—	—	—	—
Phosphorus (%)	—	—	0.03	—	—	—	—	—	—
Total impurities (%)	0.50	0.50	0.30	0.30	0.30 (excl. iron)	0.30 (excl. iron)	0.50	0.50	0.50 (excl. iron)

* These alloys are not included in BS 2870, except in appendix A, but are available in other product forms and other BS specifications

† Availability: T = tube, FS = forging stock, W = wire, RS = rods, sections, P = plate.

For essential alloying elements, limits are in **bold type**. Unless otherwise stated, figures in total impurities column include those in lighter type. Unless otherwise indicated all limits are maxima.

3.3.12(a) Copper alloys for casting: group A

Designation	PB4		LPB1		LB2		LB4		LG1		LG2	
Material	Phosphor bronze (copper-tin -phosphorus)		Leaded phosphor bronze		Leaded bronze		Leaded bronze		Leaded gunmetal		Leaded gunmetal	
Nominal composition	Cu Sn 10 Pb P		Cu Sn 7 Pb P		Cu Sn 10 Pb 10		Cu Sn 5 Pb 9		Cu Sn 3 Pb 5 Zn 8		Cu Sn 5 Pb 5 Zn 5	
Elements	min. %	max. %	min. %	max. %	min. %	max. %	min. %	max. %	min %	max. %	min. %	max. %
Copper	**Remainder**		**Remainder**		**Remainder**		**Remainder**		**Remainder**		**Remainder**	
Tin	**9.5**	**11.0**	**6.5**	**8.5**	**9.0**	**11.0**	**4.0**	**6.0**	**2.0**	**3.5**	**4.0**	**6.0**
Zinc	—	**0.5**	—	**2.0**	—	**1.0**	—	**2.0**	**7.0**	**9.5**	**4.0**	**6.0**
Lead	—	**0.75**	**2.0**	**5.0**	**8.5**	**11.0**	**8.0**	**10.0**	**4.0**	**6.0**	**4.0**	**6.0**
Phosphorus	**0.4**	**1.0**	**0.33**	—	—	**0.1**	—	**0.1***	—	—	—	—
Nickel	—	**0.5**	—	**1.0**	—	**2.0**	—	**2.0**	—	**2.0**	—	**2.0**
Iron	—	—	—	—	—	0.15	—	0.25	—	—	—	—
Aluminium	—	—	—	—	—	0.01	—	0.01	—	0.01	—	0.01
Manganese	—	—	—	—	—	0.20	—	0.20	—	—	—	—
Antimony	—	—	—	0.25	—	**0.5**	—	**0.5**	—	—	—	—
Arsenic	—	—	—	—	—	—	—	—	—	—	—	—
Iron + arsenic + antimony	—	—	—	—	—	—	—	—	—	0.75	—	0.5

Silicon	—	—	—	—	—	0.02	—	0.02	—	0.02	—	0.02
Bismuth	—	—	—	—	—	—	—	—	—	0.10	—	0.05
Sulphur	—	0.1	—	0.1	—	0.1	—	0.1	—	0.10	—	—
Total impurities	—	0.5	—	0.5	—	0.5	—	0.5	—	1.0	—	0.80

* For continuous casting, phosphorus content may be increased to a maximum of 1.5% and alloy coded with suffix /L.
† For pressure tight castings in SCB 3 the aluminium content should not be greater than 0.02.
‡ DCB 1: 0.1% lead if required.
§ DCB3: nickel to be counted as copper.
For full range of alloys and further information see BS 1400.
For essential alloying elements, limits are in **bold type**. Unless otherwise stated, figures in total impurities column include those in lighter type. Unless otherwise indicated, all limits are maxima.

3.3.12(b) Further copper alloys for casting: group A

Designation	SCB 1		SCB 3		SCB 6		DCB 1		DCB 3		PCP 1	
Material	Brass for sand casting		Brass for sand casting		Brass for brazeable castings		Brass for die casting		Brass for die casting		Brass for pressure die casting	
Nominal composition	Cu Zn 25 Pb 3 Sn 2		Cu Zn 33 Pb 2		Cu 15 As		Cu Zn 40		Cu Zn 40 Pb		Cu Zn 40 Pb	
Elements	min. %	max. %	min. %	max. %	min. %	max. %	min. %	max. %	min. %	max. %	min. %	max. %
Copper	**70.0**	**80.0**	63.0	**67.0**	83.0	**88.0**	**59.0**	63.0	**58.0**	**62.0**	**57.0**	**60.0**
Tin	**1.0**	**3.0**	—	**1.5**	—	—	—	—	—	**1.0**	—	**0.5**
Zinc	**Remainder**		**Remainder**		**Remainder**		**Remainder**		**Remainder**		**Remainder**	
Lead	**2.0**	**5.0**	1.0	**3.0**	—	**0.5**	—	0.25‡	**0.5**	**2.5**	**0.5**	**2.5**
Phosphorus	—	—	—	0.05	—	—	—	—	—	—	—	—
Nickel	—	**1.0**	—	**1.0**	—	—	—	—	—	1.0§	—	—
Iron	—	**0.75**	—	**0.75**	—	—	—	0.5	—	**0.8**	—	**0.2**
Aluminium	—	0.01	—	0.1†	—	—	—	—	—	**0.8**	—	**0.5**
Manganese	—	—	—	0.2	—	—	—	—	—	**0.5**	—	—
Antimony	—	—	—	—	—	—	—	—	—	—	—	—
Arsenic	—	—	—	—	—	—	—	—	—	—	—	—
Iron + arsenic + antimony	—	—	—	—	0.05	0.20	—	—	—	—	—	—

Silicon	—	—	—	0.05	—	—	—	—	—	0.05	—	—
Bismuth	—	—	—	—	—	—	—	—	—	—	—	—
Sulphur	—	—	—	—	—	—	—	—	—	—	—	—
Total impurities	—	1.0	—	1.0	—	1.0 (incl. lead)	—	0.75	—	2.0 excl. Ni + Pb + Al)	—	**0.5**

* For continuous casting, phosphorus content may be increased to a maximum of 1.5% and alloy coded with suffix /L.
† For pressure tight castings in SCB 3 the aluminium content should not be greater than 0.02.
‡ DCB 1: 0.1% lead if required.
§ DCB3: nickel to be counted as copper.
For full range of alloys and further information see BS 1400.
For essential alloying elements, limits are in **bold type**. Unless otherwise stated, figures in total impurities column include those in lighter type. Unless otherwise indicated, all limits are maxima.

3.3.13(a) **Copper alloys for casting: group B**

Destination	HCC1		CC1-TF		PB1		PB2		CT1		LG4	
Material	High conductivity copper		Copper-chromium		Phosphor bronze (copper + tin + phosphorus)		Phosphor bronze (copper + tin + phosphorus		Copper tin		87/7/3/3 Leaded gunmetal	
Nominal composition	—		Cu Cr 1		Cu Sn 10 P		Cu Sn 11 P		Cu Sn 10		Cu Sn 7 PB 3 Zn 3	
Elements	min. %	max. %	min. %	max. %	min. %	max. %	min. %	max. %	min. %	max. %	min. %	max. %
Copper	See note*		**Remainder**		**Remainder**		**Remainder**		**Remainder**		**Remainder**	
Tin			—	—	**10.0**	**11.5**	**11.0**	**13.0**	**9.0**	**11.0**	**6.0**	**8.0‡**
Zinc			—	—	—	0.05	—	**0.30**	—	0.03	**1.5**	**3.0**
Lead			—	—	—	0.25	—	**0.50**	—	0.25	**2.5**	**3.5**
Phosphorus			—	—	**0.5**	**1.0**	**0.15**	**0.60**	—	**0.15†**	—	—
Nickel			—	—	—	0.1	—	**0.50**	—	0.25	—	**2.0‡**
Iron			—	—	—	0.1	—	0.1	—	0.20	—	0.20
Aluminium			—	—	—	0.1	—	0.01	—	0.01	—	0.01
Manganese			—	—	—	0.05	—	—	—	0.20	—	—
Antimony			—	—	—	0.05	—	—	—	0.20	—	0.25
Arsenic			—	—	—	—	—	—	—	—	—	0.15
Iron + arsenic + antimony			—	—	—	—	—	—	—	—	—	0.40

Silicon			—	—	—	0.02	—	0.02	—	0.01	—	0.01
Bismuth			—	—	—	—	—	—	—	—	—	0.05
Magnesium			—	—	—	—	—	—	—	—	—	—
Sulphur			—	—	—	0.05	—	0.1	0	0.05	—	—
Chromium			**0.50**	**1.25**	—	—	—	—	—	—	—	—
Total impurities	—	—	—	—	—	0.60	—	0.20	—	0.80	—	0.70

* HCC1 castings shall be made from the copper grades Cu-CATH-2, Cu-EPT-2 or Cu- FRHC, as specified in BS 6017.
† For continuous casting, phosphorus content may be increased to a maximum of 1.5% and the alloy coded with the suffix /L.
‡ Tin plus half nickel content shall be within the range 7.0–8.0%.
§ HTB1 subject also to microstructure requirements: see BS 1400 Clause 6.3.
For full range of alloys and further information see BS 1400.
For essential alloying elements, limits are in **bold type**. Unless otherwise stated, figures in total impurities column include those in lighter type.
Unless otherwise indicated, all limits are maxima.

3.3.13(b) Further copper alloys for casting: group B

Destination	AB1		AB2		CMA1		HTB1		HTB3	
Material	Aluminium bronze (copper-aluminium)		Aluminium bronze (copper-aluminium)		Copper-manganese-aluminium		High tensile brass§		High tensile brass	
Nominal composition	Cu Al 10 Fe 3		Cu Al 10 Fe 5 Ni 5		Cu Mn 13 Al 8 Fe 3 Ni 3		Cu Zn 31 Al Fe Mn		Cu Zn 28 Al 5 Fe Mn	
Elements	min. %	max. %	min. %	max. %	min. %	max. %	min. %	max. %	min. %	max. %
Copper	**Remainder**		**Remainder**		**Remainder**		**57.0**	—	**55.0**	—
Tin	—	0.1	—	0.1	—	**0.50**	—	**1.0**	—	**0.20**
Zinc	—	0.5	—	0.5	—	**1.00**	**Remainder**		**Remainder**	
Lead	—	0.03	—	0.3	—	0.05	—	**0.50**	—	**0.20**
Phosphorus	—	—	—	—	—	0.05	—	—	—	—
Nickel	—	**1.0**	**4.0**	**5.5**	**1.5**	**4.5**	—	**1.0**	—	**1.0**
Iron	**1.5**	**3.5**	**4.0**	**5.5**	**2.0**	**4.0**	**0.7**	**2.0**	**1.5**	**3.25**
Aluminium	**8.5**	**10.5**	**8.8**	**10.0**	**7.0**	**8.5**	**0.5**	**2.5**	**3.0**	**6.0**
Manganese	—	**1.0**	—	**3.0**	**11.0**	**15.0**	**0.1**	**3.0**	—	**4.0**

Antimony	—	—	—	—	—	—	—	—	—	
Arsenic	—	—	—	—	—	—	—	—	—	
Iron + arsenic + antimony	—	—	—	—	—	—	—	—	—	
Silicon	—	0.2	—	0.7	—	0.15	—	0.10	—	**0.10**
Bismuth	—	—	—	—	—	—	—	—	—	—
Magnesium	—	0.05	—	0.05	—	—	—	—	—	—
Sulphur	—	—	—	—	—	—	—	—	—	—
Chromium	—	—	—	—	—	—	—	—	—	—
Total impurities	—	0.30	—	0.30	—	0.30	—	0.20	—	0.20

* HCC1 castings shall be made from the copper grades Cu-CATH-2, Cu-EPT-2 or Cu-FRHC, as specified in BS 6017.
† For continuous casting, phosphorus content may be increased to a maximum of 1.5% and the alloy coded with the suffix /L.
‡ Tin plus half nickel content shall be within the range 7.0–8.0%.
§ HTB1 subject also to microstructure requirements: see BS 1400 Clause 6.3.
For full range of alloys and further information see BS 1400.
For essential alloying elements, limits are in **bold type**. Unless otherwise stated, figures in total impurities column include those in lighter type. Unless otherwise indicated, all limits are maxima.

3.3.14(a) Copper alloys for casting: group C

Designation	LB1		LB5		G1		G3		G3-TF	
Material	Leaded bronze		Leaded bronze		Gunmetal		Nickel gunmetal		Nickel gunmetal fully heat treated	
Nominal composition	Cu Pb 15 Sn 9		Cu Pb 20 Sn 5		Cu Sn 10 Zn 2		Cu Sn 7 Ni 5 Zn 3		Cu Sn 7 Ni 5 Zn 3	
Elements	min. %	max. %	min. %	max. %	min. %	max. %	min. %	max. %	min. %	max. %
Copper	**Remainder**		**Remainder**		**Remainder**		**Remainder**		**Remainder**	
Tin	**8.0**	**10.0**	**4.0**	**6.0**	**9.5**	**10.5**	**6.5**	**7.5**	**6.5**	**7.5**
Zinc	—	1.0	—	**1.0**	**1.75**	**2.75**	**1.5**	**3.0**	**1.5**	**3.0**
Lead	**13.0**	**17.0**	**18.0**	**23.0**	—	**1.5**	**0.10**	**0.50**	**0.10**	**0.50**
Phosphorus	—	0.1	—	0.1	—	—	—	**0.02**	—	**0.02**
Nickel	—	**2.0**	—	**2.0**	—	**1.0**	**5.25**	**5.75**	**5.25**	**5.75**
Iron	—	—	—	—	—	0.15†	—	†	—	†
Aluminium	—	—	—	—	—	0.01	—	0.01	—	0.01
Manganese	—	—	—	—	—	—	—	0.20	—	0.20
Antimony	—	**0.5**	—	**0.5**	—	†	—	†	—	†
Arsenic	—	—	—	—	—	†	—	†	—	†
Silicon	—	0.02	—	0.01	—	0.02	—	0.02	—	0.02
Bismuth	—	—	—	—	—	0.03	—	0.02	—	0.02
Sulphur	—	0.1	—	—	—	0.10	—	0.10	—	0.10
Magnesium	—	—	—	—	—	—	—	—	—	—

Niobium + tantalum	—	—	—	—	—	—	—	—	—	—
Carbon	—	—	—	—	—	—	—	—	—	—
Chromium	—	—	—	—	—	—	—	—	—	—
Zirconium	—	—	—	—	—	—	—	—	—	—
Cobalt	—	—	—	—	—	—	—	—	—	—
Total impurities	—	0.30	—	0.30	—	0.50	—	0.50	—	0.50

* For continuous casting, phosphorus content may be increased to a maximum of 1.5% and the alloy coded with suffix /L.
† Iron plus antimony plus arsenic 0.20% maximum.
For full range of alloys and further information see : BS 1400.
For essential alloying elements, limits are in **bold type**. Unless otherwise stated, figures in total impurities column include those in lighter type.
Unless otherwise indicated, all limits are maxima.

3.3.14(b) **Further copper alloys for casting: group C**

Designation	SCB4		CT2		AB3		CN1		CN2	
Material	Naval brass for sand casting		Copper-tin		Aluminium-silicon bronze		Copper-nickel-chromium		Copper-nickel-niobium	
Nominal composition	Cu Zn 36 Sn		Cu Sn 12 Ni		Cu Al 6 Si 2 Fe		Cu Ni 30 Cr		CU Ni 30 NB	
Elements	min. %	max. %	min. %	max. %	min. %	max. %	min. %	max. %	min. %	max. %
Copper	**60.0**	**63.0**	**85.0**	**87.0**	**Remainder**		**Remainder**		**Remainder**	
Tin	**1.0**	**1.5**	**11.0**	**13.0**	—	0.10	—	—	—	—
Zinc	**Remainder**	—	0.4	—	0.40	—	—	—	—	—
Lead	—	**0.50**	—	0.3	—	0.03	—	0.005	—	0.005
Phosphorus	—	—	**0.05**	**0.40***	—	—	—	0.005	—	0.005
Nickel	—	—	**1.5**	**2.5**	—	0.10	**29.0**	**33.0**	**28.0**	**32.0**
Iron	—	—	—	0.20	**0.5**	**0.7**	**0.4**	**1.0**	**1.0**	**1.4**
Aluminium	—	0.01	—	0.01	**6.0**	**6.4**	—	—	—	—
Manganese	—	—		0.20	—	0.50	**0.4**	**1.0**	**1.0**	**1.4**
Antimony	—	—	—	—	—	—	—	—	—	—
Arsenic	—	—	—	—	—	—	—	—	—	—
Silicon	—	—	—	0.01	**2.0**	**2.4**	**0.20**	**0.40**	**0.20**	**0.40**
Bismuth	—	—	—	—	—	—	—	0.002	—	0.002
Sulphur	—	—	—	0.05	—	—	—	0.01	—	0.01
Magnesium	—	—	—	—	—	0.05	—	—	—	—

Niobium + tantalum	—	—	—	—	—	—	—	—	**1.20**	**1.40**
Carbon	—	—	—	—	—	—	—	0.02	—	0.02
Chromium	—	—	—	—	—	—	**1.5**	**2.0**	—	—
Zirconium	—	—	—	—	—	—	**0.05**	**0.15**	—	—
Cobalt	—	—	—	—	—	—	—	**0.05**	—	0.05
Total impurities	—	0.75	—	0.80	—	0.80	—	0.20	—	0.30

* For continuous casting, phosphorus content may be increased to a maximum of 1.5% and the alloy coded with suffix /L.
† Iron plus antimony plus arsenic 0.20% maximum.
For full range of alloys and further information see : BS 1400.
For essential alloying elements, limits are in **bold type**. Unless otherwise stated, figures in total impurities column include those in lighter type. Unless otherwise indicated, all limits are maxima.

3.3.15 Copper alloys for casting: typical properties and hardness values

Designation	Freezing range category	Tensile strength				0.2% proof stress			
		*Sand**	*Chill*	*Continuous*	*Centrifugal*	*Sand**	*Chill*	*Continuous*	*Centrifugal*
		N/mm^2	N/mm^2	N/mm^2	N/mm^2	N/mm^2	N/mm^2	N/mm^2	N/mm^2
Group A									
PB4	L	190–270	270–370	330–450	280–400	100–160	140–230	160–270	140–230
LPB1	L	190–250	220–270	270–360	230–310	80–130	130–160	130–200	130–160
LB2	L	190–270	270–280	280–390	230–310	80–130	140–200	160–220	140–190
LB4	L	160–190	200–270	230–310	220–300	60–100	80–110	130–170	80–110
LG1	L	180–220	180–270	—	—	80–130	80–130	—	—
LG2	L	200–270	200–280	270–340	220–310	100–130	110–140	100–140	110–140
SCB1	S	170–200	—	—	—	80–110	—	—	—
SCB3	S	190–220	—	—	—	70–110	—	—	—
SCB6	S	170–190	—	—	—	80–110	—	—	—
DCB1	S	—	280–370	—	—	—	90–120	—	—
DCB3	S	—	300–340	—	—	—	90–120	—	—
PCB1	S	—	280–370	—	—	—	90–120	—	—
Group B									
HCC1	S	160–190	—	—	—	—	—	—	—
CC1-TF	S	270–340	—	—	—	170–250	—	—	—
PB1	L	220–280	310–390	360–500	330–420	130–160	170–230	170–280	170–230
PB2	L	220–310	270–340	310–430	280–370	130–170	170–200	170–250	170–200
CT1	L	230–310	270–340	310–390	280–370	130–160	140–190	160–220	180–190

LG4	L	250–320	250–340	300–370	230–370	130–140	130–160	130–160	130–160
AB1	S	500–590	540–620	—	560–650	170–200	200–270	—	200–270
AB2	S	640–700	650–740	—	670–730	250–300	250–310	—	250–310
CMA1	S	650–730	670–740	—	—	280–340	310–370	—	—
HTB1	S	470–570	500–570	—	500–600	170–280	210–280	—	210–280
HTB3	S	740–810	—	—	740–930	400–470	—	—	400–500
Group C									
LB1	L	170–230	200–270	230–310	220–300	80–110	130–160	130–190	130–160
LB5	L	160–190	170–230	190–270	190–270	60–100	80–110	100–160	80–110
G1	L	270–340	230–310	300–370	250–340	130–160	130–170	140–190	130–170
G3	L	280–340	—	340–370	—	140–160	—	170–190	—
G3-TF	L	430–480	—	430–500	—	280–310	—	280–310	—
SCB4	S	250–310	—	—	—	70–110	—	—	—
CT2	L	280–330	—	300–350	300–350	160–180	—	180–210	180–210
AB3	S	460–500	—	—	—	180–190	—	—	—
CN1	S	480–540	—	—	—	300–320	—	—	—
CN2	S	480–540	—	—	—	300–320	—	—	—

continued

Designation	*Freezing range category*	*Elongation on 5.65 $\sqrt{S_o}$*				*Hardness H_B*			
		*Sand** %	*Chill* %	*Continuous* %	*Centrifugal*† %	*Sand*	*Chill*	*Continuous*	*Centrifugal*
Group A									
PB4	L	3–12	2–10	7–30	4–20	70–95	95–140	95–140	95–140
LPB1	L	3–12	2–12	5–18	4–22	60–90	85–110	85–110	85–110
LB2	L	5–15	3–7	6–15	5–10	65–85	80–90	80–90	80–90
LB4	L	7–12	5–10	9–20	6–13	55–75	60–80	60–80	60–80
LG1	L	11–15	2–8	—	—	55–65	65–80	—	—
LG2	L	13–25	6–15	13–35	8–30	65–75	80–95	75–90	80–95
SCB1	S	18–40	—	—	—	45–60	—	—	—
SCB3	S	11–30	—	—	—	45–65	—	—	—
SCB6	S	18–40	—	—	—	45–60	—	—	—
DCB1	S	—	23–50	—	—	—	60–70	—	—
DCB3	S	—	13–40	—	—	—	60–70	—	—
PCB1	S	—	25–40	—	—	—	60–70	—	—
Group B									
HCC1	S	23–40	—	—	—	40–45	—	—	—
CC1-TF	S	18–30	—	—	—	100–120	—	—	—
PB1	L	3–8	2–8	6–25	4–22	70–100	95–150	100–150	25–150
PB2	L	5–15	3–7	5–15	3–14	75–110	100–150	100–150	100–150
CT1	L	6–20	5–15	9–25	6–25	70–90	90–130	90–130	90–130
LG4	L	16–25	5–15	13–30	6–30	70–85	80–95	80–95	80–95

AB2	S	13–20	13–20	—	13–20	140–180	160–190	—	140–180
CMA1	S	18–35	27–40	—	—	160–210	—	—	—
HTB1	S	18–35	18–35	—	20–38	100–150	—	—	100–150
HTB3	S	11–18	—	—	13–21	150–230	—	—	150–230
Group C									
LB1	L	4–10	3–7	9–10	4–10	50–70	70–90	70–90	70–90
LB5	L	5–10	5–12	8–16	7–15	45–65	50–70	50–70	50–70
G1	L	13–25	3–8	9–25	5–16	70–95	85–130	90–130	70–95
G3	L	16–25	—	18–25	—	70–95	—	90–130	—
G3-TF	L	3–5	—	3–7	—	160–180	—	160–180	—
SCB4	S	18–40	—	—	—	50–75	—	—	—
CT2	L	12–20	—	8–15	10–15	75–110	—	100–150	100–150
AB3	S	20–30	—	—	—	—	—	—	—
CN1	S	18–25	—	—	—	170–200	—	—	—
CN2	S	18–25	—	—	—	170–200	—	—	—

* On separately cast test bars.
† Values apply to samples cut from centrifugal castings made in metallic moulds. Minimum properties of centrifugal castings made in sand moulds are the same as for sand castings.

These typical mechanical properties (BS 1400 : Table 16) are included to supplement the minimum requirements specified in BS 1400 in order to provide the user with guidance on design. The values give a direct indication of the properties of continuous, centrifugal or chill castings as the test pieces are taken from the castings themselves. The values quoted for sand castings are the result of tests on separately cast test bars, and therefore do not necessarily give a direct indication of properties in the castings. The wide range of properties quoted for these continuous, chill and centrifugal castings is largely due to the effect of *thickness*; values in this table are based on thickness 15–40 mm. As a general principle, material of heavier section tends towards the lower end of the range for tensile strength, proof stress and hardness, while the elongation lies at the upper end of the range. The column headed 'Freezing range category' in the table is intended for design purposes; L indicates a long cooling range, and S a short cooling range.

Current practice uses 0.2% proof stress as the basis of stress calculations in design. BS 1400 : Table 17 indicates factors by which this value may be divided to make allowance for variations in strength of castings resulting from the casting process and the effect of freezing range on the alloy.

3.3.16 Wrought aluminium and aluminium alloys: condition code

The material shall be supplied in one of the following tempers as specified by the purchaser and selected from BS 1470 : 1987 : Tables 1, 2 and 3:

F	as fabricated;
O	annealed;
H12, H14, H16, H18	strain hardened (increased order of tensile strength);
H22, H24, H28	strain hardened and partially annealed (increasing order of tensile strength);
T3	solution heat treated, cold worked and naturally aged;
T4	solution heat treated and naturally aged (the properties of some alloys in this temper are unstable);
T5	cooled from an elevated temperature shaping process and then artificially aged;
T6	solution heat treated and artificially aged;
T6510	solution heat treated and stress relieved by controlled stretching before ageing. Bars so processed are given the suffix '510' after the temper designation.

Full details of the temper designation system, including definitions of the temper, are given in BS 1470 Appendix D. See also 3.3.3, 3.3.10 and 3.3.21.

3.3.17 Unalloyed aluminium plate, sheet and strip (composition)

*Materials designation**	*Tolerance category*	*Silicon* %	*Iron* %	*Copper* %	*Manganese* %	*Magnesium* %	*Aluminium‡* %	*Zinc* %	*Gallium* %	*Titanium* %	*Others†* *Each* %	*Total* %
1080(A)	A	0.15	0.15	0.03	0.02	0.02	99.80	0.06	0.03	0.02	0.02	—
1050(A)	A	0.40	0.05	0.05	0.05	0.05	99.50	0.07	—	0.05	0.03	—
1200	A	1.0 Si + Fe		0.05	0.05	—	99.00	0.10	—	0.05	0.05	0.15

Unalloyed aluminium plate, sheet and strip (properties) – table continued from above

Materials designation	*Temper§*	*Thickness*		*Tensile strength*		*Elongation on 50 mm: Materials thicker than*					*Elongation on 5.65 √s. over 12.5 mm thick min.*
		>	⩽	*min.*	*max.*	0.5 mm	0.8 mm	1.3 mm	2.6 mm	3.0 mm	
%		mm	mm	N/mm²	N/mm²	%	%	%	%	%	%
1080(A)	F	3.0	25.0	—	—	—	—	—	—	—	—
	O	0.2	6.0	—	90	29	29	29	35	35	—
	H14	0.2	12.5	90	125	5	6	7	8	8	—

1050(A)	F	3.0	25.0	—	—	—	—	—	—	—	—
	O	0.2	6.0	55	95	22	25	30	32	32	—
	H12	0.2	6.0	80	115	4	6	8	9	9	—
	H14	0.2	12.5	100	135	4	5	6	6	8	—
	H18	0.2	3.0	135	—	3	3	4	4	—	—
1200	F	3.0	25.0	—	—	—	—	—	—	—	—
	O	0.2	6.0	70	105	20	25	30	30	30	—
	H12	0.2	6.0	90	125	4	6	8	9	9	—
	H14	0.2	12.5	105	140	3	4	5	5	6	—
	H16	0.2	6.0	125	160	2	3	4	4	4	—
	H18	0.2	3.0	140	—	2	3	4	4	—	—

* Composition in per cent (m/m) maximum unless shown as a range or a minimum.

† Analysis is regularly made only for the elements for which specific limits are shown. If, however, the presence of other elements is suspected to be, or in the case of routine analysis is indicated to be, in excess of the specified limits, further analysis should be made to determine that these other elements are not in excess of the amount specified.

‡ The aluminium content for unalloyed aluminium not made by a refining process is the difference between 100.00% and the sum of all other metallic elements in amounts of 0.010% or more each, expressed to the second decimal before determining the sum.

§ An alternative method of production, designated H2, may be used instead of the H1 routes, subject to agreement between supplier and purchaser and providing that the same specified properties are achieved.

For further information see BS 1470.

3.3.18 Aluminium alloy plate, sheet and strip: non-heat-treatable (composition)

Material designation*	Tolerance category	Silicon %	Iron %	Copper %	Manganese %	Magnesium %	Chromium %	Alum^n %	Zinc %	Other restrictions %	Titanium %	Others† Each %	Others† Total %
3103	A	0.50	0.7	0.10	0.9/1.5	0.30	0.10	Rem.	0.20	0.10 Zr + Ti	—	0.05	0.15
3105	A	0.6	0.7	0.3	0.3/0.8	0.2/0.8	0.20	Rem.	0.40	—	0.01	0.05	0.15
5005	A	0.3	0.7	0.2	0.2	0.5/1.1	0.10	Rem.	0.25	—	—	0.05	0.15
5083	B	0.40	0.40	0.10	0.4/1.0	4.0/4.9	0.05/0.25	Rem.	0.25	—	0.15	0.05	0.15
5154	B	0.50	0.50	0.10	0.50	3.1/3.9	0.25	Rem.	0.20	0.10/0.50 Mn + Cr	0.20	0.05	0.15
5251	A	0.40	0.50	0.15	0.1/0.5	1.7/2.4	0.15	Rem.	0.15	—	0.15	0.05	0.15
5454	B	0.25	0.40	0.10	0.5/1.0	2.4/3.0	0.5/2.0	Rem.	0.25	—	0.20	0.05	0.15

Aluminium alloy plate, sheet and strip: non-heat-treatable (properties) – table continued from above

Material designation*	Temper‡ %	Thickness > mm	Thickness < mm	0.2% proof stress N/mm²	Tensile strength min. N/mm²	Tensile strength max. N/mm²	Elongation on 50 mm: materials thicker than 0.5 mm %	0.8 mm %	1.3 mm %	2.6 mm %	3.0 mm %	Elongation on 5.65 $\sqrt{S_o}$ over 12.5 mm thick (min.) %
3103	F	0.2	25.0	—	—	—	—	—	—	—	—	—
	O	0.2	6.0	—	90	130	20	23	24	24	25	—
	H12	0.2	6.0	—	120	155	5	6	7	9	9	—
	H14	0.2	12.5	—	140	175	3	4	5	6	7	—
	H16	0.2	6.0	—	160	195	2	3	4	4	4	—
	H18	0.2	3.0	—	175	—	2	3	4	4	—	—
3105	O	0.2	3.0	—	110	155	16	18	20	20	—	—
	H12	0.2	3.0	115	130	175	2	3	4	5	—	—
	H14	0.2	3.0	145	160	205	2	2	3	4	—	—
	H16	0.2	3.0	170	185	230	1	1	2	3	—	—
	H18	0.2	3.0	190	215	—	1	1	1	2	—	—
5005	O	0.2	3.0	—	95	145	18	20	21	22	—	—
	H12	0.2	3.0	80	125	170	4	5	6	8	—	—
	H14	0.2	3.0	100	145	185	3	3	5	6	—	—
	H18	0.2	3.0	165	185	—	1	2	3	3	—	—
5083	F	3.0	25.0	—	—	—	—	—	—	—	—	—
	O	0.2	80.0	125	275	350	12	14	16	16	16	14
	H22	0.2	6.0	235	310	375	5	6	8	10	8	—
	H24	0.2	6.0	270	345	405	4	5	6	8	6	—

continued

Section 3.3.18 (*continued*)

Material designation*	Temper‡ %	Thickness > mm	Thickness < mm	0.2% proof stress N/mm²	Tensile strength min. N/mm²	Tensile strength max. N/mm²	Elongation on 50 mm: materials thicker than 0.5 mm %	0.8 mm %	1.3 mm %	2.6 mm %	3.0 mm %	Elongation on 5.56 $\sqrt{S_0}$ over 12.5 mm thick (min.) %
5154	O	0.2	6.0	85	215	275	12	14	16	18	18	—
	H22	0.2	6.0	165	245	295	5	6	7	8	8	—
	H24	0.2	6.0	225	275	325	4	4	8	6	5	—
5251	F	3.0	25.0	—	—	—	—	—	—	—	—	—
	O	0.2	6.0	60	160	200	18	18	18	20	20	—
	H22	0.2	6.0	130	200	240	4	5	6	8	8	—
	H24	0.2	6.0	175	275	275	3	4	5	5	5	—
	H28	0.2	3.0	215	255	285	2	3	3	4	4	—
5454	F	3.0	25.0	—	—	—	—	—	—	—	—	—
	O	0.2	6.0	80	215	285	12	14	16	18	18	—
	H22	0.2	3.0	180	250	305	4	5	7	8	—	—
	H24	0.2	3.0	200	270	325	3	4	5	6	—	—

* Composition in per cent (m/m) maximum unless shown as a range or a minimum.

† Analysis is regularly made only for the elements for which specific limits are shown. If, however, the presence of other elements is suspected to be, or in the case of the routine analysis is indicated to be, in excess of the specified limits, further analysis should be made to determine that these other elements are not in excess of the amount specified.

‡ An alternative method of production, designated H2, may be used instead of the H1 routes, subject to agreement between supplier and purchaser and providing that the same specified properties are achieved.

For further information see BS 1470 : 1987.

3.3.19 Aluminium alloy plate, sheet and strip: heat-treatable (composition)

*Material designation**	*Tolerance category*	*Silicon*	*Iron*	*Copper*	*Manganese*	*Magnesium*	*Chromium*	*Nickel*	*Zinc*	*Other restrictions*	*Titanium*	*Alum*ⁿ	Others†	
													Each	*Total*
		%	%	%	%	%	%	%	%	%	%	%	%	%
2014A	B	0.5/0.9	0.50	3.9/5.0	0.4/1.2	0.2/0.8	0.10	0.10	0.25	0.20 Zr + Ti	0.15	Rem.	0.05	0.15
Clad 2014A‡	B	0.5/0.9	0.50	3.0/5.0	0.4/1.2	0.2/0.8	0.10	0.10	0.25	0.20 Zr + Ti	0.15	Rem.	0.05	0.15
2024	B	0.50	0.50	3.8/4.4	0.3/0.9	1.2/1.8	0.10	—	0.25	—	0.15	Rem.	0.05	0.15
Clad 2024‡	B	0.50	0.50	3.8/4.4	0.3/0.9	1.2/1.8	0.10	—	0.25	—	0.15	Rem.	0.05	0.15
6082	B	0.7/1.3	0.50	0.10	0.4/1.0	0.6/1.2	0.25	—	0.20	—	0.10	Rem.	0.05	0.15

continued

Section 3.3.19 (*continued*)

Aluminium alloy plate, sheet and strip: heat-treatable (properties)

*Material designation**	*Temper§*	*Thickness*		*0.2% proof stress*	*Tensile strength*		*Elongation on 50 mm: materials thicker than*					*Elongation on 5.65 $\sqrt{S_o}$ over 12.5 mm thick (min.)*
		>	<		*min.*	*max.*	0.5 mm	0.8 mm	1.3 mm	2.6 mm	3.0 mm	
		mm	mm	N/mm^2	N/mm^2	N/mm^2	%	%	%	%	%	%
2014A	O	0.2	6.0	110	—	235	14	14	16	16	16	
	T4	0.2	6.0	22	400	—	13	14	14	14	14	
	T6	0.2	6.0	380	440	—	6	6	7	7	8	
	T451	6.0	25.0	250	400	—	—	—	—	—	14	12
		25.0	40.0	250	400	—	—	—	—	—	—	10
		40.0	80.0	250	395	—	—	—	—	—	—	7
	T651	6.0	25.0	410	460	—	—	—	—	—	—	6
		25.0	40.0	400	450	—	—	—	—	—	—	5
		40.0	60.0	390	430	—	—	—	—	—	—	5
		60.0	90.0	390	430	—	—	—	—	—	—	4
		90.0	115.0	370	420	—	—	—	—	—	—	4
		115.0	140.0	350	410	—	—	—	—	—	—	4
Clad	O	0.2	6.0	100	—	220	14	14	16	16	16	—
2014A‡	T4	0.2	1.6	240	385	—	13	14	14	—	—	—
		1.6	6.0	245	395	—	—	—	—	14	14	—
	T6	0.2	1.6	345	420	—	7	7	8	9	—	—
		1.6	6.0	355	420	—	—	—	—	9	9	—

2024	O	0.2	6.0	110	—	235	12	12	14	14	14	—
	T3	0.2	1.6	290	440	—	11	11	11	—	—	—
		1.6	6.0	290	440	—	—	—	—	12	12	—
	T351	6.0	25.0	280	430	—	—	—	—	—	10	10
		25.0	40.0	280	420	—	—	—	—	—	—	9
		40.0	60.0	270	410	—	—	—	—	—	—	9
		60.0	90.0	270	410	—	—	—	—	—	—	8
		90.0	115.0	270	400	—	—	—	—	—	—	8
		115.0	140.0	260	390	—	—	—	—	—	—	7
Clad 2024†	O	0.2	6.0	100	—	235	12	12	14	14	14	—
	T3	0.2	1.6	270	405	—	11	11	11	—	—	—
		1.6	6.0	275	425	—	—	—	—	12	12	—
6082	O	0.2	3.0	—	—	155	16	16	16	15	—	—
	T4	0.2	3.0	120	200	—	15	15	15	15	—	—
		3.0	25.0	115	200	—	—	—	—	—	15	12
	T6	0.2	3.0	255	295	—	8	8	8	8	—	—
		3.0	25.0	240	295	—	—	—	—	—	8	—
	T451	6.0	25.0	115	200	—	—	—	—	—	—	15
		25.0	90.0	115	200	—	—	—	—	—	—	15
	T651	6.0	25.0	240	295	—	—	—	—	—	—	8
		25.0	90.0	240	295	—	—	—	—	—	—	8
		90.0	115.0	230	285	—	—	—	—	—	—	7
		115.0	150.0	220	275	—	—	—	—	—	—	6

* Composition in per cent (m/m) maximum unless shown as a range or a minimum.

† Analysis is regularly made only for the elements for which specific limits are shown. If, however, the presence of other elements is suspected to be, or in the case of routine analysis is indicated to be, in excess of the specified limits, further analysis should be made to determine that these other elements are not in excess of the amount specified.

‡ Unalloyed aluminium grade 1050A is used as cladding material. The cladding thickness is 4% on each side of the material up to and including 1.6 mm thick and 2% on each side for material over 1.6 mm thick.

§ The tempers Tx51 (stress relieved by stretching) apply to plate and sheet which have been stretched after solution treatment to give a permanent set of approximately 1.5 to 3.0%.

For further information see BS 1470 : 1987.

3.3.20 Aluminium and aluminium alloy bars, extruded tube and sections for general engineering: non-heat-treatable (composition)

Material designation*	Silicon %	Iron %	Copper %	Manganese %	Magnesium %	Chromium %	Zinc %	Other restrictions %	Titanium %	Others† Each %	Others† Total %	Aluminium %
1050A	0.25	0.40	0.05	0.05	0.05	—	0.07	—	0.05	0.03	—	**99.50§ min.**
1200	1.0 Si + Fe		0.05	0.05	—	—	0.10	—	0.05	0.05	0.15	**99.00§ min.**
5083	0.4	0.4	0.10	0.40/1.0	4.0/4.9	0.05/0.25	0.25	—	0.15	0.05	0.15	**Rem.**
5154A	0.50	0.50	0.10	0.50	3.1/3.9	0.25	0.20	0.10–0.50 Mn + Cr	0.20	0.05	0.15	**Rem.**
5251	0.40	0.50	0.15	0.10/0.5	1.7/2.4	0.15	0.15	—	0.15	0.05	0.15	**Rem.**

Aluminium and aluminium alloy bars, extruded tube and sections for general engineering: non-heat-treatable (properties) – table continued from above

Material designation	Temper‡	Diameter (bar) or thickness (tube/sections)		0.2% proof stress	Tensile strength		Elongation	
		>	⩽	(min.)	min.	max.	on $5.65\sqrt{S_o}$	on 50 mm
		mm	mm	N/mm²	N/mm²	N/mm²	(min.) %	(min.) %
1050A	F	—	—	—	(60)	—	(25)	(23)
1200	F	—	—	—	(65)	—	(20)	(18)
5083	O	—	150‖	125	275	—	14	13
	F	—	150	(130)	(280)	—	(12)	(11)
5154A	O	—	150‖	85	215	275	18	16
	F	—	150	(100)	(215)	—	(16)	(14)
5251	F	—	150	(60)	(170)	—	(16)	(14)

* Composition in per cent (m/m) maximum unless shown as a range or a minimum.

† Analysis is regularly carried out for the elements for which specific limits are shown. If, however, the presence of other elements is suspected to be, or in the course of routine analysis is indicated to be, in excess of specified limits, further analysis should be made to determine that these other elements are not in excess of the amount specified.

‡ No mechanical properties are specified for materials in the F condition. The bracketed values shown for proof stress, tensile strength and elongation are typical properties and are given for information only.

§ The aluminium content for unalloyed aluminium not made by a refining process is the difference between 100% and the sum of all other metallic elements present in amounts of 0.10% or more each, expressed to the second decimal before determining the sum.

‖ No mechanical properties are specified for tube and hollow sections having a wall thickness greater than 75 mm (see BS 1474 : 1987 Clause 6).

For further information see BS 1474 : 1987.

3.3.21 Aluminium alloy bars, extruded tube and sections for general engineering: heat-treatable (composition)

Material designation*	Silicon %	Iron %	Copper %	Manganese %	Magnesium %	Chromium %	Zinc %	Other restrictions %	Other Titanium %	Others† Each %	Others† Total %	Aluminium %
2014A	0.5/0.9	0.50	3.9/5.0	0.4/1.2	0.2/0.8	0.10	0.25	0.20 Zr + Ti	0.15	0.05	0.15	Rem.
6060	0.3/0.6	0.1/0.3	0.10	0.10	0.35/0.6	0.05	0.15	—	0.10	0.05	0.15	Rem.
6061	0.4/0.8	0.7	0.15/0.4	0.15	0.8/1.2	0.04/0.35	0.25	—	0.15	0.05	0.15	Rem.
6063	0.2/0.6	0.35	0.10	0.10	0.45/0.9	0.10	0.10	—	0.10	0.05	0.15	Rem.
6063A	0.3/0.6	0.15/0.35	0.10	0.15	0.6/0.9	0.05	0.15	—	0.10	0.05	0.15	Rem.
6082	0.7/1.3	0.50	0.10	0.40/1.0	0.6/1.2	0.25	0.20	—	0.10	0.05	0.15	Rem.
6463	0.2/0.6	0.15	0.20	0.05	0.45/0.9	—	0.05	—	—	0.05	0.16	Rem.

heat treatable (properties) – continued from table above

Material designation*	Temper‡	Diameter (bar) or thickness (tube/sections)§ > mm	⩽ mm	0.2% proof stress (min.) N/mm²	Tensile strength min. N/mm²	Tensile strength max. N/mm²	Elongation on $5.65\sqrt{S_o}$ (min.) %	Elongation on 50 mm (min.) %
2014A		—	20	230	370	—	11	10
	T4	20	75	250	390	—	11	—
		75	150	250	390	—	8	—
	T6	150	200	230	370	—	8	—
		—	20	370	435	—	7	6
	T6510	20	75	435	480	—	7	—
		75	150	420	465	—	7	—
		150	200	390	435	—	7	—
6060	T4	—	150	60	120	—	15	—
	T5	—	150	100	145	—	8	—
	T6	—	150	150	190	—	8	—
6061	T4	—	150	115	190	—	16	14
	T6, T6510	—	150	240	280	—	8	7
6063	O	—	200	—	—	140	15	13
	F	—	200	—	(100)	—	(13)	(12)
	T4	—	150	70	130	—	16	14
	T4	150	200	70	120	—	13	—
	T5	—	25	110	150	—	8	7
	T6	—	150	160	195	—	8	7
	T6	150	200	130	150	—	6	—

continued

Section 3.3.21 (*continued*)

Material designation*	Temper‡	Diameter (bar) or thickness (tube/sections)§		0.2% proof stress	Tensile strength		Elongation	
							on $5.65\sqrt{S_o}$	on 50 mm
		> mm	⩽ mm	(min.) N/mm²	min. N/mm²	max. N/mm²	(min.) %	(min.) %
6063A	T4	—	25	90	150	—	14	12
	T5	—	25	160	200	—	8	7
	T6	—	25	190	230	—	8	7
6082	O	—	200	—	—	170	16	14
	F	—	200	—	(110)	—	(13)	(12)
	T4	—	150	120	190	—	16	14
		150	200	100	170	—	13	—
	T5	—	6	230	270	—	—	8
		—	20	255	295	—	8	7
	T6 / T6510	20	150	270	310	—	8	—
		150	200	240	280	—	5	—
6463	T4	—	50	75	125	—	16	14
	T6	—	50	160	185	—	10	9

* Composition in per cent (m/m) maximum unless shown as a range or a minimum.

† Analysis is regularly carried out for the elements for which specific limits are shown. If, however, the presence of other elements is suspected to be, or in the course of routine analysis is indicated to be in excess of specified limits, further analysis should be made to determine that these elements are not in excess of the amount specified.

‡ No mechanical properties are specified for materials in the F condition. The bracketed values shown for proof stress, tensile strength and elongation are typical properties and are given for information only. The temper T6510 is applicable only to bars (see 3.3.16).

§ No mechanical properties are specified for tube and hollow sections having a wall thickness greater than 75 mm (see BS 1474 : 1987 Clause 6).

3.3.22 Cast aluminium alloys: condition code

The castings shall be supplied in one of the following conditions as specified by the purchaser (see BS 1490 : 1988 Clause 5.2):

M	as cast
TS	stress relieved only
TE	precipitation treated
TB	solution treated and quenched
TB7	solution treated, quenched and stabilized
TF	solution treated, quenched and precipitation treated
TF7	solution treated, quenched and precipitation treated and stabilized

If stress relief treatment (TS) is required, details of the stress relieving procedure to be applied shall be stated on the order.

See also 3.3.3 and 3.3.16.

3.3.23 Aluminium alloy castings, group A: general purpose

Designation	LM2		LM4		LM6		LM20		LM24		LM25		LM27	
Nominal composition	Al-Si 10 Cu 2		Al-Si 5 Cu 3 Mn 0.5		Al-Si 12		Al-Si 12		Al-Si 8 Cu 3.5		Al-Si 7 Mg 0.5		Al-Si 7 Cu 2 Mn 0.5	
Nearest alloy(s) in ISO 3522	—		Al-Si 5 Cu 3		Al-Si 12 Al-Si 12 Fe		Al-Si 12 Cu Al-Si 12 Cu Fe		Al-Si 8 Cu 3 Fe		Al-Si 7 Mg		Al-Si 5 Cu 3	
Elements	min. %	max. %	min. %	max. %	min. %	max. %	min. %	max. %	min. %	max. %	min. %	max. %	min. %	max. %
Aluminium	**Remainder**		**Remainder**		**Remainder**		**Remainder**		**Remainder**		**Remainder**		**Remainder**	
Copper	**0.7**	**2.5**	**2.0**	**4.0**	—	0.1	—	0.4	**3.0**	**4.0**	—	0.20	**1.5**	**2.5**
Magnesium	—	0.3	—	0.2	—	0.1	—	0.2	—	0.30	**0.2**	**0.6**	—	0.35
Silicon	**9.0**	**11.5**	**4.0**	**6.0**	**10.0**	**13.0**	**10.0**	**13.0**	**7.5**	**9.5**	**6.5**	**7.5**	**6.0**	**8.0**
Iron	—	1.0	—	0.8	—	0.6	—	1.0	—	1.3	—	0.5	—	0.8
Manganese	—	0.5	**0.2**	**0.6**	—	0.5	—	0.5	—	0.5	—	0.3	**0.2**	**0.6**
Nickel	—	0.5	—	0.3	—	0.1	—	0.1	—	0.5	—	0.1	—	0.3
Zinc	—	2.0	—	0.5	—	0.1	—	0.2	—	3.0	—	0.1	—	1.0
Lead	—	0.3	—	0.1	—	0.1	—	0.1	—	0.3	—	0.1	—	0.2
Tin	—	0.2	—	0.1	—	0.05	—	0.1	—	0.2	—	0.05	—	0.1
Titanium	—	0.2	—	0.2	—	0.2	—	0.2	—	0.2	—	0.2*	—	0.2
Each other element†	—	—	—	0.05	—	0.05	—	0.05	—	—	—	0.05	—	0.05
Total other elements	—	0.5	—	0.15	—	0.15	—	0.20	—	0.5	—	0.15	—	0.15

* If titanium alone is used for grain refining, the amount present shall not be less than 0.05%.

† In cases where alloys are required in the modified condition, the level of modifying element(s) present is not limited by the specified maximum value for other elements.

Specified impurities are in light type. Analysis is required to verify that the contents of the specified impurities are less than the limits given in the table.

Designation	LM0		LM5		LM9		LM13		LM16		LM21		LM22	
Nominal composition	99.50 + %Al		Al-Mg5 Mn 0.5		Al-Si 12 Mg 0.5 Mn 0.5		Al-Si 12 Cu 1 Mg 2		Al-Si 5 Cu 1 Mg 0.5		Al-Si 6 Cu 4 Mn 0.4 Mg 0.2		Al-Si 5 Cu 3 Mn 0.4	
Nearest alloy(s) in ISO 3522	—		Al-Mg 5 Si 1 Al-Mg 6		Al-Si 10 Mg		Al-Si 12 Cu Al-Si 12 Cu Fe		Al-Si 5 Cu 1 Mg		Al-Si 6 Cu 4		Al-Si 5 Cu 3	
Elements	min. %	max. %	min. %	max. %	min. %	max. %	min. %	max. %	min. %	max. %	min. %	max. %	min. %	max. %
Aluminium	**99.50***	—	**Remainder**		**Remainder**		**Remainder**		**Remainder**		**Remainder**		**Remainder**	
Copper	—	0.03	—	0.10	—	0.20	**0.7**	**1.5**	**1.0**	**1.5**	**3.0**	**5.0**	**2.8**	**3.8**
Magnesium	—	0.03	**3.0**	**6.0**	**0.2**	**0.6**	**0.8**	**1.5**	**0.4**	**0.6**	**0.1**	**0.3**	—	0.05
Silicon	—	0.03	—	0.30	**10.0**	**13.0**	**10.0**	**13.0**	**4.5**	**5.5**	**5.0**	**7.0**	**4.0**	**6.0**
Iron	—	0.40	—	0.60	—	0.60	—	1.0	—	0.6	—	1.0	—	0.6
Manganese	—	0.03	**0.3**	**0.7**	**0.3**	**0.7**	—	0.5	—	0.5	**0.2**	**0.6**	**0.2**	**0.6**
Nickel	—	0.03	—	0.10	—	0.10	—	1.5	—	0.25	—	0.3	—	0.15
Zinc	—	0.07	—	0.10	—	0.10	—	0.5	—	0.1	—	2.0	—	0.15
Lead	—	0.03	—	0.05	—	0.10	—	0.1	—	0.1	—	0.2	—	0.10
Tin	—	0.03	—	0.05	—	0.05	—	0.1	—	0.05	—	0.1	—	0.05
Titanium	—	—	—	0.20	—	0.02	—	0.2	—	0.2†	—	0.2	—	0.20
Each other element‡	—	—	—	0.05	—	0.05	—	0.05	—	0.05	—	0.05	—	0.05
Total other elements‡	—	—	—	0.15	—	0.15	—	0.15	—	0.15	—	0.15	—	0.15

* The aluminium content shall be determined by difference, i.e. by subtracting the total of all other elements listed.
† If titanium alone is used for grain refining, the amount present shall be not less than 0.05%.
‡ In cases when alloys are required in the modified condition, the level of any modifying element present is not limited by the specified maximum value for other elements.
Specified impurities are shown in light type. Analysis is required to verify that the contents of the specified impurities are less than the limits given in the table. Analysis for other elements is made when their presence is suspected to be in excess of the 'each other element' limit.

For further information see BS 1490 : 1988.

3.3.25 Aluminium alloy castings, group C: special purpose and of limited application

Designation	LM12		LM26		LM28*		LM29*		LM30		LM31†	
Nominal composition	Al-Cu 10 Mg 0.3		Al-Si 10 Cu 3 Mg 1		Al-Si 18 Cu 1.5 Mg 1 Ni 1		Al-Si 23 Cu 1 Mg 1 Ni 1		Al-Si 17 Cu 4.5 Mg 0.5		Al-Zn 5 Mg 0.7 Cr 0.5 Ti	
Nearest alloy(s) in ISO 3522	—		—		—		—		—		Al-Zn 5 Mg	
Element	min. %	max. %	min. %	max. %	min. %	max. %	min. %	max. %	min. %	max. %	min. %	max. %
Aluminium	**Remainder**		**Remainder**		**Remainder**		**Remainder**		**Remainder**		**Remainder**	
Copper	**9.0**	**11.0**	**2.0**	**4.0**	**1.3**	**1.8**	**0.8**	**1.3**	**4.0**	**5.0**	—	0.10
Magnesium	**0.2**	**0.4**	**0.5**	**1.5**	**0.8**	**1.5**	**0.8**	**1.3**	**0.4**	**0.7**	**0.5**	**0.75**
Silicon	—	2.5	**8.5**	**10.5**	**17.0**	**20.0**	**22.0**	**25.0**	**16.0**	**18.0**	—	0.25
Iron	—	1.0	—	1.2	—	0.70	—	0.70	—	1.10	—	0.50
Manganese	—	0.6	—	0.5	—	0.60	—	0.60	—	0.30	—	0.10
Nickel	—	0.5	—	1.0	**0.8**	**1.5**	**0.8**	**1.3**	—	0.10	—	0.10
Zinc	—	0.8	—	1.0	—	0.20	—	0.20	—	0.20	**4.8**	**5.7**
Lead	—	0.1	—	0.2	—	0.10	—	0.10	—	0.10	—	0.05
Tin	—	0.1	—	0.1	—	0.10	—	0.10	—	0.10	—	0.05
Titanium	—	0.2	—	0.2	—	0.20	—	0.20	—	0.20	—	0.25‡
Chromium	—	—	—	—	—	0.60	—	0.60	—	—	**0.4**	**0.6**
Each other element ‖	—	0.05	—	0.05	—	0.10§	—	0.10§	—	0.10	—	0.05
Total other elements ‖	—	0.15	—	0.15	—	0.30	—	0.30	—	0.30	—	0.15

* LM28 and LM29 are also subject to metallographic structure requirements (BS 1490 : note 5.4).
† LM31 castings in M condition have to be naturally aged for 3 weeks before use, or before determination of mechanical properties.
‡ If titanium alone is used for grain refining, the amount present shall be not less than 0.05%.
§ Maximum cobalt content.
|| In cases when alloys are required in the modified condition, the level of any modifying element present is not limited by the specified maximum value for other elements.

Specified impurities are shown in light type. Analysis is required to verify that the contents of the specified impurities are less than the limits given in the table. Analysis for other elements is made when their presence is suspected to be in excess of the 'each other element' limit.

For further information see BS 1490 : 1988.

3.3.26 Aluminium alloy castings: mechanical properties

		Tensile strength		*Elongation on 5.65* $\sqrt{S_o}$	
*Designation**	*Condition*	*Sand or investment casting* *(min.)* N/mm^2	*Chill cast* *(min.)* N/mm^2	*Sand or investment casting* *(min.)* %	*Chill cast* *(min.)* %
Group A					
LM2	M	—	150	—	—
LM4	M	140	160	2	2
	TF	230	280	—	—
LM6	M	160	190	5	7
LM20	M	—	190	—	5
LM24	M	—	180	—	1.5
LM25	M	130	160	2	3
	TE	150	190	1	2
	TB7†	160	230	2.5	5
	TF	230	280	—	2
LM27	M	140	160	1	2
Group B					
LMO	M	—	—	—	—
LM5	M	140	170	3	5
LM9	M	—	190	—	3
	TE	170	230	1.5	2
	TF	240	295	—	—
LM13‡	TE	—	210	—	—
	TF	170	280	—	—
	TF7	140	200	—	—
LM16	TB	170	230	2	3
	TF	230	280	—	—
LM21	M	150	170	1	1
LM22	TB	—	245	—	8

Designation*	Condition	Tensile strength: Sand or investment casting (min.) N/mm^2	Tensile strength: Chill cast (min.) N/mm^2	Elongation on 5.65 $\sqrt{S_o}$: Sand or investment casting (min.) %	Elongation on 5.65 $\sqrt{S_o}$: Chill cast (min.) %
Group C					
LM12	M	—	170	—	—
LM26‡	TE	—	210	—	—
L28§	TE	—	170	—	—
	TF	120	190	—	—
LM29§	TE	120	190	—	—
	TF	120	190	—	—
LM30	M	—	150	—	—
	TS	—	160	—	—
LM31‖	M	215	—	4	—
	TE	215	—	4	—

* Properties are obtained on separately cast test samples (see BS 1490 : 1988 : note 5.3.1).

† After solution treatment, castings have to be heated at a temperature and for a time that will ensure reasonable stability of mechanical properties.

‡ LM13, LM26, LM28, and LM29 are subject to hardness requirements (see BS 1490: note 5.3.2 and Table 5).

§ LM28 and LM29 are subject to microstructure requirements (see BS 1490: note 5.4).

‖ LM31 castings in the M condition have to be naturally aged for 3 weeks before use, or before the determination of mechanical properties.

3.3.27 Soft solders

Grade	Tin		Antimony		Lead		Silver		Cadmium		Copper		Bismuth	Arsenic	Iron	Zinc	Aluminium	Others
	min.	max.	min.	max.	min.	max.	min.	max.	min.	max.	min.	max.	max.	max.	nax.	max.	max.	Total max.
	%	%	%	%	%	%	%	%	%	%	%	%	%	%	%	%	%	%
Tin-lead																		
A	63.0	64.0	—	0.6	Remainder		—	—	—	0.005	—	0.08	0.1	0.03	0.02	0.003	0.001	0.08
AP	63.0	64.0	—	0.2	Remainder		—	—	—	0.005	—	0.08	0.1	0.03	0.02	0.003	0.001	0.08
K	59.0	60.0	—	0.5	Remainder		—	—	—	0.005	—	0.08	0.1	0.03	0.02	0.003	0.001	0.08
KP	59.0	60.0	—	0.2	Remainder		—	—	—	0.005	—	0.08	0.1	0.03	0.02	0.003	0.001	0.08
F	49.0	50.0	—	0.5	Remainder		—	—	—	0.005	—	0.08	0.1	0.03	0.02	0.003	0.001	0.08
R	44.0	45.0	—	0.4	Remainder		—	—	—	0.005	—	0.08	0.1	0.03	0.02	0.003	0.001	0.08
G	39.0	40.0	—	0.4	Remainder		—	—	—	0.005	—	0.08	0.1	0.03	0.02	0.003	0.001	0.08
H	34.0	35.0	—	0.3	Remainder		—	—	—	0.005	—	0.08	0.1	0.03	0.02	0.003	0.001	0.08
J	29.0	30.0	—	0.3	Remainder		—	—	—	0.005	—	0.05	0.1	0.03	0.02	0.003	0.001	0.08
V	19.0	20.0	—	0.2	Remainder		—	—	—	0.005	—	0.05	0.1	0.03	0.02	0.003	0.001	0.08
W	14.0	15.0	—	0.2	Remainder		—	—	—	0.005	—	0.05	0.1	0.03	0.02	0.003	0.001	0.08

Tin-lead-antimony																		
B	49.0	50.0	2.5	3.0	Remainder		—	—	—	0.005	—	0.08	0.25	0.03	0.02	0.003	0.001	0.08
M	44.0	45.0	2.2	2.7	Remainder		—	—	—	0.005	—	0.08	0.25	0.03	0.02	0.003	0.001	0.08
C	39.0	40.0	2.0	2.4	Remainder		—	—	—	0.005	—	0.08	0.25	0.03	0.02	0.003	0.001	0.08
L	31.0	32.0	1.6	1.9	Remainder		—	—	—	0.005	—	0.08	0.25	0.03	0.02	0.003	0.001	0.08
D	29.0	30.0	1.5	1.8	Remainder		—	—	—	0.005	—	0.05	0.25	0.03	0.02	0.003	0.001	0.08
N	18.0	18.5	0.9	1.1	Remainder		—	—	—	0.005	—	0.05	0.25	0.03	0.02	0.003	0.001	0.08
Tin-antimony																		
95*A*	*Remainder*		4.75	5.25	—	0.07	—	—	—	0.005	—	0.08	0.25	0.03	0.02	0.003	0.001	0.08
Tin-silver																		
96S	Remainder		—	0.10	—	0.01	3.5	3.7	—	0.005	—	0.08	0.10	0.03	0.02	0.005	0.001	0.08
97S	Remainder		—	0.10	—	0.01	3.0	3.5	—	0.005	—	0.10	0.10	0.03	0.02	0.001	0.001	0.08
98S	Remainder		—	0.10	—	0.01	1.8	2.2	—	0.005	—	0.10	0.10	0.03	0.02	0.001	0.001	0.08
Tin-copper																		
99C	Remainder		—	0.05	—	0.01	—	0.05	—	0.002	0.45	0.85	0.10	0.03	0.02	0.001	0.001	0.08
Tin-lead-silver																		
5S	4.75	5.25	—	0.10	Remainder		1.4	1.6	—	0.005	—	0.05	0.10	0.03	0.02	0.003	0.001	0.08
62S	61.50	62.50	—	0.20	Remainder		1.8	2.2	—	0.005	—	0.08	0.10	0.03	0.02	0.003	0.001	0.08
Tin-lead-cadmium																		
T	49.0	50.0	—	0.10	Remainder		—	—	17.5	18.5	—	0.08	0.10	0.03	0.02	0.01	0.005	0.08

For further information see BS 219 : 1987. *Note*: Tin solder 998S/997S see BS 3252

3.3.28 Typical uses of soft solders

Grade	*Tin content* %	*Starts to melt at* °C	*Fully molten at* °C	*Typical uses*
Tin				
9985	min. 99.90	Melting point 232		Certain food handling equipment, special can soldering and other special applications.
9975	min. 99.75	Melting point 232		
Tin-lead				
A	64	183	185	Soldering of electrical connections to copper; soldering brass to zinc; hand soldering of electronic assemblies; hot dip coating of ferrous and non-ferrous metals; high quality sheet metal work; capillary joints including light gauge tubes in copper and stainless steel; manufacture of electronic components; machine soldering of printed circuits.
AP	64	183	185	
K	60	183	185	
KP	60	183	188	Hand and machine soldering of electronic components; can soldering.
F	50	183	212	General engineering work on copper, brass and zinc; can soldering.
R	45	183	224	
G	40	183	234	
H	35	183	244	Jointing of electric cable sheaths.
J	30	183	255	
V	20	183	276	Lamp solder; dipping solder; for service at very low temperatures (e.g. less than −60°C).
W	15	227	288	
Tin-lead-antimony				
B	50	185	204	Hot dip coating and soldering of ferrous metals; high quality engineering; capillary joints of ferrous metals; jointing of copper conductors.
M	45	185	205	
C	40	185	227	General engineering; heat exchangers; general dip soldering; jointing copper conductors.
L	32	185	243	Plumbing, wiping of lead and lead alloy cable sheathing; dip soldering.
D	30	185	248	

Tin-antimony				
95A	95*	236	243	High service temperature (e.g. greater than 100°C) and refrigeration equipment; step soldering.
Tin-silver				
96S	96*	Melting point 221		High service temperature (e.g. greater than 100°C).
97S	97*	221	223	For capillary joints in all copper plumbing installations and particularly in those installations where the lead content of solder is restricted.
98S	98*	221	230	
Tin-copper				
99C	99*	227	228	For capillary joints in all copper plumbing installations and particularly in those installations where the lead content of the solder is restricted.
Tin-lead-silver				
5S	5.25	296	301	For service both at high (e.g. greater than 100°C) and very low (e.g. less than −60°C) temperatures; soldering of silver coated substrates.
62S	62.5	Melting point	178	
Tin-lead-cadmium				
T	50	Melting point 145		Low melting point solder for assemblies that could be damaged by normal soldering temperatures; step soldering for thermal cutouts.

* Nominal value.
For further information see BS 219 : 1977 : 1987.

3.4 Metallic material sizes

3.4.1 Metallic material sizes: introduction to BS 6722 : 1986

British Standard BS 6722 supersedes BS 4229 Pt 1 and Pt 2, BS 4391 and DD5 which are now withdrawn.

In the case of wire, the dimensions recommended are those previously given in BS 4391, since they are firmly and logically established in the wire and associated industries.

For other products where a clear pattern of sizes does not exist, and where availability and demand vary from one sector of industry to another. It was considered that a list of recommended dimensions based upon the rounded R20 series (BS 2045) should be established without any attempt to distinguish between product type or between ferrous and non-ferrous materials. Suitable dimensions may then be drawn from this list to establish a range of sizes to meet best the pattern of demand.

The detailed recommendations for bar shapes previously given in BS 4229 have not therefore been included. In a similar way the recommendations previously given in DD5 for plate and sheet have been rationalized and the recommendations for thickness of sheet and plate are now referenced as for bar dimensions. Details of preferred sizes for hexagon bars are given in BS 3692.

It is recommended that applicable British Standards for metallic materials should include combinations of dimensions recommended in BS 6722 : 1986. BS 6722 gives recommended dimensions for use as a basis for establishing the sizes of metallic materials in the form of wire, bars (excluding hexagon bars) and flat products including sheet and plate:

Wire The diameters of wires should be selected from the recommended dimensions given in 3.4.2.
Bars The diameters of round bars and the thickness and widths of bars of rectangular or square cross-section should be selected from the recommended dimensions given in 3.4.3.
Flat products The widths and/or lengths for flat products (sheet strip and plate) should be selected from the recommended dimensions given in 3.4.4. The thicknesses for flat products should be selected from the recommended dimensions given in 3.4.3.

3.4.2 Recommended diameters of wires, metric

Choice			Choice			Choice		Choice	
First mm	Second mm	Third mm	First mm	Second mm	Third mm	First mm	Second mm	First mm	Second mm
0.010			0.100			1.0		10.0	
	0.011			0.112			1.12		11.2
0.012			0.125			1.25		12.5	
		0.013			0.132				
	0.014			0.140			1.40		14.0
		0.015			0.150				
0.016			0.160			1.60		16.0	
		0.017			0.170				
	0.018			0.180			1.80		18.0
		0.019			0.190				
0.020			0.200			2.00		20.0	
		0.021			0.212				
	0.022			0.224			2.25		
		0.024			0.236				
0.025			0.250			2.50			
		0.026			0.265				
	0.028			0.280			2.80		
		0.030			0.300				
0.032			0.315			3.15			
		0.034			0.335				
	0.036			0.355			3.55		
		0.038			0.375				
0.040			0.400			4.00			
		0.042			0.425				
	0.045			0.450			4.50		
		0.048			0.480				
0.050			0.500			5.00			
		0.053			0.530				
	0.056			0.560			5.60		
		0.060			0.600				
0.063			0.630			6.30			
		0.067			0.670				
	0.071			0.710			7.10		
		0.075			0.750				
0.080			0.800			8.00			
		0.085			0.850				
	0.090			0.900			9.00		
		0.095			0.950				

From BS 6722 : 1986.
For metric inch wire gauge equivalents see 3.4.7.

3.4.3 Recommended dimensions for bar and flat products

Choice		*Choice*		*Choice*		*Choice*	
First mm	*Second* mm	*First* mm	*Second* mm	*First* mm	*Second* mm	*First* mm	*Second* mm
0.10		1.0		10.0		100	
	0.11		1.1		11.0		110
0.12		1.2		12.0		120	
	0.14		1.4		14.0		140
0.16		1.6		16.0		160	
	0.18		1.8		18.0		180
0.20		2.0		20.0		200	
	0.22		2.2		22.0		220
0.25		2.5		25.0		250	
	0.28		2.8		28.0		280
0.30		3.0		30.0		300	
	0.35		3.5		35.0		
0.40		4.0		40.0			
	0.45		4.5		45.0		
0.50		5.0		50.0			
	0.55		5.5		55.0		
0.60		6.0		60.0			
	0.70		7.0		70.0		
0.80		8.0		80.0			
	0.90		9.0		90.0		

3.4.4 Recommended widths and lengths of flat products

mm	mm
400	2500
500	3000
600	4000
800	5000
1000	6000
1200	8000
1250	10000
1500	
2000	

3.4.5 Mass of metric round and square bars

Size mm	*Steel* Round kg/m	*Steel* Square kg/m	*Copper* Round kg/m	*Copper* Square kg/m	*Brass* Round kg/m	*Brass* Square kg/m	*Tin bronze* Round kg/m	*Tin bronze* Square kg/m	*Duralumin* Round kg/m	*Duralumin* Square kg/m
1.0	0.0062	0.0079	0.0071	0.0090	0.0065	0.0085	0.0069	0.0088	0.0023	0.0027
1.1	0.0075	0.0095	0.0085	0.0108	0.0081	0.0103	0.0084	0.0106	0.0029	0.0035
1.2	0.0089	0.0113	0.0101	0.0129	0.0096	0.0122	0.0100	0.0127	0.0032	0.0041
1.4	0.0120	0.0154	0.0137	0.0175	0.0130	0.0166	0.0134	0.0173	0.0044	0.0056
1.6	0.0160	0.0201	0.0181	0.024	0.0173	0.0217	0.0179	0.0225	0.0058	0.0073
1.8	0.020	0.0254	0.023	0.029	0.0216	0.0275	0.0224	0.0285	0.0073	0.0093
2.0	0.025	0.0314	0.028	0.036	0.027	0.034	0.028	0.035	0.0091	0.0114
2.5	0.039	0.0491	0.044	0.056	0.042	0.053	0.043	0.055	0.0142	0.0179
3.0	0.055	0.0707	0.063	0.080	0.060	0.076	0.062	0.079	0.0200	0.0257
3.5	0.076	0.0962	0.087	0.109	0.082	0.104	0.085	0.108	0.0277	0.0350
4.0	0.099	0.126	0.113	0.143	0.107	0.136	0.111	0.141	0.0360	0.0459
4.5	0.125	0.159	0.142	0.181	0.135	0.172	0.140	0.178	0.0455	0.0579
5.0	0.154	0.196	0.175	0.223	0.166	0.212	0.173	0.220	0.0560	0.0713
5.5	0.187	0.237	0.213	0.270	0.202	0.256	0.209	0.265	0.0680	0.0863
6.0	0.222	0.283	0.253	0.322	0.240	0.306	0.249	0.317	0.0808	0.1030
7.0	0.302	0.385	0.344	0.438	0.326	0.416	0.338	0.431	0.110	0.140
8.0	0.395	0.502	0.450	0.571	0.427	0.543	0.442	0.562	0.144	0.183
9.0	0.499	0.636	0.568	0.724	0.539	0.688	0.559	0.712	0.182	0.232
10.0	0.617	0.785	0.702	0.893	0.667	0.849	0.691	0.879	0.225	0.286
11.0	0.746	0.950	0.849	1.081	0.806	1.027	0.836	1.064	0.272	0.346
12.0	0.888	1.130	1.010	1.286	0.960	1.222	0.995	1.266	0.323	0.411
14.0	1.208	1.539	1.375	1.751	1.306	1.664	1.353	1.724	0.440	0.560
16.0	1.578	2.010	1.796	2.287	1.706	2.173	1.767	2.251	0.574	0.732
18.0	1.998	2.543	2.274	2.894	2.160	2.749	2.238	2.848	0.727	0.926

20.0	2.466	3.140	2.806	3.573	2.666	3.394	2.762	3.517	0.898	1.143
25.0	3.853	4.906	4.385	5.583	4.165	5.303	4.315	5.495	1.402	1.786
30.0	5.158	7.065	5.870	8.040	5.876	7.637	5.777	7.913	1.878	2.572
35.0	7.553	9.616	8.595	10.943	8.165	10.395	8.459	10.770	2.749	3.500
40.0	9.865	12.56	11.23	14.29	10.66	13.58	11.05	14.07	3.590	4.572
45.0	12.48	15.90	14.20	18.09	13.49	17.19	13.98	17.81	4.542	5.788
50.0	15.41	19.63	17.54	22.34	16.66	21.22	17.26	21.99	5.609	7.145
55.0	18.65	23.75	21.22	27.03	20.16	25.67	20.89	26.60	6.789	8.645
60.0	22.20	28.26	25.26	32.16	24.00	30.55	24.86	31.65	8.081	10.29
70.0	30.21	38.47	34.38	43.78	32.66	41.59	33.84	43.09	11.00	14.00
80.0	39.46	50.24	44.91	57.17	42.66	54.31	44.20	56.27	14.36	18.29
90.0	49.94	63.59	56.83	72.37	53.99	68.74	55.93	71.22	18.18	23.15
100.0	61.65	78.50	70.16	89.33	66.64	84.86	69.05	87.92	22.44	28.57
120.0	88.78	113.04	101.03	128.64	95.97	122.20	99.43	126.60	32.32	41.15
160.0	167.84	200.96	191.00	228.69	181.44	217.24	187.98	225.08	61.09	73.15
200.0	246.60	314.00	280.63	319.36	266.58	339.43	276.19	351.68	89.76	114.30
250.0	385.31	490.63	438.48	558.34	416.52	530.37	431.55	549.51	140.25	178.59
300.0	554.80	706.50	631.36	804.00	599.74	763.73	621.38	791.28	201.95	257.17

3.4.6 Hexagon bar sizes for screwed fasteners, metric

Choice	Nominal size of thread	*Hexangon bar sizes* (mm)				Mass (kg/m) (*max. bar size: steel*)
		Across flats (A/F)		*Across corners (A/C)*		
		max.	*min.*	*max.*	*min.*	
First (preferred)	M1.6	3.2	3.08	3.7	3.48	0.07
	M2	4.0	3.88	4.6	4.38	0.11
	M2.5	5.0	4.88	5.8	5.51	0.17
	M3	5.5	5.38	6.4	6.08	0.21
	M4	7.0	6.85	8.1	7.74	0.33
	M5	8.0	7.85	9.2	8.87	0.44
	M6	10.0	9.78	11.5	11.05	0.68
	M8	13.0	12.73	15.0	14.38	1.15
	M10	17.0	16.73	19.6	18.90	1.97
	M12	19.0	18.67	21.9	21.10	2.45
	M16	24.0	23.67	27.7	26.75	3.62
	M20	30.0	29.67	34.6	33.53	6.12
	M24	36.0	35.38	41.6	39.98	8.81
	M30	46.0	45.38	53.1	51.28	14.40
	M36	55.0	54.26	63.5	61.31	20.52
	M42	65.0	64.26	75.1	72.61	28.67
	M48	75.0	74.26	86.6	83.91	35.15
	M56	85.0	84.13	98.1	95.07	49.00
	M64	95.0	94.13	109.7	106.37	61.22
Second (non-preferred)	M14	22.0	21.67	25.4	24.49	3.29
	M18	27.0	26.67	31.2	30.14	4.95
	M22	32.0	31.61	36.9	35.74	6.96
	M27	41.0	40.38	47.3	45.63	11.43
	M33	50.0	49.38	57.7	55.80	17.00
	M39	60.0	59.26	69.3	66.96	24.42
	M45	70.0	69.26	80.8	78.26	32.23
	M52	80.0	79.26	92.4	89.56	43.41
	M60	90.0	89.13	103.9	100.72	55.00
	M68	100.0	99.13	115.5	112.02	67.84

The mass of common non-ferrous hexagon bars can be determined by multiplying the mass of a corresponding steel bar by one of the following conversion factors:

Brass	× 1.081
Bronze	× 1.120
Duralumin	× 0.364

For example, the mass of a hexagonal steel bar 30 mm across flats (A/F) is 6.12 kg/m. Thus the mass of a hexagonal brass bar 30 mm across flats (A/F) is 6.12 × 1.081 = 6.616 kg/m.

3.4.7 Gauge sizes and equivalents

ISWG	*British* in	*Metric* mm	*Mass* kg/m (*steel*)	*ISWG*	*British* in	*Metric* mm	*Mass* kg/m (*steel*)
50	0.0010	0.025	0.0000044	29	0.0136	0.35	0.000735
49	0.0012	0.030	0.0000057	28	0.0148	0.37	0.00087
48	0.0016	0.040	0.0000102	27	0.0164	0.4	0.00107
47	0.0020	0.050	0.000016	26	0.0180	0.45	0.00129
46	0.0024	0.061	0.000023	25	0.0200	0.5	0.00159
45	0.0028	0.071	0.000032	24	0.022	0.55	0.00192
44	0.0032	0.081	0.000041	23	0.024	0.6	0.0023
43	0.0036	0.091	0.000052	22	0.028	0.7	0.0031
42	0.0040	0.101	0.000064	21	0.032	0.8	0.0041
41	0.0044	0.112	0.000077	20	0.036	0.9	0.0052
40	0.0048	0.122	0.000092	19	0.040	1.0	0.0064
39	0.0052	0.127	0.000108	18	0.048	1.2	0.0092
38	0.0060	0.152	0.000144	17	0.056	1.4	0.0125
37	0.0068	0.172	0.000185	16	0.064	1.6	0.0163
36	0.0076	0.177	0.000231	15	0.072	1.8	0.0211
35	0.0084	0.203	0.000256	14	0.080	2.0	0.025
34	0.0092	0.230	0.000338	13	0.092	2.3	0.034
33	0.0100	0.254	0.000397	12	0.104	2.6	0.043
32	0.0108	0.27	0.000463	11	0.116	3.0	0.054
31	0.0116	0.28	0.000527	10	0.128	3.3	0.065
30	0.0124	0.32	0.000613	9	0.144	3.7	0.083

continued

Section 3.4.7 (*continued*)

ISWG	*British* in	*Metric* mm	*Mass* kg/m (*steel*)	*ISWG*	*British* in	*Metric* mm	*Mass* kg/m (*steel*)
8	0.160	4.1	0.102	1/0	0.324	8.2	0.42
7	0.176	4.5	0.123	2/0	0.348	8.8	0.48
6	0.192	4.9	0.147	3/0	0.372	9.4	0.55
5	0.212	5.4	0.178	4/0	0.400	10.2	0.64
4	0.232	5.9	0.214	5/0	0.432	11.0	0.74
3	0.252	6.4	0.25	6/0	0.464	11.8	0.86
2	0.276	7.0	0.31	7/0	0.500	12.7	1.0
1	0.300	7.6	0.36				

The mass of common non-ferrous wires can be determined by multiplying the mass of a corresponding steel wire by one of the following conversion factors

Brass	× 1.081
Bronze	× 1.120
Duralumin	× 0.364

3.5 Polymeric (plastic) materials

3.5.1 Polymeric materials (plastics)

Introduction

Polymeric materials are conventionally referred to as 'plastics'. This is a misnomer since polymeric materials rarely show plastic properties in their finished condition; in fact many of them are elastic. However, during the moulding process by which they are formed they are reduced to a plastic condition by heating them to a temperature above that of boiling water, and it is from this that they get the generic name of *plastics*.

There are two main groups of polymeric materials:

Thermoplastics These can be softened as often as they are reheated. They are not so rigid as the thermosetting plastic materials but tend to be tougher. Examples of thermoplastic polymeric materials are listed in 3.5.3.

Thermosetting plastics (*thermosets*) These undergo a chemical change during moulding and can never again be softened by reheating. This chemical change, called *curing*, is triggered by the temperature and pressure of the moulding process. These materials are harder and more brittle than the thermoplastic materials.

Polymers

Polymers are formed by combining together a large number of basic units (monomer molecules) to form long chain molecules (polymers). These polymer molecules may be one of three types as follows.

Linear polymer chain Linear polymer chains can move past each other easily, resulting in a non-rigid, flexible, thermoplastic material such as *polyethylene.*

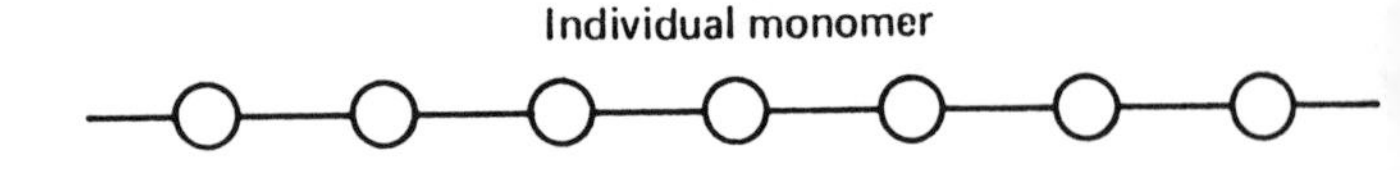

Branched linear polymer chain It is more difficult for branched linear chains to move past each other, and materials with molecules of this configuration are more rigid, harder and stronger. Such materials also tend to be less dense since the molecule chains cannot pack so closely together. Heat energy is required to break down the side branches so that the chains can flow more easily, and this raises their melting point above that for materials with a simple linear chain.

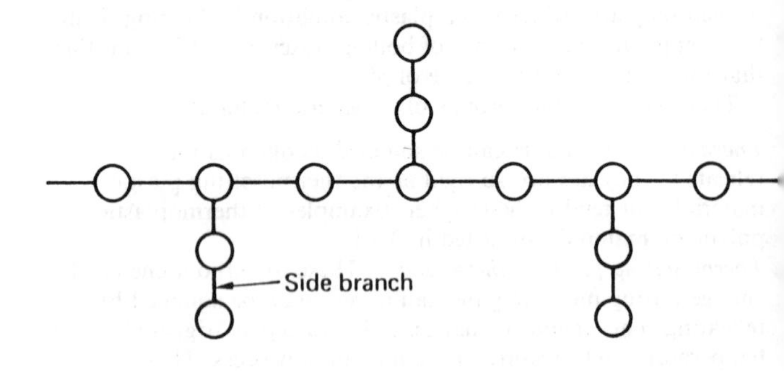

Cross-linked polymer The cross-linked molecular chain is typical of the thermosetting plastics. Thermosets are rigid and tend to be brittle once the cross-links are formed by 'curing' the material during the moulding process. The *elastomers* are an intermediate group of materials which exhibit the toughness and resilience of rubber. This is achieved by a more limited cross-linking than that of the rigid thermosets.

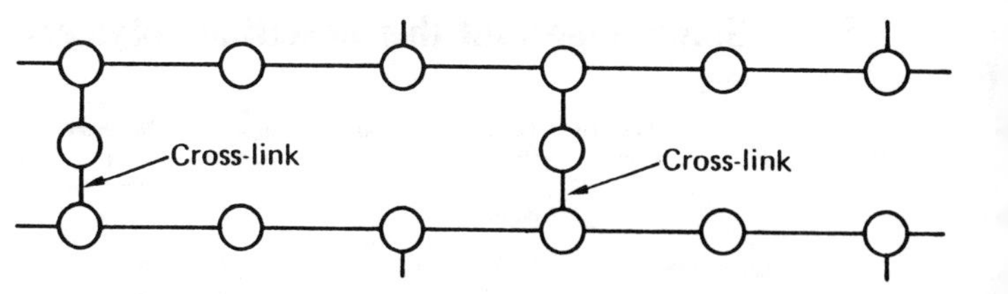

Reinforced polymeric materials

In this group of materials synthetic, polymeric materials are used to bond together strong reinforcing materials to produce high strength composites.

Glass reinforced plastics (GRP) High strength glass fibres are bonded together using polyester or epoxide resins. The fibres may be in the form of rovings (ropes), woven cloth, or chopped strand mat. Glass reinforced plastics are used for a wide range of products, including: printed circuit boards for high quality electronic equipment; safety helmets; and boat hulls and superstructures.

Laminated plastics Sheets of paper, cotton cloth, woollen cloth, or woven glass fibre are impregnated with an appropriate synthetic resin and then stacked between polished metal sheets in a hydraulic press. The combined heat and pressure cause the laminates to bond together and to cure. The moulded sheets, rods, tubes and other sections produced by the process have high strength and can be machined on conventional machined tools into screwed fastenings, bushes, gears etc. in a manner similar to metals. A typical range of such materials is available under the trade name of Tufnol.

3.5.2 Some important thermosetting polymers

Material	*Relative density*	*Tensile strength* N/mm^2	*Elongation* %	*Impact strength* J	*Maximum service temperature* °C
Phenol formaldehyde*	1.35	35–55	1.0	0.3–1.5	75
Urea formaldehyde†	1.50	50–75	1.0	0.3–0.5	75
Melamine formaldehyde†	1.50	56–80	0.7	0.2–0.4	100
Casein (cross-linked with formaldehyde)	1.34	55–70	2.5–4.0	1.5–2.0	150
Epoxides‡	1.15	35–80	5.0–10.0	0.5–1.5	200
Polyesters (unsaturated)	1.12	50–60	2.0	0.7	220
Polyesters (alkyd resins)	2.00	20–30	0.0	0.25	150
Silicones	1.88	35–45	30–40	0.4	450

* With wood flour filler.
† With cellulose filler.
‡ Rigid, unfilled.

Additives

Plasticizers These reduce the rigidity and brittleness of polymeric materials and improve their flow properties during moulding.
Fillers These are bulking agents which not only reduce the cost of the moulding powder, but have a considerable influence on the properties of a moulding produced from a given polymeric material. Fillers improve the impact strength and reduce shrinkage during moulding. Typical fillers are:

Glass fibre: good electrical properties
Wood flour, calcium carbonate: low cost, high bulk, low strength
Aluminium powder: expensive but high strength and wear resistance
Shredded paper (*cellulose*), *shredded cloth*: good mechanical strength with reasonable electrical insulation properties
Mica granules: good heat resistance and good electrical insulation properties.

Stabilizers These are added to prevent or reduce degradation, and include antioxidants, antiozonants, and ultraviolet ray absorbants.

Colorants These can be subdivided into dyestuffs, organic pigments and inorganic pigments. Dyestuffs are used for transparent and translucent plastics. Pigments have greater opacity, colour stability and heat stability than dyestuffs. They are unsuitable for transparent plastics.
Antistatic agents These provide improved surface conductivity so that static electrical charges can leak away, thus reducing the attraction of dust particles, the risk of electric shock and the risk of explosion in hazardous environments caused by the spark associated with an electrical discharge.

3.5.3 Some important thermoplastic polymers

Material	*Crystallinity* %	*Density* kg/m³	*Tensile strength* N/mm²	*Elongation* %	*Impact strength* J	T_g* °C	T_m* °C	*Maximum service temperature* °C
Polyethylene (polythene)	60†	920	11	100–600	no fracture	−120	115	85
	95‡	950	31	50–800	5–15	−120	138	125
	60	900	30–35	50–600	1–10	−25	176	150
Polypropylene	0	1070	28–53	1–35	0.25–2.5	100	—	65–85
Polystyrene	0	1400§	49	10–130	1.5–18	87	—	70
Polyvinyl chloride (PVC)	0	1300‖	7–25	240–380	—	87	—	60–105
Polytetrafluoroethylene (Teflon) (PTFE)	90	2170	17–25	200–600	3–5	−126	327	260
Polymethyl methacrylate (Plexiglass) (Perspex)	0	1180	50–70	3–8	0.5–0.7	0	—	95
Acrylonitrile-butadiene-styrene (ABS) (high impact polystyrene)	0	1100	30–35	10–140	7–12	−55	—	100

Polyamides (nylon) (properties for nylon 66)	variable	1140	50–85	60–300	1.5–15.0	50	265	120
Polyethylene teraphthalate (Terylene): one of the polyester group	60	1350	over 175	60–110	1.0	70	267	69
Polyformaldehyde[‖]	70–90	1410	50–70	15–75	0.5–2.0	−73	180	105
Polyoxymethylene[‖]	70–90	1410	60–70	15–70	0.5–2.0	−76	180	120
Polycarbonate	0	1200	60–70	60–100	10–20	150	—	130
Cellulose acetate	0	1280	24–65	5–55	0.7–7.0	120	—	70
Cellulose nitrate (highly flammable)	0	1400	35–70	10–40	3–11	53	—	—
Polyvinylidene chloride	60	1680	25–35	up to 200	0.4–1.3	−17	198	60

* T_g = glass transition temperature, T_m = melting temperature.
† Low density polyethylene.
‡ High density polyethylene.
§ Unplasticized.
‖ Plasticized.
‖ Members of the polyacetal group of plastics: these are strong and stiff with high creep resistance and resistance to fatigue.

Part 4 Computer Aided Engineering

4.1 Computer numerical control

4.1.1 Background to computer numerical control

Ever since machine tools were first used as a means of production in the engineering industry, the trend has been towards developing semi-automatic or fully automatic machines. These eliminate the high cost of manual operation and thus reduce the unit cost of each component, and also improve repeatability and quality control. Until the advent of numerical control, automatic machine tools had to be controlled by mechanical devices such as cams. Although fast and reliable, such machines were inflexible and expensive to reset when a new and different workpiece was required. For example, each new component on a single spindle automatic lathe required the manufacture of a new set of expensive cams with complex profiles. Often form tools were required as well. Thus such automation was only viable for large batch or continuous production.

With the introduction of numerical control (NC), greater operating flexibility was possible. No longer were complex and expensive cams and form tools required. Lead time was reduced to only that required to write the part program and load it into the controller of the machine. Complex profiles could be generated using standard tooling simply by entry of numerical data into the control unit.

Numerical control is the term used to describe the control of machines by instructions expressed as a series of numbers which are interpreted by an electronic control system which converts the numerical data into physical movement of the machine elements. *Computer numerical control* (CNC) is the term used when the control unit includes a computer and when sophisticated system management software is used to interpret the alphanumerical data of the part program. The information for each operation is fed from the controller to the machine where it operates the positioning mechanisms, starts and stops the spindle, coolant supply etc., changes the cutting speed and feed rate and, on some machines, changes the tools.

Early NC machines were hard wired from the discrete electronic components available at the time. They were virtually devoid of memory by current standards and had constantly to read the punched tape which contained the operating data (program).

CNC machines came into being with the development of microelectronic techniques and integrated circuits. This enabled powerful, dedicated computers using sophisticated systems management software to be built into the controller. Once loaded with the part program the controller can keep repeating the program for repetitive production. As the computing power has increased so has the range of 'canned' or permanent prerecorded cycles, thus reducing the time taken to program a component. Further, the controller has become capable of profiling the most complex shapes and contouring the most complex solids by interpolating the curves between given coordinates.

The programming of present day machines has been made even easier by the introduction of *interactive control systems*, where the operator can load the positional and cutting data directly into the controller from the component drawing by simply following the prompts on a VDU screen, without the need for a detailed program. It is now possible to extend a numerical control system so that by using a single computer and transmission lines, several machine tools (each with their own computer terminal) can be controlled from a central point. This arrangement is known as *direct numerical control* (DNC). A further development of this technique is to load the digitized data from a drawing produced by computer aided design (CAD) directly into the machine tool without the preparation of a part program. The 'language' of the CAD system is converted into the 'language' of the machine system by suitable computer software without human intervention. Such a system is known as CAD/CAM.

4.1.2 Typical applications of computer numerical control

Computer numerical control is applied to a wide range of production processes in many industries. In the engineering industries it is applied to such processes as:

(a) Machine tools, including
 Milling machines and machining centres
 Centre lathes and turning centres
 Drilling machines
 Precision, grinding machines
 EDM (spark erosion) machines
 Die sinking machines
(b) Sheet metal working machines, including
 Turret punching machines
 Riveting machines
 Forming machines
(c) Fabrication equipment, including
 Flame cutting machines
 Welding machines
 Tube bending machines
(d) Inspection machines for checking three-dimensionally contoured components.

4.1.3 Advantages and limitations of computer numerical control

It is evident from the wide and increasing use of computer numerically controlled machines in manufacturing industry that the advantages substantially outweigh the limitations.

Advantages

High productivity Although the cutting speeds and feeds for CNC machines are the same as for manually operated machines, much time is saved by rapid traversing and positioning between operations. Also a wider range of operations is possible on a CNC machine, avoiding the necessity to pass the work from one machine to another for, say, each of drilling, milling and boring. This reduces the need for expensive jigs and fixtures and avoids reserves of work in progress between operations. In addition,

CNC machines do not become tired and they maintain a constant rate of productivity. If the work is robot fed, they can work 'lights out' through the night.

Design flexibility Complex shapes are easily produced on CNC machines. In addition, contoured solids can be produced on CNC machines which cannot be produced on conventional, manually operated machines.

Management control Production rates, reduced scrap and improved quality comes under management control with CNC machines and is not influenced by operator performance.

Quality CNC machines have a higher accuracy and better repeatability than conventional machines. If the machine is fitted with adaptive control it will even sense tool failure or other variations in performance and either stop the machine or, if fitted with automatic tool changing, select backup tooling from the tool magazine before scrap is produced or the machine damaged.

Reduced lead time The lead time for CNC machines is much less than for other automatic machines. There are no complex and expensive cams and form tools; it is necessary simply to write a part program and load it into the machine memory. Complex profiles are generated using standard tooling.

Limitations

Capital cost The initial cost of CNC machines is substantially higher than for manually operated machines of the same type. However, in recent years, the cost differential has come down somewhat.

Tooling cost To exploit the production potential of CNC machine tools, specialized cutting tools are required. Although the initial cost is high, this largely reflects the cost of the tool shanks and tool holding devices which do not have to be replaced. The cost of replacement tool tips is no higher than for conventional machines.

Maintenance Because of the complexity of CNC machine tools, few small and medium companies will have the expertise to carry out more than very basic maintenance and repairs. Therefore maintenance contracts are advisable. These are expensive – approximately 10% of the capital cost per annum.

Training Programmer/operator training is required. This is usually provided by the equipment manufacturer but can be time consuming and costly.

Depreciation As with all computer based devices, CNC controllers rapidly become obsolescent. Therefore CNC machines should be amortized over a shorter period than is usual with manually operated machines and should be replaced approximately every five years.

4.1.4 Axes of control for machine tools

There are a number of axes configurations for CNC machine tools; the most common are used with vertical/horizontal milling machines and lathes as shown. Note that:

(a) The *Z* axis is always the main spindle axis.
(b) The *X* axis is always horizontal and perpendicular to the *Z* axis.
(c) The *Y* axis is perpendicular to both the *X* and *Z* axes.

Vertical milling machine: axes of control

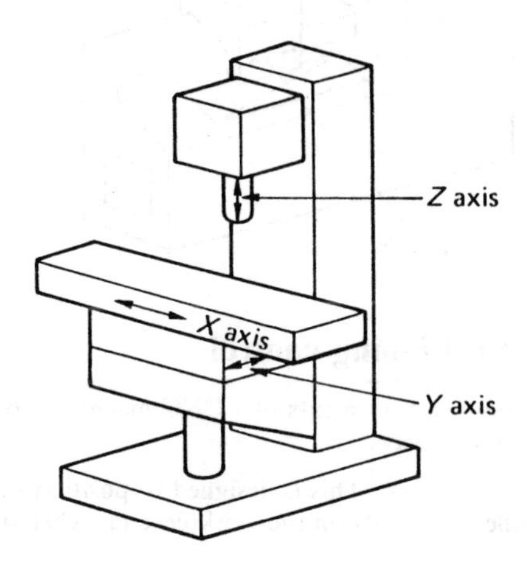

Horizontal milling machine: axes of control

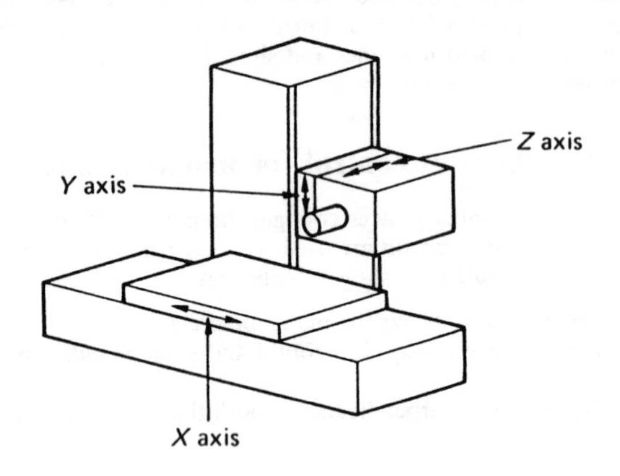

Centre lathe: axes of control

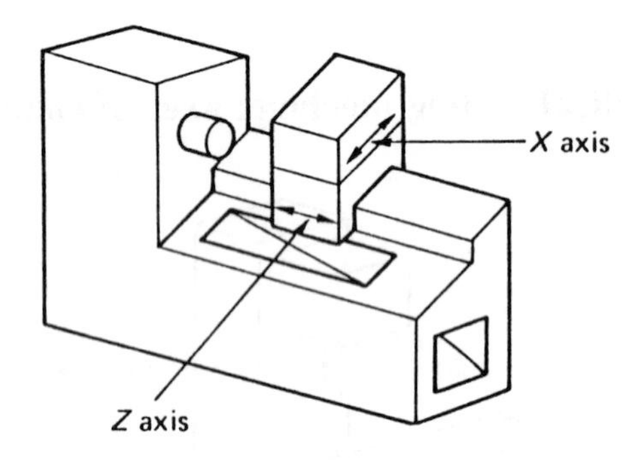

4.1.5 Positioning control

The programmed movements of a CNC machine tool can be described in four ways:

Point-to-point system This is designed to position the tool at a series of different points on the workpiece (as when drilling or punching). The machine moves the tool from point to point in rapid traverse by the shortest possible route, and this function is not under the control of the programmer. Thus machining between the points is not possible. The programmer only has positional control over the point coordinates.

Linear path system Again this is a system in which the tool moves from point to point in a straight line by the shortest distance. However, in this system the traverse rate can be controlled by the programmer and simple machining operations can be performed between the points: for example, milling a straight slot between two points.

Parallel path system Again this is a system in which the tool moves from point to point in a straight line. However, in the parallel path system the movement is always parallel to an axis. The traverse rate between the points is under the control of the programmer and simple machining operations can be performed between the points.

Continuous path system This allows more complex programmed movements involving angular movements and curves. These movements can be made in two or three axes simultaneously. This allows complex profiles and contours such as helixals to be generated.

4.1.6 Control systems

Control systems for CNC machine tools broadly fall into two categories as follows.

Open loop control

This system derives its name from the fact that there is no feedback in the system, and hence no comparison between input and output. The system uses stepper motors to drive the positioning mechanism, and these have only limited torque compared with more conventional servo motors. Further, if the drag of the mechanism causes the motor to stall and miss a step, no corrective action is taken by the system.

Open loop control

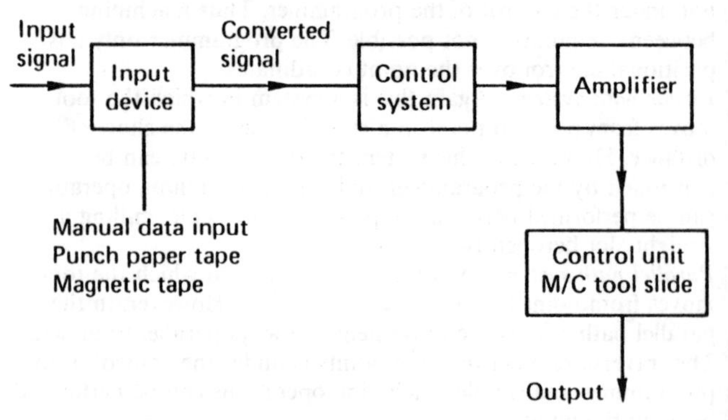

Closed loop control

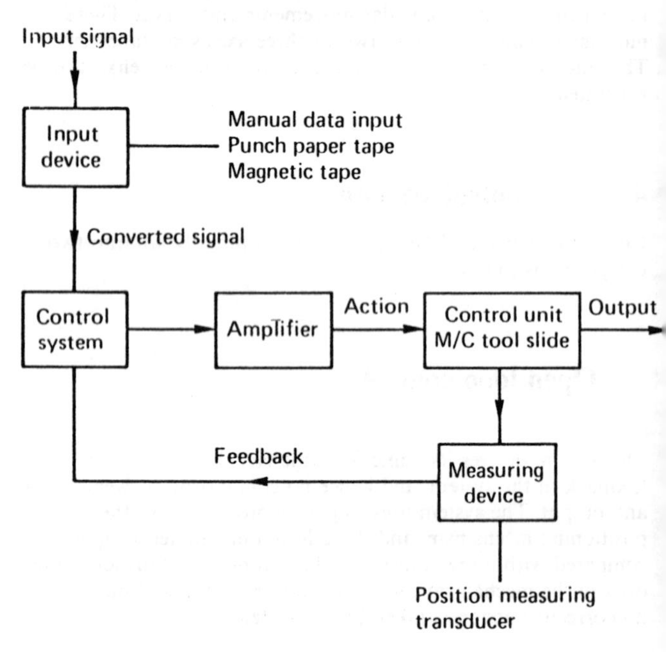

In a closed loop control system the feedback continuously influences the action of the controller and corrects any positional errors. This system allows the use of servo motors to drive the positioning mechanism, and these have a much higher torque than the stepper motors used with the open loop control system.

4.1.7 Program terminology and formats

Character

A character is a number, letter or other symbol which is recognized by the controller. An associated group of characters makes a word.

Word

A word is a group of characters which defines one complete element of information, e.g. N100. There are two types of word as follows.

Dimensional words

These are any words related to a linear dimension; that is, any word commencing with the characters X, Y, Z, I, J, K or any word in which these characters are inferred.

The letters X, Y, Z refer to dimensions parallel to the corresponding machine axes, as explained in 4.1.4.

The letters I, J, K refer to arcs of circles. The start and finish positions of the arcs are defined by X, Y, Z dimensions, whilst the centre of radius of the arc is defined using I, J, K dimensions, with

I dimensions corresponding to X dimensions
J dimensions corresponding to Y dimensions
K dimensions corresponding to Z dimensions.

Current practice favours the use of the decimal point in specifying dimension words. Thus a machine manual may stipulate that an X dimension word has the form X 4, 3, which means that the X dimension may have up to 4 digits in front of the decimal point and up to 3 digits behind the decimal point. Some older systems, still widely in use, do *not* use the decimal point but use leading and trailing zeros; for example, 25.4 would be written 0025400.

Management words

These are any words which are not related to a dimension; that is, any word commencing with the characters N, G, F, S, T, M or any word in which the above characters are inferred. Examples of management words may be as follows:

N4 Sequence number: the character N followed by up to four digits, i.e. N1 . . . N9999
G2 Preparatory function: the character G followed by up to two digits, i.e. G0 . . . G99
F4 Feedrate command: the character F followed by up to four digits
S4 Spindle speed command: the character S followed by up to four digits
T2 Tool identifier: the character T followed by up to two digits
M2 Miscellaneous commands: the character M followed by up to two digits.

Note that N, G, T and M commands *may require* leading zeros to be programmed on some older but still widely used systems, e.g. G0 would be G00, G1 would be G01 etc.

Format

Different control systems use different formats for the assembly of a block of data; thus the machine manual should always be consulted when programming. A *block* of data consists of a complete line on a program containing a complete set of instructions for the controller.

Word (or letter) address format

This is, currently, the most widely used system. Each word commences with a letter character called an *address*. Hence a word is identified by its letter character and *not* by its position in the block (in contrast to the fixed block system described below).

Thus in a word (or letter) address system, instructions which remain unchanged from a previous block may be omitted from subsequent blocks.

A typical letter address format, as given by a maker's handbook, could be:

Metric N4 G2 X4, 3 Y4, 3 Z4, 3 I4, 3 J4, 3 K4, 3 F3 S4 T2 M2
Inch N4 G2 X3, 4 Y3, 4 Z3, 4 I3, 4 J3, 4 K3, 4 F3 S4 T2 M2

Fixed block format

This is an outdated system, but is still widely used on older machines.

Instructions in blocks are always written and recorded in the same *fixed* sequence. No letter commences each word in the block, but the letter address is implicit by the position of the word in the sequence. For example, a block could read

20 1 25.6 37.450 100 2500 2 6

Because 20 is the first word in the sequence, the controller reads this as having the prefix N. Because 25.6 is the third word in the sequence, the controller reads this as having the prefix X, and so on. Thus all instructions are given in *every* block, including those instructions which remain unchanged.

4.1.8 Coded information

A CNC program contains the information for the manufacture of a component part. The CNC controller regulates the signals and sequence to the various drive units.

Codes

Block numbers	N
Preparatory functions	G
Dimensional data	X,Y,Z,I,J,K
Feed rates	F
Spindle speeds	S

Tool numbers	T
Miscellaneous functions	M

A sample of a CNC program could look like this:

```
N5  G90  G71  G00  X25.0  Y25.0  T01  M06
N10  X100.0  Y100.0  S1250
N15  G01  Z25.0  F125  M03
```

Block numbers

The block number is usually the first word which appears in any block. Blocks are numbered in steps of 5 or 10 so that additional blocks can be easily inserted in the event of an omission.

Preparatory functions (G)

These are used to inform the machine controller of the functions required for the next operation. Standardized preparatory functions are shown in the table. In practice, the actual codes used will depend upon the control system and the machine type. The codes that one system uses can vary from those of another, so reference to the relevant programming manual is essential.

Code number	*Function**	
G00	Rapid positioning, point to point	(M)
G01	Positioning at controlled feed rate, normal dimensions	(M)
G02	Circular interpolation, normal dimensions	(M)
G03	Circular interpolation CCW, normal dimensions	(M)
G04	Dwell for programmed duration	
G05	Hold: cancelled by operator	
G06, G07	Reserved for future standardization: not normally used	
G08	Programmed slide acceleration	
G09	Programmed slide deceleration	
G10	Linear interpolation, long dimensions	(M)
G11	Linear interpolation, short dimensions	(M)
G12	3D interpolation	(M)
G13–G16	Axis selection	(M)

G17	XY plane selection	(M)
G18	ZX plane selection	(M)
G19	YZ plane selection	(M)
G20	Circular interpolation CW, long dimensions	(M)
G21	Circular interpolation CW, short dimensions	(M)
G22	Coupled motion positive	
G23	Coupled motion negative	
G24	Reserved for future standardization	
G25–G29	Available for individual use	
G30	Circular interpolation CCW, long dimensions	(M)
G31	Circular interpolation CCW, short dimensions	(M)
G32	Reserved for future standardization	
G33	Thread cutting, constant lead	(M)
G34	Thread cutting, increasing lead	(M)
G35	Thread cutting, decreasing lead	(M)
G36–G39	Available for individual use	
G40	Cutter compensation, cancel	(M)
G41	Cutter compensation, left	(M)
G42	Cutter compensation, right	(M)
G43	Cutter compensation, positive	
G44	Cutter compensation, negative	
G45	Cutter compensation +/+	
G46	Cutter compensation +/−	
G47	Cutter compensation −/−	
G48	Cutter compensation −/+	
G49	Cutter compensation 0/+	
G50	Cutter compensation 0/−	
G51	Cutter compensation +/0	
G52	Cutter compensation −/0	
G53	Linear shift cancel	(M)
G54	Linear shift X	(M)
G55	Linear shift Y	(M)
G56	Linear shift Z	(M)
G57	Linear shift XY	(M)
G58	Linear shift XZ	(M)
G59	Linear shift YZ	(M)
G60	Positioning exact 1	(M)
G61	Positioning exact 2	(M)

G62	Positioning fast	(M)
G63	Tapping	
G64	Change of rate	
G65–G79	Reserved for future standardization	
G80	Fixed cycle cancel	(M)
G81–G89	Fixed cycles	(M)
G90–G99†	Reserved for future standardization	

(M) indicates modal G commands which remain in force from line to line until cancelled.

* Variations on standard codings occur not only between the different makes of controller but between different models by the same maker and even between different types of the same model. Thus again it must be stressed that the programmer/operator *must* work from the manufacturer's manual for a given machine/controller combination.

† Most control units use G90 to establish the program in *absolut* dimensional units, and G91 to establish the program in *incremental* dimensional units, however. FANUC control units use G20 in place of G90, and G21 in place of G92.

Dimensional words

A CNC machine tool will have axes which are addressed by letters (X, Y, Z etc.). The CNC program will instruct the controller to drive the appropriate machine elements to a required position parallel to the relevant axes using dimensional words (X25.0 Y-55.0) which consists of the axis letter plus a dimension. These dimensional words are sign sensitive (− or +). If there is no sign, the number is assumed positive by the controller. This adds built-in safety to a CNC program, ensuring that should a CNC programmer fail to input a minus value to a *Z* axis command the tool should move to 'safe' as shown below. That is, it moves away from the workpiece, as shown in the figure.

Consider a line of program N10 G01 X25.0 Y25.0 Z30.0. This would result in the tool moving to the coordinates X25, Y25, Z30. However, since the Z word is positive the tool will go up and not down 30 mm from the datum. To drill the component to a depth of 30 mm the line of program should read N10 G01 X25.0 Y25.0 Z-30.0.

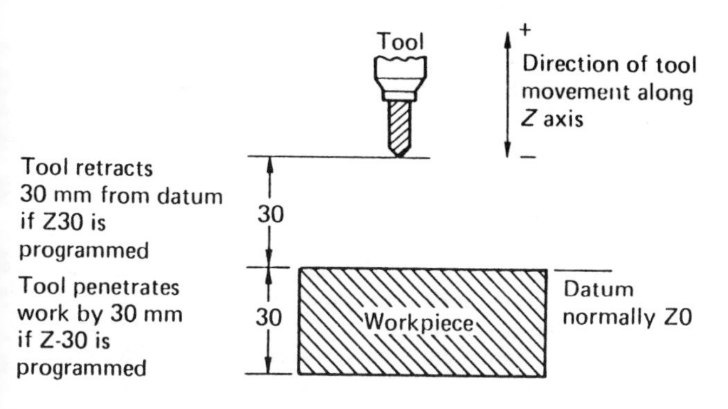

Feed rate (F)

Words commencing with F indicate to the controller the desired feed rate for machining. There are a number of ways of defining the feed rate:

(a) Millimetres/minute: F30 = 30 mm/min.
(b) Millimetres/revolution: F0.2 = 0.2 mm/rev.
(c) Feed rate number 1 to 20 indicates feed rates predetermined by the manufacture in rev/min or mm/min as appropriate. To use this system the feed rate command is prefaced by a G code. Only a few older machines use this system.

Spindle speed (S)

Words commencing with the letter S indicate to the controller the desired spindle speed for machining. Once again there are a number of ways of defining the spindle speed, each selected by use of the appropriate G code:

(a) Spindle speeds in revolutions/minute (r.p.m.)
(b) Cutting speed in metres/minute
(c) Constant cutting speed in metres/minute.

Tool numbers (T)

Each tool used during the machining of a part will have its own number (e.g. T01 for tool 1, T19 for tool 19). Most CNC machine controllers can hold information about 20 tools or more. This tool information will take the form of a tool length offset and a tool diameter/radius compensation (see 4.1.10 and 4.1.11). Where the machine is fitted with automatic tool changing it will also identify the position of the tool in the tool magazine.

Miscellaneous functions (M)

Apart from preparatory functions there are a number of other functions that are required throughout the program, e.g. 'switch spindle on', 'switch coolant on' etc. These functions have been standardized and are popularly known as M codes. The address letter M is followed by two digits. The most commonly used M codes are as follows:

M00 Program stop
M01 Optional stop
M02 End program
M03 Spindle on clockwise
M04 Spindle on counter-clockwise
M05 Spindle off
M06 Tool change
M07 Mist coolant on
M08 Flood coolant on
M09 Coolant off
M30 End of tape

4.1.9 Data input

Program data can be entered into a CNC machine by a number of methods:

Manual data input (*MDI*) This method requires data input by an operator pressing various keys on the control console.
Punched tape This is still the most common method of data input. It requires the CNC program to be encoded on tape; this can be paper tape, polyester aluminium tape or metallized tape, paper tape being the most popular. The CNC program can be loaded into the CNC machine tool memory by the use of a 'tape reader' which will decode the data from the tape.
Magnetic tape This requires the CNC program to be 'copied' to a magnetic tape or cartridge, very much in the same way as

ecording music on to cassette tape. Two major disadvantages of his method are that the recorded data is not visible on the tape, and that the data is easily corrupted under workshop conditions.

Direct numerical control (*DNC*) This requires the prepared CNC program to be stored in the memory of a remote computer. The CNC data is then transferred directly down line to the CNC machine tool by means of a suitable communications link.

4.1.10 Tool length offsets: milling

Most machining operations require the use of a number of tools, which vary in length and diameter. In order to allow for these variables, tool length offset and tool diameter compensation facilities can be used.

Tool length offsets allow for a number of tools with varying length to be programmed to a common datum or zero, as shown in the figure.

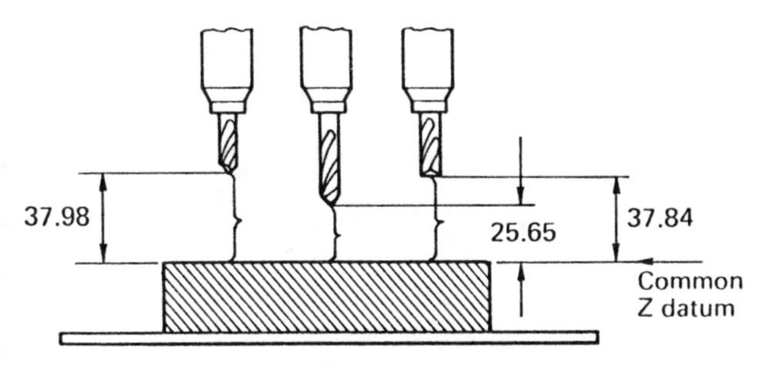

4.1.11 Cutter diameter compensation: milling

When using diameter or radius compensation, normal practice would be to program for the actual size of the component and then use the diameter compensation facility to allow for the radius of the cutter. Another use of this feature allows for the changing of tools of different diameters, without altering the CNC part program. Diameter compensation is activated by the following preparatory codes (see 4.1.8):

G41 Compensates, cutter to the left
G42 Compensates, cutter to the right

G41 Compensation to the left

The cutter is always to the *left* of the surface being machined when looking along the path of the cutter, as indicated by the arrows in the figure.

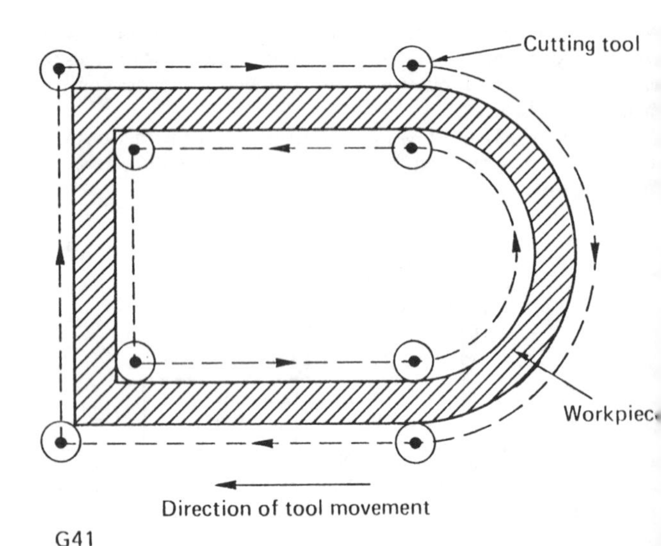

G41

G42 Compensation to the right

The cutter is always to the right of the surface being machined when looking along the path of the cutter, as indicated by the arrows in the figure.

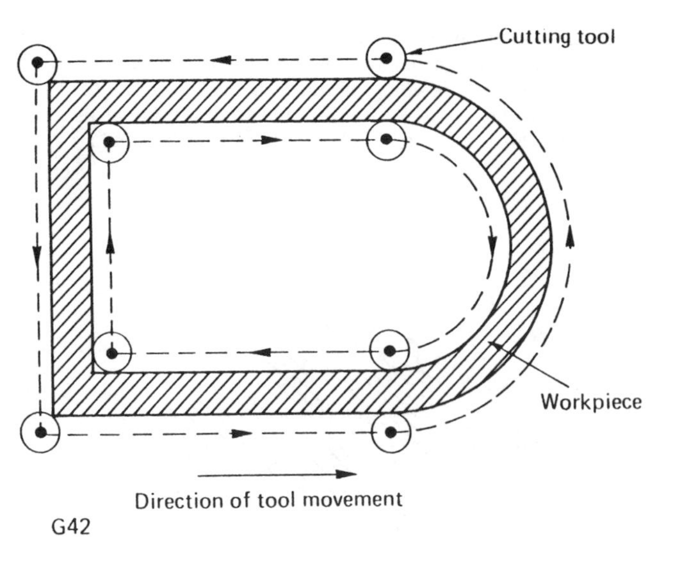

G40 Turning compensation on and off

Whenever G41 or G42 is activated, the cutter diameter is compensated during the next move in the *X* and *Y* axes, as shown. The preliminary movement of the cutter before cutting commences is called *ramping on*.

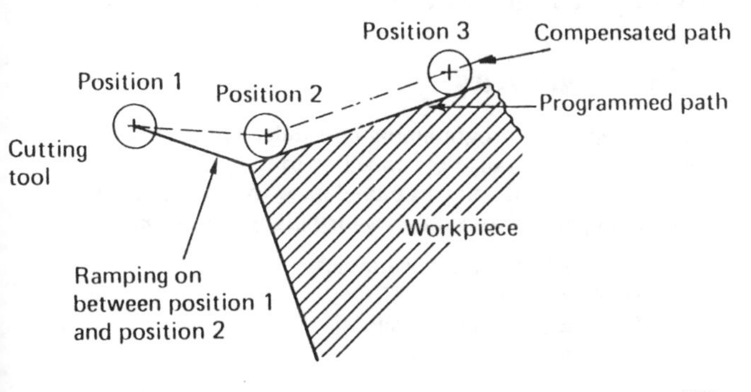

Similarly G40 causes the compensation to be cancelled on the next *X* and *Y* movements as shown, and is known as *ramping off.*

Ramping on and ramping off allow the feed servo motor to accelerate to the required feed rate, and to decelerate at the end of the cut whilst the cutter is clear of the work. It therefore follows that diameter compensation can never be applied or cancelled when the cutting tool is in direct contact with the workpiece.

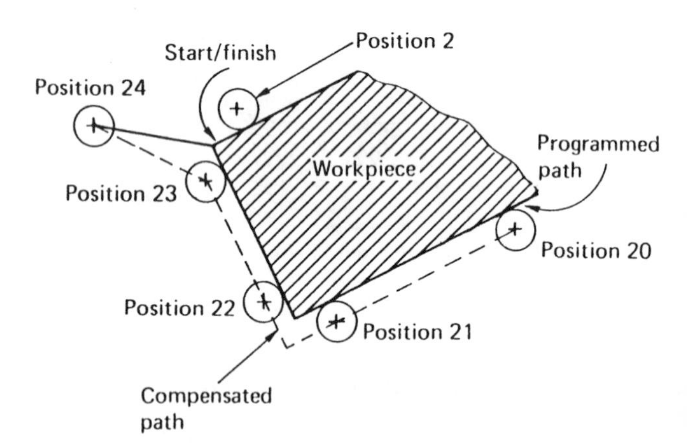

4.1.12 Programming techniques: milling

Canned cycles

To save repetitive programming on similar operations, CNC controllers offer a range of canned or fixed cycles. It is only necessary to provide dimensional data with the required G code. Some examples of canned cycles for milling are as follows:

G80 Cancels fixed or canned cycles
G81 Drilling cycles
G82 Drilling cycles with dwell
G83 Deep hole drilling cycle

G84 Tapping cycle
G85 Boring cycle
G86 Boring cycle with dwell
G87/88 Deep hole boring cycle

G81 Drilling cycle

One of the most popular canned cycles is the drilling cycle G81. The machine movements involved in drilling a series of holes are shown and are as follows:

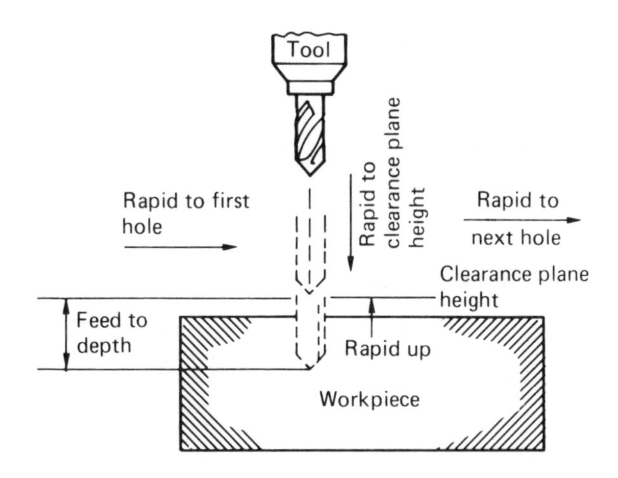

(a) Rapid to centre of first hole
(b) Rapid to clearance plane height
(c) Feed to depth of hole
(d) Rapid up to clearance plane height
(e) Rapid to centre of next hole
(f) Repeat for as many holes as required.

The only data which needs to be programmed is:

Tool number
Hole position (X, Y)
Hole depth (Z)
Spindle speed (S)
Feed rate (F).

4.1.13 Programming example: milling

Component

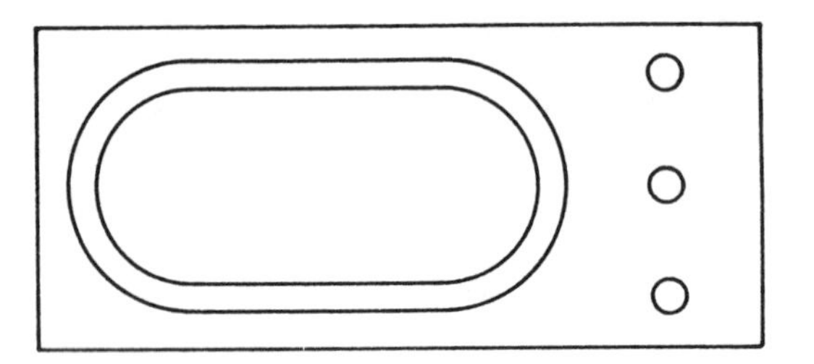

Material: aluminium alloy BS 1474 : 1987 type 5154(A)
condition 0.

Machining data

Tool no.	*Tool description*	*Spindle speeds*	*Feed rates*	
			Vertical	*Horizontal*
T01	10 mm dia. slot drill	1500 rev/min	70 mm/min	100 mm/min
T02	no. 2 centre drill	2500 rev/min	40 mm/min	—
T03	8 mm dia. twist drill	1760 rev/min	60 mm/min	—

The tool change position will be X – 100.0, Y – 100.0. The appropriate M code in the program for tool changing will move the tool to these coordinates and retract the tool up the *Z* axis to a 'home' position clear of the work to facilitate manual tool change.

Centre line path/point programming will be used, and to avoid complexity no diameter compensation will be shown in this example.

Dimensional data

The dimensions shown provide the *X*, *Y*, *Z* data for the 10 mm wide and 8 mm deep slot and the 8 mm diameter and 12 mm deep holes. The numbers in the circles refer to the tool positions as described in the specimen program to follow. The *Z* datum (Z0) would be the top face of the workpiece.

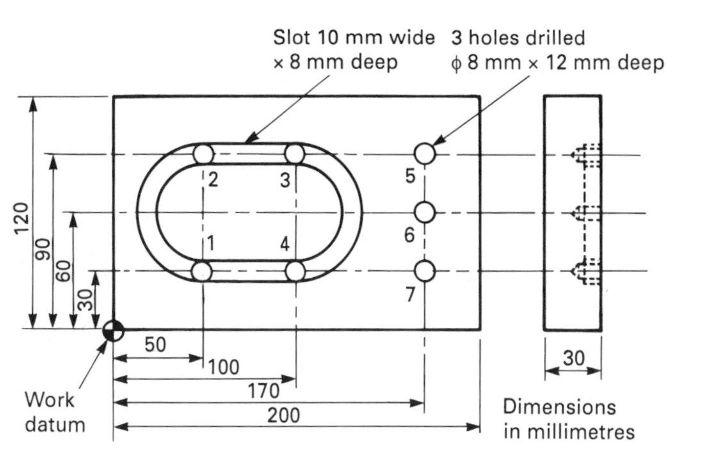

Specimen program

The format of the following program example would be suitable for the Bridgeport BOSS 6 software. When evaluating the program, reference should be made to the coded information given in 4.1.8.

CNC listing	*Description*
%	Per cent symbol = start of program/tape.
N5 G90 G71 G00 G75	Set up default preparatory codes. G75 is special to BOSS 6 software.

N10 X−100.0 Y−100.0 S1500 T01 M06	Rapid move to tool change (home) position. Set spindle speed (rev/min). Select tool required and insert first tool (slot drill). Stop control for tool change.
N15 X50.0 Y30.0	Restart control. Rapid move to position 1.
N20 Z1.0 M03	Rapid tool move to 1.0 mm above workpiece. Start up spindle (speed set in block N10).
N25 G01 Z−8.0 F70 M07	Linear feed rate move to required depth (70 mm/min). Mist coolant on.
N30 G02 X50.0 Y90.0 150.0 J60.0 F100	Circular interpolation to X and Y coordinates at position 2, using I and J coordinates for interpolation centres. Increase feed rate (horizontal) to 100 mm/min.
N35 G01 X100.0 Y90.0	Linear feed rate move as set in block N30 to position 3.
N40 G02 X100.0 Y30.0 100.0 J60.0	Circular interpolation to X and Y coordinates at position 4 at feed rate set in block N30.
N45 G01 X50.0 Y30.0	Linear feed rate move as set in block N30 to position 1.
N50 G00 Z1.0	Rapid move tool clear of workpiece along Z axis
N55 X−100.0 Y−100.0 S2500 T02 M06	Rapid move to tool change (home) position and stop spindle. Remove tool 1 and insert tool 2 (centre drill) Set spindle speed to 2500 rev/min ready for drilling.
N60 X170.0 Y90.0	Restart control. Rapid move to position 5.
N65 Z1.0 M03	Rapid move to 1.0 mm above workpiece. Start up spindle (speed set to 2500 rev/min in block N55).

N70 G81 X170.0 Y90.0 Z−5.0 F40 M07	Start drilling cycle (see 4.1.12) and centre drill first hole (position 5) to depth at 40 mm/min feed rate. Mist coolant on.
N75 X170.0 Y60.0	C/drill second hole (position 6).
N80 X170.0 Y30.0	C/drill third hole (position 7).
N85 G80	Cancel drilling cycle.
N90 G00−X100.0 Y−100.0 S1760 T03 M06	Rapid move to tool change (home) position and stop spindle. Remove tool 2. Insert tool 3 (twist drill). Set spindle speed to 1760 rev/min ready for drilling.
N95 X170.0 Y90.0	Rapid move to position 5.
N100 Z1.0 M03	Rapid move tool to 1 mm above workpiece. Start spindle.
N105 G81 X170.0 Y90.0 Z−12.0 F60 M07	Start drilling cycle and drill first hole to depth (12 mm) at position 5 with 60 mm/min feed rate. Mist coolant on.
N110 X170.0 Y60.0	Drill second hole (position 6).
N115 X170.0 Y30.0	Drill third hole (position 7).
N120 G80	Turn spindle off.
N125 G00 X−100.0 Y−100.0 M06	Return tool to tool change (home) position and stop spindle. Ready for repeat of program.
N130 M02	End or program.
N135 M30	End of tape.

4.1.14 Tool offsets: lathe

On a CNC lathe, to keep a common datum with all the tools on the turret, tool length offsets (TLO) are required in both the *X* and *Z* axes as shown.

On a CNC centre lathe the turret will hold a number of different tools. Each tool will have its own *X* and *Z* offset, which will become operative when the tool is called into the program. When the turret is indexed all the tools will take up a different position relative to the workpiece. As can be seen in the diagram, since the various tools protrude from the turret by different distances in terms of X and Z, different tool length offsets will need to be set for each tool.

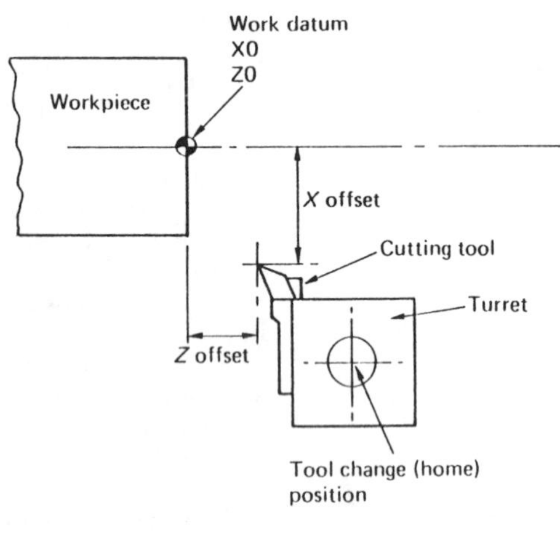

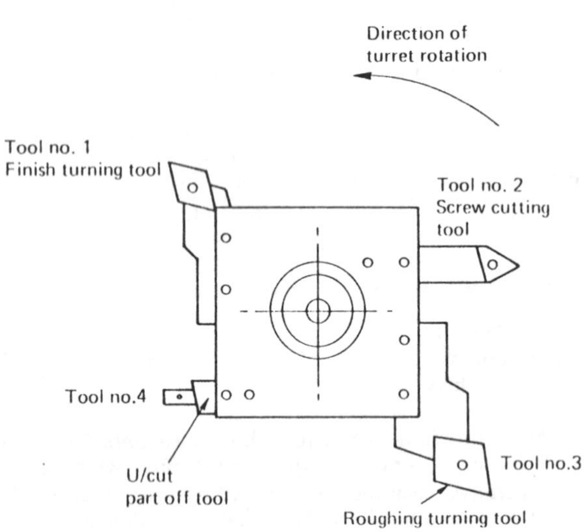

4.1.15 Tool nose radius compensation: lathe

Tool nose radius compensation (TNRC) is used in a similar manner to diameter compensation when milling. Consequently the same preparatory codes (G codes) are used to activate and deactivate tool nose radius compensation. TNRC reduces the complex and repetitive calculations required for tool paths. The programmer can program as if sharp pointed tools were being used. The codes are as follows

G41 Compensates tool nose radius to the left
G42 Compensates tool nose radius to the right
G40 Cancels tool nose radius compensation

G41 Compensation to the left

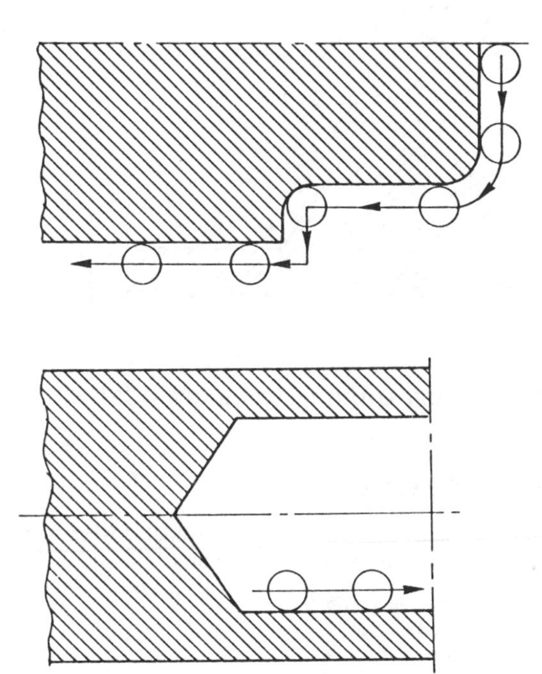

G42 Compensation to the right

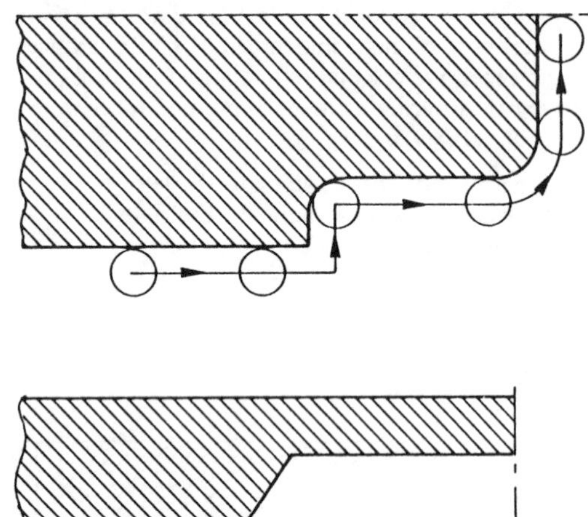

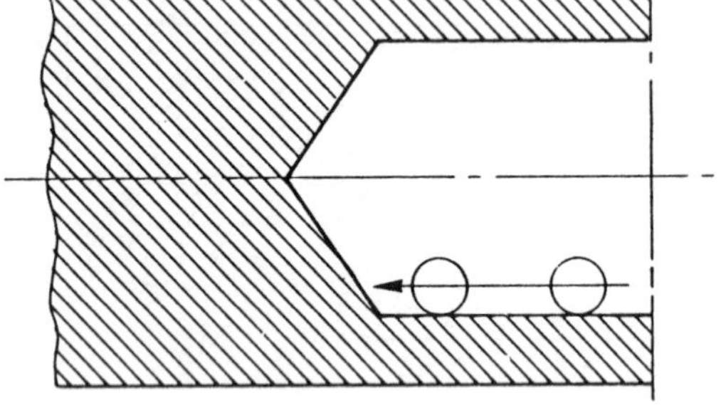

4.1.16 Programming techniques: lathe

Canned cycles

Examples of some of the canned cycles available when using CNC centre lathe controllers are as follows:

G66/67 Contouring cycles
G68/69 Roughing cycle
G81 Turning cycle

G82	Facing cycle
G83	Deep hole drilling cycle
G84/85	Straight threading cycles
G88	Auto grooving cycle

G68 Roughing cycle

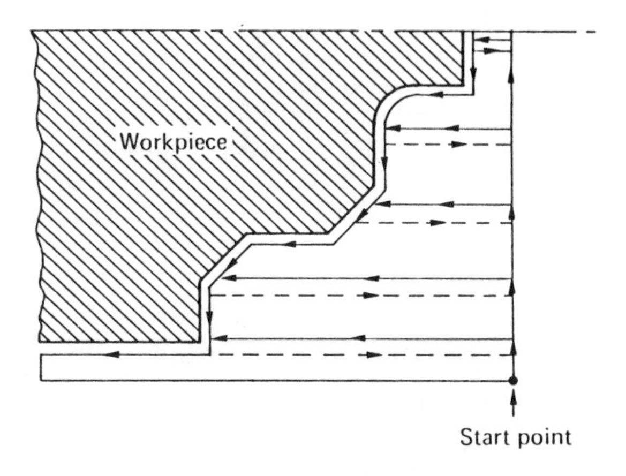

This cycle is used for large amounts of stock removal. The cycle is activated by a G68 code. The machine moves are shown and are as follows:

(a) Rapid move to start point
(b) A number of linear roughing passes (the number varies with depth of cut)
(c) A profiling pass, leaving on a finish allowance.

After the roughing cycle is completed the component would be finish turned to size.

G83 Deep hole drilling cycle

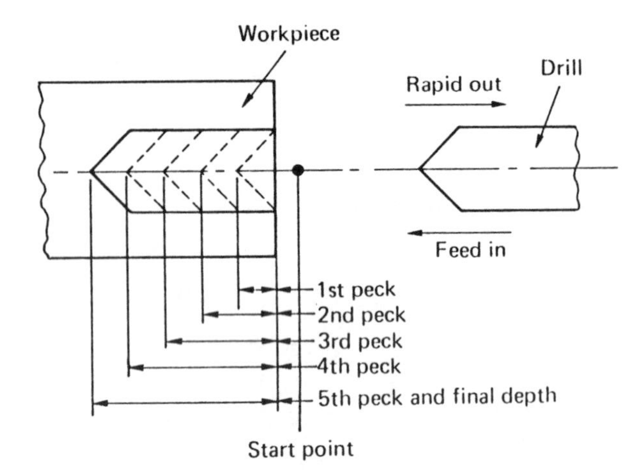

The deep hole drilling cycle is used to drill holes with a high depth/diameter ratio, and provides 'flute clearance' during the cycle. The cycle is activated by a G83 code. The moves involved are shown and are as follows:

(a) Rapid move to start point
(b) Feed to first peck depth
(c) Rapid move out to start point
(d) Rapid in just short of first peck
(e) Feed to second peck depth
(f) Repeat movements (c), (d), (e) for each successive peck depth until required depth is achieved.

4.1.17 Programming example: lathe

An example CNC program follows. The program is to

(a) Rough turn leaving 0.5 mm on diameters and faces
(b) Finish turn the part to size
(c) Part off to length.

Component

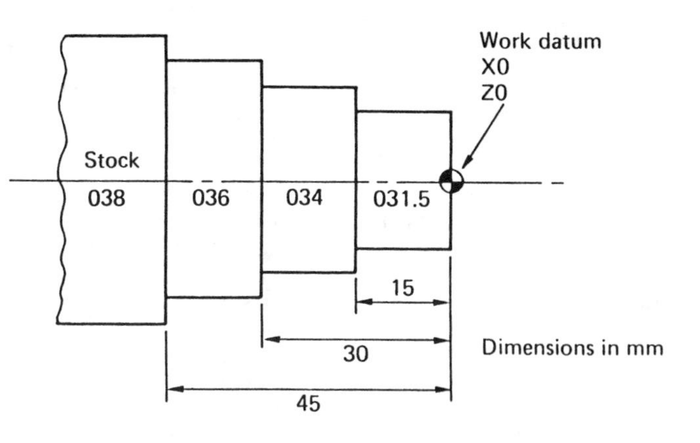

Material: aluminium alloy BS 1474 : 1987 type 5154(A) condition 0.

Tool and machining data

Tool no.	*Tool description*	*Spindle speed*	*Feed rates*
T101	Turning tool for roughing	130 m/min	0.2 mm/rev
T202	Turning tool for finishing	2500 rev/min	0.05 mm/rev
T303	Part off tool	120 m/min	0.05 mm/rev

Specimen program

(a) The format of the program would be suitable for a GE 1050 CNC controller.
(b) Diameter programming is used in this example
(c) Tool change position (home position) is X177.8 Z254.

CNC program listing	*Description*
%	Start of program/tape.
N0010 G71	Metric input.
N0020 G95	Feed rate, mm/rev.
N0030 G97 S1000 M03	Direct rev/min spindle speed. 1000 rev/min switch on spindle.
N0040 G00 M08	Rapid move set. Switch on coolant.
N0050 G53 X177.8 Z254.0 T0	Cancels work offset. Moves turret to home position. Cancels tool offsets.
N0060 T100	Rotates turret to position 1.
N0070 G54 X00 Z2.0 T101	Activates work offset. Rapid move to coordinates. Activates tool offset number 1 with tool number 1.
N0080 G92 R0 S2000	Sets up parameters for constant surface cutting speed (CSS) (maximum 2000 rev/min).
N0090 G96 S130	Activates CSS at 130 m/min.
N0100 G01 X0.0 Z0.5 F0.2	Linear feed rate move at 0.2 mm/rev.
N0110 X36.5	Linear feed rate move at 0.2 mm/rev.
N0120 Z.50.0	Turning beyond end of component to reduce diameter for parting off. Linear feed rate moves at 0.2 mm/rev.
N0130 G00 X37.0	Rapid move of tool off workpiece.
N0140 Z0.5	Rapid move of tool off workpiece.
N0150 X34.5	Rapid move of tool off workpiece.
N0160 G01 Z−29.5	Linear feed rate move.
N170 G00 X35.0	Rapid move.
N0180 Z0.5	Rapid move
N0190 X32.0	Rapid move
N0200 G01 Z−14.5	Linear feed rate move.

N0120 G00	Rapid move.
N0220 G53 X177.8 Z254.0 T0	Cancels work and tool offsets and moves turret to home position.
N0230 T200	Rotates turret to position 2.
N0240 G54 X10.0 Z10.0 T202	Activates work offset. Rapid move to coordinates. Activates tool offset number 2 with tool number 2.
N0250 G41 X0.0 Z0.05	Moves to coordinates and activates tool nose radius compensation (TNRC).
N0260 G97 S2500	Direct rev/min, 2500 rev/min.
N0270 G01 Z0.0 F0.05	Linear feed rate move at 0.05 mm/rev.
N0280 X31.5 N0290 Z – 15.0 N0300 X34.0 N0310 Z – 30.0 N0320 X36.0 N0330 Z – 45.0	Linear feed rate moves to profile part to size.
N0340 G40	Cancels TNRC.
N0350 G00	Rapid move.
N0360 G53 X177.8 Z254.0 T0	Cancels work offset. Rapid move to home position. Cancels tool offsets.
N0370 T300	Rotates turret to position 3.
N0380 G54 X38.0 Z – 45 T303	Activates work offset. Rapid move to coordinates. Activates tool offset number 3 with tool number 3.
N0390 G92 R38 S1000	Sets up parameters for constant surface cutting speed.
N0400 G96 S120	Activates CSS at 120 m/min.
N0410 G01 X – 2.0 F0.05	Linear feed rate move.
N0420 G00 X38.0 M05	Rapid clear of work. Switch off spindle.
N0430 G53 X177.8 Z254.0 T0	Cancels work and tool offsets. Rapid to home position.
N0440 M02	End of program.

4.1.18 Glossary of terms

Absolute programming A system of programming where all positional dimensions are related to a common datum.
Adaptive control A system of sensors which changes speeds/feeds in response to changes in cutting loads.
Address In programming, a symbol which indicates the significance of the information immediately following that symbol.
Backlash 'Wasted' movements between interacting mechanical parts due to wear and/or manufacturing tolerance.
Binary coded decimal A method of representing decimal numbers by a series of binary numbers.
Binary number A number system with a base of 2.
Bit An abbreviation of 'binary digit'.
Block A line or group of words which contains all the instructions for one operation.
Byte A group of 8 bits.
CAM Computer aided manufacture.
Canned cycle An operation which has been preprogrammed and which can be called up by a single instruction.
Circular interpolation A type of contouring control which uses the information contained in a single instruction to produce movement along the arc of a circle.
CLF Cutter location file.
Closed loop control A system in which a signal depending on the output is fed back to a comparing device so that the output can be compared with the input, and a corrective signal generated if necessary.
Continuous path system A system in which the tool path results from the coordinated simultaneous motion of the work and/or cutter along two or more axes.
Cutter compensation An adjustment which compensates for the difference between the actual and programmed cutter diameters. See also *tool length offset*.
Datum The reference position from which all absolute coordinates are taken.
DNC Direct numerical control.
DO loop A loop back to a repeated instruction in a program.
Encoder A device which is used to convert the position of a moving device into an electronic signal.

Feed rate The rate at which the cutting tool is advanced into the workpiece.
Incremental system A system by which each positional dimension is measured from the preceding position.
Interpolation The joining up of programmed points to make a smooth curve by computation.
Linear path system A point-to-point system in which the tool or work moves only in straight lines.
MDI Manual data input: a means of manually entering instructions to a controller, usually via a key panel.
Numerical control Control of machine movements by the direct insertion of numerical data.
Open loop system A system where there is a single forward path between the input instruction and the output signal with no feedback.
Parallel path system A point-to-point system in which the tool or work moves only in straight lines parallel to any axis.
Parity A checking method to help determine if the tape has been prepared correctly. The standard for even parity is that of the International Standards Organization (ISO), whereas the standard for odd parity is that of the Electronic Industries Association (EIA).
Part program A program in machine control language and format required to accomplish a given task.
Point-to-point system A system in which the controlled motion is required only to reach a given end point, with no path control during the movements from one point to the next.
Post-processor A set of computer instructions which transforms tool centre line data into machine movement commands using the tape code and format required by a specific machine tool control system.
Rapid traverse Movements at a high traverse rate, normally used to save time when positioning the cutter before cutting commences.
Servo system An automatic control system, incorporating power amplification and feedback, designed to make a machine table follow the programmed route.
Spindle speed The rotational speed of the cutting tool or workpiece.
Subroutine A sequence of instructions or statements used to perform an operation which is frequently required. It is prepared

by the part programmer and temporarily stored in the controller memory.

Tape punch A device for transferring instructions to a punched tape by perforating it with holes.

Tape reader A device for sensing and transmitting the instructions recorded on a punched or magnetic tape.

Tool length offset (*TLO*) An instruction which adjusts the position of the spindle along the *Z* axis of a milling machine to take account of different lengths of cutting tool. On a lathe, offset is parallel to both the *X* and *Z* axes.

Word A set of characters which give a single complete instruction to a machine's control system.

Word address A block of characters preceded by a literal symbol to identify them.

4.2 Computer aided design

4.2.1 An introduction to computer aided design

Computer aided design (CAD) is the application of a computer system which can be used to solve or enhance the solution of design and draughting problems. It not only eases the work of the draughtsperson in preparing drawings in both two and three dimensions (pictorial representations), but can be extended to provide:

(a) Geometric modelling: wire frame, solid modelling
(b) Finite element analysis: techniques to solve thermal and stress problems
(c) Testing
(d) Documentation.

For the architect and civil engineer, the ability to draw not only buildings but whole estates and complexes in three dimensions and then change the viewpoint at the touch of a button is of inestimable value.

By far the most widely used application of CAD in small and medium engineering companies is a draughting aid. The capabilities of a typical draughting system could be:

(a) The production of 'library symbols' such as BS 308 conventions, pneumatic symbols, hydraulic symbols, electrical symbols and electronic symbols
(b) The production of three-view orthographic drawings using these symbols, to save having to repeatedly draw small details (e.g. screwed fastenings)
(c) The automatic production of pictorial drawings from orthographic drawings
(d) The automatic shading or hatching of section drawings
(e) The facility to make major or minor changes to a drawing without redrawing

(f) The production of printed circuit board (PCB) layouts
(g) The production of plant layouts
(h) The production of parts lists, bills of materials etc. from the digitized data of the drawing.

When analysis and modelling facilities are required, a very powerful computer must be used together with complex and expensive software.

An example of a 'wire frame' three-dimensional representation which could be produced on a mini computer is shown.

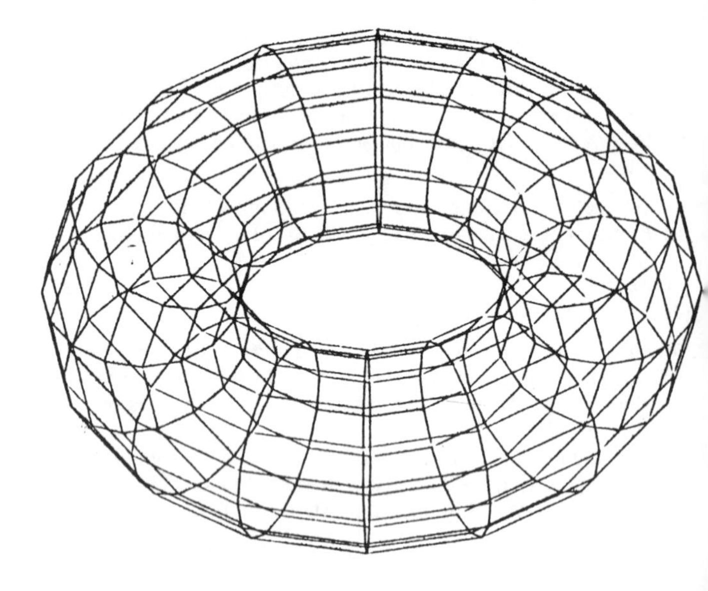

4.2.2 CAD system hardware

The heart of any CAD system is the computer. Various configurations are used to provide the considerable computing power which any but the simplest CAD software requires, and yet to ensure that the system is loaded economically.

Computer configurations

Stand alone computers, where each user has access to a single computer. Normally this is in the form of the more powerful microcomputers (personal computers).
Centralized processing, where one computer (normally a mainframe) supports a number of terminals. Response times can sometimes be relatively slow on this type of system, particularly if a large number of users are all working together.

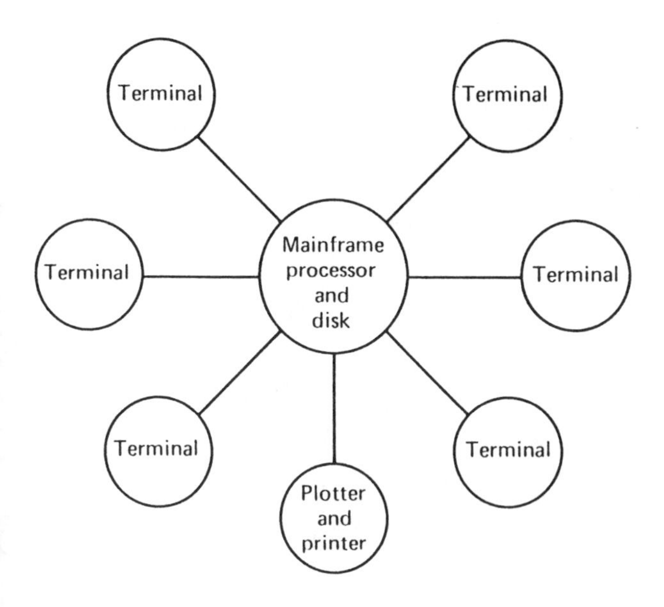

Shared centralized processing This type of system is more costly than centralized processing, but it has the big advantage that if one of the computers fails the whole system is not disabled.
Integrated system With this configuration a number of computers are networked together so that system files can be shared. This arrangement also allows plotter, printers and disk drives to become a shared resource, resulting in more economical

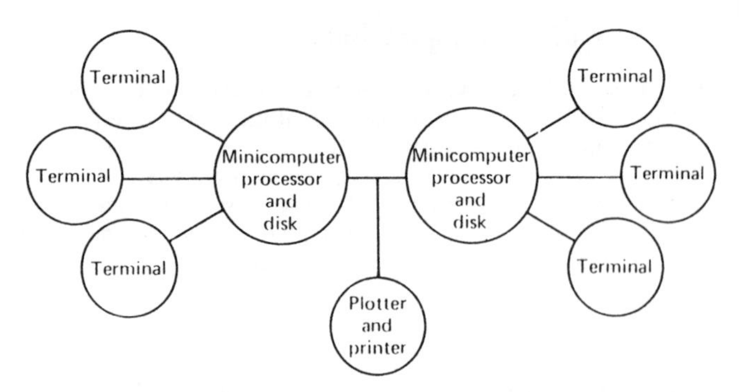

loading of the system, faster response time and less chance of total disablement. The initial capital outlay is lower, as the system can be started up with only a few work stations; additional work stations can be added to the network as demand grows.

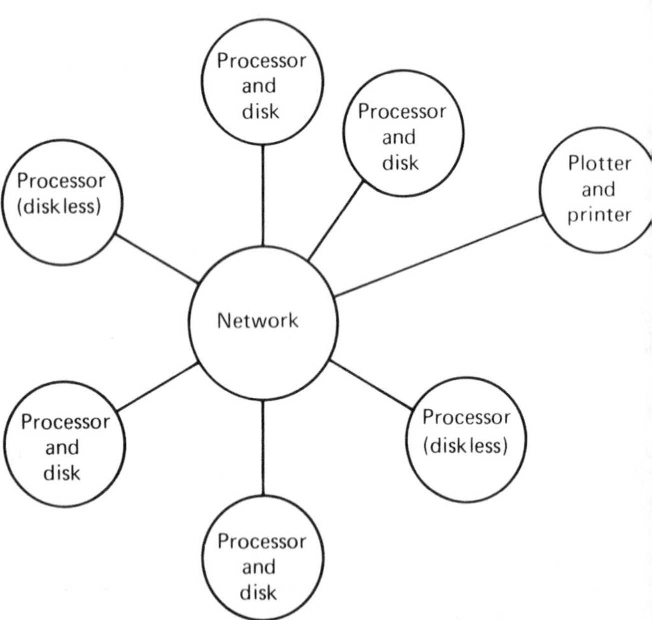

Visual display units (VDUs)

Storage tubes These were, for the most part, a Tectronix product. It was the main work station (display) used on high quality installations in the 1970s. The storage tube has the advantages of high definition and none of the flicker of the earlier stroke or vector VDUs. This results from the fact that, once written, the picture is stored in the screen phosphor without refresh. Unfortunately this system has a slow update rate and limited colour capability.
Vector display This system has the advantage that standard cathode ray tubes can be used, and it was the system most widely used by IBM until the introduction of its 5080 Colormaster product in 1983. Vector displays have a faster update response than storage tubes and are better matched to the high speed CPU performance of modern computers. Unfortunately, vector systems have limited colour capability and a tendency to flicker as the screen is continuously refreshed. This flicker becomes more noticeable as the picture becomes more complex.
Raster display Raster scan, although more complex and costly, overcomes both the fast update and the flicker problem. It provides full colour capability and high definition. Either screen or tablet update can be used, and complex images in full colour can be presented without flicker. This has encouraged software to be written with ever increasing features such as three-dimensional solid modelling, robotic kinematics, work cell simulation, and 3D piping.

Input devices

Keyboards These are familiar to all computer operators and are user friendly. They are used to enter commands, text and parameter values.
Programmable function box This is used in conjunction with the keyboard. Each key can be programmed to provide a predetermined set of commands to the computer; this saves having to key in commands each time they are required.
Joystick This is a two-axis control for providing rapid movement of the cursor. It is familiar to players of video games. When used with a CAD system it allows more rapid cursor movement than is possible from the keyboard. However, the positional accuracy is low and is dependent upon operator skill.

Data tablet This is the most widely used form of digitizer. The data tablet detects the position of a fixed or hand held cursor on a designated digitizing surface. The tablet contains an electromagnetic, electrostatic or electroresistive grid which corresponds to the resolution of the VDU. Thus *X* and *Y* coordinates on the tablet can be mapped directly on to the screen. There are various types of cursors for use with data tablets:

(a) The *digitizing cursor* with a cross-hair sight or bull's-eye which provides absolute coordinate outputs
(b) The *mouse*, which can be moved freely over the data tablet and is useful for 'sketching'
(c) The *stylus*, which can be used for freehand 'sketching' and menu picking with a data tablet.

Output devices

Hard copy can be printed from digitized data in a number of ways.

Flat bed plotter The paper is fixed in position on the bed of the plotter, which is a flat surface. The pen moves along the *X* and *Y* axes to draw the image. The carriage moves along the *X* axis and the penhead moves along the *Y* axis on a bridge mounted on the carriage. There is often a 'home' position to which the penhead returns, not only at the start and end of a drawing but also when pens need to be automatically changed for different line thicknesses and colours. The flat bed plotters will accept any type of writing medium and are useful for producing transparencies on acetate sheet.

Drum or roller bed plotters The bed rotates to provide the *X* axis movement and the pen carriage moves along the *Y* axis. This arrangement allows large drawings to be produced, yet occupies little floor space. These plotters are more limited than flat bed plotters in the materials they will accept.

Printer/plotters These produce the line by means of a dot matrix head, which is much faster in operation than a conventional penhead. The line quality tends not to be so good, and they are more complex to maintain. There are two basic systems:

(a) *Non-impact*, which uses a pulsed ink jet

(b) *Impact*, in which a 'ribbon' is struck by a stylus matrix to transfer ink to the paper.

Electrostatic plotters These require a raster input across the entire medium width for each forward incremental movement of the paper. Rows of styluses plot the drawing on the paper as a series of fine point electrostatic charges. Where the charges appear they attract a toner on to the paper and produce a permanent copy. These plotters are rapid in use and have a very high resolution.

Laser beam plotters These are similar to electrostatic plotters except that, in place of the physical styluses, a beam of laser light is used to control the electrostatic charge on the paper surface.

4.2.3 CAD system software

Besides the computer hardware, the other essential feature of CAD system is the CAD system software. CAD applications software falls into one of the following groups.

Draughting software

This comprises two-dimensional draughting and dimensioning software which can be interfaced to a suitable plotter.

Three-dimensional modelling software

Wire frame This type of modeller describes the corners and edges of a model; it can lead to the view looking ambiguous. An example was shown in 4.2.1.

Surface models These describe corners, edges and faces between edges. They are usually used when a component has a complex surface, such as a car panel. Information relating to surface intersections and surface area can be extracted from the shaded surface model.

Solid models These provide detailed information concerning area, volume and centre of gravity of a component part. Solid models can be built up from standard three-dimensional shapes and modified to give the desired result. This type of software requires a high level of computing power to work effectively.

A computer's operating system consists of software supplied by the computer manufacturer, which is 'booted' in on occasions when the machine is started up, and under the control of which the computer always operates. The operating system ensures that the facilities of the machine are coordinated so as to make optimum use of the CAD system. This includes controlling the various input and output devices, and the allocation of storage to programs and their data.

In mainframe or minicomputers, multiprogramming is nearly always employed. This involves the storage and execution of several programs at the same time. The benefit of multiprogramming is that different parts of the computer system can be used by different programs at the same time, for example allowing calculation of one program to take place whilst another is using an input device to obtain data. The operating system and the use of multiprogramming thus ensure efficient use of all the computer's components and peripherals.

4.2.4 Computer aided design and manufacture (CAD/CAM)

The integration of computer aided design with computer aided manufacture involves the sharing of the database between these distinct elements. The advantages of such a system are:

(a) There is consistent reliability of information relating to design and manufacture.
(b) CNC programs can be constructed in much shorter times.
(c) Complex parts are programmed without the need for lengthy calculations.
(d) On-screen proofing of CNC program tool paths reduces scrap and damaged tool costs.
(e) There is a reduction in lead time from the initial design to completion of manufacture.

4.2.5 Advantages and limitations of computer aided design

Advantages

(a) There are substantial improvements in productivity during the design and draughting processes.
(b) Drawings can be produced to very high levels of accuracy and consistent house styles.
(c) Product design can be improved.
(d) It is easy to make modifications without complete redrawing.
(e) The storage of digital data on disk or tape is simple, and storage space is reduced.
(f) Digitized data can be used as a basis for
Costing and estimating
Purchasing
Production planning and control
Control of labour costs (cost control)
Quality control (reduced scrap).
(g) Digitized CAD data can be integrated with CNC machine tools and robots to provide CAD/CAM cells.

Limitations

(a) Hardware and software costs for CAD are very high.
(b) Powerful CAD systems require regular and expensive maintenance. Maintenance contracts are advisable.
(c) Expensive and time consuming operator training and updating is required.
(d) Initial setup can be expensive whilst libraries of conventions and symbols are prepared and digitized to suit company products.
(e) A suitable ergonomic environment is required to avoid operator fatigue and ensure economic use of the system.

4.3 Industrial robots

4.3.1 An introduction to robotics

An industrial robot is a general purpose, programmable machine possessing certain anthropomorphic (human-like) characteristics. The most typical anthropomorphic characteristic of a robot is its arm. This arm, together with the robot's capability to be programmed, makes it ideally suited to a variety of production tasks, including machine loading, spot welding, spray painting and assembly. The robot can be programmed to perform a sequence of mechanical motions, and it can repeat that motion sequence indefinitely until reprogrammed to perform some other job.

Manufacturers use robots mostly to reduce manning levels. Robots, used either with other robots or with other machines, have two major advantages compared with traditional machines. First, they allow almost total automation of production processes, leading to increased rates of production better quality control and an increased response to varying demand. Second, they permit the adaptability, at speed, of the production unit. The production line can be switched rapidly from one product to another similar product, for example from one model of car to another. Again, when a breakdown immobilizes one element in the production unit, that element's function can be replaced quickly.

Adaptable production units are known as flexible manufacturing systems (FMS). A flexible unit would comprise a small number of robots and computer controlled machine tools working together to produce or part-produce a particular component or assembly. The logical development of such systems is to integrate a number of these flexible cells into a fully automated workshop or factory.

It must be remembered that the robot, although a highly sophisticated device, cannot by itself solve all the problems that can be solved by the human operator. It must therefore be associated with additional techniques, for example computer aided manufacture (CAM).

The term *robotics* has two currently accepted meanings:

(a) In the strictest sense of the word, it implies the further development of automation by improving the robot as we know it at present.
(b) In the broader sense, it involves the development not only of the robot itself, but also processes associated with the robot, for example computer aided design (CAD), or the consideration of the robot as a machine with special properties in association with other machines, for example, flexible manufacturing cells or systems.

4.3.2 Robot control

An industrial robot shares many attributes in common with a computer numerical control (CNC) machine tool. The type of technology used to operate CNC machine tools is also used to actuate the robot's mechanical arm. However, the uses of the robot are more general, typically involving the handling of work parts. Also, the programming of the robot is different from CNC part programming. Traditionally, CNC programming has been performed away from the machine tool, 'off line', with the machine commands being contained in a punched tape. Robot programming, on the other hand, can be accomplished 'on line', with the instructions being retained in the robot's electronic memory. In spite of these differences, there are definite similarities between robots and CNC machine tools in terms of power drive technologies, feedback systems, the use of computer control, and even some of the industrial applications.

4.3.3 Robot arm geometry

A robot must be able to reach workpieces and tools. This requires a combination of an arm and a wrist subassembly, plus a 'hand', usually called the *end effector*. The robot's sphere of influence is based upon the volume into which the robot's arm can deliver the wrist subassembly. A variety of geometric configurations have been researched and their relative kinematic capabilities appraised. To date, the robot manufacturers have specialized in the following geometric configurations:

(a) Cartesian coordinates: three linear axes

(b) Cylindrical coordinates: two linear axes and one rotary axis
(c) Spherical coordinates: one linear axis and two rotary axes
(d) Revolute coordinates: three rotary axes.

Cartesian coordinate robots

Cartesian coordinate robots consist of three orthogonal linear sliding axes, the manipulator hardware and the interpolator. The control algorithms are similar to those of CNC machine tools. Therefore the arm resolution and accuracy will also be of the order of magnitude of machine tool resolution.

An important feature of a cartesian robot is its equal and constant spatial resolution; that is, the resolution is fixed in all axes of motions and throughout the work volume of the robot arm. This is not the case with other coordinate systems.

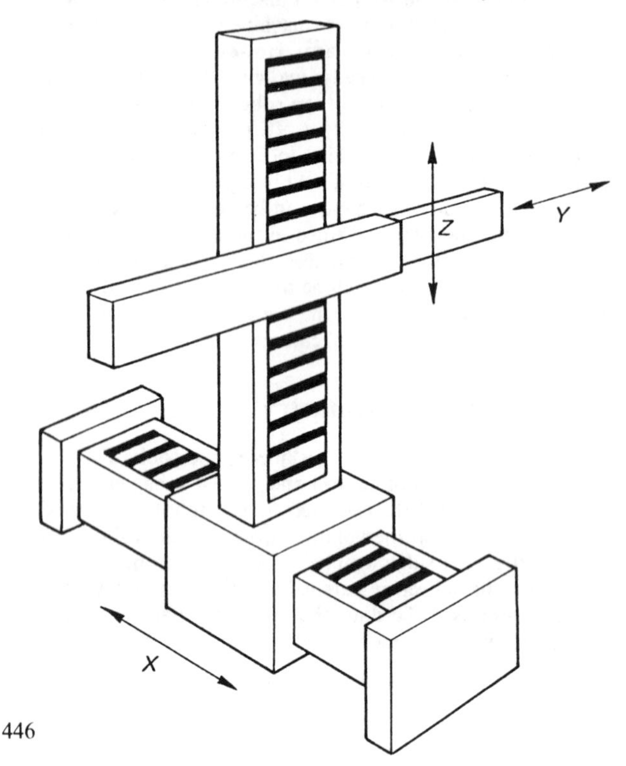

Cylindrical coordinate robots

Cylindrical coordinate robots consist of a horizontal arm mounted on a vertical column, which in turn is mounted on a rotary base. The horizontal arm moves in and out, the carriage moves vertically up and down on the column, and these two units rotate as a single assembly on the base. The working volume is therefore the annular space of a cylinder.

The resolution of the cylindrical robot is not constant and depends on the distance between the column and the wrist along the horizontal arm. Given the standard resolution of an incremental digital encoder on the rotary axis and arm length of only 1 m, then the resolution at the hand at full arm extension will be of the order of 3 mm. This is two orders of magnitude larger than is regarded as the state of the art in machine tools (0.01 mm). This is one of the drawbacks of cylindrical robots as compared to those with cartesian frames. Cylindrical geometry robots do offer the advantage of higher speed at the end of the arm provided by the rotary axis, but this is often limited by the moment of inertia of the robot arm.

In robots which contain a rotary base, good dynamic performance is difficult to achieve. The moment of inertia reflected at the base drive depends not only on the weight of the object being carried but also on the distance between the base shaft and the manipulated object. This is regarded as one of the main drawbacks of robots containing revolute joints.

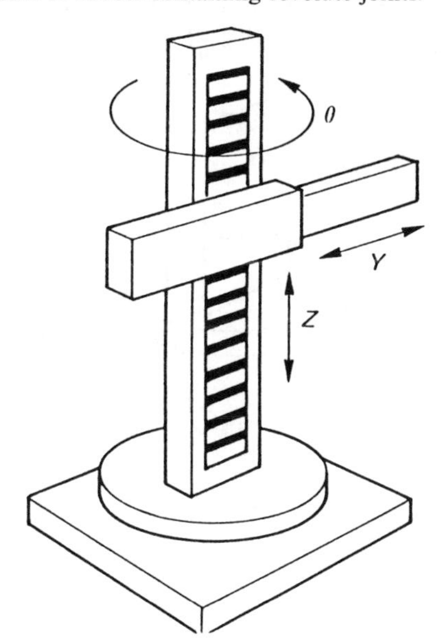

Spherical coordinate robots

The kinematic configuration of spherical coordinate robot arms is similar to the turret of a tank. These arms consist of a rotary base, an elevated pivot, and a telescopic arm which moves in and out. The magnitude of rotation is usually measured by incremental encoders mounted on the rotary axes. The working envelope is a thick spherical shell.

The disadvantage of spherical robots compared with their cartesian counterparts is that there are two axes having a low resolution, which varies with the arm length.

The main advantage of spherical robots over the cartesian and cylindrical ones is a better mechanical flexibility. The pivot axis in the vertical plane permits convenient access to the base or under-the-base level. In addition, motions with rotary axes are much faster than those along linear axes.

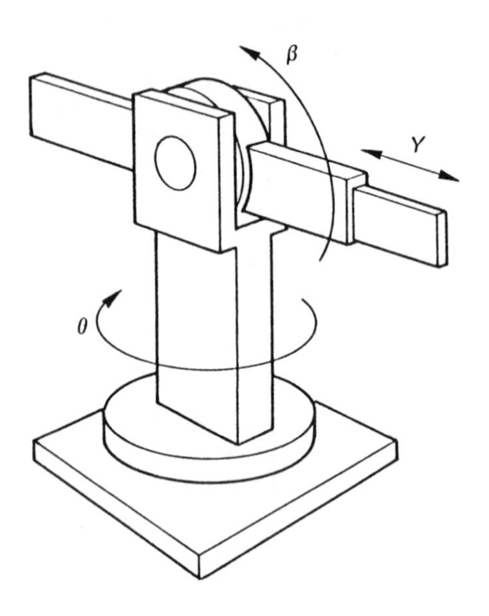

Revolute coordinate robots

'he revolute, or articulated, robot consists of three rigid
nembers connected by two rotary joints and mounted on a
otary base. It closely resembles the human arm. The end effector
s analogous to the hand, which attaches to the forearm via the
vrist. The elbow joint connects the forearm and the upper arm,
.nd the shoulder joint connects the upper arm to the base.
ometimes a rotary motion in the horizontal plane is also
rovided at the shoulder joint.

Since the revolute robot has three rotary axes it has a
elatively low resolution, which depends entirely on the arm
ength. Its accuracy is also the poorest since the articulated
tructure accumulates the joint errors at the end of the arm. The
.dvantages of such a structure and configuration is that it can
nove at high speeds and has excellent mechanical flexibility,
vhich has made it the most popular medium-sized robot.

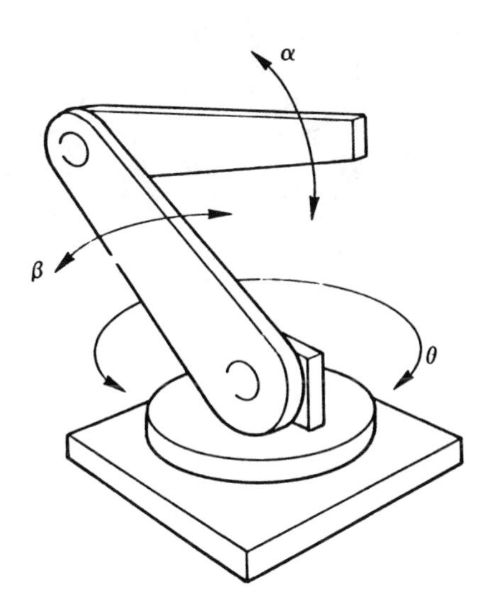

The wrist

The end effector is connected to the mainframe of the robot through the wrist. The wrist includes three rotary axes, denoted by roll, pitch and yaw. The roll (or twist) is a rotation in a plane perpendicular to the end of the arm; pitch (or bend) is a rotation in a vertical plane; and yaw is a rotation in the horizontal plane through the arm. However, there are applications which require only two axes of motion in the wrist.

In order to reduce weight at the wrist, the wrist drives are sometimes located at the base of the robot, and the motion is transferred with rigid links or chains. Reduction of weight at the wrist increases the maximum allowable load and reduces the moment of inertia, which in turn improves the dynamic performance of the robot arm. The pitch, roll and yaw movements of the wrist can be seen on the robot shown.

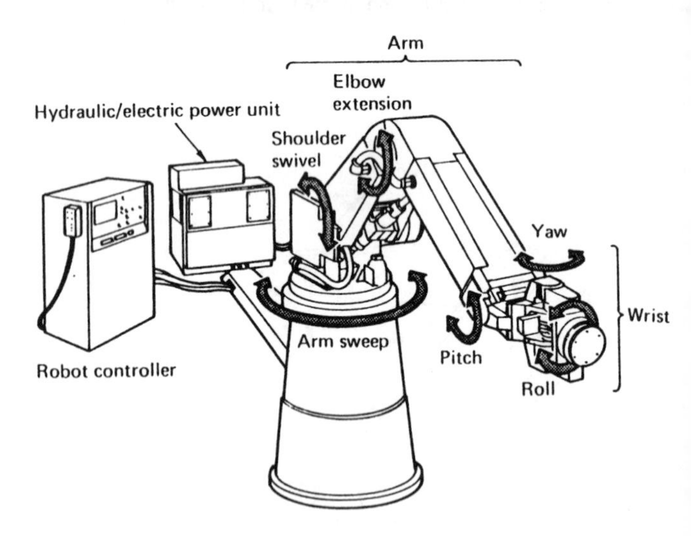

Part 5 Cutting Tools

5.1 Twist drills, reamers, countersinking and counterboring cutters

5.1.1 Twist drill sizes, metric

Dimensions in millimetres

Nominal diameter	*Parallel shank jobber series*		*Parallels shank stub drills*		*Parallel shank long series*		*Morse taper (MT) shank two-flute twist and multiflute core drills*			*Oversize Morse taper shank*	
	Flute length	*Overall length*	*Flute length*	*Overall length*	*Flute length*	*Overall length*	*Flute length*	*Overall length*	*MT no.*	*Overall length*	*MT no.*
0.20	2.5	19									
0.22	2.5	19									
0.25	3	19									
0.28	3	19									
0.30	4	19									
0.32	4	19									
0.35	4	19									
0.38	4	19									
0.40	5	20									
0.42	5	20									
0.45	5	20									
0.48	5	20									
0.50	6	22	3	20							
0.52	6	22									
0.55	7	24									
0.58	7	24									
0.60	7	24									
0.62	8	26									
0.65	8	26									
0.68	9	28									
0.70	9	28									

0.72	9	28				
0.75	9	28				
0.78	10	30				
0.80	10	30	5	24		
0.82	10	30				
0.85	10	30				
0.88	11	32				
0.90	11	32				
0.92	11	32				
0.95	11	32				
0.98	12	34				
1.00	12	34	6	26	33	56
1.05	12	34				
1.10	14	36			37	60
1.15	14	36				
1.20	16	38	8	30	41	65
1.25	16	38				
1.30	16	38			41	65
1.35	18	40				
1.40	18	40			45	70
1.45	18	40				
1.50	18	40	9	32	45	70
1.55	20	43				
1.60	20	43			50	76
1.65	20	43				
1.70	20	43			50	76
1.75	22	46				
1.80	22	46	11	36	53	80
1.85	22	46				
1.90	22	46			53	80

continued

Section 5.1.1 (*continued*)

Nominal diameter	*Parallel shank jobber series*		*Parallel shank stub drills*		*Parallel shank long series*		*Morse taper (MT) shank two-flute twist and multiflute core drills*			*Oversize Morse taper shank*	
	Flute length	*Overall length*	*Flute length*	*Overall length*	*Flute length*	*Overall length*	*Flute length*	*Overall length*	*MT no.*	*Overall length*	*MT no.*
1.95	24	49									
2.00	24	49	12	38	56	85					
2.05	24	49									
2.10	24	49			56	85					
2.15	27	53									
2.20	27	53	13	40	59	90					
2.25	27	53									
2.30	27	53			59	90					
2.35	27	53									
2.40	30	57			62	95					
2.45	30	57									
2.50	30	57	14	43	62	95					
2.55	30	57									
2.60	30	57			62	95					
2.65	30	57									
2.70	33	61			66	100					
2.75	33	61									
2.80	33	61	16	46	66	100					
2.85	33	61									
2.90	33	61			66	100					
2.95	33	61									
3.00	33	61	16	46	66	100	33	114	1		
3.10	36	65			69	106					
3.20	36	65	18	49	69	106	36	117	1		

3.40	39	70			73	112			
3.50	39	70	20	52	73	112	39	120	1
3.60	39	70			73	112			
3.70	39	70			73	112			
3.80	43	75	22	55	78	119	43	123	1
3.90	43	75			78	119			
4.00	43	75	22	55	78	119	43	123	1
4.10	43	75			78	119			
4.20	43	75	22	55	78	119	43	123	1
4.30	47	80			82	126			
4.40	47	80			82	126			
4.50	47	80	24	58	82	126	47	128	1
4.60	47	80			82	126			
4.70	47	80			82	126			
4.80	52	86	26	62	87	132	52	133	1
4.90	52	86			87	132			
5.00	52	86	26	62	87	132	52	133	1
5.10	52	86			87	132			
5.20	52	86	26	62	87	132	52	133	1
5.30	52	86			87	132			
5.40	57	93			91	139			
5.50	57	93	28	66	91	139	57	138	1
5.60	57	93			91	139			
5.70	57	93			91	139			
5.80	57	93	28	66	91	139	57	138	1
5.90	57	93			91	139			

continued

Section 5.1.1 (*continued*)

Nominal diameter	*Parallel shank jobber series*		*Parallel shank stub drills*		*Parallel shank long series*		*Morse taper (MT) shank two-flute twist and multiflute core drills*			*Oversize Morse taper shank*	
	Flute length	*Overall length*	*Flute length*	*Overall length*	*Flute length*	*Overall length*	*Flute length*	*Overall length*	*MT no.*	*Overall length*	*MT no.*
6.00	57	93	28	66	91	139	57	138	1		
6.10	63	101			97	148					
6.20	63	101	31	70	97	148	63	144	1		
6.30	63	101			97	148					
6.40	63	101			97	148					
6.50	63	101	31	70	97	148	63	144	1		
6.60	63	101			97	148					
6.70	63	101			97	148					
6.80	69	109	34	74	102	156	69	150	1		
6.90	69	109			102	156					
7.00	69	109	34	74	102	156	69	150	1		
7.10	69	109			102	156					
7.20	69	109	34	74	102	156	69	150	1		
7.30	69	109			102	156					
7.40	69	109			102	156					
7.50	69	109	34	74	102	156	69	150	1		
7.60	75	117			109	165					
7.70	75	117			109	165					
7.80	75	117	37	79	109	165	75	156	1		
7.90	75	117			109	165					
8.00	75	117	37	79	109	165	75	156	1		
8.10	75	117			109	165					
8.20	75	117	37	79	109	165	75	156	1		
8.30	75	117			109	165					

8.40	75	117			109	165			
8.50	75	117	37	79	109	165	75	156	1
8.60	81	125			115	175			
8.70	81	125			115	175			
8.80	81	125	40	84	115	175	81	162	1
8.90	81	125			115	175			
9.00	81	125	40	84	115	175	81	162	1
9.10	81	125			115	175			
9.20	81	125	40	84	115	175	81	162	1
9.30	81	125			115	175			
9.40	81	125			115	175			
9.50	81	125	40	84	115	175	81	162	1
9.60	87	133			121	184			
9.70	87	133			121	184			
9.80	87	133	43	89	121	184	87	168	1
9.90	87	133			121	184			
10.00	87	133	43	89	121	184	87	168	1
10.10	87	133			121	184			
10.20	87	133	43	89	121	184	87	168	1
10.30	87	133			121	184			
10.40	87	133			121	184			
10.50	87	133	43	89	121	184	87	168	1
10.60	87	133			121	184			
10.70	94	142			128	195			
10.80	94	142	47	95	128	195	94	175	1
10.90	94	142			128	195			
11.00	94	142	47	95	128	195	94	175	1

continued

Section 5.1.1 (*continued*)

Nominal diameter	*Parallel shank Jobber series*		*Parallel shank stub drills*		*Parallel shank long series*		*Morse taper (MT) shank two-flute twist and multiflute core drills*			*Oversize Morse taper shank*	
	Flute length	*Overall length*	*Flute length*	*Overall length*	*Flute length*	*Overall length*	*Flute length*	*Overall length*	*MT no.*	*Overall length*	*MT no.*
11.10	94	142			128	195					
11.20	94	142	47	95	128	195	94	175	1		
11.30	94	142			128	195					
11.40	94	142			128	195					
11.50	94	142	47	95	128	195	94	175	1		
11.60	94	142			128	195					
11.70	94	142			128	195					
11.80	94	142	47	95	128	195	94	175	1		
11.90	101	151			134	205					
12.00	101	151	51	102	134	205	101	182	1	199	2
12.10	101	151			134	205					
12.20	101	151	51	102	134	205	101	182	1	199	2
12.30	101	151			134	205					
12.40	101	151			134	205					
12.50	101	151	51	102	134	205	101	182	1	199	2
12.60	101	151			134	205					
12.70	101	151			134	205					
12.80	101	151	51	102	134	205	101	182	1	199	2
12.90	101	151			134	205					
13.00	101	151	51	102	134	205	101	182	1	199	2
13.10	101	151			134	205					
13.20	101	151	51	102	134	205	101	182	1	199	2
13.30	108	160			140	214					
13.40	108	160			140	214					

13.50	108	160	54	107	140	214	108	189	1	206	2
13.60	108	160			140	214					
13.70	108	160			140	214					
13.80	108	160	54	107	140	214	108	189	1	206	2
13.90	108	160			140	214					
14.00	108	160	54	107	140	214	108	189	1	206	2
14.25	114	169			144	220	114	212	2	206	2
14.50	114	169	56	111	144	220	114	212	2	206	2
14.75	114	169			144	220	114	212	2	206	2
15.00	114	169	56	111	144	220	114	212	2	206	2
15.25	120	178			149	227	120	218	2	206	2
15.50	120	178	58	115	149	227	120	218	2	206	2
15.75	120	178			149	227	120	218	2	206	2
16.00	120	178	58	115	149	227	120	218	2	206	2
16.25					154	235	125	223	2	206	2
16.50			60	119	154	235	125	223	2	206	2
16.75					154	235	125	223	2	206	2
17.00					154	235	125	223	2	206	2
17.25					158	241	130	228	2	206	2
17.50					158	241	130	228	2	206	2
17.75					158	241	130	228	2	206	2
18.00					158	241	130	228	2	206	2
18.25					162	247	135	233	2	256	3
18.50					162	247	135	283	2	256	3
18.75					162	247	135	283	2	256	3
19.00					162	247	135	233	2	256	3
19.25					166	254	140	238	2	261	3

continued

Section 5.1.1 (*continued*)

Nominal diameter	*Parallel shank long series*		*Morse taper (MT) shank two-flute twist and multi-flute core drills*			*Oversize Morse taper shank*	
	Flute length	*Overall length*	*Flute length*	*Overall length*	*MT no.*	*Overall length*	*MT no.*
19.50	166	254	140	238	2	261	3
19.75	166	254	140	238	2	261	3
20.00	166	254	140	238	2	261	3
20.25	171	261	145	243	2	266	3
20.50	171	261	145	243	2	266	3
20.75	171	261	145	243	2	266	3
21.00	171	261	145	243	2	266	3
21.25	176	268	150	248	2	271	3
21.50	176	268	150	248	2	271	3
21.75	176	268	150	248	2	271	3
22.00	176	268	150	248	2	271	3
22.25	176	268	150	248	2	271	3
22.50	180	275	155	253	2	276	3
22.75	180	275	155	253	2	276	3
23.00	180	275	155	253	2	276	3
23.25	180	275	155	276	3	—	—
23.50	180	275	155	276	3	—	—
23.75	185	282	160	281	3	—	—
24.00	185	282	160	281	3	—	—
24.25	185	282	160	281	3	—	—
24.50	185	282	160	281	3	—	—
24.75	185	282	160	281	3	—	—
25.00	185	282	160	281	3	—	—
25.25			165	286	3	—	—
25.50			165	286	3	—	—
25.75			165	286	3	—	—
26.00			165	286	3	—	—
26.25			165	286	3	—	—
26.50			165	286	3	—	—
26.75			170	291	3	319	4
27.00			170	291	3	319	4
27.25			170	291	3	319	4
27.50			170	291	3	319	4
27.75			170	291	3	319	4
28.00			170	291	3	319	4
28.25			175	296	3	324	4
28.50			175	296	3	324	4
28.75			175	296	3	324	4
29.00			175	296	3	324	4
29.25			175	296	3	324	4
29.50			175	296	3	324	4
29.75			175	296	3	324	4
30.00			175	296	3	324	4
30.25			180	301	3	329	4
30.50			180	301	3	329	4

Nominal diameter	Morse taper (MT) shank two-flute twist and multi-flute core drill			Oversize Morse taper shank	
	Flute length	Overall length	MT no.	Overall length	MT no.
30.75	180	301	3	329	4
31.00	180	301	3	329	4
31.25	180	301	3	329	4
31.50	180	301	3	329	4
31.75	185	306	3	334	4
32.00	185	334	4	—	—
32.50	185	334	4	—	—
33.00	185	334	4	—	—
33.50	185	334	4	—	—
34.00	190	339	4	—	—
34.50	190	339	4	—	—
35.00	190	339	4	—	—
35.50	190	339	4	—	—
36.00	195	344	4	—	—
36.50	195	344	4	—	—
37.00	195	344	4	—	—
37.50	195	344	4	—	—
38.00	200	349	4	—	—
38.50	200	349	4	—	—
39.00	200	349	4	—	—
39.50	200	349	4	—	—
40.00	200	349	4	—	—
40.50	205	354	4	392	5
41.00	205	354	4	392	5
41.50	205	354	4	392	5
42.00	205	354	4	392	5
42.50	205	354	4	392	5
43.00	210	359	4	397	5
43.50	210	359	4	397	5
44.00	210	359	4	397	5
44.50	210	359	4	397	5
45.00	210	359	4	397	5
45.50	215	364	4	402	5
46.00	215	364	4	402	5
46.50	215	364	4	402	5
47.00	215	364	4	402	5
47.50	215	364	4	402	5
48.00	220	369	4	407	5
48.50	220	369	4	407	5
49,00	220	369	4	407	5
49.50	220	369	4	407	5
50.00	220	369	4	407	5
50.50	225	374	4	412	5
51.00	225	412	5	—	—
52.00	225	412	5	—	—
53.00	225	412	5	—	—

continued

Section 5.1.1 (*continued*)

Nominal diameter	Morse taper (MT) shank two-flute twist and multi-flute core drill			Oversize Morse taper shank	
	Flute length	Overall length	MT no.	Overall length	MT no.
54.00	230	417	5	—	—
55.00	230	417	5	—	—
56.00	230	417	5	—	—
57.00	235	422	5	—	—
58.00	235	422	5	—	—
59.00	235	422	5	—	—
60.00	235	422	5	—	—
61.00	240	427	5	—	—
62.00	240	427	5	—	—
63.00	240	427	5	—	—
64.00	245	432	5	499	6
65.00	245	432	5	499	6
66.00	245	432	5	499	6
67.00	245	432	5	499	6
68.00	250	437	5	504	6
69.00	250	437	5	504	6
70.00	250	437	5	504	6
71.00	250	437	5	504	6
72.00	255	442	5	509	6
73.00	255	442	5	509	6
74.00	255	442	5	509	6
75.00	255	442	5	509	6
76.00	260	447	5	514	6
77.00	260	514	6	—	—
78.00	260	514	6	—	—
79.00	260	514	6	—	—
80.00	260	514	6	—	—
81.00	265	519	6	—	—
82.00	265	519	6	—	—
83.00	265	519	6	—	—
84.00	265	519	6	—	—
85.00	265	519	6	—	—
86.00	270	524	6	—	—
87.00	270	524	6	—	—
88.00	270	524	6	—	—
89.00	270	524	6	—	—
90.00	270	524	6	—	—
91.00	275	529	6	—	—
92.00	275	529	6	—	—
93.00	275	529	6	—	—
94.00	275	529	6	—	—
95.00	275	529	6	—	—
96.00	280	534	6	—	—
97.00	280	534	6	—	—
98.00	280	534	6	—	—
99.00	280	534	6	—	—
100.00	280	534	6	—	—

For further information see BS 328.

5.1.2 Twist drills: equivalent sizes

Number (gauge) size	*Metric size* mm	*Fractional size* in	*Decimal equivalent* in
80	0.35		0.0135
79	0.38		0.0145
78	0.40		0.0160
77	0.45		0.0180
76	0.50		0.0200
75	0.52		0.0210
74	0.58		0.0225
73	0.60		0.0240
72	0.65		0.0250
71	6.65		0.0260
70	0.70		0.0280
69	0.75		0.0292
68		$\frac{1}{32}$	0.0310
67	0.82		0.0320
66	0.85		0.0330
65	0.90		0.0350
64	0.92		0.0360
63	0.95		0.0370
62	0.98		0.0380
61	1.00		0.0390
60	1.00		0.0400
59	1.05		0.0410
58	1.05		0.0420
57	1.10		0.0430
56		$\frac{3}{64}$	0.0465
55	1.30		0.0520
54	1.40		0.0550
53	1.50		0.0595
52	1.60		0.0635
51	1.70		0.0670
50	1.80		0.0700
49	1.85		0.0730
48	1.95		0.0760
47	2.00		0.0785
46	2.05		0.0810
45	2.10		0.0820
44	2.20		0.0860
43	2.25		0.0890
42		$\frac{3}{32}$	0.0935
41	2.45		0.0960
40	2.50		0.0980
39	2.55		0.0995
38	2.60		0.1015
37	2.65		0.1040
36	2.70		0.1065
35	2.80		0.1100
34	2.80		0.1110
33	2.85		0.1130
32	2.95		0.1160
31	3.00		0.1200
30	3.30		0.1285
29	3.50		0.1360
28		$\frac{9}{64}$	0.1405
27	3.70		0.1440
26	3.70		0.1470
25	3.80		0.1495
24	3.90		0.1520
23	3.90		0.1540
22	4.00		0.1570
21	4.00		0.1590
20	4.10		0.1610
19	4.20		0.1660
18	4.30		0.1695
17	4.40		0.1730
16	4.50		0.1770
15	4.60		0.1800
14	4.60		0.1820
13	4.70		0.1850
12	4.80		0.1890
11	4.90		0.1910
10	4.90		0.1935
9	5.00		0.1960
8	5.10		0.1990
7	5.10		0.2010
6	5.20		0.2040
5	5.20		0.2055
4	5.30		0.2090
3	5.40		0.2130
2	5.60		0.2210
1	5.80		0.2280

Continued on right

Letter size	*Metric size* mm	*Fractional size* in	*Decimal equivalent* in
A		$\frac{15}{64}$	0.2340
B	6.00		0.2380
C	6.10		0.2420
D	6.20		0.2460
E		$\frac{1}{4}$	0.2500
F	6.50		0.2570
G	6.60		0.2610
H		$\frac{17}{64}$	0.2660
I	6.90		0.2720
J	7.00		0.2770

continued

Section 5.1.2 (*continued*)

Letter size	*Metric size* mm	*Fractional size* in	*Decimal equivalent* in
K		$\frac{9}{32}$	0.2810
L	7.40		0.2900
M	7.50		0.2950
N	7.70		0.3020
O	8.00		0.3160
P	8.20		0.3230
Q	8.40		0.3320
R	8.60		0.3390

Letter size	*Metric size* mm	*Fractional size* in	*Decimal equivalent* in
S	8.80		0.3480
T	9.10		0.3580
U	9.30		0.3680
V		$\frac{3}{8}$	0.3770
W	9.80		0.3860
X	10.10		0.3970
Y	10.30		0.4040
Z	10.50		0.4130

5.1.3 BA threads: tapping and clearance drills

BA no.	*Tapping size drill*		*Clearance size drill*	
	mm	*Number or fraction size*	mm	*Number, letter or fraction size*
0	5.10	7	6.10	C
1	4.50	16	5.50	2
2	4.00	22	4.85	11
3	3.40	$\frac{9}{64}$ in	4.25	18
4	3.00	31	3.75	26
5	2.65	37	3.30	30
6	2.30	$\frac{3}{32}$ in	2.90	32
7	2.05	46	2.60	38
8	1.80	50	2.25	43
9	1.55	52	1.95	48
10	1.40	54	1.75	50
11	1.20	$\frac{3}{64}$ in	1.60	$\frac{1}{16}$ in
12	1.05	59	1.40	54
13	0.98	62	1.30	55
14	0.78	$\frac{1}{32}$ in	1.10	57
15	0.70	70	0.98	62
16	0.60	73	0.88	65

5.1.4 ISO metric tapping and clearance drills, coarse thread series

Nominal size	*Tapping drill size* (mm)		*Clearance drill size* (mm)		
	Recommended 80% *engagement*	*Alternative* 70% *engagement*	*Close fit*	*Medium fit*	*Free fit*
M1.6	1.25	1.30	1.7	1.8	2.0
M2	1.60	1.65	2.2	2.4	2.6
M2.5	2.05	2.10	2.7	2.9	3.1
M3	2.50	2.55	3.2	3.4	3.6
M4	3.30	3.40	4.3	4.5	4.8
M5	4.20	4.30	5.3	5.5	5.8
M6	5.00	5.10	6.4	6.6	7.0
M8	6.80	6.90	8.4	9.0	10.0
M10	8.50	8.60	10.5	11.0	12.0
M12	10.20	10.40	13.0	14.0	15.0
M14	12.00	12.20	15.0	16.0	17.0
M16	14.00	14.25	17.0	18.0	19.0
M18	15.50	15.75	19.0	20.0	21.0
M20	17.50	17.75	21.0	22.0	24.0
M22	19.50	19.75	23.0	24.0	26.0
M24	21.00	21.25	25.0	26.0	28.0
M27	24.00	24.25	28.0	30.0	32.0
M30	26.50	26.75	31.0	33.0	35.0
M33	29.50	29.75	34.0	36.0	38.0
M36	32.00	—	37.0	39.0	42.0
M39	35.00	—	40.0	42.0	45.0
M42	37.50	—	43.0	45.0	48.0
M45	40.50	—	46.0	48.0	52.0
M48	43.00	—	50.0	52.0	56.0
M52	47.00	—	54.0	56.0	62.0

5.1.5 ISO metric tapping and clearance drills, fine thread series

Nominal size	*Tapping drill size* (mm)		*Clearance drill size* (mm)		
	Recommended 80% *engagement*	*Alternative* 70% *engagement*	*Close fit*	*Medium fit*	*Free fit*
M6	5.20	5.30	6.4	6.6	7.0
M8	7.00	7.10	8.4	9.0	10.0
M10	8.80	8.90	10.5	11.0	12.0
M12	10.80	10.90	13.0	14.0	15.0
M14	12.50	12.70	15.0	16.0	17.0
M16	14.50	14.75	17.0	18.0	19.0
M18	16.50	16.75	19.0	20.0	21.0
M20	18.50	18.75	21.0	22.0	24.0
M22	20.50	20.75	23.0	24.0	26.0
M24	22.00	22.25	25.0	26.0	28.0
M27	25.00	25.25	28.0	30.0	32.0
M30	28.00	28.25	31.0	33.0	35.0
M33	31.00	31.25	34.0	36.0	38.0
M36	33.00	—	37.0	39.0	42.0
M39	36.00	—	40.0	42.0	45.0
M42	39.00	—	43.0	45.0	48.0

5.1.6 ISO unified tapping and clearance drills, coarse thread series

Nominal size	*Tapping drill size*		*Clearance drill size*	
in	mm	in	mm	*Letter or* in
$\frac{1}{4} \times 20$	5.20	$\frac{13}{64}$	6.50	$\frac{17}{64}$ or F
$\frac{5}{16} \times 18$	6.60	$\frac{17}{64}$	8.00	$\frac{21}{64}$ or O
$\frac{3}{8} \times 16$	8.00	$\frac{5}{16}$	9.80	$\frac{25}{64}$ or W

$\frac{7}{16} \times 14$	9.40	$\frac{3}{8}$	11.30	$\frac{29}{64}$
$\frac{1}{2} \times 13$	10.80	$\frac{27}{64}$	13.00	$\frac{33}{64}$
$\frac{9}{16} \times 12$	12.20	$\frac{31}{64}$	14.75	$\frac{37}{64}$
$\frac{5}{8} \times 11$	13.50	$\frac{17}{32}$	16.25	$\frac{41}{64}$
$\frac{3}{4} \times 10$	16.50	$\frac{21}{32}$	19.50	$\frac{47}{64}$
$\frac{7}{8} \times 9$	19.25	$\frac{49}{64}$	20.25	$\frac{51}{64}$
1×8	22.25	$\frac{7}{8}$	25.75	$1\frac{1}{64}$
$1\frac{1}{8} \times 7$	25.00	$\frac{63}{64}$	26.00	$1\frac{9}{64}$
$1\frac{1}{4} \times 7$	28.25*	$1\frac{7}{64}$	28.25	$1\frac{17}{64}$
$1\frac{3}{8} \times 6$	30.50*	$1\frac{13}{64}$	30.75	$1\frac{25}{64}$
$1\frac{1}{2} \times 6$	34.00*	$1\frac{21}{64}$	34.00	$1\frac{33}{64}$
$1\frac{3}{4} \times 5$	39.50*	$1\frac{35}{64}$	45.00	$1\frac{49}{64}$
$2 \times 4\frac{1}{2}$	45.50*	$1\frac{25}{32}$	52.00	$2\frac{1}{64}$

* Nearest standard metric size: approx. 0.25 mm over recommended inch size.

5.1.7 ISO unified tapping and clearance drills, fine thread series

Nominal size	*Tapping drill size*		*Clearance drill size*	
in	mm	*Letter or* in	mm	*Letter or* in
$\frac{1}{4} \times 28$	5.50	$\frac{7}{32}$	6.50	F
$\frac{5}{16} \times 24$	6.90	I	8.00	O
$\frac{3}{8} \times 24$	8.50	R	9.80	W
$\frac{7}{16} \times 20$	9.90	$\frac{25}{64}$	11.30	$\frac{29}{64}$
$\frac{1}{2} \times 20$	11.50	$\frac{29}{64}$	13.00	$\frac{33}{64}$
$\frac{9}{16} \times 18$	12.90	$\frac{33}{64}$	14.75	$\frac{37}{64}$
$\frac{5}{8} \times 18$	14.50	$\frac{37}{64}$	16.50	$\frac{41}{64}$
$\frac{3}{4} \times 16$	17.50	$\frac{11}{16}$	19.50	$\frac{49}{64}$
$\frac{7}{8} \times 14$	20.50	$\frac{13}{16}$	22.75	$\frac{57}{64}$
1×12	23.25	$\frac{59}{64}$	25.80	$1\frac{1}{64}$
$1\frac{1}{8} \times 12$	26.50	$1\frac{3}{64}$	29.00	$1\frac{9}{64}$
$1\frac{1}{4} \times 12$	29.50	$1\frac{11}{64}$	32.50	$1\frac{17}{64}$
$1\frac{3}{8} \times 12$	33.00	$1\frac{19}{64}$	35.50	$1\frac{25}{64}$
$1\frac{1}{2} \times 12$	36.00	$1\frac{27}{64}$	38.50	$1\frac{33}{64}$

5.1.8 ISO metric tapping and clearance drills, miniature series

Nominal size		Pitch		Tapping drill size		Clearance drill size	
ISO mm	*ASA B1.10* mm	mm	*Threads per inch*	mm	*Number or fraction*	mm	*Number or fraction*
S-0.3	0.30 unm	0.080	318	0.25	—	0.32	—
(S-0.35)	(0.35 unm)	0.090	282	0.28	—	0.38	79
S-0.4	0.40 unm	0.100	254	0.35	80	0.45	77
(S-0.45)	(0.45 unm)	0.100	254	0.38	79	0.50	76
S-0.5	0.50 unm	0.125	203	0.42	78	0.55	75,74
(S-0.55)	(0.55 unm)	0.125	203	0.45	77	0.60	73
S-0.6	0.60 unm	0.150	169	0.50	76	0.65	72
(S-0.7)	(0.70 unm)	0.175	145	0.58	74	0.78	$\frac{1}{32}$ in
S-0.8	0.80 unm	0.200	127	0.65	72	0.88	66, 65
(S-0.9)	(0.90 unm)	0.225	113	0.72	70	0.98	62
S-1.0	1.00 unm	0.250	102	0.80	$\frac{1}{32}$ in	1.10	57
(S-1.1)	(1.10 unm)	0.250	102	0.90	65	1.20	$\frac{3}{64}$ in
S-1.2	1.20 unm	0.250	102	1.00	61	1.30	55
(S-1.4)	(1.40 unm)	0.300	85	1.15	$\frac{3}{64}$ in	1.50	53

5.1.9 Hand reamers

Hand reamer

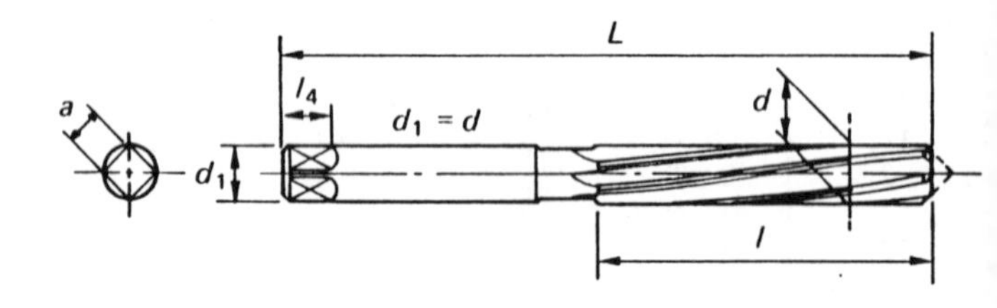

Hand reamer with long taper lead

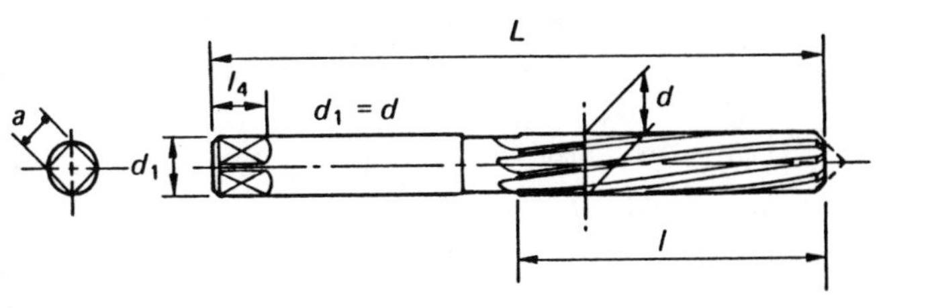

Dimensions in millimetres

Preferred cutting diameters* d	Cutting edge length l	Overall length L	Driving square a (h12)	l_4
1.5	20	41	1.12	4
1.6	21	44	1.25	
1.8	23	47	1.40	
2.0	25	50	1.60	
2.2	27	54	1.80	
2.5	29	58	2.00	
2.8	31	62	2.24	5
3.0				
3.5	35	71	2.80	
4.0	38	76	3.15	6
4.5	41	81	3.55	
5.0	44	87	4.00	7
5.5	47	93	4.50	
6.0				

Preferred cutting diameters* d	Cutting edge length l	Overall length L	Driving square (h12)	l_4
7.0	54	107	5.60	8
8.0	58	115	6.30	9
9.0	62	124	7.10	10
10.0	66	133	8.00	11
11.0	71	142	9.00	12
12.0	76	152	10.00	13
13.0				
14.0	81	163	11.20	14
15.0				
16.0	87	175	12.50	16
17.0				
18.0	93	188	14.00	18
19.0				
20.0	100	201	16.00	20
21.0				

continued

Section 5.1.9 (*continued*) Dimensions in millimetres

*Preferred cutting diameter** d	*Cutting edge length* l	*Overall length* L	*Driving square* a (h12)	l_4
22	107	215	18.00	22
23				
24				
25	115	231	20.00	24
26				
27				
28	124	247	22.40	26
30				
32	133	265	25.00	28
34				
35	142	284	28.00	31
36				
38				
40	152	305	31.50	34
42				

*Preferred cutting diameter** d	*Cutting edge length* l	*Overall length* L	*Driving square* (h12)	l_4
44				
45	163	326	35.50	38
46				
48				
50	174	347	40.00	42
52				
55				
56	184	367	45.00	46
58				
60				
62				
63	194	387	50.00	51
67				
71	203	406	56.00	56

*The diameters in bold type should be used whenever possible.
This table is based on a table from ISO 236/1, except that the latter uses the symbols l for L and l_1 for l. For full range and further information see BS 328 : Pt 4 : 1983.

5.1.10 Long flute machine reamers

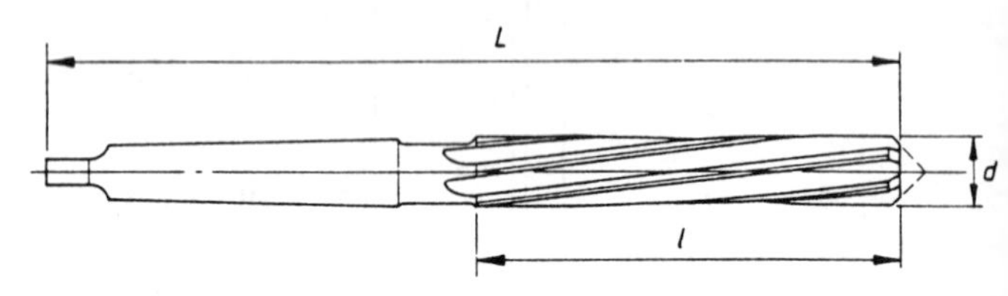

Dimensions in millimetres

<table>
<tr><th>Preferred cutting diameter*
d</th><th>Cutting edge length
l</th><th>Overall length
L</th><th>Morse taper shank</th></tr>
<tr><td>7</td><td>54</td><td>134</td><td rowspan="8">no, 1</td></tr>
<tr><td>8</td><td>58</td><td>138</td></tr>
<tr><td>9</td><td>62</td><td>142</td></tr>
<tr><td>10</td><td>66</td><td>146</td></tr>
<tr><td>11</td><td>71</td><td>151</td></tr>
<tr><td>12</td><td rowspan="2">76</td><td rowspan="2">156</td></tr>
<tr><td>13</td></tr>
<tr><td>14</td><td rowspan="2">81</td><td>161</td></tr>
<tr><td>15</td><td>181</td><td rowspan="9">no. 2</td></tr>
<tr><td>16</td><td rowspan="2">87</td><td rowspan="2">187</td></tr>
<tr><td>17</td></tr>
<tr><td>18</td><td rowspan="2">93</td><td rowspan="2">193</td></tr>
<tr><td>19</td></tr>
<tr><td>20</td><td rowspan="2">100</td><td rowspan="2">200</td></tr>
<tr><td>21</td></tr>
<tr><td>22</td><td rowspan="2">207</td><td rowspan="2">207</td></tr>
<tr><td>23</td></tr>
<tr><td>24</td><td rowspan="3">115</td><td rowspan="3">242</td><td rowspan="6">no. 3</td></tr>
<tr><td>25</td></tr>
<tr><td>26</td></tr>
<tr><td>27</td><td rowspan="3">124</td><td rowspan="3">251</td></tr>
<tr><td>28</td></tr>
<tr><td>30</td></tr>
</table>

<table>
<tr><th>Preferred cutting diameters*
d</th><th>Cutting edge length
l</th><th>Overall length
L</th><th>Morse taper shank</th></tr>
<tr><td>32</td><td>133</td><td>293</td><td rowspan="12">no. 4</td></tr>
<tr><td>34</td><td rowspan="3">142</td><td rowspan="3">302</td></tr>
<tr><td>35</td></tr>
<tr><td>36</td></tr>
<tr><td>38</td><td rowspan="3">152</td><td rowspan="3">312</td></tr>
<tr><td>40</td></tr>
<tr><td>42</td></tr>
<tr><td>44</td><td rowspan="3">163</td><td rowspan="3">323</td></tr>
<tr><td>45</td></tr>
<tr><td>46</td></tr>
<tr><td>48</td><td rowspan="3">174</td><td rowspan="2">334</td></tr>
<tr><td>50</td></tr>
<tr><td>52</td><td>371</td><td rowspan="9">no. 5</td></tr>
<tr><td>55</td><td rowspan="4">184</td><td rowspan="4">381</td></tr>
<tr><td>56</td></tr>
<tr><td>58</td></tr>
<tr><td>60</td></tr>
<tr><td>62</td><td rowspan="3">194</td><td rowspan="3">391</td></tr>
<tr><td>63</td></tr>
<tr><td>67</td></tr>
<tr><td>71</td><td>203</td><td>400</td></tr>
</table>

* The diameters in bold type should be used whenever possible.
This table is based on a table from ISO 236/II, except that the latter uses the symbols l for L and l_1 for l. For tool definitions, full range and further information see BS 328 : 4 : 1983.

5.1.11 Machine chucking reamers with Morse taper shanks

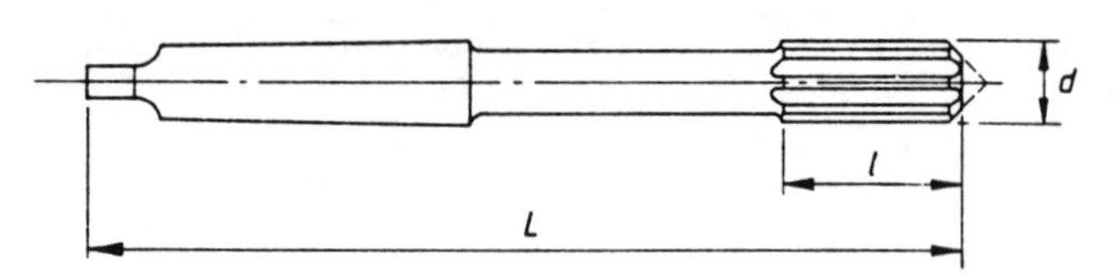

Dimensions in millimetres

Preferred cutting diameter d*	*Cutting edge length l*	*Overall length L*	*Morse taper shank*
5.5	26	138	no.1
6			
7	31	150	
8	33	156	
9	36	162	
10	38	168	
11	41	175	
12	44	182	
13			
14	47	189	
15	50	204	no. 2
16	52	210	
17	54	214	
18	56	219	
19	58	223	
20	60	228	
22	64	237	
24	68	268	no. 3
25			
26	70	273	
28	71	277	
30	73	281	
32	77	317	no. 4
34	78	321	
35			
36	79	325	
38	81	329	
40			
42	82	333	
44	83	336	
45			
46	84	340	
48	86	344	
50			

*The diameters in bold type should be used whenever possible.
This table is based on a table from ISO 521. For tool definitions, full range and further information see BS 328 : Pt 4 : 1983.

5.1.12 Shell reamers with taper bore

Shell reamer with taper bore

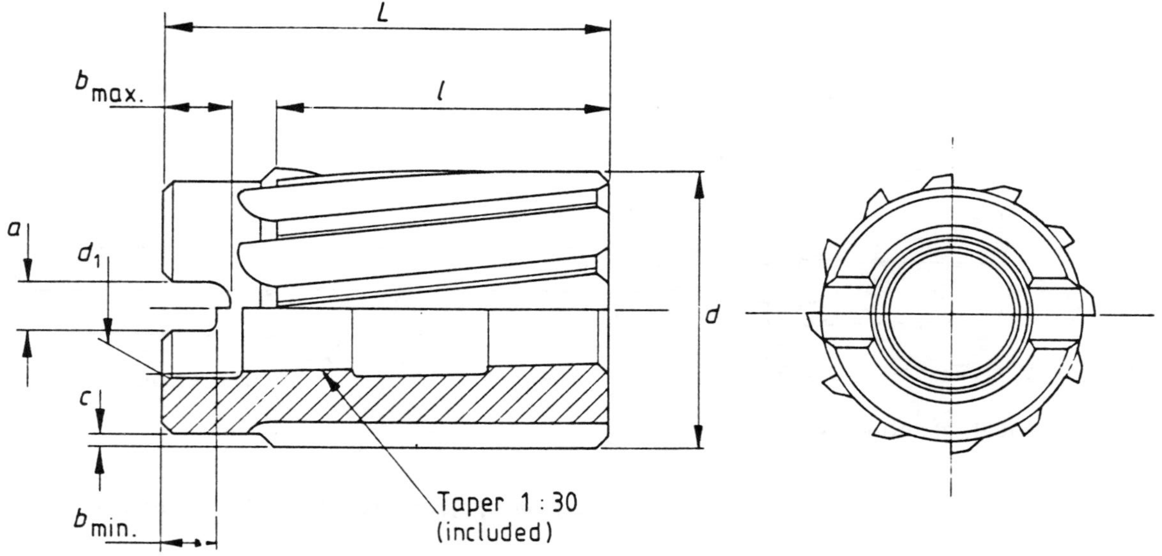

continued

Arbor for shell reamer with taper bore

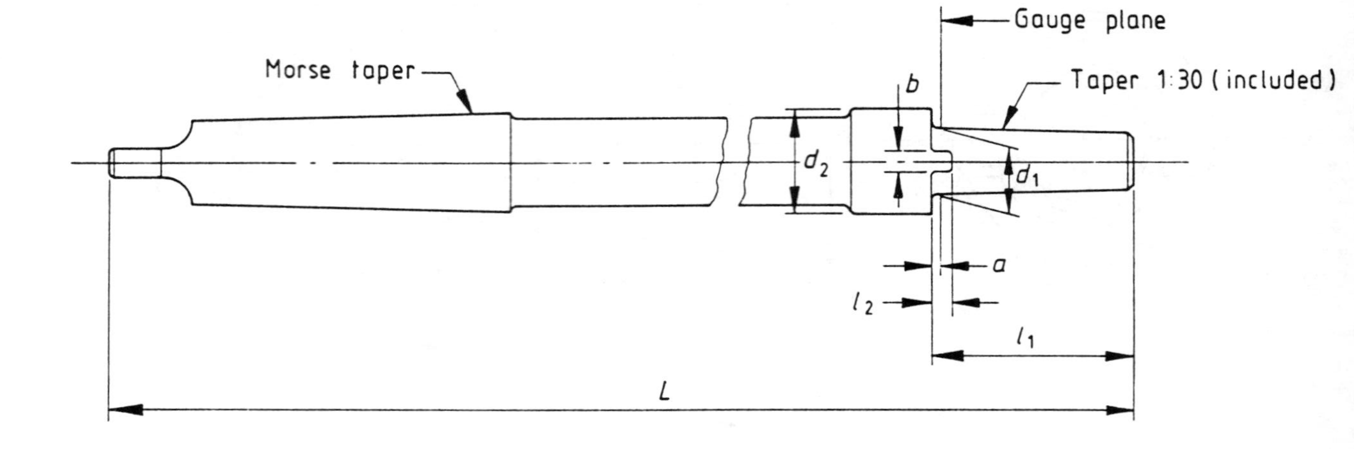

Dimensions in millimetres

Reamer diameter d			Diameter of large end of taper bore	Width of driving slot	Depth of driving slot b		Relief depth	Cutting edge length	Overall length
Over	Up to and including	Preferred sizes	d_1	a (H13)*	min.	max.	C max.	l	L
19.9	23.6	—	10					28	40
23.6	30.0	25 26 27 28 30	13	4.3	5.4	7.0	1.0	32	45
30.0	35.5	32 34 35	16	5.4	6.2	8.3	1.5	36	50
35.5	42.5	36 38 40 42	19	6.4	7.8	10.2	1.5	40	56

continued

Section 5.1.12 (*continued*)

Dimensions in millimetres

Reamer diameter d			*Diameter of large end of taper bore*	*Width of driving slot*	*Depth of driving slot b*		*Relief depth*	*Cutting edge*	*Overall length*
Over	*Up to and including*	*Preferred sizes*	d_1	*a* (H13)*	*min.*	*max.*	*C* *max.*	*length* *l*	*L*
42.5	50.8	45 47 48 50	22	7.4	8.6	11.3	1.5	45	63
50.8	60.0	52 55 58 60	27	8.4	9.3	12.5	2.0	50	71
60.0	71.0	62 65 70	32	10.4	10.5	14.5	2.0	56	80

71.0	85.0	72 75 80 85	40	12.4	11.2	16.2	2.5	63	90
85.0	101.6	90 95 100	50	14.4	13.1	18.7	2.5	71	100

* For values of the tolerance H13, see BS 328 : Pt 4 Appendix B.

The dimensions shown in this table are in accordance with ISO 2402, except that the latter does not include preferred diameters. For further information see BS 328 : Pt 4 : 1983.

5.1.13 Hand taper pin reamer

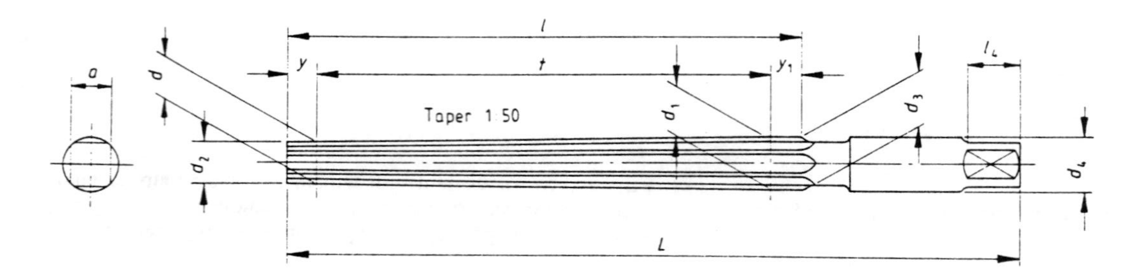

d nom.	d_1	t	y	y_1	d_2	d_3	l	d_4 (h11)	L	a (h12)	l_4
0.6	0.76	8	5	7	0.5	0.90	20		38	†	†
0.8	1.04	12	5	7	0.7	1.18	24		42	0.90	4
1.0	1.32	16	5	7	0.9	1.46	28		46	1.12	4
1.2	1.60	20	5	7	1.1	1.74	32		50	1.40	4
1.5	2.00	25	5	7	1.4	2.14	37	$d_4 = d_3$	57	1.80	4
2.0	2.70	35	5	8	1.9	2.86	48		68	2.24	5
2.5	3.20	35	5	8	2.4	3.36	48		68	2.80	5
3.0	3.90	45	5	8	2.9	4.06	58	4.0	80	3.15	6
4.0	5.10	55	5	8	3.9	5.26	68	5.0	93	4.00	7
5.0	6.20	60	5	8	4.9	6.36	73	6.3	100	5.00	8
6.0	7.80	90	5	10	5.9	8.00	105	8.0	135	6.30	9
8.0	10.60	130	5	10	7.9	10.80	145	10.0	180	8.00	11
10.0	13.20	160	5	10	9.9	13.40	175	12.5	215	10.00	13
12.0	15.60	180	10	20	11.8	16.00	210	14.0	255	11.20	14
16.0	20.00	200	10	20	15.8	20.40	230	18.0	280	14.00	18
20.0	24.40	220	10	20	19.8	24.80	250	22.4	310	18.00	22
25.0	29.80	240	15	45	24.7	30.70	300	28.0	370	22.40	26
30.0	35.20	260	15	45	29.7	36.10	320	31.5	400	25.00	28
40.0	45.60	280	15	45	39.7	46.50	340	40.0	430	31.50	34
50.0	56.00	300	15	45	49.7	56.90	360	50.0	460	40.00	42

* For the values of the tolerances h11 and h12 see BS 328 : Pt 4 : 1983 Appendix B.

† This shank size is smaller than the size range for which a size of driving square is specified in ISO 237. A parallel shank should be used without a square.

This table is in accordance with ISO 3465, except that in the latter, for values of d equal to or less than 2.5 mm, d_4 has a constant value equal to 3.15 mm. The values of a and l_4 are in accordance with ISO 237. For further information see BS 328 : Pt 4 : 1983.

5.1.14 Counterbores with parallel shanks and integral pilots

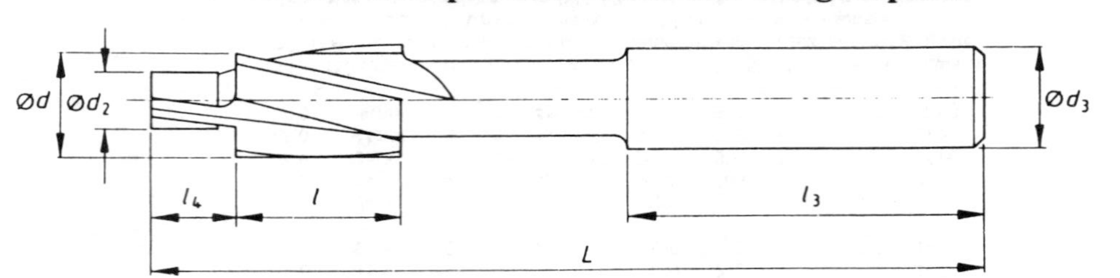

General dimensions

Dimensions in millimetres

*Cutting diameter d (z9)** *over*	*to*	*Pilot diameter* d_2	*Shank diameter* d_3 *(h9)**	*Overall length L*	*Cutting length l*	*Shank length* l_3	*Pilot length (approx.)* l_4
2.00†	3.15	For all cutting diameters: $d/3$ min.	$d_3 = d$	45	7		d_2
3.15	5.00	Limits of tolerance on selected pilot diameter: e8.*	$d_3 = d$	56	10		d_2
5.00	8.00	The selected pilot diameter is to be specified, when	5.0	71	14	31.5	d_2
8.00	12.50	ordering, to suit the pilot hole diameter	8.0	80	18	35.5	d_2
12.50	20.00		12.5	100	22	40.0	d_2

* For values of the tolerances z9, e8 and h9 see tables 11, 8 and 10 BS 328 : Pt 5 : 1983 Appendix A.

† Includes 2 mm.

This table is in accordance with ISO 4206 except that the latter uses l_1 for L, l_2 for l and d_1 for d.

Preferred cutting diameters d (z9)	*Pilot diameter* d_2 (38)	*Cap screw size*	*Cap screw head diameter*
6.0	2.5 3.2 3.4*	M3	5.5
8.0	3.3 4.3 4.5*	M4	7.0
10.0	4.2 5.3 5.5*	M5	8.5
11.0	5.0 6.4 6.6*	M6	10.0
15.0	6.8 8.4 9.0*	M8	13.0
18.0	8.5 10.5 11.0*	M10	16.0
20.0	10.2 13.0 14.0*	M12	18.0

* These are the preferred pilot diameters, being the diameters of clearance holes for the sizes of cap screw indicated.
For further information see BS 328: Pt 5: 1983

5.1.15 Counterbores with Morse taper shanks and detachable pilots

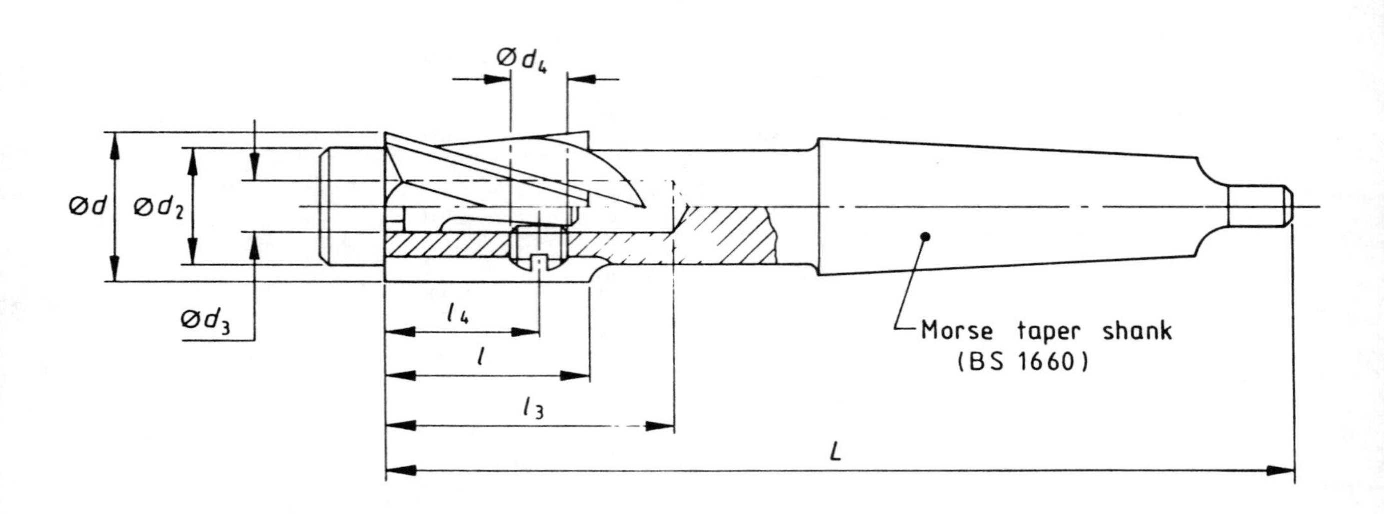

General dimensions

Dimensions in millimetres

Cutting diameter d (z9)*		Pilot diameter d_2 (e8)*		Diameter of hole for pilot d_3 (H8)	Set screw size d_4	Overall length L	Cutting length l	Pilot shank L_3	Set screw position l_4	Morse taper shank no.
over	to	over	to							
12.5	16.0	5.0	14.0	4	M3	132	22	30	16	2
16.0	20.0	6.3	18.0	5	M4	140	25	38	19	2
20.0	25.0	8.0	22.4	6	M5	150	30	46	23	2
25.0	31.5	10.0	28.0	8	M6	180	35	54	27	3
31.5	40.0	12.5	35.5	10	M8	190	40	64	32	3
40.0	50.0	16.0	45.0	12	M8	236	50	76	42	4
50.0	63.0	20.0	56.0	16	M10	250	63	88	53	4

* For values of the tolerances z9, e8 and H8 see tables 11, 8 and 12 in BS 328 : Pt 5 : 1983 Appendix A.
This table is in accordance with ISO 4207 except that the latter uses l_1 for L, l_2 for l and d_1 for d.

continued

Section 5.1.15 (*continued*)

Diameters

Dimensions in millimetres

Preferred cutting diameters d (z9)	*Pilot diameter* d_2 (e8)	*Pilot shank diameter* d_3 (f7)	*Cap screw size*	*Cap screw head diameter*
15.0	6.8 8.4 9.0*	4.0	M8	13.0
18.0	8.5 10.2 10.5	5.0	M10	16.0
20.0	11.0* 13.0 14.0*		M12	18.0
24.0	12.0 15.0 16.0*	6.0	M14	21.0
26.0	14.0 15.5 17.0	8.0	M16	24.0
30.0	18.0 19.0 20.0*		M18	27.0
33.0	17.5 19.5	10.0	M20	30.0
36.0	21.0 22.0* 23.0		M22	33.0
40.0	24.0* 25.0 26.0*		M24	36.0

* These are the preferred pilot diameters, being the diameters of clearance holes for the sizes of cap screw indicated.
For further information see BS 328 : Pt 5.

5.1.16 Detachable pilots for counterbores

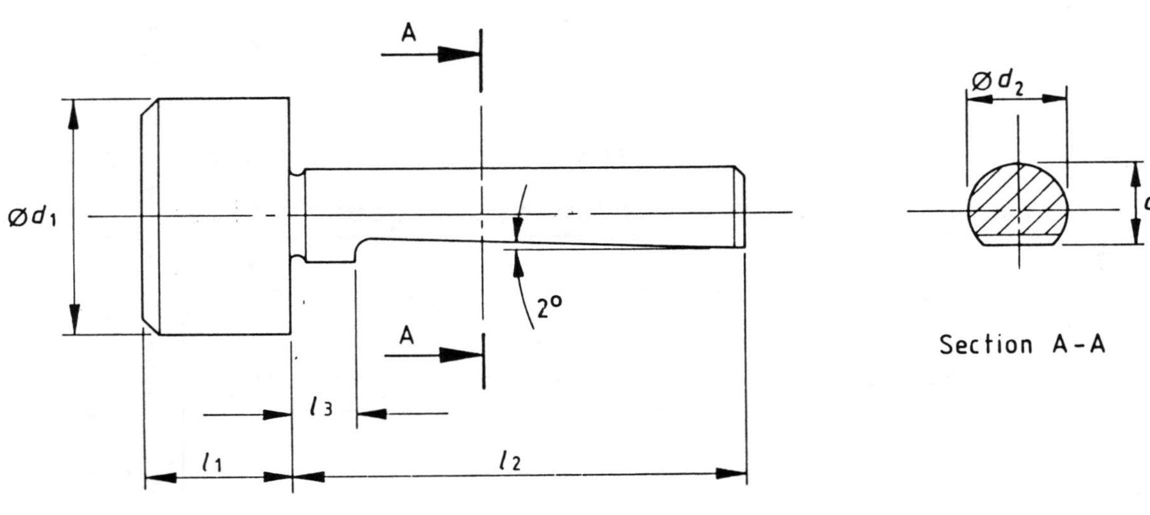

continued

Section 5.1.16 (*continued*) Dimensions in millimetres

Pilot shank diameter d_2 (f7)*	Pilot diameter d_1 (e8)*		$a\ {}^{0}_{-0.1}$	Pilot length l_1	Pilot shank length l_2	l_3
	over	to				
4	5.0	6.3	3.6	5	20	3
4	6.3	8.0	3.6	6	20	3
4	8.0	10.0	3.6	7	20	3
4	10.0	12.5	3.6	8	20	4
4	12.5	14.0	3.6	10	20	4
5	6.3	8.0	4.6	6	23	3
5	8.0	10.0	4.6	7	23	3
5	10.0	12.5	4.6	8	23	4
5	12.5	16.0	4.6	10	23	4
5	16.0	18.0	4.6	12	23	4
6	8.0	10.0	5.5	7	28	4
6	10.0	12.5	5.5	8	28	4
6	12.5	16.0	5.5	10	28	4
6	16.0	20.0	5.5	12	28	5
6	20.0	22.4	5.5	15	28	5
8	10.0	12.5	7.5	8	32	4
8	12.5	16.0	7.5	10	32	4
8	16.0	20.0	7.5	12	32	5
8	20.0	25.0	7.5	15	32	5
8	25.0	28.0	7.5	18	32	5
10	12.5	16.0	9.1	10	40	5
10	16.0	20.0	9.1	12	40	5
10	20.0	25.0	9.1	15	40	5
10	25.0	31.5	9.1	18	40	6
10	31.5	35.5	9.1	22	40	6
12	16.0	20.0	11.3	12	50	5
12	20.0	25.0	11.3	15	50	5
12	25.0	31.5	11.3	18	50	6
12	31.5	40.0	11.3	22	50	6
12	40.0	45.0	11.3	27	50	6
16	20.0	25.0	15.2	15	60	6
16	25.0	31.5	15.2	18	60	6
16	31.5	40.0	15.2	22	60	6
16	40.0	50.0	15.2	27	60	6
16	50.0	56.0	15.2	30	60	6

* For values of the tolerances f7 and e8 see tables 8 and 9 in BS 328 : Pt 5 : 1983 Appendix A.
This table is in accordance with ISO 4208. For further information see BS 328 : Pt 5 : 1983.

5.1.17 Countersinks with parallel shanks

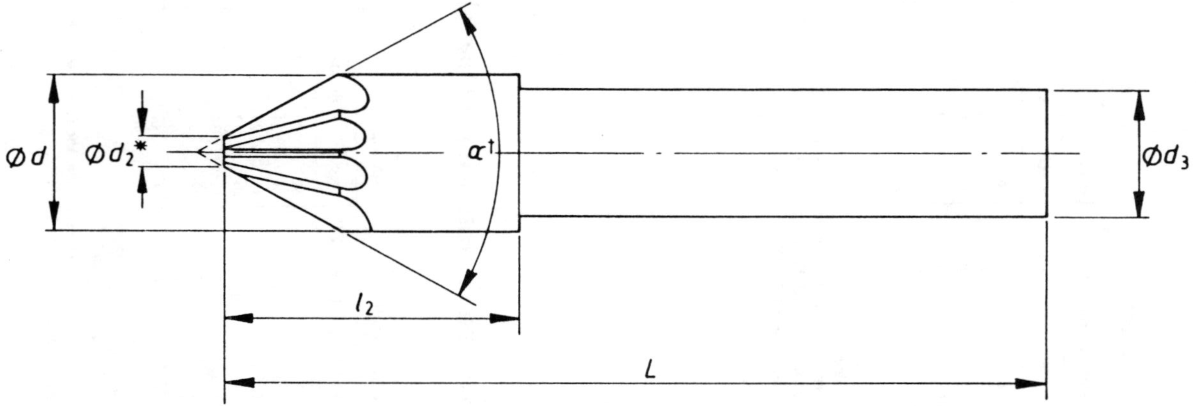

continued

Section 5.1.17 (*continued*)

Dimensions in millimetres

Nominal size d	Small diameter* d_2	Overall length L†		Body length l_2†		Shank diameter d_3 (h9)‡
		$\alpha=60°$	$\alpha=90°$ and 120°	$\alpha=60°$	$\alpha=90°$ and 120°	
8.0	1.6	48	44	16	12	8
10.0	2.0	50	46	18	14	8
12.5	2.5	52	48	20	16	8
16.0	3.2	60	56	24	20	10
20.0	4.0	64	60	28	24	10
25.0	7.0	69	65	33	29	10

* Front end design optional.
† Tolerance on α is $_{-1}^{\ 0}$ degrees.
‡ For values of the tolerance h9 see table 10 in BS 328 : Pt 5 : 1983 Appendix A.
This table is in accordance with ISO 3294, except that the latter uses l_1 for L and d_1 for d. For further information see BS 328 : Pt 5 : 1983.

5.1.18 Countersinks with Morse taper shanks

Dimensions in millimetres

Nominal size d	Small diameter* d_2	Overall length L†		Body length l_2†		Morse taper shank no.
		$\alpha=60°$	$\alpha=90°$ and 120°	$\alpha=60°$	$\alpha=90°$ and 120°	
16.0	3.2	97	93	24	20	1
20.0	4.0	120	116	28	24	2
25.0	7.0	125	121	33	29	2
31.5	9.0	132	124	40	32	2
40.0	12.5	160	150	45	35	3
50.0	16.0	165	153	50	38	3
63.0	20.0	200	185	58	43	4
80.0	25.0	215	196	73	54	4

* Front end design optional.
† Tolerance on α is $_{-1}^{\ 0}$ degrees.
This table is in accordance with ISO 3293, except that the latter uses l_1 for L and d_1 for d. For further information see BS 328 : Pt 5 : 1983.

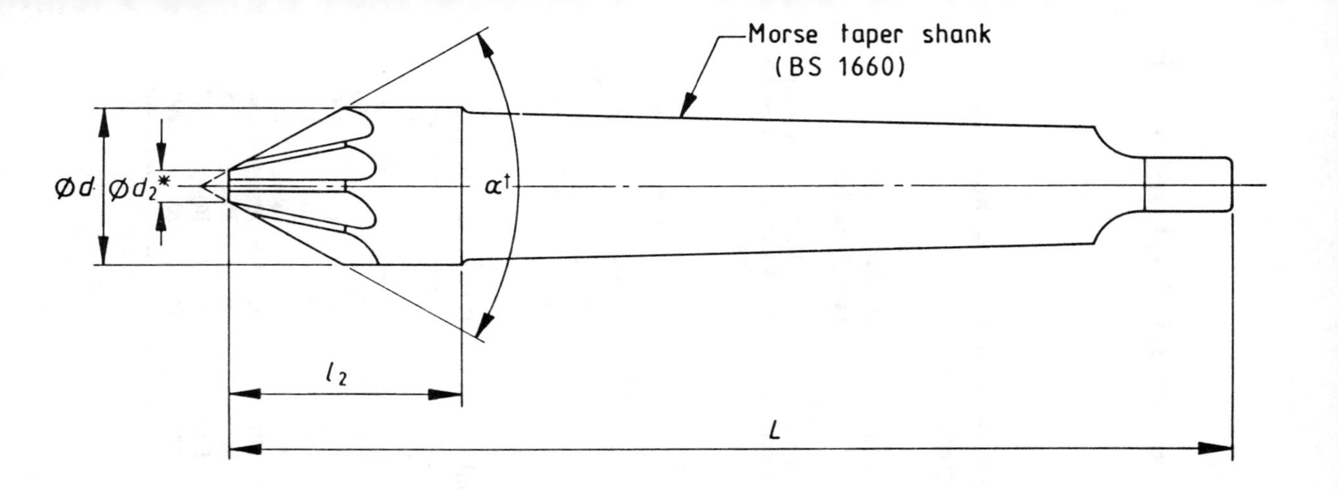

Morse taper shank
(BS 1660)
$\varnothing d$
$\varnothing d_2$*
α†
l_2
L

5.2 Single point cutting tools

5.2.1 Single point cutting tools: butt welded high speed steel

Light turning and facing tool

No. 1 Right hand as drawn
No. 2 Left hand opposite to drawing

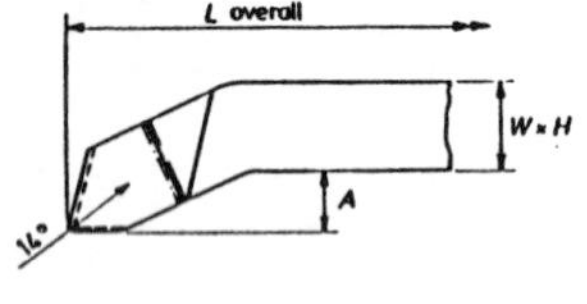

Preferred sizes (mm)		
H	*W*	*L*
12	12	100
16	16	110
20	20	125
25	16	200
32	20	250
40	25	315
(20	16)	140
(25	20)	200

Straight nosed roughing tool

No. 3 Right hand as drawn
No. 4 Left hand opposite to drawing

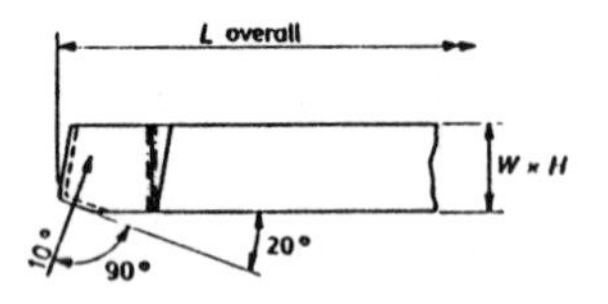

Preferred sizes (mm)		
H	*W*	*L*
12	12	100
16	16	110
20	20	125
25	16	200
32	20	250
40	25	315
(20	16)	200
(25	20)	200

Knife tool or side-cutting tool

No. 7 Right hand as drawn
No. 8 Left hand opposite to drawing

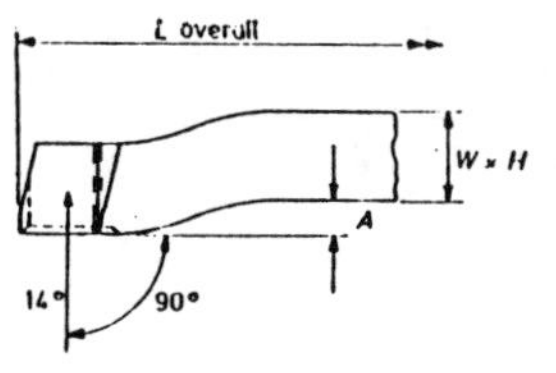

NOTE. A = from 0.3W to 0.5W

Preferred sizes (mm)		
H	*W*	*L*
12	12	100
16	16	110
20	20	125
25	16	200
32	20	250
40	25	315
(20	16)	140
(25	20)	200

External screw-cutting tool

No. 13 As drawn

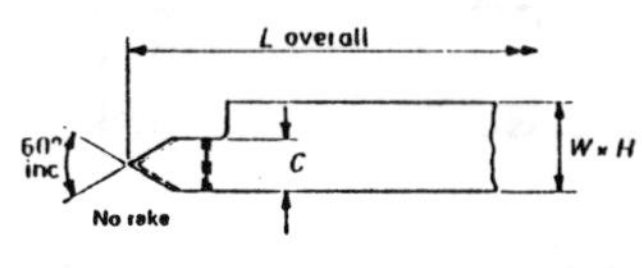

NOTE. C = from 0.5W to 0.75W

Preferred sizes (mm)		
H	*W*	*L*
12	12	100
16	16	110
20	20	125
25	16	200
32	20	250
40	25	315
(20	16)	140
(25	20)	200

Parting-off tool

No. 16RH Right hand as drawn
No. 16LH Left hand opposite to drawing

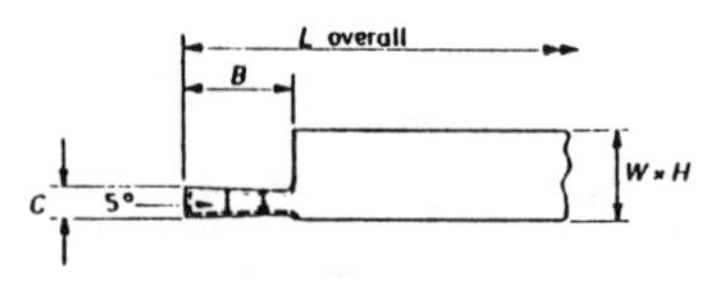

Preferred sizes (mm)		
H	*W*	*L*
12	12	100
16	16	110
20	20	125
25	16	200
32	20	250
40	25	315
(20	16)	140
(25	20)	200

Facing tool

No. 19 Right hand as drawn

No. 20 Left hand opposite to drawing

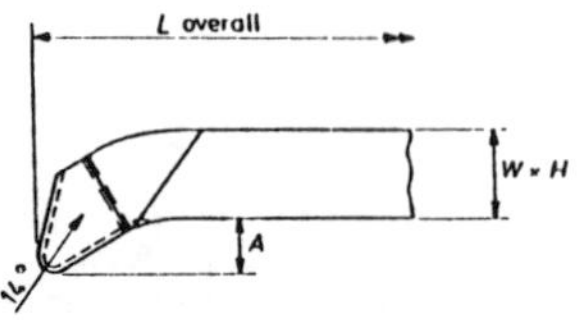

Preferred sizes (mm)		
H	*W*	*L*
12	12	100
16	16	110
20	20	125
25	16	200
32	20	250
40	25	315
(20	16)	140
(25	20)	200

Round nosed planing or shaping tool

No. 17 Cuts either right hand or left hand

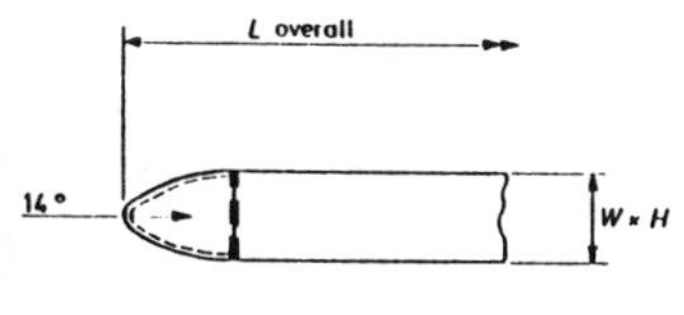

Preferred sizes (mm)

H	*W*	*L*
12	12	100
16	16	110
20	20	125
25	25	200
32	32	315
40	40	315
25	16	200
32	20	250
40	25	315
(20	16)	140
(25	20)	200
(50	40)	400

Right-angle recessing tool

No. 25 Right hand as drawn
No. 26 Left hand opposite to drawing

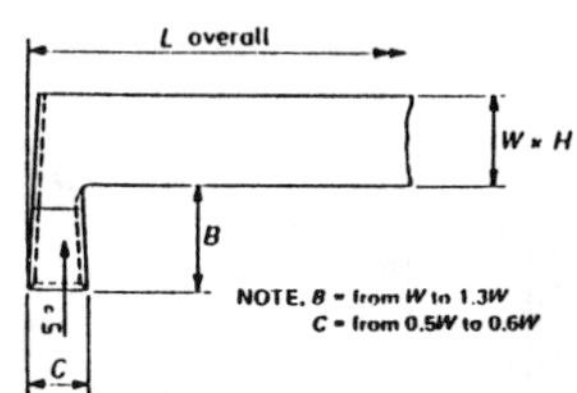

Preferred sizes (mm)

H	*W*	*L*
12	12	100
16	16	110
(20	16)	140
(25	20)	200

Right-angle parting-off tool

No. 27 Right hand as drawn
No. 28 Left hand opposite to drawing

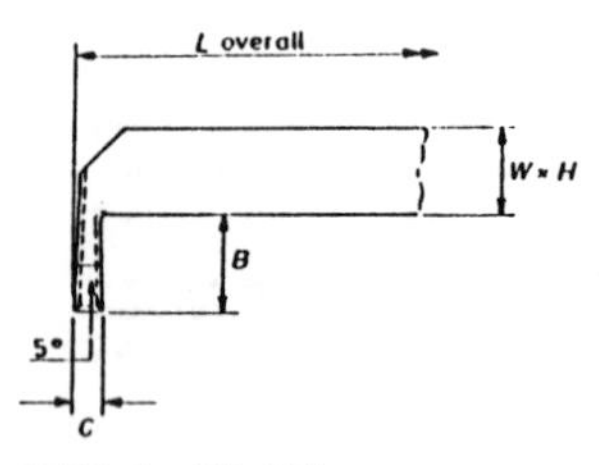

Preferred sizes (mm)

H	*W*	*L*
12	12	100
16	16	110
(20	16)	140
(25	20)	200

Cranked turning or recessing tool

No. 39 Right hand as drawn
No. 40 Left hand opposite to drawing

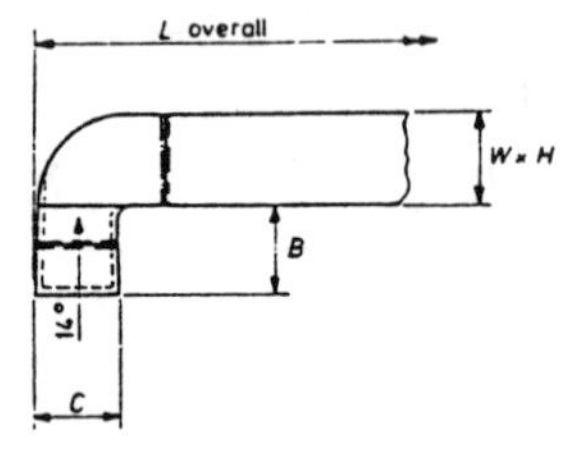

Preferred sizes (mm)

H	*W*	*L*
12	12	100
16	16	110
20	20	125
(20	16)	140
(25	20)	200

Hardened blank

No. 47

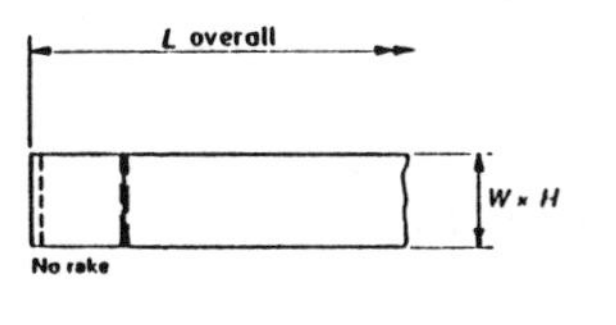

Preferred sizes (mm)

H	*W*	*L*
12	12	100
16	16	110
20	20	125
25	25	200
32	32	315
40	40	315
25	16	200
32	20	250
40	25	315
(20	16)	140
(25	20)	200
(50	40)	400

Hardened blank

No. 62

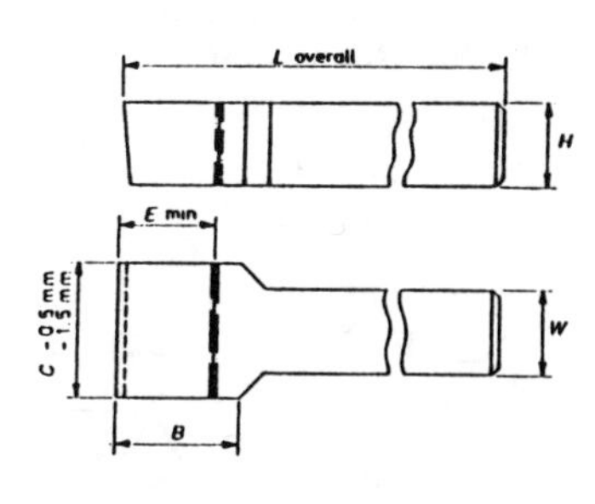

Preferred sizes (mm)

H	*W*	*C*	*B*	*E*	*L*
16	16	20	25	16	140
16	16	25	25	16	140
20	20	25	25	18	140
20	20	32	32	25	200
25	25	40	36	28	200

Boring tool

No. 50 Square nose
No. 50A V-nose for internal screw cutting
No. 50B Round nose

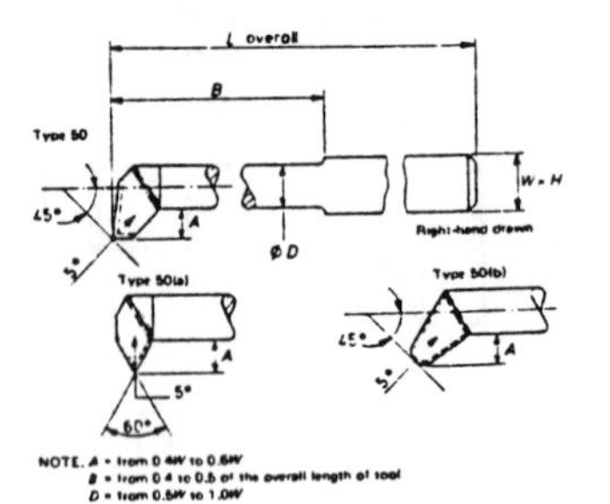

Preferred sizes (mm)		
H	*W*	*L*
12	12	160
16	16	200
(20	16)	200
(25	20)	250

Swan-necked finishing tool

No. 52 Cuts either right hand or left hand

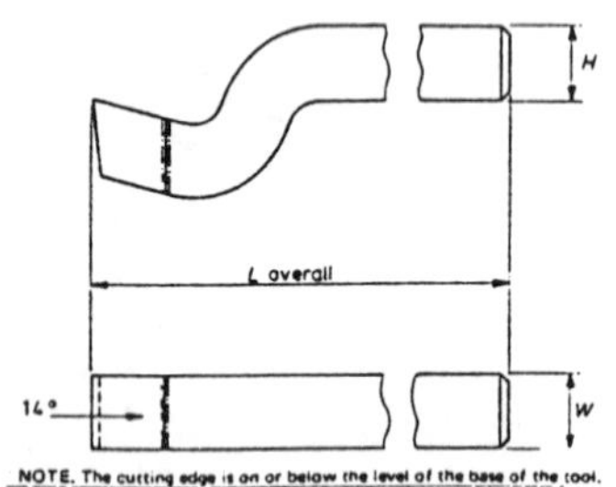

Preferred sizes (mm)		
H	*W*	*L*
40	25	355
(20	16)	200
(25	20)	250

For further details, including non-preferred sizes, nomenclature and shank sections, see BS 1296 : Pts 1 to 4 inclusive.

5.2.2 Tool bits: ground high speed steel

Round section tool bits

Dimensions in millimetres

diameter (*h*12)*	L^{+0}_{-3} 63	80	100	160	180
4	×	×	×	—	—
5	×	×	×	—	—
6	×	×	×	×	—
8	—	×	×	×	—
10	—	×	×	×	×
12	—	—	×	×	×
16	—	—	×	×	×
18	—	—	—	—	×

Square section tool bits

Dimensions in millimetres

breadth (*h*13)*	*height* (*h*13)*	L^{+0}_{-3} 63	80	100	160	180
4	4	×	—	—	—	—
5	5	×	—	—	—	—
6	6	×	×	×	×	×
8	8	×	×	×	×	×
10	10	×	×	×	×	×
12	12	×	×	×	×	×
16	16	—	—	×	×	×
20	20	—	—	—	×	×
25	25	—	—	—	—	×

Rectangular section tool bits

Dimensions in millimetres

breadth (h13)*	*height* (h13)*	L^{+0}_{-3} 100	160	200
4	6	×	—	—
	8	×	—	—
5	8	×	—	—
	10	×	—	—
6	10	—	×	×
	12	—	×	×
8	12	—	×	×
	16	—	×	×
10	16	—	×	×
	20	—	×	×
12	20	—	×	×
	25	—	—	×
16	25	—	—	×
	—	—	—	—

* For tolerance sizes see BS 4500. For further information see BS 1296.

5.3 Milling cutters

5.3.1 Cylindrical cutters

Light duty cylindrical cutter

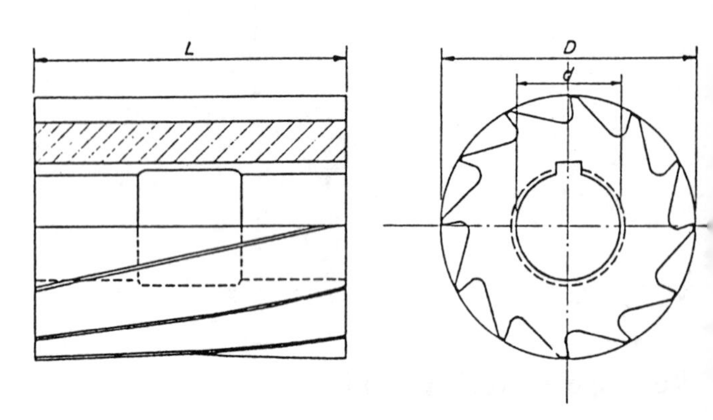

High power cylindrical cutter

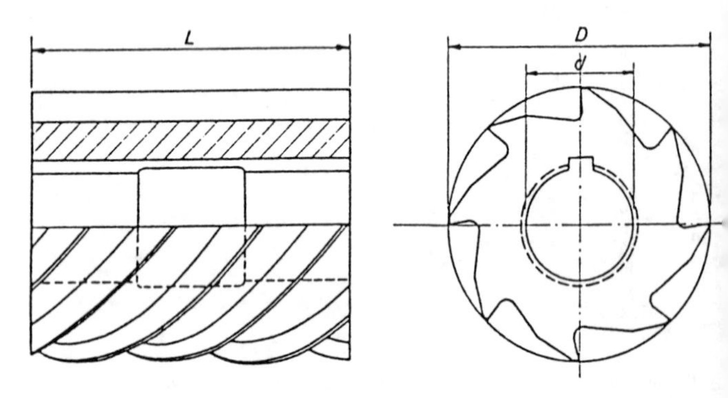

The dimensions of light duty or high power cylindrical cutters shall be as given in the table. These cutters are normally supplied with left hand helix as shown in the figures. The cutters shall have keyways in accordance with BS 122 : Pt 3 Clause 3.2.

For further information, see BS 122 : Pt 3 : 1987.

Dimensions in millimetres

Diameter of cutter D (js16)*	*Diameter of bore* d (H7)*	*Lengths* L (js15)*
50	22	40, 63, 80
63	27	50,70
80	32	63, 80, 100, 125
100	40	70, 100, 125, 160
125	50	125, 200

*For tolerances see BS4500: Pt 1.

5.3.2 High helix cylindrical cutters

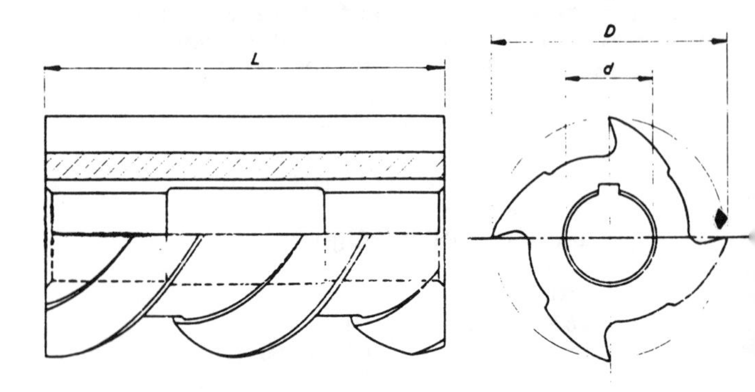

Dimensions in millimetres

Diameter of cutter D (js16)*	*Diameter of bore* d (H7)*	*Lengths* L (js15)*
80	32	70, 100, 160
100	40	70, 100, 160
125	50	70, 100, 160

* For tolerances see BS 4500 : Pt 1.

The dimensions of high helix cylindrical cutters shall be as given in the table. These cutters are normally supplied with left hand helix as shown in the figure. The cutters shall have keyways in accordance with BS 122 : Pt 3 Clause 3.2.

For further information see BS 122 : Pt 3 : 1987.

5.3.3 Side and face cutters

Light duty side and face cutter

High power side and face cutter

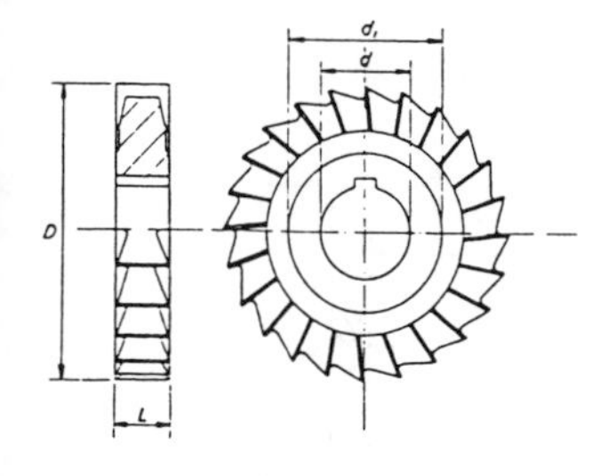

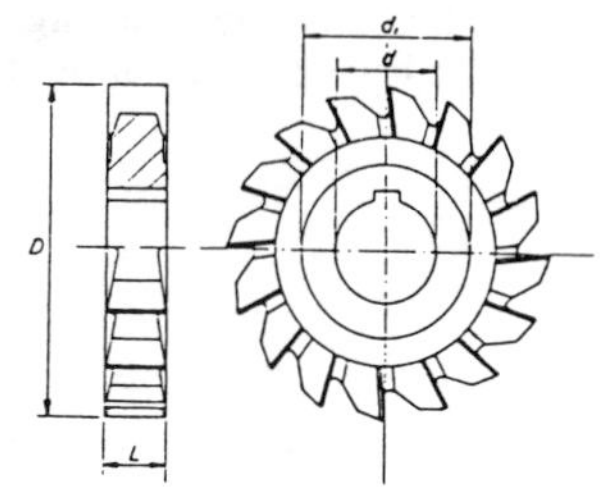

Dimensions in millimetres

Diameter of cutter D (js16)*	*Diameter of boss* d_1 (min.)	*Diameter of bore* d (H7)*	*Width of cutting edges and boss*† L (k11)*
50	27	16	6, 8, 10
63	34	22	6, 8, 10, 12, (14), 16
80	41	27	6, 8, 10, 12, (14), 16, (18), 20
100	47	32	6, 8, 10, 12, (14), 16, (18), 20, (22), 25
125	47	32	8, 10, 12, (14), 16, (18), 20, (22), 25, (28)
160	55	40	10, 12, (14), 16, (18), 20, (22), 25, (28), 32
200	55	40	12, (14), 16, (18), 20, (22), 25, (28), 32, (36), 40

* For tolerances see BS 4500 : Pt 1.

† Dimensions in parentheses are least preferred.

The dimensions of light duty or high power side and face cutters shall be as given in the table. The cutters shall have keyways in accordance with BS 122 : Pt 3 Clause 3.2. Each side of a cutter may be ground to provide $\frac{1}{4}°$ side clearance, when the clearance shall be amplified by recessing.

For further information see BS 122 : Pt 3 : 1987.

5.3.4 Staggered tooth side and face cutters

The dimensions of staggered tooth side and face cutters shall be as given in the table. The cutters shall have keyways in accordance with BS 122 : Pt 3 : Clause 3.2. Each side of a cutter may be ground to provide $\frac{1}{4}°$ side clearance, when the clearance shall be amplified by recessing.

For further information see BS 122 : Pt 3 : 1987.

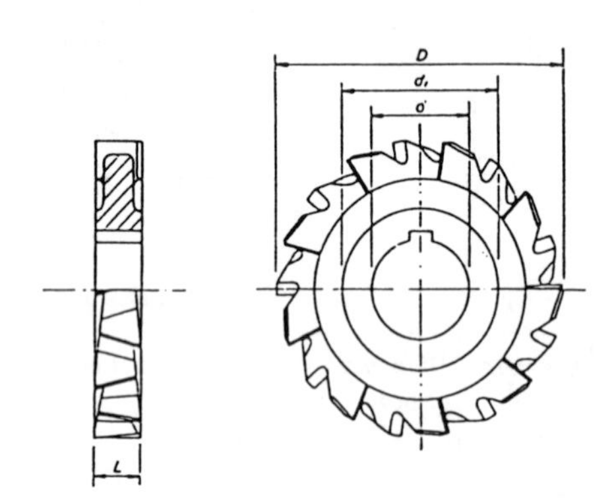

Dimensions in millimetres

Diameter of cutter D (js16)*	*Diameter of boss* d_1 (min.)	*Diameter of bore* d (H7)*	*Width*† L (k11)*
63	34	22	6, 8, 10, 12, (14), 16
80	41	27	6, 8, 10, 12, (14), 16, (18), 20
100	47	32	6, 8, 10, 12, (14), 16, (18), 20, (22), 25
125	47	32	8, 10, 12, (14), 16, (18), 20, (22), 25, (28)
160	55	40	10, 12, (14), 16, (18), 20, (22), 25, (28), 32
200	55	40	12, (14), 16, (18), 20, (22), 25, (28), 32, (36), 40

* For tolerances see BS 4500 : Pt 1.

† Dimensions in parentheses are least preferred.

5.3.5 Slotting cutters

The dimensions of slotting cutters shall be as given in the table. The cutters shall have each side ground to provide side clearance and the clearance shall, where the width and diameter of the cutter permit, be amplified by recessing. The cutters shall have keyways in accordance with BS 122 : Pt 3 Clause 3.2. The use of these cutters for cutting keyways is not recommended as the width of the slot produced cannot be guaranteed. If, however, the cutters are required for cutting keyways to BS 46 : Pt 1, the special tolerances should be agreed between the purchaser and the manufacturer.

For further information see BS 122 : Pt 3 : 1987.

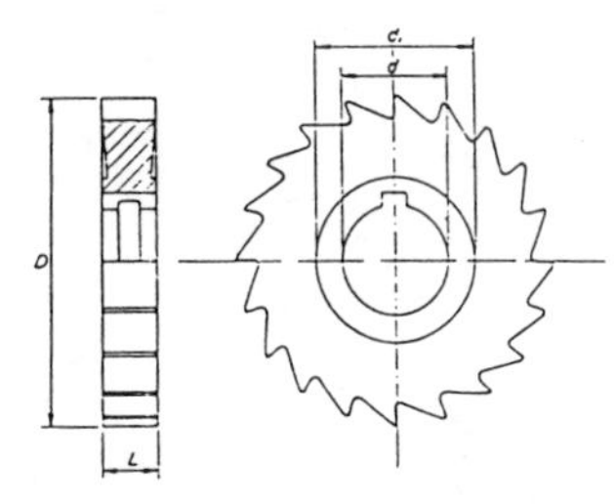

Dimensions in millimetres

Diameter of cutter D (js16)*	*Diameter of boss* d_1 (min.)	*Diameter of bore* d (H7)*	*Width†* L (js4)*
50	27	16	6, 7, 8, 10
63	34	22	6, 7, 8, 10, 12, 14
80	41	27	6, 7, 8, 10, 12, 14, 16, 18
100	47	32	6, 7, 8, 10, 12, 14, 16, 18, 20, (22), 25
125	47	32	8, 10, 12, 14, 16, 18, 20, (22), 25
160	55	40	10, 12, 14, 16, 18, 20, (22), 25, (28), 32
200	55	40	12, 14, 16, 18, 20, (22), 25, (28), 32, (36), 40

* For tolerances see BS 4500 : Pt 1.

† Dimensions in parentheses are least preferred.

5.3.6 Metal slitting saws without side chip clearance: fine teeth

The dimensions of metal slitting saws without side chip clearance shall be as given in the tables in this section for fine teeth and in 5.3.7 for coarse teeth. The value for the tooth pitch in relation to the number of teeth of a saw of a given diameter is expressed as an approximate rounded figure. The saws shall have side clearance either up to the bore or up to the boss.

For further information see BS 122 : Pt 3 : 1987.

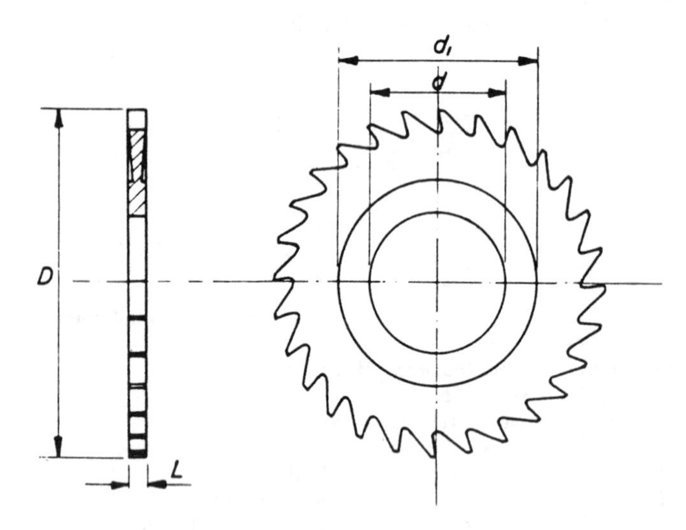

Dimensions in millimetres

Diameter of saw D (js16)*		20	25	32	40	50	63	80	100	125	160	200	250	315
Diameter of boss d_1 (min.)		—	—	—	—	—	—	34	34	34	47	63	63	80
Diameter of bore d (H7)*		5	8	8	10	13	16	22	22	22	32	32	32	40
Width L (js11)*	*Tooth pitch*	*Number of teeth*												
0.2	0.8	80			128									
0.25				100		128								
0.3	1.0	64	80		100									
0.4				80			128							
0.5			64			100								
0.6	1.25	48			80			128	160					
0.8				64			100			160				
1.0			48			80			128					
1.2	1.6	40			64			100			160			
1.6				48			80			128				
2.0		32		40			64			100			160	200
2.5	2.0				48			80			128			200
3.0				40			64			100			160	
4.0					40	48			80			128		
5.0	2.5							64			100		128	160
6.0							48		64	80		100		
				3.15			4.0		5.0			6.3		

* For tolerances see BS 4500 : Pt 1.

5.3.7 Metal slitting saws without side chip clearance: coarse teeth

The value for the tooth pitch in relation to the number of teeth of a saw of a given diameter is expressed as an approximate rounded figure. The saws shall have side clearance either up to the bore or up to the boss.

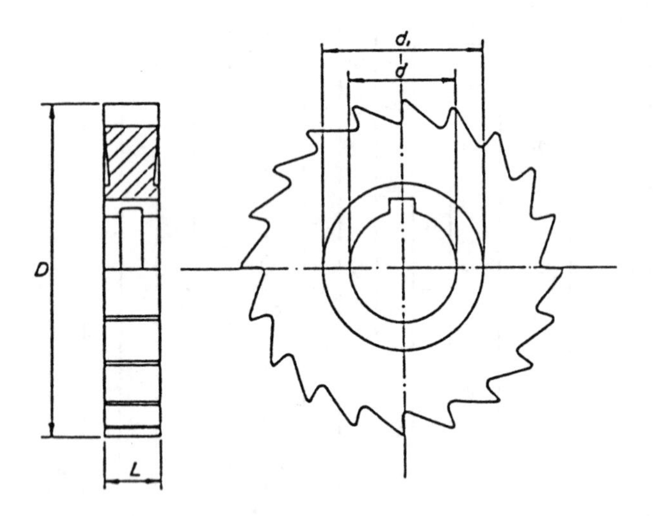

Dimensions in millimetres

Diameter of saw D (js16)*		32	40	50	63	80	100	125	160	200	250	315
Diameter of boss d_1 (min.)		—	—	—	—	34	34	34	47	63	63	80
Diameter of bore d (H7)		8	10	13	16	22	22	22	32	32	32	40
Width L (js11)*	*Tooth pitch*	*Number of teeth*										
0.3			48	64								
0.4	2.5	40			64							
0.5				48								
0.6			40			64						
0.8	3.15	32			48							
1.0				40			64	80				
1.2			32			48			80			
1.6	4.0	24			40			64				
2.0				32			48			80	100	
2.5			24			40			64			100
3.0	5.0	20			32			48			80	
4.0			20	24			40			64		
5.0					24	32		40	48			80
6.0							32			48	64	
	6.3			8.0			10.0			12.5		

* For tolerances see BS 4500 : Pt 1.

5.3.8 Metal slitting saws with side chip clearance

Type A: staggered teeth

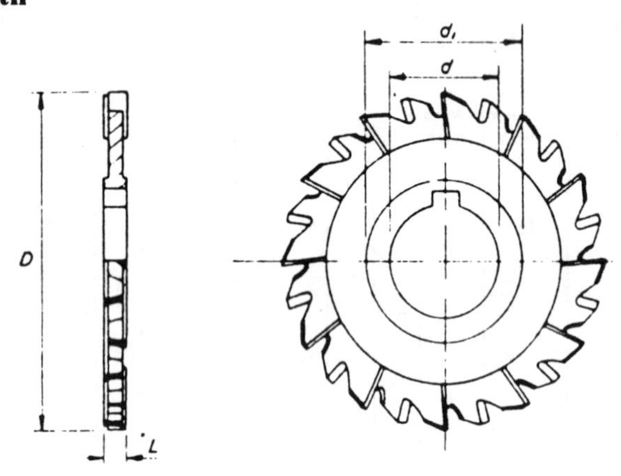

Type B: straight teeth

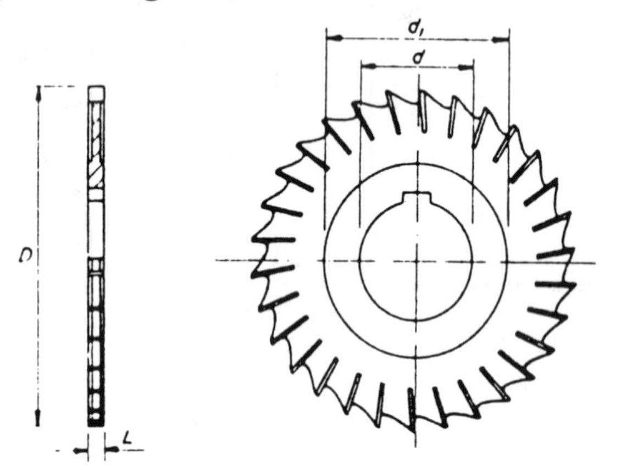

Dimensions in millimetres

Diameter of saw D (js16)*	63	80	100	125	160	200	250
Diameter of boss d_1 (min.)	—	34	34	34	47	63	63
Diameter of bore d (H7)*	16	22	22	22	32	32	32

Type A: staggered teeth

Width L (js10)*	*Number of teeth (and pitch)*						
4.0, 5.0, 6.0	28 (7.1)	32 (7.8)	36 (8.7)	40 (9.8)	44 (11.4)	52 (12.0)	64 (12.3)

Type B: straight teeth

Width L (js10)*	*Number of teeth (and pitch)*						
1.6, 2.0, 2.5, 3.0	32 (6.2)	36 (7.0)	40 (7.8)	44 (8.9)	48 (10.5)	56 (11.2)	68 (11.5)

* For tolerances see BS 4500 : Pt 1.
For further information see BS 122 : Pt 3 : 1987.

5.3.9 Convex milling cutters

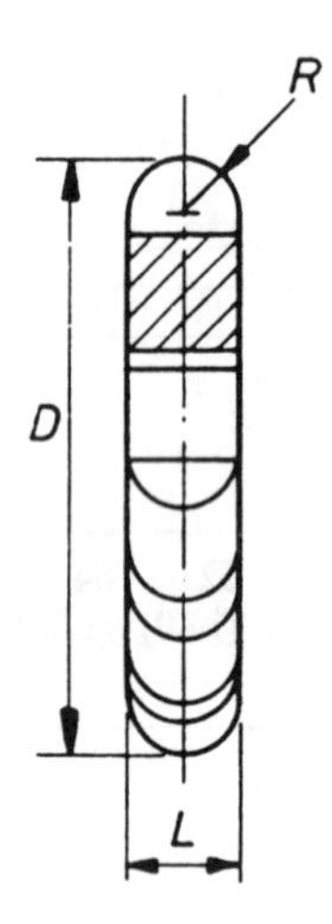

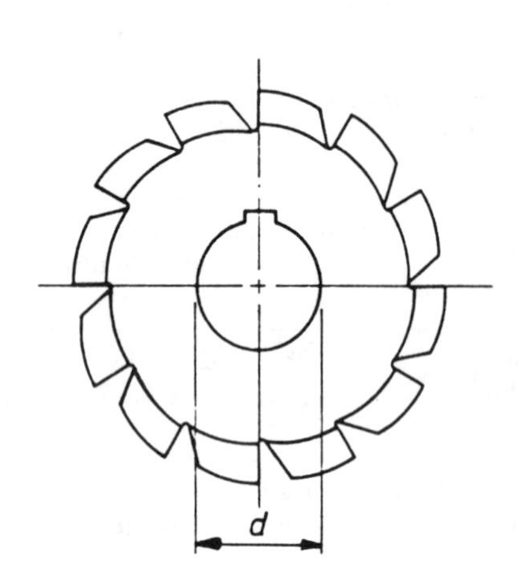

5.3.10 Concave milling cutters

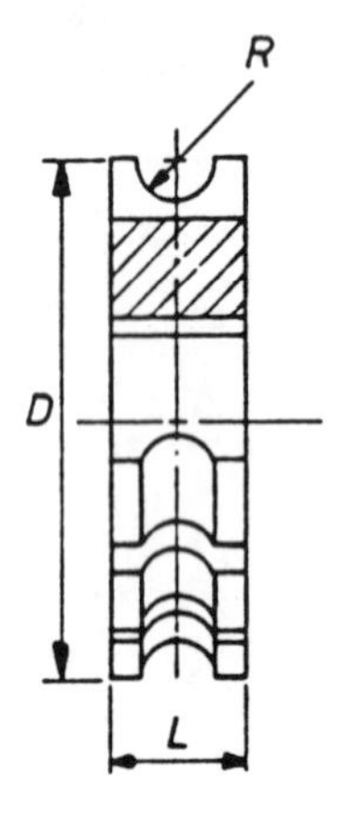

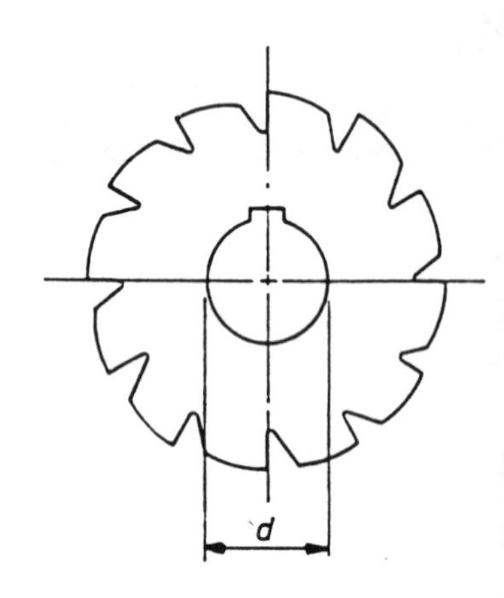

The dimensions of convex milling cutters shall be as given in the table. The cutters shall have keyways in accordance with BS 122 : Pt 3 Clause 3.2.

For further information see BS 122 : Pt 3 : 1987.

Dimensions in millimetres

R (k11)*	D (js16)*	d (H7)*	L
1	50	16	2
1.25			2.5
1.6			3.2
2			4
2.5	63	22	5
3.15 or 3			6.3 or 6
4			8
5			10
6.3 or 6	80	27	12.6 or 12
8			16
10	100	32	20
12.5 or 12			25 or 24
16	125		32
20			40

* For tolerances see BS 4500 : Pt 1.

The dimensions of concave milling cutters shall be as given in the table. For these cutters, radius *R* is struck from the outside diameter of the cutter and chamfers have been eliminated from the intersection of the profile and the outside diameter. The cutters shall have keyways in accordance with BS 122 : Pt 3 Clause 3.2.

For further information see BS 122 : Pt 3 : 1987.

Dimensions in millimetres

R (N11)*	D (js16)*	d (h7)*	L
1	50	16	6
1.25			
1.6			8
2			9
2.5	63	22	10
3.15 or 3			12
4			16
5			20
6.3 or 6	80	27	24
8			32
10	100	32	36
12.6 or 12			40
16	125		50
20			60

* For tolerances see BS 4500 : Pt 1.

5.3.11 Corner rounding concave milling cutters

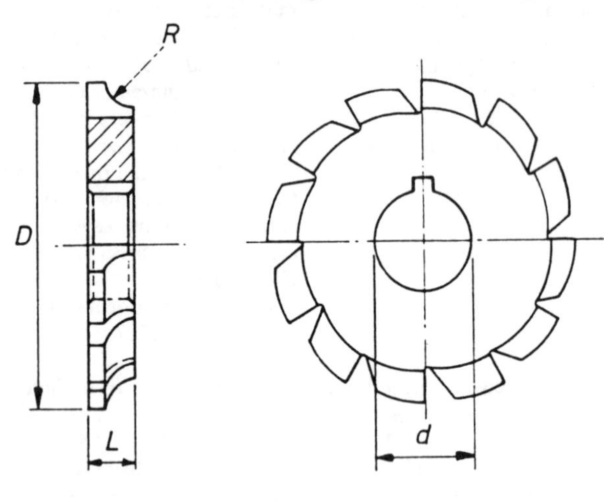

The dimensions of corner rounding concave milling cutters shall be as given in the table. For these cutters, radius R is struck from the outside diameter of the cutter and chamfers have been eliminated from the intersection of the profile and the outside diameter. The cutters shall have keyways in accordance with BS 122 : Pt 3 Clause 3.2.

For further information see BS 122 : Pt 3 : 1987.

Dimensions in millimetres

R (N11)*	*D* (js16)*	*d* (H7)*	*L*
1	50	16	4
1.25			
1.6			5
2			
2.5	63	22	
3.15 or 3			6
4			8
5			10
6.3 or 6	80	27	12
8			16
10	100	32	18
12.5 or 12			20
16	125		24
20			28

* For tolerances see BS 4500 : Pt 1.

5.3.12 Double equal angle milling cutters

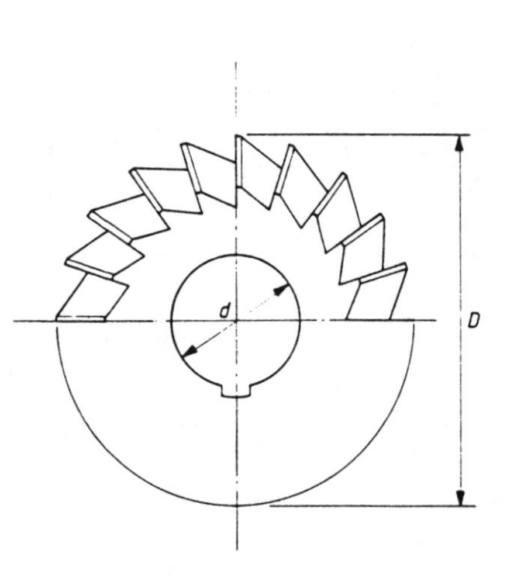

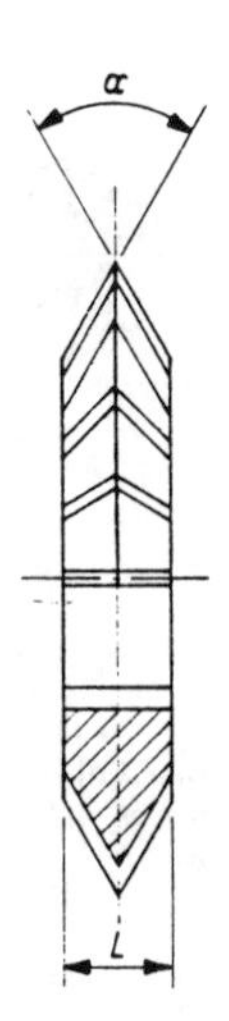

D (js16)* mm	d (H7)* mm	α (±15′)* degrees	L (js16)* mm
50	16	45	8
		60	10
		90	14
63	22	45	10
		60	14
		90	20
80	27	45	12
		60	18
		90	22
100	32	45	18
		60	25
		90	32

* For tolerances see BS 4500 : Pt 1.

The dimensions of double equal angle milling cutters shall be as given in the table. The cutters shall have keyways in accordance with BS 122 : Pt 3 Clause 3.2.

For further information see BS 122 : Pt 3 : 1987.

5.3.13 T-slot cutters with Morse taper shanks

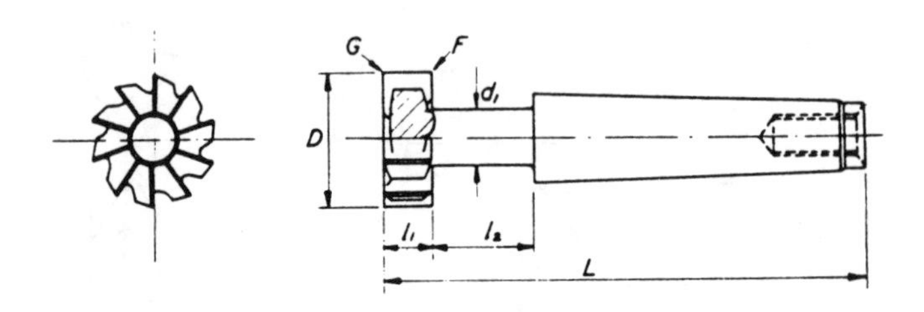

Dimensions in millimetres

T-slot	*T-slot cutter*							
*Nominal size of slot**	*Diameter of cutter* D (h12)†	*Width of cutter* l_1 (h12)†	*Diameter of neck* d_1 (max.)	*Length of neck* l_2	*No. of Morse taper shank, tapped*	*Overall length* L	*Radius* G (max.)	*Radius* F (max.)
10	18	8	8	17^{+1}_{-0}	1	82	1.0	0.6
12	21	9	10	20^{+1}_{-0}	2	98	1.0	0.6
14	25	11	12	23^{+1}_{-0}	2	103	1.6	0.6
18	32	14	15	28^{+1}_{-0}	2	111	1.6	1.0
22	40	18	19	34^{+1}_{-0}	3	138	2.5	1.0
28	50	22	25	42^{+1}_{-0}	4	173	2.5	1.0
36	60	28	30	51^{+1}_{-0}	4	188	2.5	1.0
42	72	35	36	58^{+1}_{-0}	5	229	4.0	1.6
48	85	40	42	64^{+1}_{-0}	5	240	6.0	2.0
54	95	44	44	71^{+1}_{-0}	5	251	6.0	2.0

* See BS 2485.
† For tolerances see BS 4500 : Pt 1.

The dimensions of T-slot cutters with Morse taper shanks shall be as given in the table. However, the cutters may be made with square corners throughout, as an alternative to the radiused corners *G* and *F* shown. It is recommended that the corners be radiused when considerations of strength preclude the use of slots with square corners. The cutter teeth shall be either straight (as shown) or staggered. The cutters shall be designated by the nominal size of the slot.

For further information see BS 122 : Pt 3 : 1987.

5.3.14 Shell end mills

The dimensions of shell end milling cutters shall be as given in the table. However, the boss d_5 and the side clearance S are optional. The milling cutters shall not be reversible on their arbors and the direction of rotation shall be specified by describing them as either right hand or left hand cutters. Milling cutters for right hand rotation with right hand helical cutting edges are normally supplied.

For further information see BS 122 : Pt 3 : 1987.

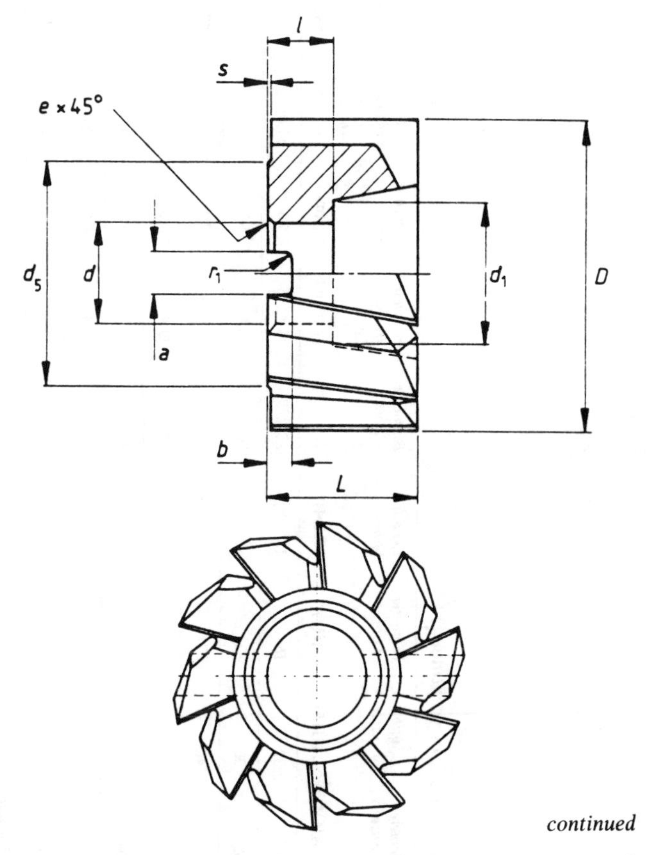

continued

Section 5.3.14 (*continued*)

Dimensions in millimetres

Diameter of cutter	*Length of cutter*	*Diameter of bore*	*Length of bore*	*Diameter of boss*	*Width of driving slot*	*Depth of driving slot*	*Maximum radius of driving slot*	*Diameter of boss*	*Chamfer on bore*	*Shoulder*
D (js16)*	L (H15)*	d (H7)*	l (H14)*	d_1	a_1 (min.)	b_1 (min.)	r_1	d_5	e	S
40	32	16	18	22	8.4	5.6	1.0	33	$0.6^{+0.2}_{-0}$	0.5
50	36	22	20	30	10.4	6.3	1.2	41	$0.6^{+0.2}_{-0}$	0.5
63	40	27	22	38	12.4	7.0	1.2	49	$0.8^{+0.2}_{-0}$	0.5
80	45	27	22	38	12.4	7.0	1.2	49	$0.8^{+0.2}_{-0}$	0.5
100	50	32	25	45	14.4	8.0	1.6	59	$0.8^{+0.2}_{-0}$	0.5
125	56	40	28	56	16.4	9.0	2.0	71	$1.0^{+0.3}_{-0}$	0.5
160	63	50	31	67	18.4	10.0	2.0	91	$1.0^{+0.3}_{-0}$	0.5

* For tolerances see BS 4500 : Pt 1.

5.3.15 Arbors for shell end mills

The dimensions of spigots, tenons and retaining bolts for shell end mills shall be as given in the tables.

For further information see BS 122 : Pt 3 : 1987.

Spigot

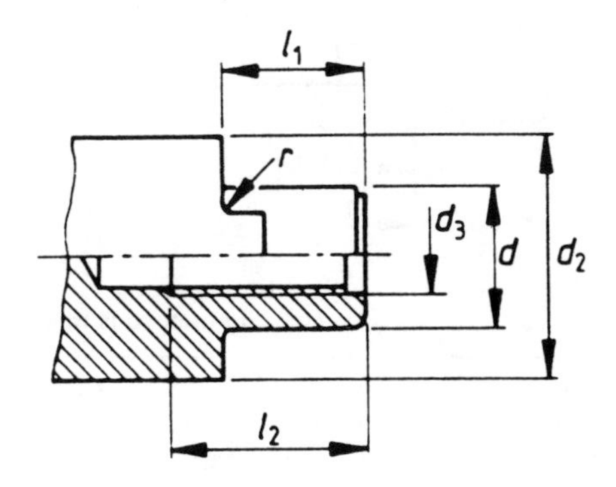

Dimensions in millimetres

d (h6)*	l_1 (max.)	d_2	d_3	l_2 (min.)	r (max.)
16	17^{+0}_{-1}	32	M8	22	0.6
22	19^{+2}_{-1}	40	M10	28	0.6
27	21^{+0}_{-1}	48	M12	32	0.8
32	24^{+0}_{-1}	58	M16	36	0.8
40	27^{+0}_{-1}	70	M20	45	1.0
50	30^{+0}_{-1}	90	M24	50	1.0

* For tolerances see BS 4500 : Pt 1.

continued

Tenon

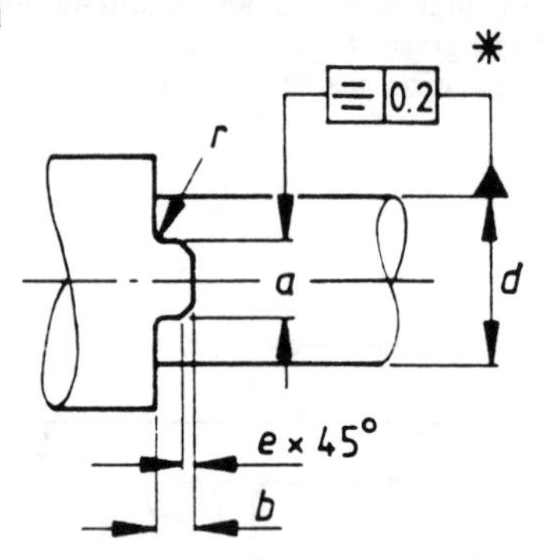

Dimensions in millimetres

	Arbor			*Chamfer*
d	*a*	*b*	*r* (max.)	*e*
16	8	5.0	0.6	$0.6^{+0.2}_{-0}$
22	10	5.6		
27	12	6.3	0.8	$0.8^{+0.2}_{-0}$
32	14	7.0		
40	16	8.0	1.0	$1.0^{+0.3}_{-0}$
50	18	9.0		

* See BS 308 : Pt 3.

Retaining bolt

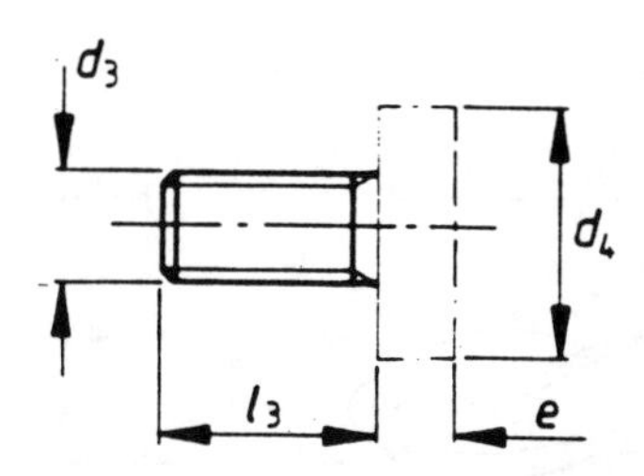

Dimensions in millimetres

Spigot diameter (nominal)	d_3	l_3	d_4 (max.)*	e
16	M8	16^{+3}_{-0}	20	6
22	M10	18^{+3}_{-0}	28	7
27	M12	22^{+3}_{-0}	35	8
32	M16	26^{+3}_{-0}	42	9
40	M20	30^{+3}_{-0}	52	10
50	M24	36^{+3}_{-0}	63	10

* The shape of the head of the bolt is not specified.

5.3.16 Screwed shank end mills: normal series

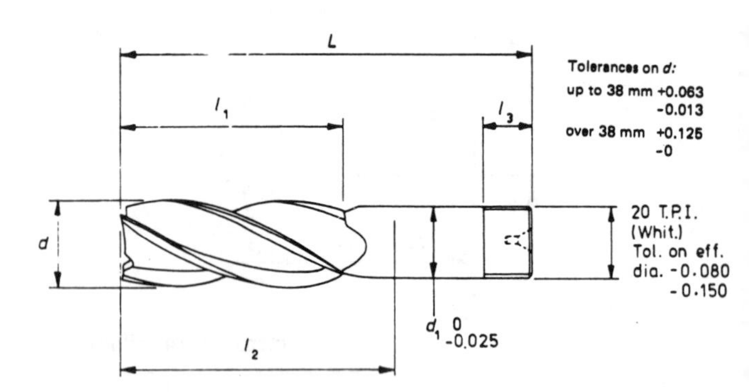

Dimensions in millimetres

<table>
<tr><th>Cutter diameter
d</th><th>Cut length
l_1</th><th>Shank diameter
d_1</th><th>Nominal length below chuck
l_2</th><th>Overall length
L</th><th>Thread length
l_3</th></tr>
<tr><td>2.5</td><td>6.5</td><td>6</td><td>13.5</td><td>51</td><td rowspan="13">9.5</td></tr>
<tr><td>3</td><td>9.5</td><td>6</td><td>16.5</td><td>54</td></tr>
<tr><td>3.5</td><td rowspan="3">12.5</td><td rowspan="3">6</td><td rowspan="3">19.5</td><td rowspan="3">57</td></tr>
<tr><td>4</td></tr>
<tr><td>4.5</td></tr>
<tr><td>5</td><td rowspan="3">16</td><td rowspan="3">6</td><td rowspan="3">23</td><td rowspan="3">60.5</td></tr>
<tr><td>5.5</td></tr>
<tr><td>6</td></tr>
<tr><td>6.5</td><td>16</td><td rowspan="2">10</td><td rowspan="2">22.5</td><td rowspan="2">60.5</td></tr>
<tr><td>7</td><td>15</td></tr>
<tr><td>7.5</td><td rowspan="2">18</td><td rowspan="2">10</td><td rowspan="2">25.5</td><td rowspan="2">63.5</td></tr>
<tr><td>8</td></tr>
</table>

<table>
<tr><th>Cutter diameter
d</th><th>Cut length
l_1</th><th>Shank diameter
d_1</th><th>Nominal length below chuck
l_2</th><th>Overall length
L</th><th>Thread length
l_3</th></tr>
<tr><td>8.5</td><td rowspan="4">21</td><td rowspan="4">10</td><td rowspan="4">28.5</td><td rowspan="4">66.5</td><td rowspan="16">9.5</td></tr>
<tr><td>9</td></tr>
<tr><td>9.5</td></tr>
<tr><td>10</td></tr>
<tr><td>10.5</td><td rowspan="2">19</td><td rowspan="2">12</td><td rowspan="2">28.5</td><td rowspan="2">66.5</td></tr>
<tr><td>11</td></tr>
<tr><td>11.5</td><td>22.5</td><td rowspan="3">12</td><td rowspan="3">32</td><td rowspan="3">70</td></tr>
<tr><td>12</td><td>24</td></tr>
<tr><td>13</td><td>24.5</td></tr>
<tr><td>14</td><td>28.5</td><td>12</td><td>35</td><td>73</td></tr>
<tr><td>15</td><td rowspan="2">26.5</td><td rowspan="2">16</td><td rowspan="2">38</td><td rowspan="2">77</td></tr>
<tr><td>16</td></tr>
<tr><td>17</td><td>32</td><td rowspan="2">16</td><td rowspan="2">41</td><td rowspan="2">80</td></tr>
<tr><td>18</td><td>35</td></tr>
<tr><td>19</td><td rowspan="2">38</td><td rowspan="2">16</td><td rowspan="2">44.5</td><td rowspan="2">83.5</td></tr>
<tr><td>20</td></tr>
<tr><td>21</td><td>38</td><td>25</td><td>42.5</td><td>95</td><td rowspan="8">15</td></tr>
<tr><td>22</td><td rowspan="3">41.5</td><td rowspan="3">25</td><td rowspan="3">46</td><td rowspan="3">98.5</td></tr>
<tr><td>23</td></tr>
<tr><td>24</td></tr>
<tr><td>25</td><td>44.5</td><td rowspan="2">25</td><td rowspan="2">49</td><td rowspan="2">101.5</td></tr>
<tr><td>26</td><td>43</td></tr>
<tr><td>28</td><td rowspan="2">46</td><td rowspan="2">25</td><td rowspan="2">52</td><td rowspan="2">104.5</td></tr>
<tr><td>30</td></tr>
</table>

Section 5.3.16 (*continued*)

Cutter diameter d	*Cut length* l_1	*Shank diameter* d_1	*Nominal length below chuck* l_2	*Overall length* L	*Thread length* l_3
32	49	25	55.5	108	15
34					
35	52.5	25	58.5	111	
36					
38	55.5	25	62	114.5	
40	58.5	25	65	117.5	
42	60.5				
44	63.5	25	68	120.5	
45					
32	51	32	58.5	112.5	
33					
34					
35	54	32	62	116	
36					
38					
40	55.5	32	63.5	117.5	
42	54	32	62	116	
44	57	32	65	119	
45					
50	65	32	73	127	

For further information see BS 122 : Pt 4 : 1980.

5.3.17 Screwed shank slot drills: normal series

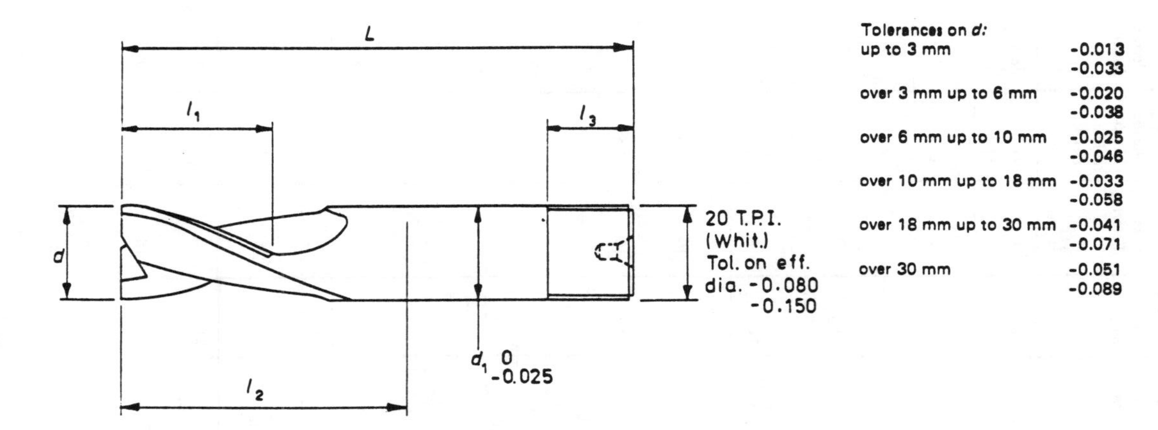

Tolerances on *d*:	
up to 3 mm	-0.013 -0.033
over 3 mm up to 6 mm	-0.020 -0.038
over 6 mm up to 10 mm	-0.025 -0.046
over 10 mm up to 18 mm	-0.033 -0.058
over 18 mm up to 30 mm	-0.041 -0.071
over 30 mm	-0.051 -0.089

continued

Section 5.3.17 (*continued*)

Cutter diameter d	*Cut length* l_1	*Shank diameter* d_1	*Nominal length below chuck* l_2	*Overall length* L	*Thread length* l_3
1.5	2.5	6	11	48.5	9.5
2	3	6	11.5	49	
2.5	4.5	6	13.5	51	
3	7				
3.5	7.5	6	15	52.5	
4	9.5				
4.5					
5					
5.5	11	6	18	55.5	
6			19	56.5	
6.5	11	10	20.5	58.5	
7					
7.5					
8	12.5	10	21.5	59.5	
8.5	14.5	10	22.5	60.5	
9					
9.5					
10					
10.5	17.5	12	27	65	
11					
11.5					
12	19	12	28.5	66.5	
13					
14	22	12	30.5	68.5	
15	22	16	33	72	
16					
17	24	16	35	74	
18					
19	25.5	16	38	77	
20					

Dimensions in millimetres

Cutter diameter d	*Cut length* l_1	*Shank diameter* d^1	*Nominal length below chuck* l_2	*Overall length* L	*Thread length* l_3
21	25.5	25	46.0	98.5	
22	25.5	25	47.5	100	
23	25.5	25	49	101.5	
24	25.5	25	50.5	103	
25	27	25	42.5	95	
26					
27	28.5	25	41	93.5	
28	30	25	42.5	95	
29	30	25	41	93.5	
30					
32	38	25	49	101.5	
34					
35	39.5	25	50.5	103	
36					
38	43	25	54	106.5	15
40	46	25	58.5	111	
42	47.5	25	60	112.5	
44	51	25	63.5	116	
45					
32	35	32	63.5	117.5	
34	35	32	65	119	
35	39.532	57	111		
36					
38	43	32	60.5	114.5	
40	46	32	63.5	117.5	
42	47.5				
44	47.5	32	65	119	
45					
50	51	32	63.5	117.5	

For further information see BS 122 : Pt 4 : 1980.

5.3.18 Screwed shank slot drills, ball nosed: normal series

Tolerances on *d*:	
up to 3 mm	-0.013 -0.033
over 3 mm up to 6 mm	-0.020 -0.038
over 6 mm up to 10 mm	-0.025 -0.046
over 10 mm up to 18 mm	-0.033 -0.058
over 18 mm up to 30 mm	-0.041 -0.071
over 30 mm	-0.051 -0.089

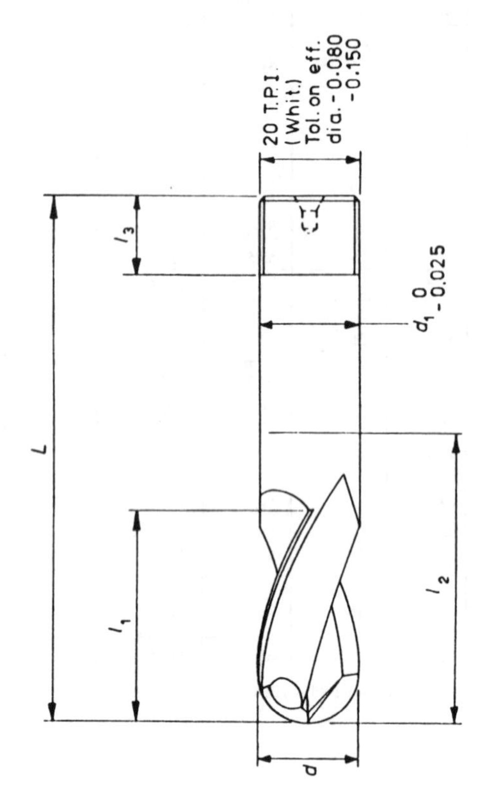

Dimensions in millimetres

Cutter diameter d	*Cut length* l_1	*Shank diameter* d_1	*Nominal length below chuck* l_2	*Overall length* L	*Thread length* l_3
2	3	6	11.5	49	9.5
2.5	4.5	6	13.5	51	
3	7				
4	9.5	6	15	52.5	
5					
6	11	6	19	56.5	
7	11	10	20.5	58.5	
8	12.5	10	21.5	59.5	
9	14.5	10	20.5	58.5	
10	14.5	10	22.5	60.5	
11	17.5	12	27	65	
12	19	12	28.5	66.5	
13					
14	22	12	30.5	68.5	
15	22	16	33	72	
16					
17	24	16	34	73	
18	24	16	35	74	
19	25.5	16	38	77	
20					
22	25.5	25	47.5	100	15
24	25.5	25	50.5	103	

continued

Section 5.3.18 (*continued*)

Dimensions in millimetres

Cutter diameter d	*Cut length* l_1	*Shank diameter* d_1	*Nominal length below chuck* l_2	*Overall length* L	*Thread length* l_3
25	28.5	25	44.5	97	15
26					
28	30	25	42.5	95	
30	30	25	41	93.5	
32	36.5	25	47.5	100	

For further information see BS 122 : Pt 4 : 1980.

5.4 Bonded abrasives

5.4.1 Example of the complete marking of an abrasive wheel

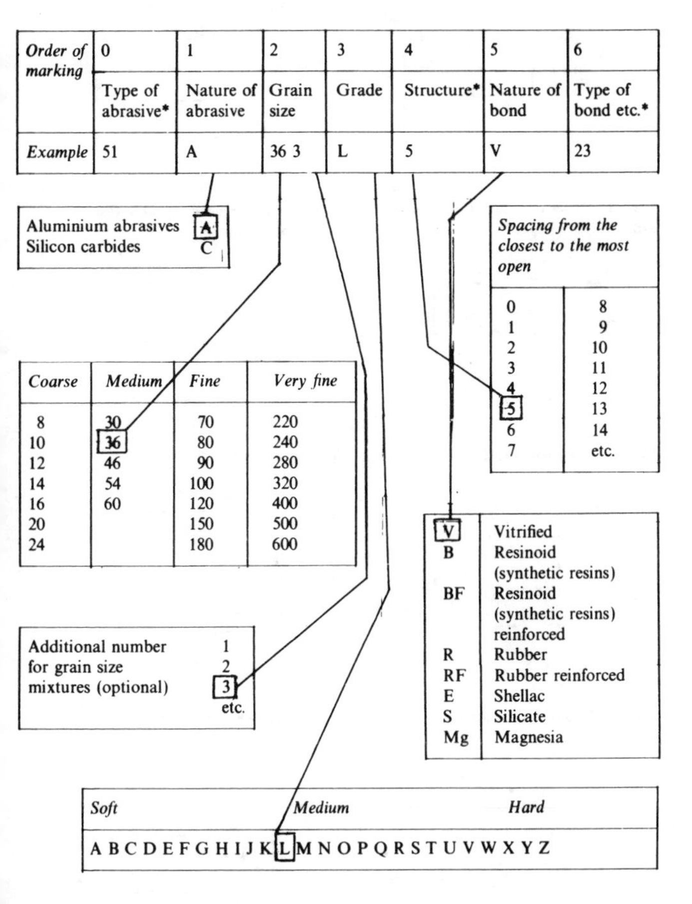

Order of marking	0	1	2	3	4	5	6
	Type of abrasive*	Nature of abrasive	Grain size	Grade	Structure*	Nature of bond	Type of bond etc.*
Example	51	A	36 3	L	5	V	23

Nature of abrasive	
Aluminium abrasives	A
Silicon carbides	C

Coarse	*Medium*	*Fine*	*Very fine*
8	30	70	220
10	36	80	240
12	46	90	280
14	54	100	320
16	60	120	400
20		150	500
24		180	600

Additional number for grain size mixtures (optional)
1
2
3
etc.

Spacing from the closest to the most open	
0	8
1	9
2	10
3	11
4	12
5	13
6	14
7	etc.

Symbol	Nature of bond
V	Vitrified
B	Resinoid (synthetic resins)
BF	Resinoid (synthetic resins) reinforced
R	Rubber
RF	Rubber reinforced
E	Shellac
S	Silicate
Mg	Magnesia

Soft	*Medium*	*Hard*
A B C D E F G H I J K	L M N O P Q R	S T U V W X Y Z

*Symbols at positions 0 and 6 are the manufacturer's own choice.

5.4.2 Classification of wheel and product shapes by type numbers

For further information see BS 4481 : Pt 1 : 1981.

Type 1 Straight wheels

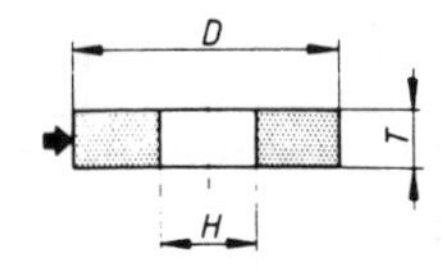

Type 2 Cylinder wheels

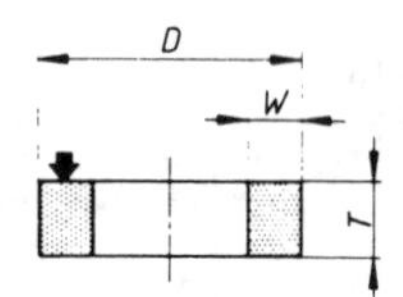

Type 3 Taper one side (for use only with straight flanges)

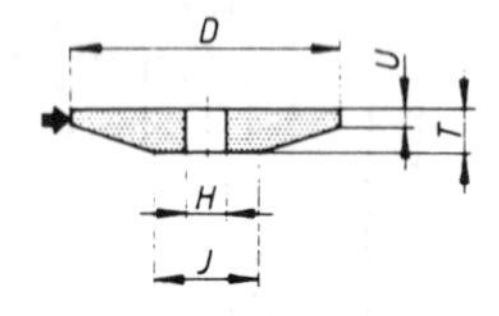

Type 4 Taper sided portable (for use with tapered flanges)

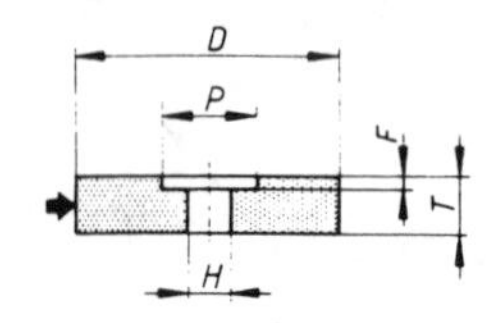

Type 5 Recessed one side

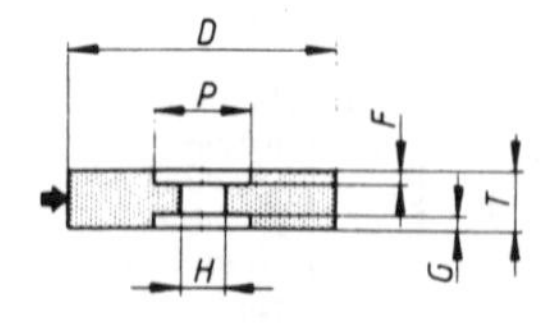

Type 6 Straight cup wheel

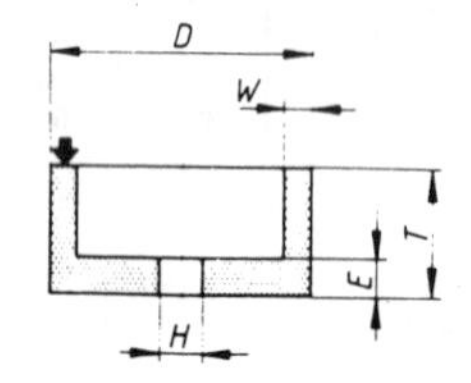

Type 7 Double recessed wheel

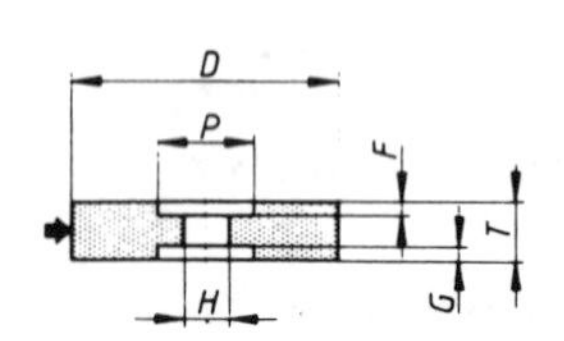

Type 9 Double cup wheels

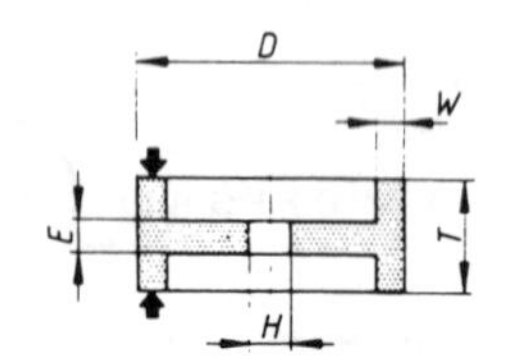

Type 11 Taper cup wheels

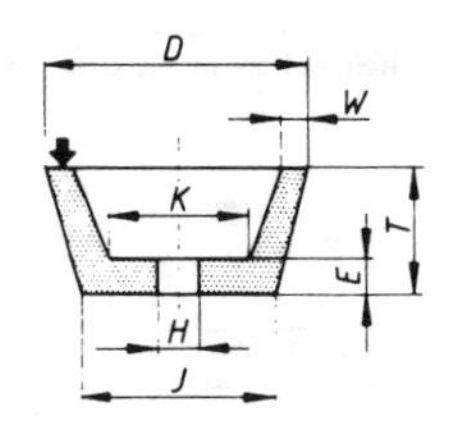

Type 12 Dish wheels

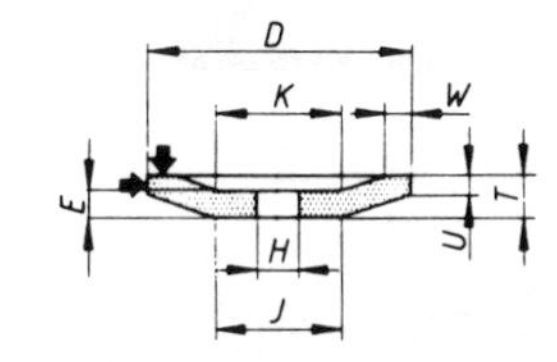

Type 13 Saucer wheels

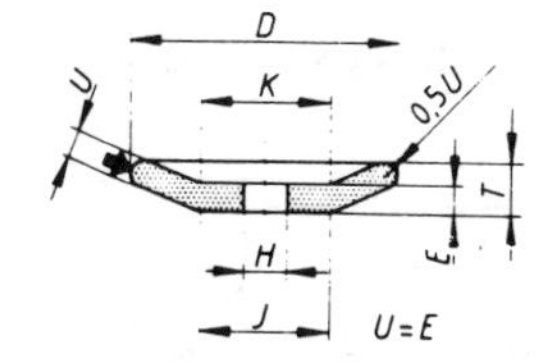

Type 16 Cone

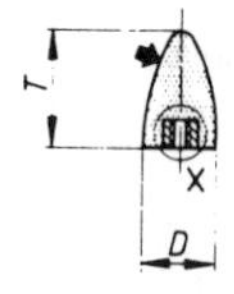

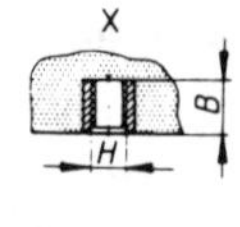

Type 17 Cone

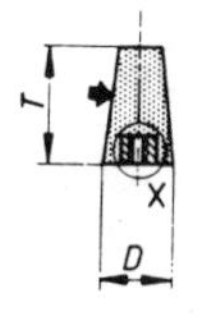

Type 18 Plug

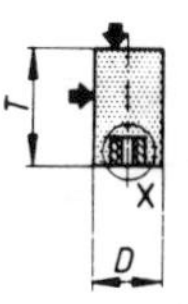

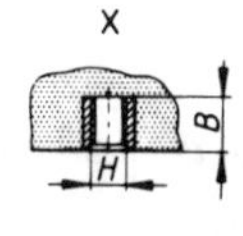

Type 18R Plug

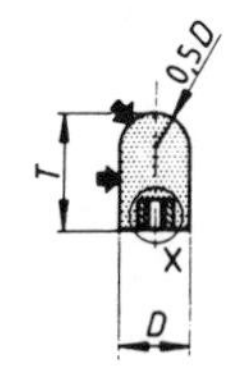

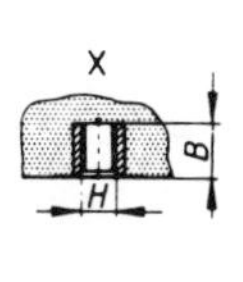

Type 19 Cone

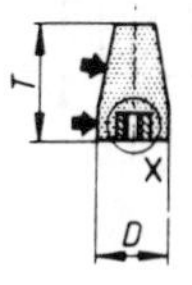

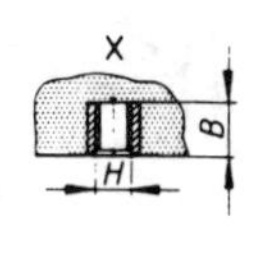

Type 20 Relieved one side

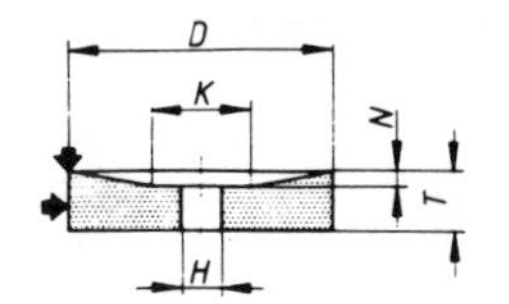

Type 21 Relieved two sides

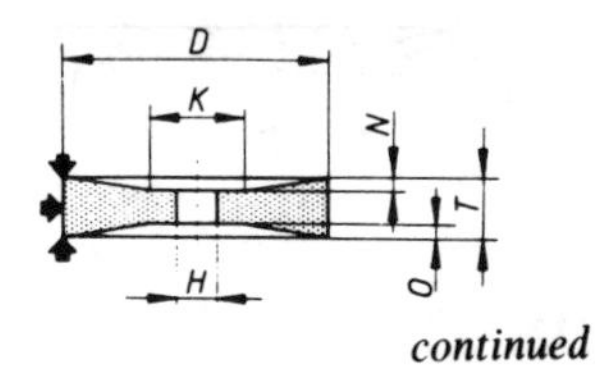

continued

Type 22 Relieved o/s recess o/s

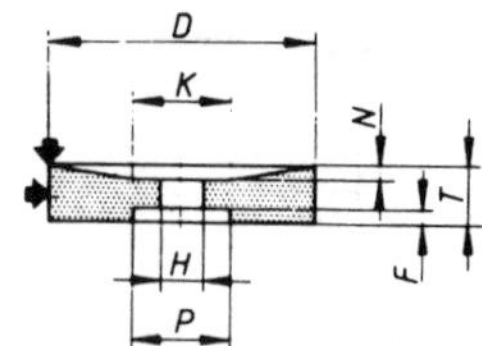
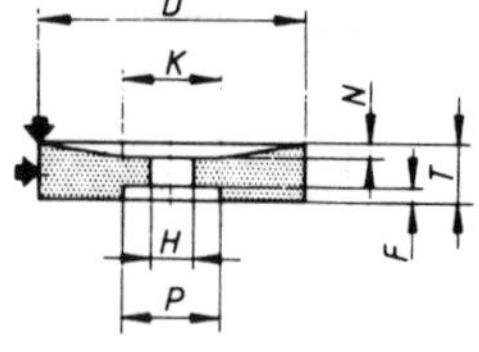

Type 23 Relieved o/s recess same side

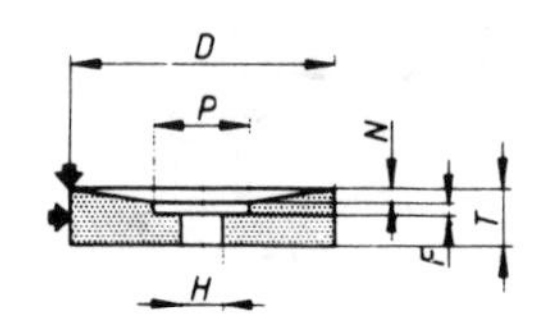

Type 24 Relieved o/s recessed b/s

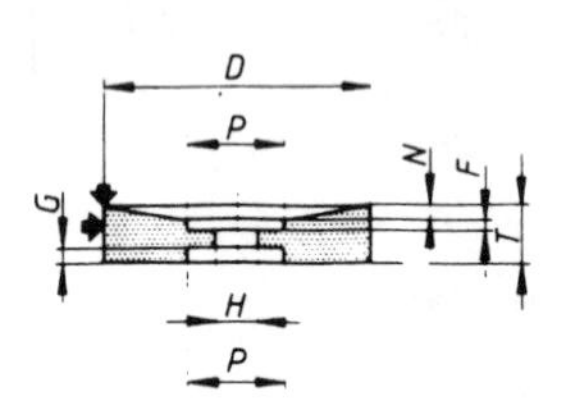

Type 25 Relieved b/s recessed o/s

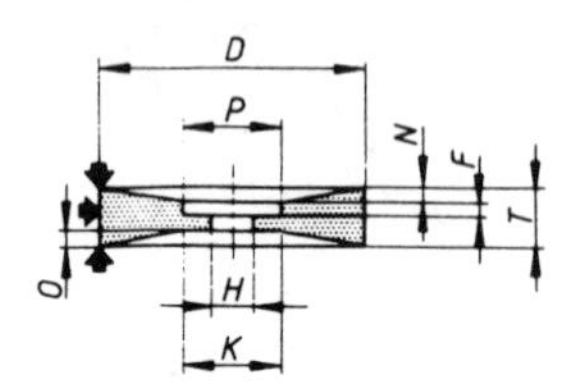

Type 25 Relieved and recessed b/s

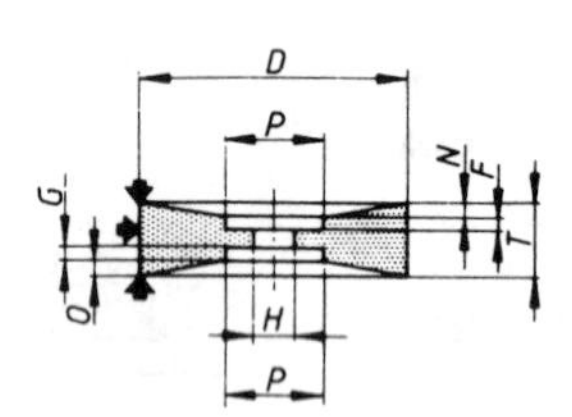

Type 27 Depressed centre

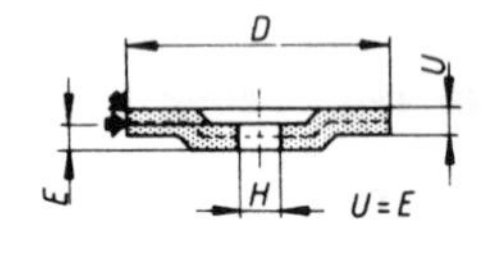

Type 28 Coolie hat

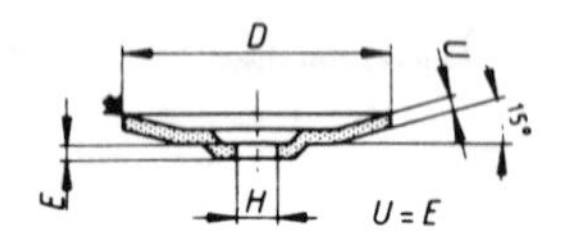

5.4.3 Maximum permissible peripheral speeds of abrasive wheels

The maximum speeds listed in this table are not necessarily the recommended speeds of operation for optimum grinding efficiency. For higher speeds and further information see BS 4481 : Pt 1 : 1981.

Machine classification and grinding operation		*Type of wheel* (section 5.4.2)	*Max. speed* m/s	*Special conditions*
	External cylindrical	1, 5, 7, 20–26	35	
	Tool room (universal)	1, 5, 7	35	
	Crankshaft	1, 5, 7	43	
	Camshaft	1, 5, 7	43	
	Thread	1	60	
	Thread	5, 7	45	
	Thread	1	45	Thicker than 35 mm

continued

Section 5.4.3 (*continued*)

Machine classification and grinding operation		*Type of wheel* (section 5.4.2)	*Max. speed*	*Special conditions*
	Centreless	1, 5, 7	35	
	Control wheels	1, 5, 7	12	
	Internal	1, 5	35	
		52	50	Without overhang
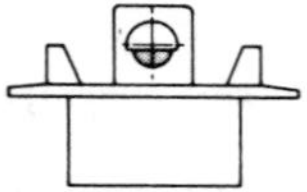	Surface			
	Horizontal spindle, reciprocating table	1, 5, 7	35	
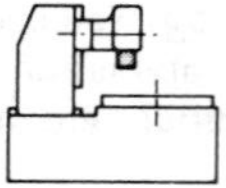	Horizontal spindle, rotary table	1, 5, 7	35	

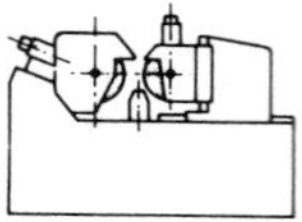

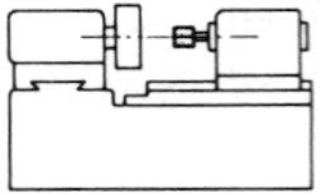

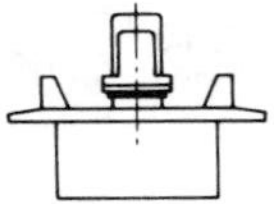

	Surface			
	Vertical spindle, reciprocating table	2, 37	25	Inorganic bonds
			30	Organic bonds
		6	30	
		35, 36	32	
	Vertical spindle, rotary table	2, 37	25	Inorganic bonds
			30	Organic bonds
		6	30	
		35, 36	32	
	Duplex	2, 37	25	Inorganic bonds
			30	Organic bonds
		6	30	
		35, 36	32	
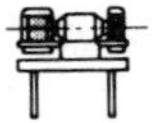	Off-hand grinding and fettling			
	Bench	1, 5, 7	35	
	Floor stand	1	50	Organic bond only
	Side grinding	6, 35, 36	32	

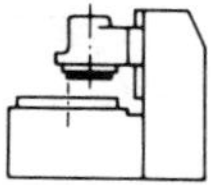

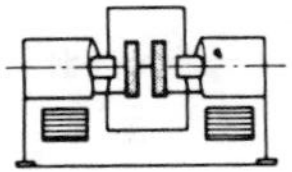

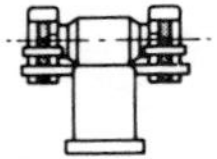

continued

Section 5.4.3 (*continued*)

Machine classification and grinding operation		*Type of wheel* (section 5.4.2)	*Max. speed* m/s	*Special conditions*
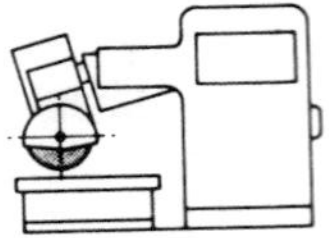	Billet and slab			
	Mechanical control	1	63	Special high density organic bond
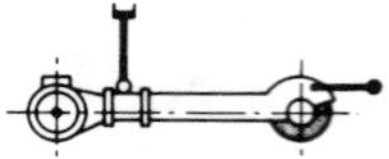	Swing frame, manual control	1	50	Organic bond only
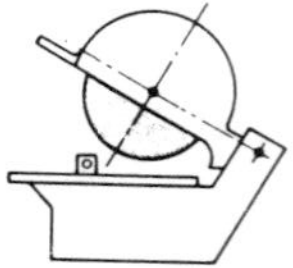	Cutting off	1	80	Reinforced organic bond only
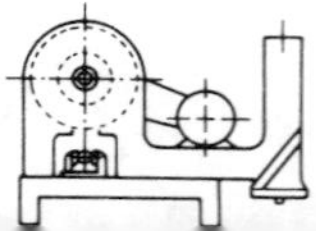	Cutting off (fully guarded)	1	80	Organic bonds only

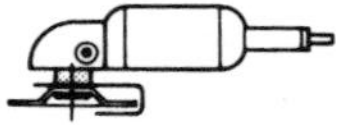	Portable, right angle			
	Grinding	6, 11	50	Organic bonds only
		27	80	Reinforced organic bonds only
	Cutting off	1, 27	80	Reinforced organic bonds only
	Portable, vertical spindle grinder	6, 11	50	Organic bonds only
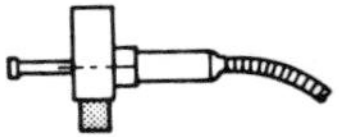	Portable, straight grinder	1, 4	50	Organic bonds only
		16, 17, 18, 18R, 19	50	
		52	50	Without overhang
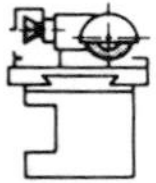	Tool and cutter	1, 5, 7	35	
	Grinding and sharpening	6, 11, 12, 13	32	

5.5 Carbide cutting tool materials

5.5.1 Coromant carbide grades for turning

The feed should be chosen so that the average chip thickness is equal to or greater than 0.1 mm per tooth per rev.

ISO category P (Blue)
Steel, cast steel, stainless steel, long chipping malleable iron

Basic grades

CT515 (P01–P15)
Titanium based grade with a greater resistance to oxidation than conventional grades. For high quality surface finish in steel and stainless steel applications. Favourable conditions.

S1P (P01–P15)
Finishing and light roughing of steel and steel castings. Favourable conditions. High cutting speeds, moderate feeds.

GC415 (P05–P30)
Finishing and light roughing of steel and steel castings. The high wear resistance and good resistance to plastic deformation permit high metal removal rates.

continued on next page

ISO category M (Yellow)
Steel, cast steel, manganese steel, alloy cast iron, austenitic stainless steel castings, malleable iron, free cutting steel, heat resistant alloys

Basic grades

GC415 (M10–M25)
Finishing and light roughing of rolled or forged stainless steel. Comparatively high cutting speeds.

GC425 (M15–M25)
Finishing and light roughing of rolled or forged stainless steel. Medium cutting speeds and feeds.

GC235 (M25–M40)
Finishing and roughing of austenitic stainless steel castings and stainless steel with difficult skin. Low speeds. Good edge security.

ISO category K (Red)
Cast iron, chilled cast iron, short chipping malleable iron, hardened steel, non-ferrous metals, plastics, wood

Basic grades

H1P (K01–K15)
Finishing and light roughing of cast iron. Also for alloyed cast iron, bronze and brass. High cutting speeds and moderate feeds.

GC3015 (K05–K20)
Finishing and light roughing of low and high tensile cast iron, malleable iron and nodular cast iron. High wear resistance permits high metal removal rates.

Supplementary grades

H10 (K10)
For machining of aluminium. Good edge sharpness.

GC415 (K05–K20)
Finishing and light roughing of cast iron, malleable iron and nodular cast iron. High wear resistance.

continued on next page

ISO category P (Blue) *continued*

Steel, cast steel, stainless steel, long chipping malleable iron

Supplementary grades

GC425 (P10–P35)
Light and medium roughing of steel and steel castings. High cutting speed and relatively high feed. High wear resistance. All round grade for steel machining.

GC435 (P15–P40)
Light and medium roughing of steel and steel castings. Can be used under unfavourable conditions. Medium cutting speeds and feeds.

Supplementary grades

S10T (P01–P15)
Threading in steel, cast steel and stainless materials. Medium to high cutting speed. Favourable conditions. Good edge sharpness.

GC015 (P05–P30)
Finishing and light roughing of steel and steel castings. High wear resistance.

GC225 (P10–P30)
Threading and grooving in steel, cast steel and stainless materials. High wear resistance permits high cutting speed. Relatively favourable conditions.

GC1025 (P10–P35)
Light and medium roughing of steel and steel castings. High wear resistance.

S30T (P20–P40)
Threading in steel, cast steel and stainless materials. Medium cutting speed. Unfavourable conditions. Good edge sharpness.

GC135 (P25–P45)
Light and medium roughing of steel and steel castings. Unfavourable conditions. Medium cutting speeds and feeds.

S6 (P35–P45)
Roughing of steel, stainless steel and steel castings. Difficult conditions. Low cutting speeds, heavy feeds.

GC235 (P30–P50)
Cut off and other toughness demanding operations in steel and stainless steel. Suitable for low speed and unfavourable conditions. Good toughness.

ISO category K (Red) *continued*

Cast iron, chilled cast iron, short chipping malleable iron, hardened steel, non-ferrous metals, plastics, wood

Supplementary grades

GC315 (K05–K25)
Light and medium roughing of cast iron and other short chipping materials. Less favourable conditions. Medium speeds, heavy feeds.

GC435 (K05–K25)
Finishing and light roughing of cast iron under less favourable conditions. High wear resistance.

H13A (K15–K25)
Combines good abrasive wear resistance and toughness for medium to rough turning of heat resistant and titanium alloys. Roughing of cast iron materials under moderate speeds and high feeds. Suitable also for plastics, rubber and wood.

H20 (K20–K25)
Heavy roughing of cast iron. Unfavourable conditions. Low speeds, heavy feeds.

H10F (K20–K30)
For machining of heat resistant and titanium alloys under unfavourable conditions. Good edge strength.

Courtesy of SANDVIK

5.5.2 Coromant carbide turning tools: selecting the toolholder system

The various toolholder systems are designed to suit different application areas. To help in the choice of suitable toolholders for the various operations, the most important factors have been graded according to suitability, 1 to 5. Grade 5 is the most suitable, becoming less suitable down to grade 1. If a toolholder is not graded, then it should not be used for that operation. Below the brief description of the clamping system follows a grade chart and then a list of inserts available for the system.

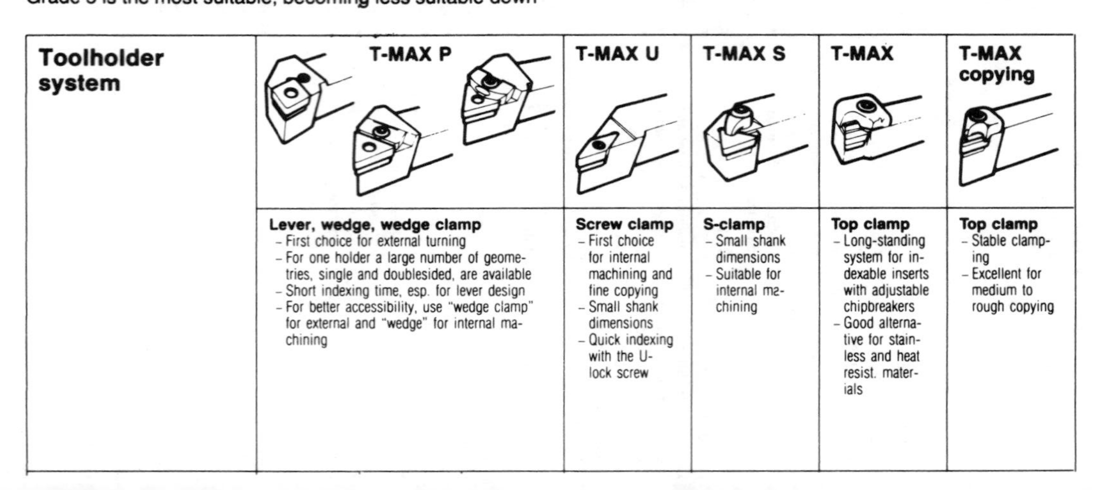

Toolholder system	T-MAX P	T-MAX U	T-MAX S	T-MAX	T-MAX copying
	Lever, wedge, wedge clamp – First choice for external turning – For one holder a large number of geometries, single and doublesided, are available – Short indexing time, esp. for lever design – For better accessibility, use "wedge clamp" for external and "wedge" for internal machining	**Screw clamp** – First choice for internal machining and fine copying – Small shank dimensions – Quick indexing with the U-lock screw	**S-clamp** – Small shank dimensions – Suitable for internal machining	**Top clamp** – Long-standing system for indexable inserts with adjustable chipbreakers – Good alternative for stainless and heat resist. materials	**Top clamp** – Stable clamping – Excellent for medium to rough copying

Operations and other factors							
External roughing	5	3	4	2	2	4	4
External finishing	4	4	4	5	4	2	4
Internal roughing	5	3	3	2	3		4
Internal finishing	4	4	3	5	5		4
Chip flow	5	5	4	5	3	2	3
Indexing time	5	5	3	2(4)[2]	4	2	3
Accessibility	2(4)[1]	4	4	5			5
Programme versatility (size, geometries, etc)	5	3	3	4	3	1	2

continued

5.5.2 (*continued*)

Insert type					
	- Single-sided - Double-sided - With or without form-sintered chipbreaker	- Positive basic shape - With or without form-sintered chipbreaker	- Positive basic shape - Form-sintered chipbreaker - Two tolerance classes G and M - Plain positive inserts also fit these holders	- Positive or negative basic shapes - Plain inserts - Two tolerance classes U and G	- 55° point angle - Single-sided - 16 mm cutting edge length - Form-sintered chipbreakers in various witdths

[1]) With 55° inserts type DNMG.
[2]) With U-Lock screw.

Courtesy of SANDVIK

5.5.3 Coromant carbide turning tools: selecting the insert

In 5.5.4 the most important factors affecting the choice of insert type are set out on the left. On the basis of these factors, the insert characteristics have been graded for suitability from 1 to 5. Grade 5 is the most suitable, becoming less suitable down to grade 1. If an insert is not graded, then it should not be used.

In the insert choice tables in 5.5.4 it is stated that 80° (i.e. C-shaped) T-MAX P inserts have 2/4 or 4/8 cutting edges per insert. The 4 and 8 cutting edges are valid when using both the 80° and 100° corners of the insert.

Start using the insert choice tables by finding the nearest material type (Coromant material classification, CMC). Go on to establish the working area in question, and then find the insert most suitable for the toolholder that has been selected. If the operation is affected by intermittent machining, vibrations or limited machine power, this should be taken into consideration in the final choice of insert. Feed rates s and depths of cut a are as follows:

Extreme finishing:
$s=0.05$–0.15 mm/rev
$a=0.25$–2.0 mm
Finishing:
$s=0.1$–0.3 mm/rev
$a=0.5$–2.0 mm
Light roughing:
$s=0.2$–0.5 mm/rev
$a=2.0$–4.0 mm
Roughing
$s=0.4$–1.0 mm/rev
$a=4.0$–10.0 mm
Heavy roughing:
$s=1.0$ mm/rev
$a=6.0$–20.0 mm

If difficulty should arise in finding a suitable insert for the toolholder previously selected, it may be a better solution to choose an insert first and then go back to choose a suitable toolholder or maybe even a different toolholder system.

5.5.4 Coromant carbide turning tools: comparison of insert types

Inserts have been graded for suitability for the listed operations from 1 to 5. A grade 5 indicates that the insert is most suitable.

Insert type: T-MAX P

CMC No.	Material type	Working area	DNMM -71	DNMG -15	DNMG -61	DNMA	TNMM	TNMM -71	TNMM -41	TNMG	TNMG -15	TNMG -23	TNMG -61	TNMG-QF	TNMA	CNMM	CNMM -82	CNMM -71
		Edges per insert	2	4	4	4	3	3	3	6	6	6	6	6	6	2/4	2/4	2/4
01 02 03 06	Long chipping	Extreme finishing			2								2	5				
		Finishing	1	2	5		1	1		1	2		5	5		1		1
		Light roughing	4	5	4		3	4		4	5		3	3		3	1	4
		Roughing	5	2			4	5	3	2	2					4	4	5
		Heavy roughing	2				2	2	3							2	5	2
07 08 09	Short chipping	Finishing	1	4	2	4	2	1	1	2	4		2	2	4	2	1	1
		Light roughing	1	4	1	5	2	1	1	3	4		1	1	5	2	1	1
		Roughing	1	2		5	2	1	1	1	2				5	2	1	1
		Heavy roughing	1			2	2	1	1						4	2	1	1
05	Stainless	Extreme finishing			1							1	1	5				
		Finishing		2	3		1		1	2	2	5	3	5		1		
		Light roughing	2	3	3		2	2	2	2	3	4	3	3		2	1	2
		Roughing	3	1			2	3	5	1	1	1				2	3	3
		Heavy roughing	1				1	1	4							1	3	1
20	Heat resistant	Extreme finishing			1							2	1	5				
		Finishing		2	3		1		1	2	2	5	3	3		1		
		Light roughing	1	2	2		1	1	3	3	2	4	2	1		1	1	1
		Roughing	1	1			1	1	4	1	1	2				1	1	1
30 33	Soft (Al,Cu,etc.)	Extreme finishing			1							1	1	4				
		Finishing		1	4					1	1	3	4	4				
		Light roughing	1	2	3			1		1	2	3	3	2				1
		Roughing	1	1	1			1		1	1		1					1
04 10	Hard[1])	Finishing				3	4	3	1	1	1				4	4	3	1
		Light roughing				1	2	3							3	3	3	
Intermittent machining			3	2	2	3	4	3	5	3	2		2	2	4	3/4	5	3/4
Vibration tendencies			3	1	3		3	3	3	2	1	5	3	2		3	3	3

Insert type: T-MAX P

CMC No.	Material type	Working area / Edges per insert	CNMG	CNMG -15	CNMG -23	CNMG -61	CNMG-QF	CNMA	SNMM	SNMM -31	SNMM -41	SNMM -71	SNMG	SNMG -15	SNMG -23	SNMG -61	SNMG-QF	SNMA	RCMX	RCMX -E	RNMG
			4/8	4/8	4/8	4/8	4/8	4/8	4	4	4	4	8	8	8	8	8	8	–	–	–
01 02 03 06	Long chipping	Extreme finishing				2	5									2	5				
		Finishing	1	2		5	5		1			1	1	2		5	5		1	2	1
		Light roughing	4	5		3	3		3	1		4	4	5		3	3		3	3	2
		Roughing	2	2					4	4	3	5	2	2					4	2	4
		Heavy roughing							2	5	3	2							3	2	3
07 08 09	Short chipping	Finishing	2	4		2	2	4	2	1	1	1	2	4		2	2	4	3	2	2
		Light roughing	3	4		1	1	5	2	1	1	1	3	4		1	1	5	4	2	3
		Roughing	1	2				5	2	1	1	1	1	2				5	3	2	3
		Heavy roughing						4	2	1	1	1						4	3	2	
05	Stainless	Extreme finishing			1	1	5								1	1	5				
		Finishing	2	2	5	3	5		1		1		2	2	5	3	5		2	3	2
		Light roughing	2	3	4	3	2		2	1	2	2	2	3	4	3	2		3	4	2
		Roughing	1	1	1				2	3	5	3	1	1	1				2	3	1
		Heavy roughing							1	3	4	1							2	2	
20	Heat resistant	Extreme finishing			2	1	5								2	1	5				
		Finishing	2	2	5	3	3		1		1		2	2	5	3	3		2	2	2
		Light roughing	3	2	4	2	1		1	1	3	1	3	2	4	2	1		2	2	3
		Roughing	1	1	2				1	1	4	1	1	1	2				2	2	1
30 33	Soft (Al, Cu, etc.)	Extreme finishing			1	1	4								1	1	4				
		Finishing	1	1	3	4	4						1	1	3	4	4		1	2	1
		Light roughing	1	2	3	3	2					1	1	2	3	3	2		1	2	1
		Roughing	1	1		1						1	1	1		1			1	2	1
04 10	Hard[1])	Finishing	1	1				4	4	1	3	1	1	1				4	5	3	3
		Light roughing						4	3	1	3							4	4	2	3
Intermittent machining			3	2		3	3	4	4	4	5	3	3	2		3	3	4	5	5	4
Vibration tendencies			2	1	5	3	2		3	3	3	3	2	1	5	3	2			2	
Limited power			2	1	5	3	3	1	3	4	4	4	2	1	5	3	3	1	2	3	1

[1]) HB >400

5.5.4 (*continued*)

Insert type: T-MAX U

CMC No.	Material type	Working area	VBMM -53	VBMA	DCMM -52	DCMM -53	DCMA	TCMM -52	TCMM -53	TCMA	CCMM -52	CCMM -53	CCMA	SCMM -52	SCMM -53	SCMA	RCMM -52
		Edges per insert	2	2	2	2	2	3	3	3	2	2	2	4	4	4	–
01 02 03 06	Long chipping	Extreme finishing	1		1	5		1	5		1	5		1	5		1
		Finishing	4		4	4		4	4		4	4		4	4		4
		Light roughing	5		5			5			5			5			5
		Roughing	1		1			1			1			1			1
		Heavy roughing															
07 08 09	Short chipping	Finishing	4	5	4	3	5	4	3	5	4	3	5	4	3	5	4
		Light roughing	4	4	4		4	4		4	4		4	4		4	4
		Roughing	1		1			1			1			1			1
		Heavy roughing															
05	Stainless	Extreme finishing	2		2	5		2	5		2	5		2	5		2
		Finishing	5	1	5	4	1	5	4	1	5	4	1	5	4	1	5
		Light roughing	4	1	4		1	4		1	4		1	4		1	4
		Roughing	1		1			1			1			1			1
		Heavy roughing															
20	Heat resistant	Extreme finishing	1		1	4		1	4		1	4		1	4		1
		Finishing	2	1	2	3	1	2	3	1	2	3	1	2	3	1	2
		Light roughing	3	1	3		1	3		1	3		1	3		1	3
		Roughing	1		1			1			1			1			1
30 33	Soft (Al, Cu, etc.)	Extreme finishing	2		2	5		2	5		2	5		2	5		2
		Finishing	4	1	4	4	1	4	4	1	4	4	1	4	4	1	4
		Light roughing	5	1	5		1	5		1	5		1	5		1	5
		Roughing	2		2			2			2			2			2
04 10	Hard[1])	Finishing		2			2			2			2			2	
		Light roughing															
Intermittent machining					2	1	2	2	1	2	2	1	2	2	1	2	3
Vibration tendencies			5	2	4	3	2	4	3	2	4	3	2	4	3	2	2
Limited power			5	2	4	4	2	4	4	2	4	4	2	4	4	2	3

[1] HB >400

Insert type: T-MAX S and T-MAX

CMC No.	Material type	Working area / Edges per insert	TPMR TPGR	TPMR TPGR -21	TCGR	SPMR SPGR	TPUN TPGN *	SPUN SPGN *	TNUN TNGN	SNUN SNGN	KNUX -11	KNUX -12	KNUX -13	KNMX -71	KNMX -73
			3	3	3	4	3	4	6	8	2	2	2	2	2
01 02 03 06	Long chipping	Extreme finishing	1	4	4	1									1
		Finishing	4	5	5	4	1	1	1	1	4	3	1	4	5
		Light roughing	4	1	1	4	4	4	3	3	3	4	3	5	5
		Roughing	2			2	4	4	4	4	1	2	4	5	2
		Heavy roughing					3	3	3	3					
07 08 09	Short chipping	Finishing	3	3	3	3	4	4	4	4	3	2	1	2	2
		Light roughing	2	1	1	2	4	4	5	5	2	3	3	2	1
		Roughing	2			2	3	3	5	5	1	2	2	2	1
		Heavy roughing					1	1	4	4					
05	Stainless	Extreme finishing	2	4	4	2									1
		Finishing	4	4	4	4	3	3			4	2	1	2	3
		Light roughing	4	1	1	4	5	5			5	4	3	3	3
		Roughing	2			2	5	5			2	3	4	3	1
		Heavy roughing					3	3							
20	Heat resistant	Extreme finishing	1	3	3	1									
		Finishing	3	2	2	3	3	3			4 5[2]	2 4[2]	1 2[2]	2	2
		Light roughing	2			2	5	5			3 3[2]	5 5[2]	3 4[2]	2	2
		Roughing	2			2	5	5			1	3 2[2]	4 5[2]	2	1
30 33	Soft (Al, Cu, etc.)	Extreme finishing	1	4	4	1									
		Finishing	4	4	4	4	2	2			4 5[2]	2 4[2]	1 2[2]	2	3
		Light roughing	3	2	2	3	2	2			2 3[2]	4 5[2]	3 4[2]	2	3
		Roughing	2			2	2	2			1	2 2[2]	3 5[2]	2	2
04 10	Hard[1])	Finishing							3	3					
		Light roughing							2	2					
Intermittent machining			2	1	1	2	3	3	4	4	2	3	3	3	2
Vibration tendencies			4	4	4	4	3	3			4	3	3	3	5
Limited power			4	4	4	4	3	3	1	1	4	3	3	3	5

[1] HB >400
[2] Valid for KNUX-F with sharp cutting edges.

* Valid for T-Max toolholders (top-clamping). When using a T-Max S toolholder with loose chipbreaker, reduce grading values somewhat.

Courtesy of SANDVIK

5.5.5 Coromant carbide turning tools: selecting the insert size

Minimum cutting edge length

1. Determine the largest depth of cut, 'a'.
2. Determine the necessary effective cutting edge length, L, while also considering the entering angle κ of the toolholder, and the depth of cut, a.

L = effective cutting edge

l = cutting edge length

κ = holder's effective angle

The minimum necessary cutting edge length, L, can then be determined from the table below.

Entering angle κ		Cutting depth (a) mm. 1	2	3	4	5	6	7	8	9	10	15
		Necessary effective cutting-edge length (L) mm.										
	90	1	2	3	4	5	6	7	8	9	10	15
105	75	1,5	2,1	3,1	4,1	5,2	6,2	7,3	8,3	9,3	11	16
120	60	1,2	2,3	3,5	4,7	5,8	7	8,2	9,3	11	12	18
135	45	1,4	2.9	4,3	5,7	7,1	8,5	10	12	13	15	22
150	30	2	4	6	8	10	12	14	16	18	20	30
165	15	4	8	12	16	20	24	27	31	35	39	58

Copying

During copying, the copying angle β must be considered. For in-copying, $\kappa_1 = \kappa + \beta$, for outcopying, $\kappa_1 + \kappa - \beta$.

In-copying

Out-copying

κ = holder's entering angle
κ_1 = effective entering angle

In-copying: $\kappa_1 = \kappa + \beta$
Out-copying: $\kappa_1 = \kappa - \beta$

Note! When turning up to a shoulder, the depth of cut 'a' can greatly increase, as shown in the sketch below. To enable the insert to handle the increase in cut, it might be necessary to choose a larger size insert, or add an extra facing operation to the layout.

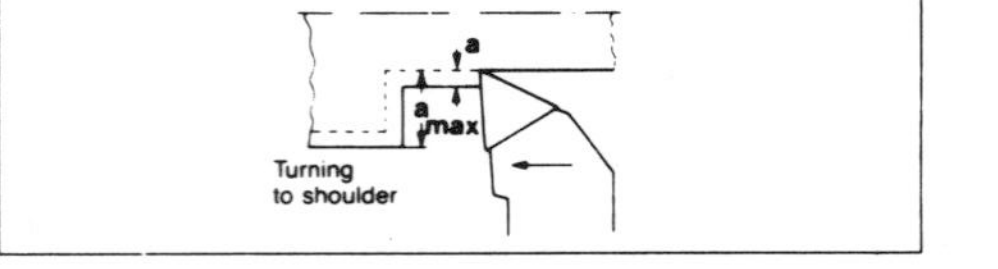

Maximum cutting edge length

The table shows the maximum recommended effective cutting edge length L_{max} for various insert shapes and geometries. Make sure that the chosen L value does not exceed the maximum values recommended in the table.

The values given in the table indicate L_{max} for continuous turning. A deeper cut can normally be taken with an insert for a limited period, when turning a short section workpiece.

Inserts	L_{max}	Inserts	L_{max}	Inserts	L_{max}	Inserts	L_{max}
TCMA, TCMM-52, TNMA, TNMG, TNMG-15, TNMG-23, TNMM, TNMM-41, TNMM-71, TPGN, TPGR, TPMR, TPUN	 $L_{max} = \frac{1}{2} \times l$	TCGR, TCMM-53, TNMG-61, TNMG-QF, TPGR-21, TPMR-21	 $L_{max} = \frac{1}{4} \times l$	DCMA, DCMM-52, DNMA, DNMG-15, DNMM-71	 $L_{max} = \frac{1}{2} \times l$	DCMM-53, DNMG-61	 $L_{max} = \frac{1}{4} \times l$
SCMA, SCMM-52, SNMA, SNMG, SNMG-15, SNMG-23, SNMM, SNMM-31, SNMM-41, SNMM-71, SPGN, SPGR, SPMR, SPUN	 $L_{max} = \frac{2}{3} \times l$	SCMM-53, SNMG-61, SNMG-QF	$L_{max} = \frac{1}{3} \times l$	CCMA, CCMM-52, CNMA, CNMG, CNMG-15, CNMG-23, CNMM, CNMM-62, CNMM-71	 $L_{max} = \frac{2}{3} \times l$	CCMM-53, CNMG-61, CNMG-QF	 $L_{max} = \frac{1}{3} \times l$
RCMM-52, RCMX, RCMX-E, RNMG	 $L_{max} = 0.4 \times d$	VBMA, VBMM-53	 $L_{max} = \frac{1}{4} \times l$	KNMX-71, KNMX-73, KNUX-11, KNUX-12, KNUX-13	 $L_{max} = \frac{1}{2} \times l$		

The values given in the table indicate the maximum L_{max} for continuous turning. A deeper cut can nomally be taken with an insert for a limited period, when turning a short section workpiece.

Courtesy of SANDVIK

5.5.6 Coromant carbide turning tools: selecting the nose radius and feed

Rough machining

- Select the largest possible nose radius to obtain a strong cutting edge.
- A large nose radius permits larger feeds.
- Select a smaller radius if there is a tendency towards vibration.
- For roughing the most commonly used radii are 1,2–1,6 mm.
- Maximum recommended feed rate 2/3 × the nose radius.

Finish machining

The surface finish and tolerances are affected by the combination of nose radius and feed.
The theoretical value of the surface finish can be calculated from the following formula:

$$R_t = \frac{s^2}{8r} \times 1000 \ (\mu m)$$

where:
R_t = profile depth in μm
r = nose radius in mm
s = feed per revolution, mm/r

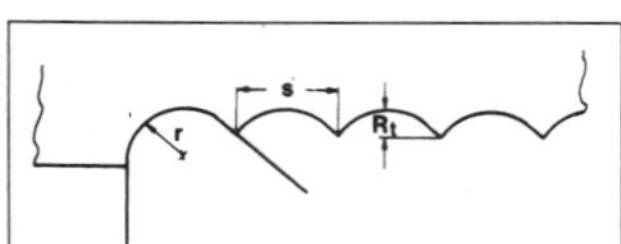

It is more usual to express the surface finish in terms of the arithmetical average, R_a. There is no mathematical connection between the profile depth and the R_a-value but the table below shows the connection between R_a and R_t, depending on the nose radius and the feed.

Round inserts must be treated differently. The larger radii which directly influences the surface finish, have a positive effect on the finish that it is possible to achieve at a certain feed. The table below indicates the connection between feed, insert diameter and surface finish.

Surface finish R_a μm	R_t μm	Diameter of the insert 10	12	16	20	25	32
		Feed					
0,6	1,6	0,25	0,28	0,32	0,36	0,40	0,45
1,6	4	0,40	0,44	0,51	0,57	0,63	0,71
3,2	10	0,63	0,69	0,80	0,89	1,00	1,13
6,3	16	0,80	0,88	1,01	1,13	1,26	1,43
8	25	1,00	1,10	1,26	1,42	1,41	1,79
32	100	2,00	2,20	2,54	2,94	3,33	3,59

Surface finish R_a µm	R_t µm	Nose radius, mm 0,4	0,8	1,2	1,6	2,4
		Feed, mm/r				
0,6	1,6	0,07	0,10	0,12	0,14	0,17
1,6	4	0,11	0,15	0,19	0,22	0,26
3,2	10	0,17	0,24	0,29	0,34	0,42
6,3	16	0,22	0,30	0,37	0,43	0,53
8	25	0,27	0,38	0,47	0,54	0,66
32	100				1,08	1,32

- The surface finish can often be improved by using higher cutting speeds and neutral or positive rakes.

- Select a smaller radius if there is a tendency to vibrate.

- Uncoated grades normally produce a better surface finish than coated grades.

Rake angle and angle of inclination

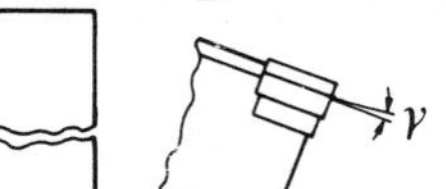

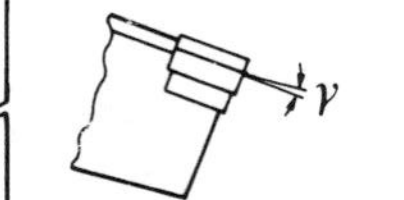

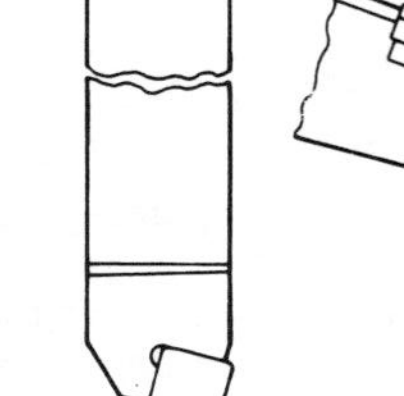

The cutting angles given on the ordering pages are for a plain master insert without chipbreakers. The effective cutting angles are dependent on the insert geometry being used, the effective rake angle is obtained by adding together the insert's and the holder's rake angle.

γ = Rake angle
λ = Angle of inclination

Courtesy of SANDVIK

5.5.7 Coromant carbide turning tools: nominal cutting speeds and feeds

The recommendations are valid for rough turning
with Sandvik Corona grades and use of cutting fluid.

Approximate tool life with C40 : 1 hour
Approximate tool life with C45/60: 2 hours (or 1 hour with approx. 20% higher speed)

ISO	CMC No.	Material		Specific cutting force k_s 0,4 N/mm²	Brinell hardness HB	Feed mm/rev 0,1–0,2–0,3–0,4 Cutting speed m/min			
P (BLUE)	01.1	Non-alloy carbon steel	C=0,15%	1900	125	85-	65-	55-	45
	01.2		C=0,35%	2100	150	70-	55-	45-	40
	01.3		C=0,60%	2250	200	50-	40-	35-	30
	02.1	Alloy steel	Annealed	2100	180	60-	45-	40-	30
	02.2		Hardened and tempered	2600	275	40-	30-	25-	20
	02.2		Hardened and tempered	2700	300	35-	25-	20-	15
	02.2		Hardened and tempered	2850	350	25-	20-	15-	10
	03.1	High-alloy steel	Annealed	2600	200	40-	30-	25-	20
	03.2		Hardened	3900	325	25-	20-	15-	10
	05.1	Stainless steel Annealed	Martensitic/ferritic	2300	200	40-	30-	25-	20
	05.2		Austenitic	2450	175	35-	25-	20-	15

	06.1	**Steel castings**		Non-alloy	2000	180	50-	40-	35-	15
	06.2			Low-alloy	2500	200	40-	30-	25-	20
	06.3			High-alloy	2700	225	35-	25-	20-	15
K (RED)	**04**	**Hard steel**		Hardened steel	4500	55 HRC	20-	15-	15-	10
	06.33			Manganese steel 12%	3600	250	25-	20-	15-	10
	08.1	**Cast-iron, low tensile**			1100	180	60-	45-	40-	30
	08.2	**Cast-iron, high tensile**			1500	260	40-	30-	25-	20
	20.11	**Heat-resistant alloys**	Iron base	Annealed	3000	200	15-	10		
	20.12			Aged	3050	280	10-	10		
	20.21, 20.31		Nickel or cobalt base	Annealed	3500	250	10-	5		
	20.22, 20.32			Aged	4150	350	10-	5		
	20.24, 20.33			Cast	4150	320	5-	5		
	30	**Aluminium alloys**			900	90	290-	240-	210-	180
	33.1	**Bronze-Brass alloys**		Lead alloys, Pb>1%	700	110	210-	170-	150-	130
	33.2			Brass, red brass	750	90	140-	115-	100-	85
	33.3			Bronze and lead-free copper incl. electro-lytic copper	1750	100	85-	70-	60-	55

For a cutting depth ⩾1,5 mm the nose radius should be ⩾1,0 mm. For a cutting depth <1,5 mm the nose radius should be <1,0 mm.

Courtesy of SANDVIK

5.5.8 Coromant carbide and turning tools: insert wear and tool life

Problem	Cause	Remedy
Flank and notch wear		
a. Rapid flank wear causing poor surface finish or out of tolerance.	a. A too high cutting speed or insufficient wear resistance.	Reduce the cutting speed. Select a more wear resistant grade.
b/c. Notch wear causing poor surface finish & risk of edge breakage.	b/c. Oxidation or excessive attrition wear caused by a hard surface.	Select an Al_2O_3 coated grade for steel machining. For work hardening materials select a smaller entering angle or a more wear resistant grade.
Crater wear		
Excessive crater wear causing a weakened edge. Cutting edge break through on the trailing edge causes poor surface finish.	Diffusion wear due to too high cutting temperatures on the rake face.	Select an Al_2O_3 coated grade. Select a positive insert geometry. Reduce the speed (and feed) to obtain a lower temperature.

Problem	Cause	Remedy
Plastic deformation a b Plastic deformation (edge depression (a) or flank impression (b)) leading to poor chip control and poor surface finish. Risk of excessive flank wear leading to insert breakage.	A too high cutting temperature in combination with a high pressure.	Select a harder grade with better resistance to plastic deformation. (a) Reduce cutting speed. (b) Reduce feed.
Built-up edge Built-up edge (B.U.E.) causing poor surface finish and cutting edge frittering when the B.U.E. is torn away.	Workpiece material is welded to the insert due to:	
	Low cutting speed.	Increase cutting speed.
	Negative cutting geometry.	Select a positive geometry.
	"Sticky" material, e.g. certain stainles steels and pure aluminium.	Increase cutting speed drastically. If tool life turns out to be short, apply coolant in large quantities.

Courtesy of SANDVIK

continued

Section 5.5.8 (*continued*)

Problem	Cause	Remedy
Chip hammering The part of the cutting edge not in cut is damaged through chip hammering. Both the top side and the support for the insert, can be damaged.	The chips are of an excessive length and are deflected against the cutting edge.	Change the feed slightly. Select an alternative insert geometry. Change the entering angle of the holder.
Frittering Small cutting edge fractures (frittering) causing poor surface finish and excessive flank wear.	Grade too brittle. Insert geometry too weak. Built-up edge.	Select tougher grade. Select an insert with a stronger geometry. Increase cutting speed or select a positive geometry.

Problem	Description	Cause	Remedy
Thermal cracks	Small cracks perpendicular to the cutting edge causing frittering and poor surface finish.	Thermal cracks due to temperature variations caused by:	
		– Intermittent machining.	Select a tougher grade with better resistance to thermal shocks.
		– Varying coolant supply.	Coolant should be applied copiously or not at all.
Insert breakage	Insert breakage that damages not only the insert but also the shim & workpiece.	Grade too brittle.	Select a tougher grade.
		Excessive load on the insert.	Reduce the feed and/or the depth or cut.
		Insert geometry too weak.	Select a stronger geometry, preferably a single sided insert.
		Insert size is too small.	Select a thicker/larger insert.

Courtesy of SANDVIK

5.5.9 Coromant carbide grades for milling

The feed should be chosen so that the average chip thickness is equal to or greater than 0.1 mm per tooth per rev.

ISO category P (Blue)
Steel, cast steel, stainless steel, long chipping malleable iron

Basic grades

GC120 (P10–P30)
Milling steel under good conditions at high speeds. This grade is superior for face milling and side and face milling operations.

SMA (P15–40)
Developed especially for milling of steel and steel castings. The wear resistance in relation to its toughness is exceptional.

S6 (P30–P40)
Roughing of carbon steel, stainless steel and steel castings at low cutting speeds under difficult working conditions. Used for large cutting depths and heavy feeds.

Supplementary grades

S1P (P05–P15)
Finishing and light roughing of steel and steel castings at high cutting speeds and moderate feeds under favourable working conditions. Withstands very high cutting temperatures.

CT520 (P05–P25)
Ti-based Cermet. Semi-finishing and finishing steel, at normal to high cutting speeds.

ISO category M (Yellow)
Steel, cast steel, manganese steel, alloy cast iron, austenitic stainless steel castings, malleable iron, free cutting steel, heat resistant alloys

Basic grades

H13A (M15–M25)
Combines good abrasive wear resistance and toughness for milling of heat resistant alloys under moderate cutting conditions.

Supplementary grades

GC235 (M25–M40)
Coated grade with high toughness and edge security. Suitable for milling of austenitic stainless steel.

R4 (M40)
Finishing and roughing of stainless austenitic steel castings with sand inclusions and difficult rolling or casting skin. Low cutting speeds and heavy feeds. Very high resistance to thermal cracking.

Grades for special applications

H10F (M30)
Fine grain carbide, extremely good resistance to notch wear. Suitable for milling of heat resistant alloys. Unique grade for low speed machining. Suitable for a wide variety of aerospace materials.

ISO category K (Red)
Cast iron, chilled cast iron, short chipping malleable iron, hardened steel, non-ferrous metals, plastics, wood

Basic grades

GC3015 (K01–K25)
Double coated grade for roughing and semi-finishing of cast iron. Excellent wear resistance combined with very good toughness makes it suitable for a wide application range.

HM (K10–K20)
Developed especially for milling low alloy cast iron, e.g. castings for the automotive industry. Very high resistance to wear and plastic deformation.

GC320 (K10–K25)
Double coated grade for roughing low alloyed castings under fairly difficult working conditions. Very good combination of wear resistance and edge toughness. Gives low edge frittering on the workpiece.

H13A (K15–K30)
Combines good abrasive wear resistance and toughness for milling of cast iron under moderate cutting conditions.

ISO category P (Blue)
Steel, cast steel, stainless steel, long chipping malleable iron

Supplementary grades
SM30 (P20–P40)
Milling of steel and steel castings in operations where there are simultaneous demands for toughness, wear resistance and resistance to thermal cracking. Wide range of applications.

GC235 (P30–P45)
Coated grade with high toughness and edge security. Suitable for unfavourable conditions.

R4 (P40–P50)
Finishing and roughing of stainless austenitic steel castings with sand inclusions and difficult casting skin. Low cutting speeds and heavy feeds. Very high resistance to thermal cracking.

ISO category M (Yellow)
Steel, cast steel, manganese steel, alloy cast iron, austenitic stainless steel castings, malleable iron, free cutting steel, heat resistant alloys

ISO category K (Red)
Cast iron, chilled cast iron, short chipping malleable iron, hardened steel, non-ferrous metals, plastics, wood

Supplementary grades
H1P (K05–K15)
Finishing and roughing of cast iron, bronze and brass. High cutting speeds and moderate feeds.

SMA (K10–K25)
Nodular and regular cast irons, in light to medium machining. Moderate speed and feed conditions. Very good combination of edge toughness and wear resistance.

CC650 (K05–K20)
Mixed ceramic grade. Can be successful for alloyed and regular cast iron mainly found in the automotive industry. Can be used with conventional cutting data but also at elevated speed. Extremely high resistance to wear and plastic deformation.

Grades for special applications
H10 (K10)
Suitable for machining aluminium. Excellent edge sharpness.

CD10 (K101)
Polycrystalline synthetic diamond grade. Can be used for finishing operations with high demand on surface finish. Only to be used in non-ferrous and non-metallic materials. Extremely high wear resistance.

Courtesy of SANDVIK

5.5.10 Coromant carbide milling cutters: nominal cutting speed values

T-MAX facemills and square shoulder facemills

CMC = Coromant Material Classification

The feed should be chosen so that the average chip thickness is equal or greater than 0,1 mm per tooth per rev.

CMC No.	Material		Brinell hardness HB	GC120	SMA	S6	S1P	CT 520	SM30	GC235	R4
				Feed mm/tooth							
				0,2 – 0,1	0,4 – 0,2 – 0,1	0,4 – 0,2 – 0,1	0,4 – 0,2 – 0,1	0,25 – 0,05	0,4 – 0,2 – 0,1	0,2 – 0,1	0,4 – 0,2 – 0,1
				Cutting speed m/min							
01.1	Non-alloy steel	C<0.25%	110	300 - 390	180 - 250 - 310	100 - 130 - 160	170 - 235 - 300	100 – 400	135 - 185 - 235		
01.3	Non-alloy steel	C<0.8%	150	180 - 255	120 - 145 - 205	65 - 85 - 100	105 - 150 - 200	100 – 400	90 - 110 - 150		
01.5	Non-alloy steel	C<1.4%	310	165 - 210	95 - 130 - 170	50 - 75 - 85	90 - 125 - 165		70 - 100 - 125		
02.1	Low-alloy steel	Annealed	125-225	200 - 250	120 - 160 - 200	65 - 85 - 105	115 - 155 - 190	80 – 300	90 - 120 - 150		
02.2	Low-alloy steel	Hardened	220-450	130 - 150	70 - 100 - 125	40 - 55 - 65	95 - 120		55 - 75 - 95		
03.11	High-alloy steel	Annealed	150-250	170 - 225	110 - 140 - 180	60 - 80 - 90	135 - 180	80 – 300	80 - 105 - 135		
03.22	High-alloy steel	Hardened	250-500	110 - 150	65 - 90 - 120	40 - 50 - 60	90 - 110		50 - 65 - 90		
03.13	HSS, Annealed		150-250	160 - 195	90 - 125 - 155	50 - 60 - 75	95 - 120	80 – 250	70 - 95 - 120		30 - 45 - 60
03.21	High-alloy tool steel	Hardened	250-350	120 - 150	70 - 95 - 120	30 - 40 - 50	70 - 90		55 - 75 - 90		
05.1	Stainless steel annealed	Ferr. Mart.	150-270		120 - 165 - 210	80 - 105 - 130*)	190 - 245	100 – 200	110 - 150 - 190	100 - 190*)	
05.2	Stainless steel annealed	Aust.	150-220		95 - 130 - 180	65 - 85 - 100*)	150 - 185	100 – 200	85 - 115 - 150	80 - 170*)	
06.1	Cast steel	Non-alloy	150	180 - 225	100 - 145 - 180	60 - 75 - 95	140 - 175		75 - 110 - 135		
06.2	Cast steel	Low-alloy	150-250	150 - 190	90 - 120 - 150	50 - 65 - 80	115 - 145		65 - 90 - 110		
06.3	Cast steel	High-alloy	160-200	110 - 130	65 - 90 - 100	35 - 45 - 55	80 - 100		50 - 65 - 75		25 - 35 - 40
06.31	Stainless steel castings	Ferr. Mart.	200		50 - 70 - 80	30 - 40 - 50	70 - 95		45 - 60 - 70		20 - 30 - 35
06.32	Stainless steel castings	Aust.	200		50 - 60	18 - 25 - 35	55 - 75		45 - 55		15 - 18 - 25

CMC No.	Material		Brinell hardness HB	GC3015		HM	GC320	H13A	H1P	SMA	H10F	H10
				Feed mm/tooth								
				0,3	0,2	0,4 – 0,2 – 0,1	0,4 – 0,2	0,4 – 0,2 – 0,1	0,4 – 0,2 – 0,1	0,4 – 0,2 – 0,1	0,4 – 0,2 – 0,1	0,2 – 0,1
				Cutting speed m/min								
04.1	Hardened[1][2] steel		HRC 50-65						10 - 15			
06.33	Cast manganese steel 12-14% Mn		250			15 - 20 - 30		12 - 18 - 20	20 - 30 - 40	15 - 20 - 30	12 - 18 - 25	
07.1	Malleable cast iron	Shortchip	110-145	120/250	150/300	100 - 125 - 150	115 - 145	65 - 80 - 95	125 - 150 - 175	100 - 125 - 150		
07.2	Malleable cast iron	Longchip	200-230	70/150	110/200	90 115 - 135	105 - 130	50 - 65 - 80	100 - 125 - 150	90 - 115 - 135		
08.1	Grey cast iron	Low tensile	180	120/250	150/300	85 - 120 - 155	95 - 140	70 - 95 - 120	90 - 130 - 170	85 - 120 - 155		
08.2	Grey cast iron	High tensile, alloyed	260	80/170	110/250	70 - 90 - 115	80 - 105	50 - 70 - 90	75 - 100 - 125	70 - 90 - 115		
09.1	Nodular cast iron, SG iron	Ferr.	160	70/110	80/140	70 - 90 - 115	80 - 105	50 - 65 - 80	90 - 110 - 125	70 - 90 - 115		
09.2	Nodular cast iron, SG iron	Pearl.	250	70/110	70/120	65 - 85 - 100	75 - 100	45 - 60 - 70	80 - 100 - 115	65 - 85 - 100		
10.1	Chilled[1][2][3] cast iron		HRC 40-60						10 - 25			
20.1	Fe-based alloys		180-300					10 - 35			10 - 35	
20.2	Ni-based alloys		220-300					10 - 20				
20.3	Co-based alloys		220-300								10 - 20	
23.4	Ti-alloys		300-400					20 - 80			20 - 80	
30.1	Aluminium alloys	Non cast	30-150					200 - 500				200 - 600
30.2	Aluminium alloys	Cast	40-185					250 - 450				250 - 500
30.3	Aluminium, non alloy (Al 99%)							250 - 1000				500 - 2000

[1]) Negative rake should be used
[2]) Negative primary land may be necessary
[3]) Increase the feed for entering angles less than 75°
[4]) If edge build-up, increase the cutting speed to 180-200 m/min
[5]) For T-MAX long edge milling cutter R215.3 use initial values 90-120 m/min.
[6]) For T-MAX long edge milling cutter R215.3 use initial values 70-90 m/min.

continued

T-MAX side and facemills

CMC No.	Material	Brinell hardness HB	GC120	SMA	S6	CT520	SM30	R4
			Average chip thickness h_m¹) 0,05–0,12 mm					
			Cutting speed m/min.					
01.	Non-alloy steel	110-310	140 - 240	130 - 250	70 - 135	100 - 400	80 - 185	
02.	Low-alloy steel	125-450	130 - 210	85 - 180	45 - 80	80 - 300	55 - 135	
03.	High-alloy steel	150-500	120 - 180	60 - 120	30 - 65	80 - 300	40 - 90	
05.	Stainless steel	150-270			40 - 90	100 - 200	55 - 125	30 - 60
06.	Cast steel	150-250	130 - 210	55 - 115	25 - 60		35 - 85	20 - 45

CMC No.	Material	Brinell hardness HB	GC3015	HM	GC320	H13A	H1P	SMA
			Average chip thickness h_m¹) 0,05–0,12 mm					
			Cutting speed m/min.					
04.	Hardened steel	HRC 50-65					10 - 15	
07.	Malleable cast iron	110-230	70 - 300	55 - 100	75 - 110	25 - 70	65 - 120	55 - 100
08.	Grey cast-iron	180-260	80 - 300	60 - 120	80 - 125	35 - 85	60 - 140	60 - 120
09.	Nodular cast-iron, SG iron	160-250	70 - 140	40 - 80	60 - 80	25 - 50	50 - 90	40 - 80
10.	Chilled cast-iron	HRC 40-60					8 - 12	
30.	Aluminium alloys	30-100		300 - 600		210 - 400		
33.	Bronze and Brass alloys	60-150		110 - 200		75 - 140	130 - 240	

Endmills, speed

CMC No.	Material	Brinell hardness HB	T-MAX				Solid carbide	Brazed helical
			SMA	S6	SM30	P30	S6	P40
			Cutting speed m/min.					
01.	Non-alloy steel	110-310	130 - 190	80 - 120	100 - 140	80 - 120	65 - 95	60 - 80
02.	Low-alloy steel	125-450	80 - 170	45 - 105	60 - 125	40 - 70	35 - 85	30 - 70
03.	High-alloy steel	150-500	70 - 155	40 - 100	55 - 120	20 - 70	30 - 80	30 - 70
05.	Stainless steel	150-270		55 - 90	65 - 110	60 - 80	45 - 70	40 - 65
06.	Cast steel	150-250	55 - 130	35 - 80	40 - 100		30 - 65	30 - 60
CMC No.	Material	Brinell hardness HB	HM	H13A	SMA	P30	H13A	K20
			Cutting speed m/min.					
04.	Hardened steel	HRC 50-65	10 - 25	8 - 18				
07.	Malleable cast iron	110-230	80 - 120	60 - 90	80 - 120		50 - 80	50 - 80
08.	Grey cast-iron	180-260	50 - 115	50 - 90	50 - 115	60 - 90	50 - 70	50 - 70
09.	Nodular cast-iron, SG iron	160-250	40 - 80	30 - 60	40 - 80	40 - 80	30 - 60	30 - 60
10.	Chilled cast-iron	HRC 40-60	10 - 35	8 - 25			8 - 20	8 - 20
30.	Aluminium alloys	30-100						400 - 900
33.	Bronze and Brass alloys	60-150	100 - 160	80 - 120			80 - 120	80 - 120

continued

Section 5.5.10 (*continued*)

Endmills, feed

Type of cutter	Average chip thickness h_m[1]), mm						
	D=3 - 4	D=6 - 8	D=10 - 12	D=16	D=20	D=25 - 32	D=40 - 50
T-MAX				0,04 - 0,06	0,05 - 0,07	0,06 - 0,12	0,10 - 0,15
T-MAX drilling			0,03 - 0,05	0,03 - 0,06	0,04 - 0,08	0,05 - 0,10	0,06 - 0,13
Solid carbide/brazed	0,005 - 0,008	0,010 - 0,018	0,015 - 0,025	0,03 - 0,04	0,04 - 0,05	0,04 - 0,08	0,05 - 0,12

Correction factor feed/tooth

$S_z = f_1 \cdot h_m$	$\frac{D}{a_r}$	50	40	20	10	5	2,5	2	1,5	1
	f_1	7,1	6,3	4,5	3,2	2,3	1,7	1,6	1,4	1,6

Courtesy of SANDVIK

5.5.11 Coromant carbide milling cutters: machining economy and cutting data

Cost picture

The total machining cost per item is made up of the following three components:

(a) Machine and labour costs during the machining operation
(b) Tool costs
(c) Fixed handling costs.

These costs vary as shown in the graph. At a certain chip removal the costs reach a minimum which corresponds to the economic combination of cutting data.

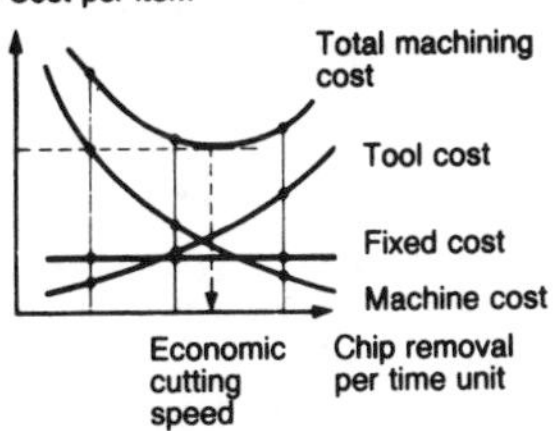

Cutting depth

To obtain the best tool economy the largest possible cutting depth a_a should be chosen, i.e. up to two-thirds of the available full cutting edge length should be used. There are several restricting factors:

(a) The power and stability of the machine
(b) The strength of the workpiece
(c) The clamping arrangement.

The cutting depth is directly proportional to the power.

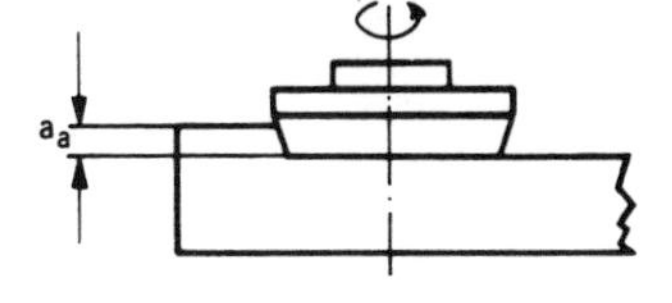

Feed

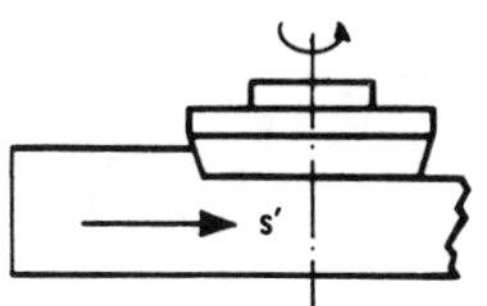

When selecting the feed s', there are several factors to be considered: cutter type, carbide grade, surface finish, material and machine power. It should be noted, however, that carbide milling should not be employed with too small a feed per insert. The feed is not directly proportional to the power. Large feed per tooth lowers the power requirement for machining a given volume of material per time unit. For the same table feed a coarse pitch cutter requires less power than a fine pitch one.

Cutting speed

The primary aim in selecting a cutting speed should be to obtain an economical tool life. The cutting speed has a greater effect on the tool life than the feed or cutting depth.

Cutting speed is given by

$$v = \frac{\pi D n}{1000} \quad \text{m/min}$$

Surface finish

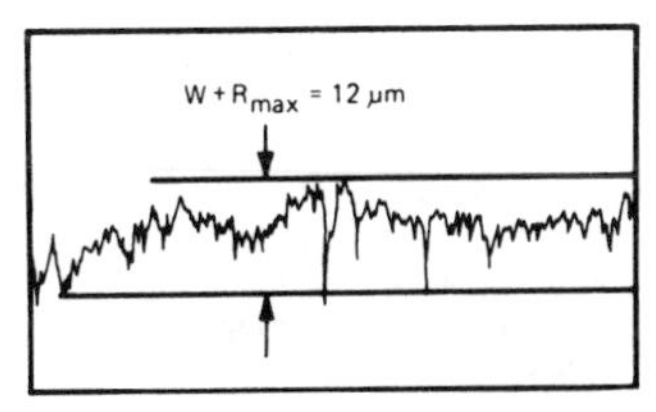

The surface finish is an important factor in milling and is affected by the machine condition, cutter design and geometry, cutting data and the workpiece shape and clamping.

5.5.12 Coromant carbide grades for drilling

ISO category P (Blue)
Steel, cast steel, stainless steel, long chipping malleable iron

Grades for T-MAX U short hole drills

GC3015 (P01–P35)
The high wear resistance choice. Very good wear resistance at high cutting speeds. Most suitable for peripheral inserts. Very good for peripheral inserts in combination with GC235 central inserts.

GC-A (P15–P45)
The first choice grade within the ISO P application area. The universal grade for low to relatively high cutting speeds. Suitable for both central and peripheral inserts.

GC235 (P25–P50)
The tough choice. Excellent grade for unstable conditions and low to moderate cutting speeds. Suitable for both central and peripheral inserts. Very good for central inserts in combination with GC3015 peripheral inserts.

Grades for deep hole drills

GC415 (P01–P35)
Extremely high wear resistance and good protection against plastic deformation. Very high metal removal over a wide application field.

ISO category M (Yellow)
Steel, cast steel, manganese steel, alloy cast iron, austenitic stainless steel castings, malleable iron, free cutting steel, heat resistant alloys

Grades for T-MAX U short hole drills

H13A (M15–M25)
The first choice for heat resistant alloys. Good edge sharpness, wear resistance and toughness. Suitable for both peripheral and central inserts.

CG235 (M20–M40)
The first choice for austenitic stainless steel. Good edge toughness and good resistance against built-up edge. Suitable for both peripheral and central inserts.

Grades for deep hole drills

GC235 (M20–M40)
The first choice for austenitic stainless steel. Good edge toughness and good resistance against built-up edge.

S6 (M30–M40)
Suitable for difficult machining conditions. Good edge toughness.

ISO category K (Red)
Cast iron, chilled cast iron, short chipping malleable iron, hardened steel, non-ferrous metals, plastics, wood

Grades for T-MAX U short hole drills

GC3015 (K01–K25)
The high wear resistant choice. Very good wear resistance at high cutting speeds. Very good for peripheral inserts in combination with H13A central inserts.

H13A (K10–K30)
The universal grade for low to moderate cutting speeds. Suitable for both peripheral and central inserts.

Grades for deep hole drills

GC415 (K01–K20)
Very high wear resistance at high cutting speeds. Most suitable for favourable conditions.

GC435 (K05–K25)
Good edge toughness in combination with good wear resistance at moderate to high cutting speeds.

ISO category P (Blue) Steel, cast steel, stainless steel, long chipping malleable iron	**ISO category M (Yellow)** Steel, cast steel, manganese steel, alloy cast iron, austenitic stainless steel castings, malleable iron, free cutting steel, heat resistant alloys	**ISO category K (Red)** Cast iron, chilled cast iron, short chipping malleable iron, hardened steel, non-ferrous metals, plastics, wood
GC435 (P20–P45) Can be used under unfavourable conditions. Comparatively high cutting speeds and feeds. Very high wear resistance. All round grade for machining steel. **GC235** (P25–P50) Suitable all round grade for T-MAX drilling. Combines good wear resistance at low to moderate cutting speeds with excellent toughness behaviour. Good resistance against built-up edge. **S2** (P15–P25) Suitable grade for skiving operations. High wear resistance combined with good toughness. **S6** (P35–P45) Good toughness. Low cutting speeds. For difficult machining conditions.		

Courtesy of SANDVIK

5.5.13 Coromant carbide drill types for short holes

			T-MAX U		
	Coromant Delta S-drills	Coromant Delta drills[1]	Solid drills[1]	Stack drills[1]	Solid BT adapted[1]
Drill diameter	2,50 - 12,00 mm	9,50 - 20,00 mm	17,5 - 58 mm	27 - 59 mm	17,5 - 58 mm
Hole depth	3 × diameter 6 × diameter	3,5 × diameter 5 × diameter	2 × diameter 2,5 × diameter	2,5 × diameter	2,5 × diameter
Hole tolerance	IT 10	IT 9 (3,5×D) IT 10 (5×D)	±0,2 mm	±0,2 mm	±0,2 mm
Surface finish	R_a 3 μm	R_a 1–2 μm (3,5×D) R_a 2–4 μm (5×D)	R_a 6–10 μm	R_a 6–10 μm	R_a 6–10 μm
Diameter adjustment	No	No	Non rotating: Max 4,2 mm radial (depending on diameter) Rotating: ±0,15 mm (with eccentric sleeve)		No
Cutting fluid	External Emulsion or neat oil	Internal Emulsion or neat oil	Internal Emulsion	Internal Emulsion	Internal Emulsion
Shank	Cylindrical	Whistle notch	Whistle notch	Whistle notch	BT
Machines	FMS (flexible machining systems), M/C:s, NC and NC-lathes, CNC, automatics, centre and turret lathes and milling machines.				

	T-MAX U				
	Solid Varilock adapted[1]	**Solid drills**	**Trepanning drills**	**Hard-Cut drills**	**Duodex drills**
Drill diameter	17,5–58 mm	60–80 mm	60–110 mm	2–6 mm	19–88 mm
Hole depth	2,5 × diameter	2,5 × diameter	2,5 × diameter	5 × diameter	6,5 × diameter
Hole tolerance	±0,2 mm	±0,2 mm	Adjustable max 1 mm on dia.	For removal of broken taps	IT 13–14
Surface finish	R_a 5 μm	R_a 6–10 μm	R_a 6–10 μm		R_a 10 μm
Diameter adjustment	No	No	Cartridge: ±0,5 mm	No	No
Cutting fluid	Internal Emulsion	Internal Emulsion	Internal Emulsion	No	Internal Emulsion or neat oil
Shank	Varilock	Varilock	Varilock	Cylindrical	Cylindrical and Morse taper
Machines	FMS (flexible machining systems), M/C:s, NC and NC-lathes, CNC, automatics, centre and turret lathes and milling machines.				

[1] Chamfering insert can be used.

Courtesy of SANDVIK

5.5.14 Coromant carbide drills: cutting data

Coromant Delta S-drills R410.5

Material				Cutting speed	Drill diameter, mm		
Description	CMC No.	Condition	HB		2,50–5,50	5,51–8,50	8,51–12,00
				m/min.	Feed mm/r		
Unalloyed steel	01.1	Non-hardened with C 0,05–0,25%	90–200	35–45	0,13–0,17	0,20–0,26	0,23–0,31
	01.2	Non-hardened with C 0,25–0,55%	125–225	25–40	0,10–0,16	0,14–0,23	0,17–0,28
	01.3	Non-hardened with C 0,55–0,80%	150–250	25–40	0,10–0,16	0,14–0,23	0,17–0,28
	01.4	High carbon and carbon tool steel	180–275	25–40	0,10–0,16	0,14–0,23	0,17–0,28
Low alloy steel	02.1	Non-hardened	150–260	30–40	0,13–0,17	0,18–0,24	0,23–0,31
High alloy steel	03.13	Annealed HSS	150–250	25–35	0,09–0,12	0,12–0,16	0,16–0,22
Stainless steel	05.1	Ferritic Martensitic Cr 13–25%	150–270	10–20	0,10–0,16	0,13–0,21	0,15–0,26
	05.2	Austenitic Ni >8%, Cr 18–25%	150–275	10–15	0,09–0,13	0,13–0,17	0,17–0,23
Steel castings	06.1	Unalloyed	–225	17–30	0,10–0,16	0,13–0,21	0,17–0,27
	06.2	Low alloyed (alloying elements ≤5%)	150–250	13–20	0,09–0,13	0,14–0,20	0,20–0,26
Malleable cast iron	07.1	Ferritic (short chipping)	110–145	30–50	0,14–0,22	0,19–0,31	0,25–0,40
	07.2	Pearlitic (long chipping)	150–270	30–40	0,10–0,14	0,15–0,21	0,19–0,25
Grey cast iron	08.1	Low tensile strength	150–220	30–50	0,14–0,23	0,19–0,31	0,25–0,41
	08.2	High tensile strength	200–330	25–35	0,10–0,14	0,15–0,21	0,20–0,28
Nodular cast iron	09.1	Ferritic	125–230	30–40	0,14–0,18	0,21–0,28	0,27–0,37
	09.2	Pearlitic	200–300	25–35	0,11–0,15	0,15–0,20	0,20–0,27
Aluminium alloys	30.11	Wrought and cold drawn	30–80	55–95	0,15–0,25	0,18–0,31	0,25–0,41
	30.21	Cast	40–100				
Copper and copper alloys	33.1	Free cutting alloys Pb ≥1%	–100	50–70	0,15–0,20	0,19–0,25	0,24–0,32
	33.2	Brass and leaded bronzes Pb≤1%					

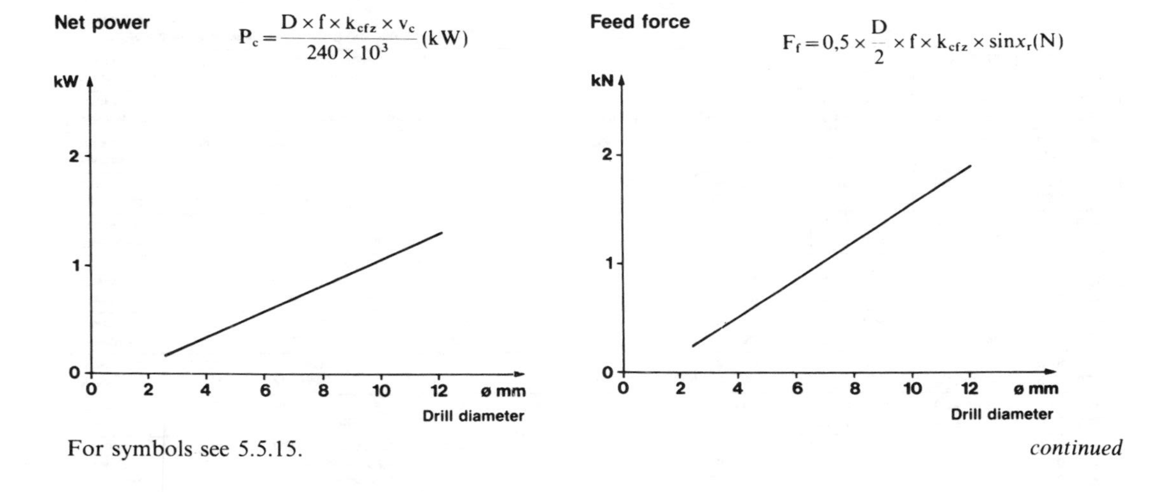

For symbols see 5.5.15.

continued

Coromant Delta drills R411.5, RA411.5

Material				Cutting speed	Drill diameter, mm[1])		
Description	CMC No.	Condition	HB		9,50–14	14,01–17	17,01–30
				m/min.	Feed mm/r		
Unalloyed steel	01.1	Non-hardened 0,05–0,25% C	90–200	75–100	0,14–0,22	0,15–0,25	0,18–0,31
	01.2	Non-hardened 0,25–0,55% C	125–225	68–92	0,15–0,23	0,18–0,26	0,20–0,30
	01.3	Non-hardened 0,55–0,80% C	150–225	68–92	0,15–0,23	0,18–0,26	0,20–0,30
	01.4	High carbon and carbon tool steel	180–225	68–92	0,15–0,23	0,18–0,26	0,20–0,30
Low alloy steel	02.1	Non-hardened	150–260	56–90	0,14–0,22	0,18–0,26	0,18–0,28
	02.2	Hardened	220–400	36–66	0,14–0,22	0,15–0,25	0,18–0,26
High alloy steel	03.1	Annealed	150–250	38–68	0,15–0,20	0,18–0,25	0,20–0,27
	03.2	Hardened	250–400	38–58	0,15–0,20	0,17–0,20	0,18–0,24
Stainless steel	05.1	Ferritic Martensitic 13–25% Cr	150–270	26–54	0,14–0,21	0,17–0,24	0,18–0,27
	05.2	Austenitic Ni >8%, 18–25% Cr	150–270	26–54	0,14–0,20	0,16–0,23	0,19–0,25
Steel castings	06.1	Unalloyed	90–225	68–92	0,17–0,23	0,19–0,25	0,20–0,26
	06.2	Low alloyed (alloying elements ≤5%)	150–250	48–75	0,15–0,21	0,17–0,23	0,19–0,25
Malleable cast iron	07.1	Ferritic (short chipping)	110–145	75–120	0,15–0,26	0,18–0,30	0,21–0,39
	07.2	Pearlitic (long chipping)	150–270	77–113	0,15–0,25	0,16–0,29	0,18–0,35
Grey cast iron	08.1	Low tensile strength	150–220	85–115	0,19–0,31	0,23–0,39	0,26–0,46
	08.2	High tensile strength	200–330	56–100	0,19–0,30	0,24–0,36	0,28–0,44
Nodular cast iron	09.1	Ferritic	125–230	65–106	0,16–0,26	0,20–0,35	0,23–0,41
	09.2	Pearlitic	200–300	56–96	0,15–0,25	0,18–0,33	0,21–0,39
Aluminium alloys	30.1	Wrought and cold drawn	40–150	96–150	0,21–0,33	0,18–0,41	0,18–0,41
	30.2	Cast	40–150	96–150	0,21–0,33	0,18–0,41	0,18–0,41
Copper and copper alloys	33.1	Free cutting alloys (Pb ≥1%)	50–160	46–150	0,16–0,29	0,20–0,35	0,25–0,44
	33.2	Brass and leaded bronzes (Pb ≤1%)	50–160	46–150	0,16–0,29	0,20–0,35	0,25–0,44

[1]) In unstable conditions when using 5 × D drill, the feed must be reduced when starting drilling.

Graphs for Coromant Delta drills R411.5, RA411.5

The graphs show nominal values which should not be regarded as strict recommendations. The values may need adjusting depending on the machining conditions e.g., the type of material.

Note that only net power ratings are given. Allowance must be made for the efficiency of the machine and the cutting edge wear.

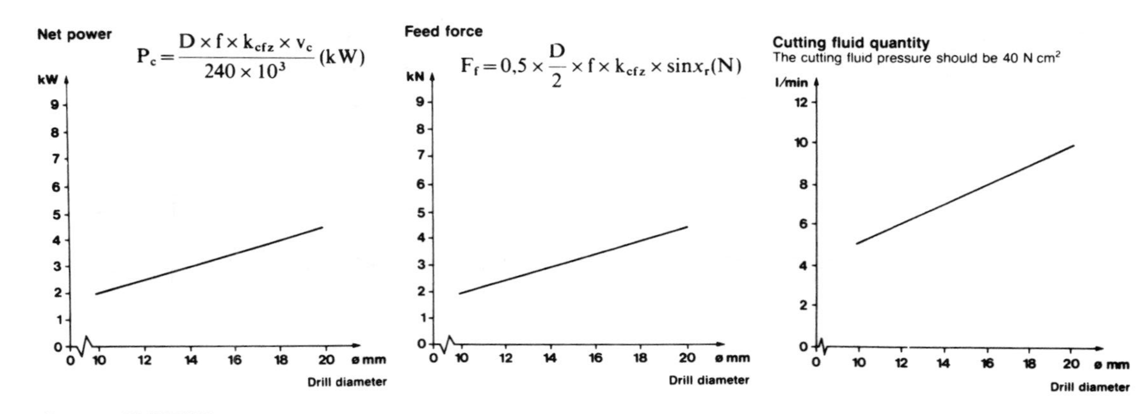

Courtesy of SANDVIK

5.5.15 Coromant carbide drills: designations and formulae

Designation acc. to ISO	Old designation	Terminology	Unit
v_c	v	Cutting speed	m/min
n	n	Spindle speed	r/min
D	D	Drill diameter	mm
v_f	s'	Feed speed	mm/min
f	s	Feed per rev.	mm/r
f_z	s_z	Feed per tooth	mm/z
k_c	k_s	Specific cutting force	N/mm^2
$k_{c\ 0,4}$	$k_{s\ 0,4}$	Specific cutting force for $f_z = 0,4$	N/mm^2
k_{cfz}	k_{sm}	Specific cutting force for feed per edge	N/mm^2
F_f	–	Feed force	N
$F_{f\mu}$	–	Feed force caused by friction	N
M_c	–	Torque	Nm
M_μ	–	Torque caused by friction	Nm
P_c	P	Net power (cutting power)	kW
P_μ	–	Power caused by friction	kW
a_p	a	Cutting depth	mm
$\varkappa_r$	–	Tool cutting edge angle	Degrees
γn	–	Tool normal rake angle	Degrees
q	Q	Cutting fluid quantity	l/min
p	p	Cutting fluid pressure	N/cm^2

Cutting depth, a_p

Solid drilling

Trepanning

Counterboring

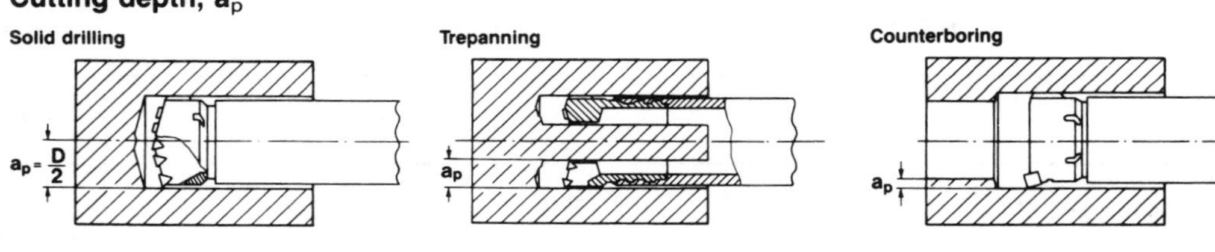

Tool cutting edge angle, $\varkappa_r$
Tool normal rake angle, γ_n

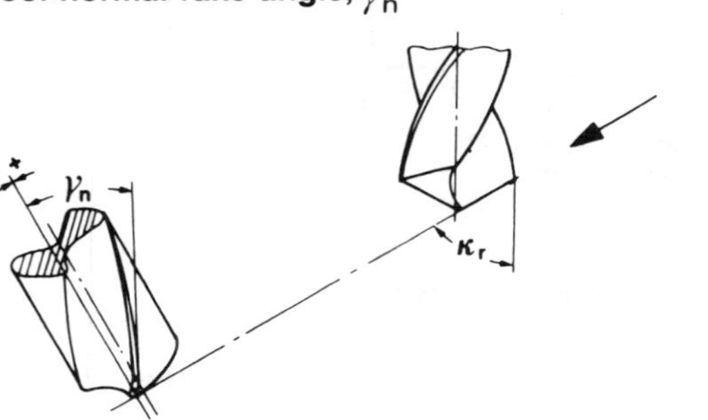

Specific cutting force for feed per edge, k_{cfz}

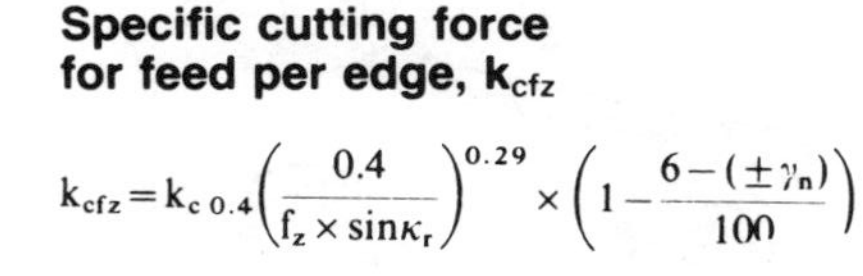

$$k_{cfz} = k_{c\,0.4}\left(\frac{0.4}{f_z \times \sin\kappa_r}\right)^{0.29} \times \left(1 - \frac{6 - (\pm\gamma_n)}{100}\right)$$

Section 5.5.15 (*continued*)

	Drills without guide pads	Drills with guide pads
	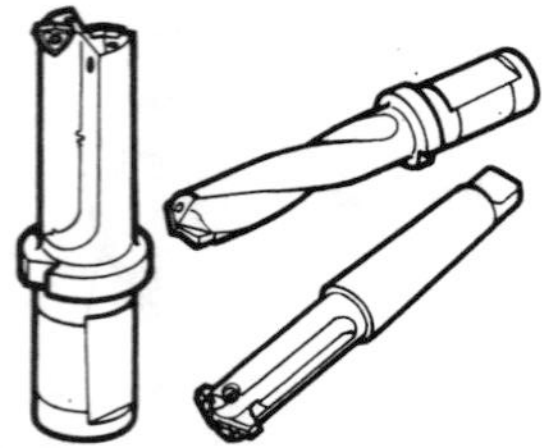 T-MAX U, Coromant Delta, Duodex drills and Coromant Delta S	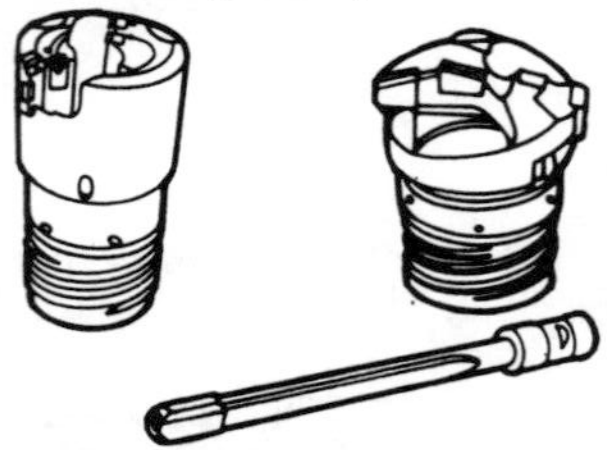 Ejector, STS and gun drills
Cutting speed	$v_c = \frac{\pi D n}{1000}$ m/min	$v_c = \frac{\pi D n}{1000}$ m/min
Feed speed	$v_f = fn$ mm/min	$v_f = fn$ mm/min
Feed force*	$F_f = 0.5 a_p f k_{ctz} \sin\kappa_r$ N	$F_f = 0.5 a_p f k_{ctz} \sin\kappa_r$ N

Torque*	$M_c = \frac{Dfk_{ctz}a_p}{2000}\left(1 - \frac{a_p}{D}\right)$ N m	$M_c + M\mu = \frac{D \times f \times k_{ctz} \times a_p}{2000}\left(1{,}17 - \frac{a_p}{D}\right)$ Nm
Net power*†	$P_c = \frac{a_p fk_{ctz} v_c}{60 \times 10^3}\left(1 - \frac{a_p}{D}\right)$ kW	$P_c + P\mu = \frac{a_p fk_{ctz} v_c}{60 \times 10^3}\left(1.17 - \frac{a_p}{D}\right)$ kW

* Feed force, torque and power at idling are not included in these formulae.

† The power requirement is calculated on the basis of an unused tool, i.e. tool without wear. For a tool with normal wear, the power requirement is 10–30% higher, depending upon the size of the drill.

continued

Specific cutting force for f_z=0,4 for different materials

Material Description	CMC No.	Condition	HB	Specific cutting force $k_{c\ 0,4}$[1]) N/mm²
Unalloyed steel	01.1	C=0,15%	125	**1900**
	01.2	C=0,35%	150	**2100**
	01.3	C=0,60%	200	**2250**
Low alloy steel	02.1	Non-hardened	180	**2100**
	02.2	Hardened and tempered	275	**2600**
	02.2	Hardened and tempered	300	**2700**
	02.2	Hardened and tempered	350	**2850**
High alloy steel	03.1	Annealed	200	**2600**
	03.2	Hardened	325	**3900**
Stainless steel	05.1	Martensitic/ferritic	200	**2300**
	05.2	Austenitic	175	**2450**
Steel castings	06.1	Unalloyed	180	**2000**
	06.2	Low alloyed	200	**2500**
	06.3	High alloyed	225	**2700**
Hard steel	04	Hardened steel	55 HRC	**4500**
	06.33	Manganese steel 12%	250	**3600**
Malleable cast iron	07.1	Ferritic	130	**1100**
	07.2	Pearlitic	230	**1100**
Grey cast iron	08.1	Low tensile strength	180	**1100**
	08.2	High tensile strength	260	**1500**
Nodular cast iron	09.1	Ferritic	160	**1100**
	09.2	Pearlitic	250	**1800**

Chilled cast iron	10		400	**3000**
Heat resistant alloys	20.11	Fe-base, annealed	200	**3000**
	20.12	Fe-base, aged	280	**3050**
	20.21, 20.31	Ni- or Co-base, annealed	250	**3500**
	20.22, 20.32	Ni- or Co-base, aged	350	**4150**
	20.24, 20.33	Ni- or Co-base, cast	320	**4150**
Aluminium alloys	30.11	Non heat treatable	60	**500**
	30.12	Heat treatable	100	**800**
Aluminium alloys, cast	30.21	Non heat treatable	75	**750**
	30.22	Heat treatable	90	**900**
Copper and copper alloys	33.1	Lead alloys, Pb>1%	110	**700**
	33.2	Brass, red brass	90	**750**
	33.3	Bronze and leadfree copper including electrolytic copper	100	**1750**

[1]) The $k_{c\,0,4}$-values are valid for: $f_z = 0{,}4$ mm/z
$\varkappa_r = 90°$
$\gamma_n = +6°$

Courtesy of SANDVIK

5.5.16 Coromant carbide drills: regrinding

Regrind the Delta S-drill as a conventional twist drill with thinned chisel point.

Because the Delta S geometry has been removed, the feed per revolution should be reduced by approximately 25%

Because the TiN coating will be ground off, the cutting speed should be reduced by approximately 20%

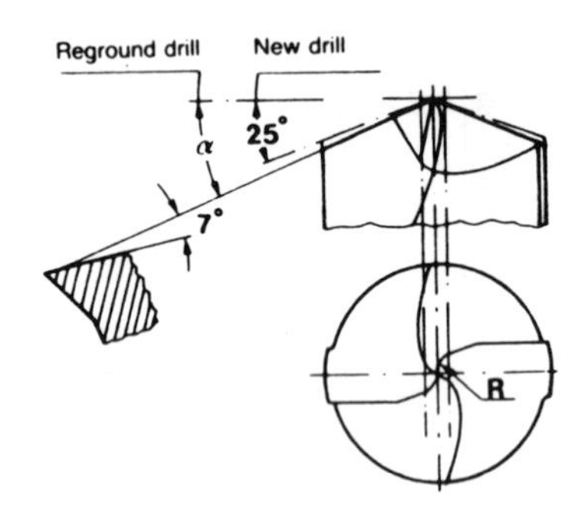

Coromant Delta drills R411.5

Grinding wheel and honing stick recommendations

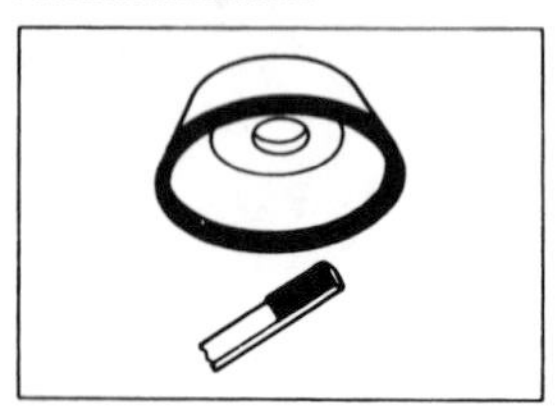

Grinding wheel:

- Diamond grinding wheel type D 11V9.
- Bond, bakelite or synthetic resin.
- Grain size 120–240 mesh ~124–64 μm.
- Diamond concentration 75–100 carats/cm^3.
- Cutting fluid emulsion 3%.

Honing stick:

- Diamond.
- Grain size 250–300 mesh ~64–53 μm.

Geometry

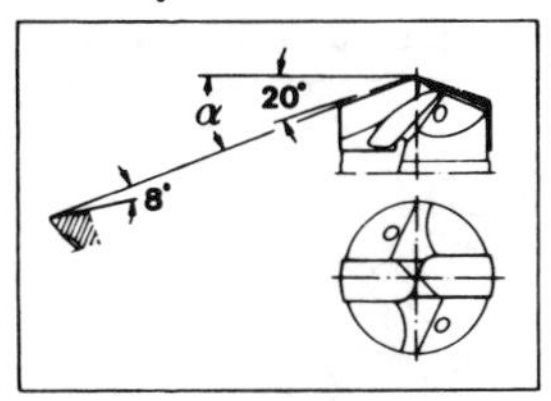

Lead angle α 20–22°.
(Point angle 136–140°.)
Clearance angle 8°.
When regrinding, change the lead angle α.

Clamping

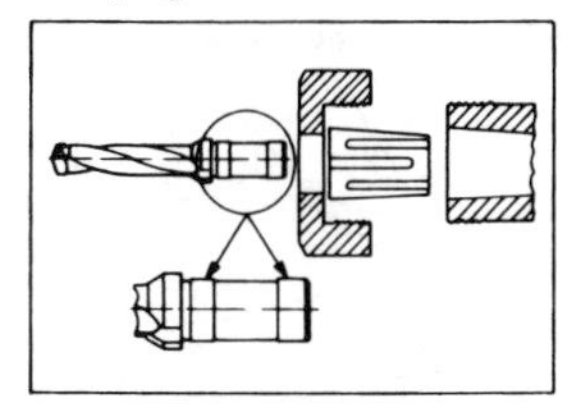

Clamp on drill shank diameter.

Set the fixture

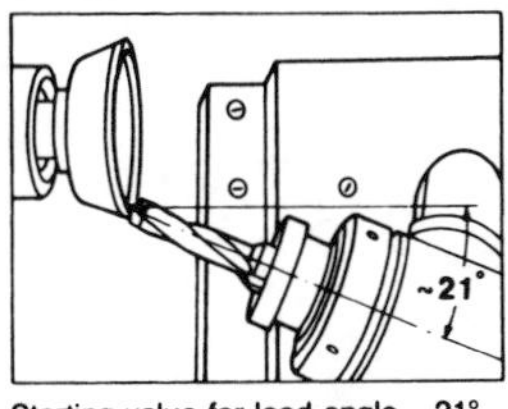

Starting value for lead angle ~21°.

NOTE! Picture showing the set up from above.

Setting value for clearance angle 8°.

NOTE! Picture showing the set up from the side.

Setting the cutting edge in relation to the machine table

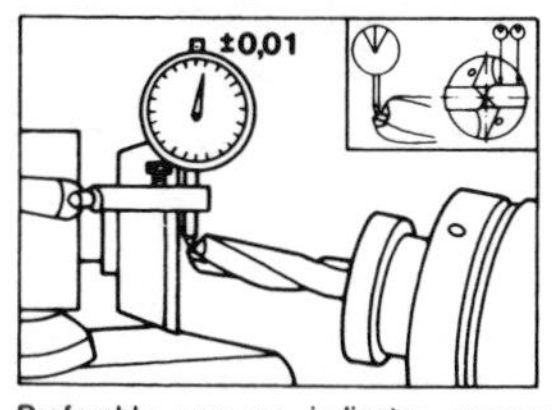

Preferably use an indicator, recommended max. deviation ±0,01 mm.

Grinding

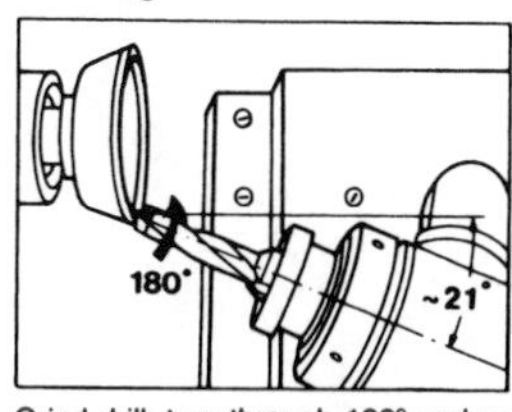

Grind drill, turn through 180° and repeat grind. Best result achieved when separating the grinding into roughing and finishing. Thus, start rough grinding, turn through 180° and repeat rough grinding. Thereafter repeat the cycle, for finish grinding.

Honing of negative land

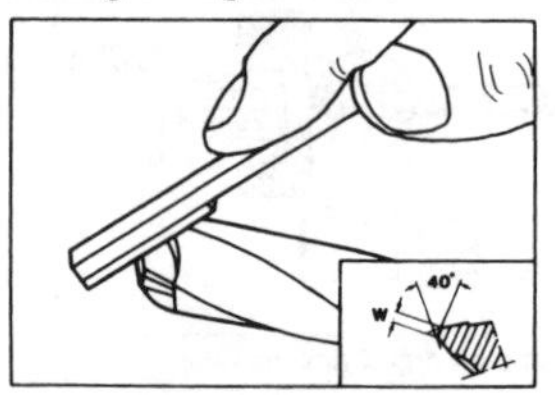

It is important that the negative land is of equal size on both sides of the centre.
Recommended values, mm

Drill dia.	
9,50–11,50	w=0,11
11,51–14,00	w=0,13
14,01–17,00	w=0,15
17,01–20,00	w=0,17

Honing of the periphery corner

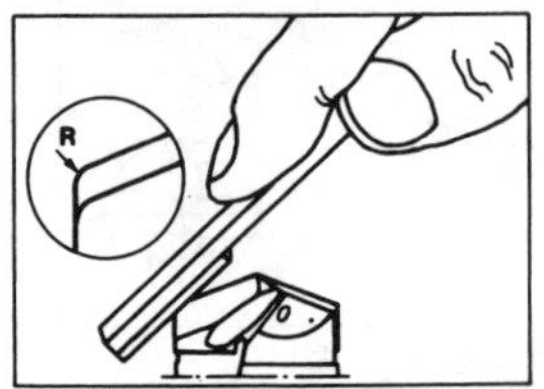

Hone the pheriphery corner to R≈0,1 mm.
It is important that the periphery corner is of equal size on both side of the centre.

Courtesy of SANDVIK

Appendix 1

British Standards: orders and information

To place an order

Orders should be directed to BSI Publications at Linford Wood, Milton Keynes, MK14 6LE. Subscribing members of BSI should not send payment with their order and will be invoiced in the usual way. Non-members should send the correct remittance with their order.

Orders are preferred by post, telex or fax. The telex number is 825777 and the fax number is 0908 322484. Urgent orders for the priority service must be received before 1500 hours, by telex, fax, or by telephone through BSI Publications at Milton Keynes, tel: 0908 221166 (call queuing system).

Priority service orders will be despatched by first class mail the same working day. The charge for this service is 10% of the invoice value with a minimum of £1 and a maximum of £50.

Personal callers may purchase standards over the counter at BSI's two sales counters: Hampden House, 61 Green Street, London W1Y 3RM and 3 York Street, Manchester M2 2AT. The counters are open between 0900 and 1700, Monday to Friday. All normal subscribing member discounts apply.

British Standards can also be purchased from BSI Sales Agents. However, BSI subscribing member discounts are not available from these sources. See the BSI Catalogue for a full list of agents or contact BSI Publications.

Photocopies of withdrawn standards can be purchased from BSI Information Services at Milton Keynes, tel: 0908 226888 (call queuing system) or fax: 0908 221435.

BSI Addresses

BSI Head Office

BSI
2 Park Street
London
W1A 2BS
Tel: 071 629 9000
Tx: 266933 BSILONG
Fax: 071 629 0506

BSI Standards

Chemical and Health Department
Construction Department
Electrical Department
Information Systems Department
Mechanical Department

BSI
2 Park Street
London
W1A 2BS
Tel: 071 629 9000
Tx: 266933 BSILONG
Fax: 071 629 0506

Multitechnics Department
BSI
3 York Street
Manchester
M2 2AT
Tel: 061 832 3731
Tx: 665969 BSIMAN G
Fax: 061 832 2895

BSI Publications
Linford Wood
Milton Keynes
MK14 6LE
Tel: 0908 221166
Fax: 0908 322484

BSI Information Services
Linford Wood
Milton Keynes
MK14 6LE
Tel: 0908 226888
Fax: 0908 221435

BSI Membership Services
Linford Wood
Milton Keynes
MK14 6LE
Tel: 0908 226777
Fax: 0908 320856

BSI quality assurance

Certification and Assessment Services
BSI
PO Box 375
Milton Keynes
MK14 6LL
Tel: 0908 220908
Tx: 827682 BSIQAS G
Fax: 0908 220671

Inspectorate
BSI
PO Box 391
Milton Keynes
MK14 6LW
Tel: 0908 220908
Tx: 827682 BSIQAS G
Fax: 0908 220671

BSI testing

BSI
Maylands Avenue
Hemel Hempstead
Herts
HP2 4SQ
Tel: 0442 230442
Tx: 82424 BSIHHC G
Fax: 0440 231442

Appendix 2

Public libraries (UK) holding sets of British Standards

The following are UK public libraries which hold sets of British Standards. Attention is drawn to the law of copyright; no part of a BSI publication may be reproduced without the prior permission of BSI. Students and lecturers will often be able to find sets in their college libraries.

England

Avon	Bristol	*Central Library*
Bedfordshire	Bedford	*Public Library*
	Luton	*Central Library*
Berkshire	Bracknell	*Central Library*
	Reading	*Central Library*
	Slough	*Central Library*
Buckinghamshire	Aylesbury	*Public Library*
	Milton Keynes	*Central Library*
Cambridgeshire	Cambridge	*Central Library*
Cheshire	Chester	*Public Library*
	Crewe	*Public Library*
	Ellesmere Port	*Central Library*
	Warrington	*Public Library*
Cleveland	Hartlepool	*Central Library*
	Middlesbrough	*Central Library*
Cumbria	Barrow-in-Furness	*Central Library*
Derbyshire	Derby	*Central Library*
	Matlock	*Public Library*
Devonshire	Exeter	*Central Library*
	Plymouth	*Central Library*
Dorset	Poole	*Arndale Reference Library*
Durham	Durham	*Public Library*
Essex	Colchester	*Public Library*

	Grays	*Public Library*
	Southend-on-Sea	*Public Library*
	Witham	*Public Library*
Gloucestershire	Cheltenham	*Public Library*
	Gloucester	*Gloucestershire Technical Information Service*
Hampshire	Basingstoke	*Public Library*
	Farnborough	*Public Library*
	Portsmouth	*Central Library*
	Southampton	*Central Library*
	Winchester	*Public Library*
Hereford and Worcester	Redditch	*Public Library*
Hertfordshire	Stevenage	*Central Library*
Humberside	Grimsby	*Central Library*
	Hull	*Central Library*
	Scunthorpe	*Public Library*
Kent	Chatham	*Public Library*
Lancashire	Blackburn	*Public Library*
	Burnley	*Central Library*
	Lancaster	*Public Library*
	Preston	*Central Library*
	Skelmersdale	*Public Library*
Leicestershire	Leicester	*Information Centre*
Lincolnshire	Lincoln	*Public Library*
Greater London	Barking	*Central Library*
	Barnet	*Hendon Central Library*
	Bexley	*Central Library*
	Brent	*Central Library*
	Bromley	*Central Library*
	Croydon	*Central Library*
	Ealing	*Central Library*
	Enfield	*Palmers Green Public Library*
	Greenwich	*Woolwich Public Library*
	Hammersmith	*Central Library*
	Haringey	*Central Library*
	Harrow	*Central Reference Library*

	Havering	*Romford Central Library*
	Hounslow	*Feltham Public Library*
	Islington	*Central Library*
	Kensington and Chelsea	*Central Library*
	Lambeth	*Tate Library*
	Lewisham	*Deptford Public Library*
	Merton	*Wimbledon Public Library*
	Newham	*Stratford Public Library*
	Redbridge	*Ilford Central Library*
	Sutton	*Central Library*
	Waltham Forest	*Central Library*
	Wandsworth	*Battersea District Library*
	Westminster	*Central Reference Library*
Greater Manchester	Ashton-under-Lyne	*Public Library*
	Bolton	*Public Library*
	Bury	*Central Library*
	Manchester	*Central Library*
	Oldham	*Central Library*
	Rochdale	*Central Library*
	Stockport	*Central Library*
	Wigan	*Central Library*
Merseyside	Liverpool	*Central Reference Library*
	St Helens	*Central Library*
Norfolk	Norwich	*Central Library*
Northamptonshire	Northampton	*Central Library*
Northumberland	Morpeth	*Public Library*
Nottinghamshire	Mansfield	*Central Library*
	Nottingham	*Central Library*
Oxfordshire	Oxford	*Central Library*
Somerset	Bridgwater	*Public Library*
Staffordshire	Burton-upon-Trent	*Public Library*
	Cannock	*Public Library*
	Stafford	*Public Library*
	Stoke-on-Trent	*Hanley Central Library*
Suffolk	Lowestoft	*Central Library*
Surrey	Woking	*Public Library*

East Sussex	Brighton	*Reference Library*
West Sussex	Crawley	*Public Library*
Tyne and Wear	Gateshead	*Public Library*
	Newcastle-upon-Tyne	*Central Library*
	North Shields	*Central Library*
	South Shields	*Central Library*
	Washington	*Central Library*
Warwickshire	Rugby	*Business Information Service*
West Midlands	Birmingham	*Central Library*
	Coventry	*Public Library*
	Dudley	*Public Library*
	Walsall	*Central Library*
	West Bromwich	*Sandwell Central Library*
	Wolverhampton	*Central Library*
Wiltshire	Trowbridge	*Public Library*
South Yorkshire	Barnsley	*Central Library*
	Doncaster	*Central Library*
	Rotherham	*Central Library*
	Sheffield	*Central Library*
North Yorkshire	Northallerton	*Public Library*
	York	*Public Library*
West Yorkshire	Bradford	*Central Library*
	Dewsbury	*Public Library*
	Huddersfield	*Public Library*
	Leeds	*Central Library*
	Wakefield	*Central Library*

Wales

South Glamorgan	Cardiff	*Public Library*
West Glamorgan	Swansea	*Central Library*

Scotland

Central	Falkirk	*Public Library*
Grampian	Aberdeen	*Public Library*

Lothian	Edinburgh	*Central Library*
Strathclyde	East Kilbride	*Central Library*
	Glasgow	*Mitchell Library*
Tayside	Dundee	*Central Library*

Northern Ireland

Antrim	Ballymena	*Public Library*
	Belfast	*Central Library*
Connagh	Portadown	*Information Services*
Tyrone	Omagh	*Public Library Headquarters*

Appendix 3

Contributing companies

CUP Ltd
Continental Technical Products Division
Cottage Leap
Clifton Road
Rugby
Warwickshire CV21 3RQ
Tel: 0788 571482/7
Fax: 0788 536608

David Brown Gear Industries Ltd
Park Gear Works
Huddersfield HD4 5DD
Tel: 0484 22180
Fax: 0484 514732

National Broach & Machine Co
17500 Twenty-Three Mile Road
Mt Clemens
Michigan 48044
USA
Tel: 313 263 0100
Fax: 313 263 4571

Sandvik Coromant UK
Manor Way
Halesowen
West Midlands B62 8QZ
Tel: 021 550 4700
Fax: 021 550 0977

Tucker Fasteners Ltd
Walsall Road
Birmingham B42 1BP
Tel: 021 356 4811
Fax: 021 356 1598

Index